Basic Fundamentals in Hearing Science

Basic Fundamentals in Hearing Science

Tony L. Sahley, PhD, CCC-A
Frank E. Musiek, PhD, CCC-A

PLURAL
PUBLISHING
INC.

5521 Ruffin Road
San Diego, CA 92123

e-mail: info@pluralpublishing.com
Website: http://www.pluralpublishing.com

Typeset in 10½/13 Palatino by Flanagan's Publishing Services, Inc.
Printed in the United States of America by Bang Printing, Inc.

Cover and Figure Illustrations: Copyright © 2014 Terry M. Paczko

Library of Congress Cataloging-in-Publication Data

Sahley, Tony L., author.
  Basic fundamentals in hearing science / Tony L. Sahley, Frank E. Musiek.
      p. ; cm.
  Includes bibliographical references and index.
  ISBN 978-1-59756-549-3 (alk. paper) — ISBN 1-59756-549-0 (alk. paper)
  I. Musiek, Frank E., author. II. Title.
  [DNLM: 1. Auditory Perception—physiology. 2. Hearing—physiology.
3. Acoustics. 4. Ear—physiology. 5. Psychoacoustics. WV 272]
  QP462.2
  612.8'5—dc23
                              2014028313

Contents

Foreword

Hearing science is a multidisciplinary subject that is rooted in a diverse array of fields, including physics, engineering, anatomy, physiology, cell biology, and psychology. Bringing together the vast reservoir of knowledge from all these disciplines into a single textbook that does justice to the field's complexity without alienating its readers is not a simple task and few have done so effectively. Sahley and Musiek are among the exceptions. Drawing on their many years of combined teaching and research experience/expertise in clinical audiology, hearing science, and auditory neuropharmacology, as well as their combined expertise in general medical physiology, neuroanatomy, and neurophysiology, they have done a masterful job of making this complex body of knowledge approachable and straightforward. The book is organized into 10 chapters, each describing a different core aspect of hearing science. The book's first two chapters are introductory to students new to science, providing an overview of what science is and summarizing basic concepts, quantities, and measurement systems that are used to describe and characterize the physical world. These chapters set the stage for Chapters 3 and 4, focusing on the terminology of hearing science and the application of its basic principles. Chapters 5 and 6 describe harmonic motion and all the properties of sound waves and how they are measured, while Chapter 7 journeys into the domain of acoustics, examining the propagation of sound waves through space and the complex interactions that shape the sound field. This provides a perfect segue into Chapter 8, summarizing the principles and concepts of psychoacoustics, the science of auditory perception. This chapter deals with what we hear and how the psychophysical attributes of sound vary with changes in the physical parameters of auditory stimulation. The last two chapters focus on the biology of hearing, beginning with a summary of terminology used to describe the various components and principles of nervous system organization (Chapter 9) and ending with a review of the anatomy and physiology of the three subdivisions of the ear (Chapter 10). Each of these chapters is characterized by a well-organized text that is prefaced by an inspiring quote and a list of terms to be defined, and each ends with a clear and succinct summary of concepts and principles introduced. Those chapters with a more quantitative bent also include numerous questions and/or problems to encourage students to put their knowledge to work or think beyond the boundaries of the book's pages. The text is written with meticulous and thorough attention to detail and accuracy. This is especially apparent with regard to the formulas and tables provided for the computations of the Bel, decibel, and RMS amplitude. An additional feature that adds to the attractiveness and flair of the book is the frequent reference to historic discoveries and to those who made them. Concepts presented in the text are beautifully complemented by illustrations, graphs, and equations. This is a book I wish I had had when I was a student, and I believe it will become a first choice textbook among undergraduate and graduate students. It will provide quick answers to questions, both simple and complex, and will provide ever-deepening insights into hearing science when knowledge of details is the goal.

—James A. Kaltenbach, PhD
Director of Otology Research
The Cleveland Clinic

Preface

Basic Fundamentals in Hearing Science was written as a textbook to be used primarily at the undergraduate level. It was originally intended as a replacement textbook in response to the unfortunate discontinuation of an earlier hearing science textbook, authored by J. D. Durrant and J. H. Lovrinic (1995), which by the way also inspired much of the textbook. The organizational approach to this book is somewhat different from what is generally found in books that deal with the same or similar subject matter. Throughout the text, the goal has been to unravel, decompress, and diligently explain in a stepwise fashion, difficult and often cumbersome concepts in order to facilitate their assimilation by non-physics and/or non-mathematics majors. Potentially confounding descriptions have intentionally been avoided. Our intent in *Basic Fundamentals in Hearing Science* has been to take concepts that are likely to be obscure and to clarify them using a writing style that promotes greater understanding and comprehension.

With the writing of any textbook that endeavors to cover the introductory basics, there is always a difficult question that needs to be addressed. That question is what information should and what information should not be included? There is also the matter of how much of the intended information should be included? The resolution to this problem was guided to some extent by simply recollecting how much of the information can actually be covered in a one-semester undergraduate hearing science course. Every attempt was made to compose and organize this textbook in much the same way that an undergraduate hearing science course is generally taught. Because the branch of physics known as "mechanics," provides much of the foundation for the subject matter of hearing science, we placed the subject of hearing science within the larger historical context of Newtonian physics. In this way, we sought to provide clear organized explanations of the metric system, measurement scales, exponential and scientific notation, and logarithms.

In *Basic Fundamentals in Hearing Science,* separate chapters are dedicated to basic scientific and metric measurement terminology, and throughout the text, those same basic principles and terms are applied to the subject matter of hearing science. From the beginning, we thought it was necessary and appropriate to define not only "hearing science," but also the meaning of "science" in general. Understandably, this was no easy task and what began as a simple definition of science at the start of the textbook soon grew into the entire first chapter. Hence, the textbook begins with a definition and survey of the philosophy and practice of science, with an emphasis on theory-driven investigation. At the end of the chapter, we also provided a guide to help students in the writing of a scientific manuscript. Information of this kind is rarely, if ever, provided in a hearing science textbook.

In another chapter, the meaning and significance of harmonic motion, or uniform circular motion, is thoroughly addressed. This includes a survey of simplified trigonometry, with an emphasis on the unit circle, phase angles, radians, measures of amplitude, and different approaches in both the conception and computation of a root-mean-square (RMS) amplitude. Also addressed are factors that influence harmonic motion, such as mass, stiffness, and subsequently, frequency, as well as clear explanations of friction (damping, resistance) and impedance. In yet a subsequent and rather lengthy chapter, a significant degree of attention is devoted to the measurement of sound. This chapter provides clear descriptions of the many types and classifications of sounds, waveform interactions, clear explanations of sound-fields, sound-level meters, distortion, types of microphones, spectral analysis, and spectral shaping, including descriptions of both analog and digital filtering. We also thought it was important to provide clear descriptions of the history, derivation, and computation of the decibel, with comprehensive tables of decibel notation and a list of decibel problems to be solved. Such a degree of attention to the decibel cannot be found in any other text dedicated to the subject of hearing science. This stands as one of

the ways in which *Basic Fundamentals in Hearing Science* encourages thinking and problem solving rather than learning by rote memorization.

Separate chapters are also devoted to acoustics and to psychoacoustics. The separate chapter on acoustics is primarily a consideration of the behavior of sound waves in different sound-field situations. The chapter on psychoacoustics not only provides a historical psychophysical perspective, with clear presentations of the laws and methods of Weber, Fechner, and Stevens, but also provides a survey of more contemporary issues in psychoacoustics. This chapter is clearly relevant to the needs of the audiologist, and we anticipate that students enrolled in doctor of audiology (AuD) programs will also find the chapter on psychoacoustics to be useful. A separate chapter is included that covers basic nervous system terminology as well as accurate descriptions of both the structure and function of the 12 pairs of cranial nerves. Finally, there is a chapter (Chapter 10) devoted more specifically to the anatomy and physiology of hearing. Chapter 10 has been reprinted from *Disorders of the Auditory System* with modifications and updates, with the permission of Plural Publishing.

Acknowledgments

For me, the prospect of writing a textbook on hearing science was daunting. Therefore, I am grateful to a number of individuals who have supported and assisted me in the completion of this undertaking. I would first like to express my unremitting gratitude to my former advisor, present colleague, and coauthor Frank Musiek, without whose support, influence, and guidance this book would not have been completed. Frank has provided me with encouragement, insight, and clarity of thought on a number of collaborative efforts over the years, as I have come to place a high value on his integrity and judgment. The authors would also like to thank Emily C. Parsons, who unfailingly and dependably dedicated her time, support, encouragement, and assistance in helping to bring this work to completion. Sincere thanks also to Terry M. Paczko for his tireless and professional dedication in the essential creation, compilation, organization, and often arduous editing of many of the high-resolution figures that appear throughout Chapters 1 through 8. With sincere gratitude, we also thank Brian C. J. Moore for graciously providing the high-resolution images that appear as Figures 8–1 and 8–6, as well as to John D. Durrant for graciously providing the high-resolution images that appear as Figures 8–9 and 8–12. I am also grateful to John J. Bazyk and Myrita S. Wilhite from the School of Health Sciences for their academic and collegial support, and to Benjamin Wallace for his steadfast encouragement during the time this book was being written. We would also like to thank Lutoni Carter for photography. *Finally, I would like to thank my wife Joan who kept me on target with her patience, love, and encouragement throughout the completion of this endeavor.*—TLS

As the second author (FM), I would like to acknowledge the opportunity provided me by Tony Sahley to contribute to this book. His outstanding work ethic, attention to detail, and devotion to this endeavor serves as a lesson to us all. I would also like to acknowledge the past and present members of the Neuroaudiology Lab at the University of Connecticut for their help with facets of this book. Finally, the both of us would like to extend our gratitude to the patient, helpful, and kind Plural staff, both directly and indirectly, for their flexibility and understanding during the completion of this book.—FM

Chapter 1

What Is Science?

It is difficult to say how science actually began. Science may have had no real beginning and may be as old as perception, beginning in the evolutionary scale with the capacity to generalize in perceiving an object. In observation, both science and perception look to underlying generalities, seeing in the observed object the uniformities of nature.

Boring, 1957, p. 5

Alphabetized Listing of Key Terms Discussed in Chapter 1

abstract section of a manuscript

alternate hypothesis

antecedent variable

asking a question

attribute variable

Bacon, Francis (1561–1626)

between-test reliability

confounding variable

consequent variable

construct

construct validity

criterion variable

deductive logic

dependent variable

descriptive statistics

determinism

discussing the results

discussion section of a manuscript

empirical observation

empiricism

external validity

Galilei, Galileo (1564–1642)

hearing science

hypothesis

hypothesis testing

hypotheses

hypothetical construct

independent variable

inductive logic

inferential

inferential statistics

interjudge reliability

internal validity

interobserver reliability

interrater reliability

intertest reliability

intervening variable

intrarater reliability

intratest reliability

introduction section of a manuscript

Kuhn, Thomas

mean (average)

method(s) section of a manuscript

normal science

null hypothesis

observation

Occam's razor

operational definition	single-case investigation	test-retest reliability
parsimony		time-series investigation
reference section of a manuscript	single hypothesis-driven research	Type I error
reporting the results	standard deviation	Type II error
results section of a manuscript	statistics	validity
science	theoretical validity	variable
scientific experiment	theory	variance
scientific law	theory-driven hypotheses	William of Occam
scientific method	theory-driven research	

What Is Hearing Science?

Hearing science may be defined as the investigation, measurement, and description of all of the physical properties that relate to the production and to the perception of the disturbance known as sound. To be sure, the study of hearing science represents a narrow discipline within the broader scope of physics. Overall, it is a subdiscipline of science that addresses issues pertaining to the measurement of sound, and to the human experience of hearing.

The Roots of Science

The word *science* is derived from the Latin word, *scientia*, which means knowledge (Dirckx, 2005), whose Greek root means to know and to discern one thing from another (Stutz, 2006). Historically, science has represented a defiance of obscurantism and a nobility of purpose in the search for truth under the most adverse circumstances

(Hawking, 2002). Intellectually, science has created a way of thinking in which fear, superstition, and blind obedience to authority are replaced by a form of reasoned, open-minded inquiry that is rooted in observation and experiment (Ferris, 2002). The word *science* in *hearing science* denotes several attributes common to all the sciences. It is used with the understanding that a set of systematic procedures are used in problem solving, decision making, and communicating knowledge to others in a manner that can be objectively evaluated and replicated (Maxwell & Satake, 1997; Schiavetti & Metz, 2002).

The Definition of Science

A sensible place to begin a textbook on hearing science is with a consideration of the general discipline and overall practice of science. Science may be defined as the observation, identification, description, experimental investigation, and theoretical explanation of natural phenomena. Science, therefore, seeks to understand all of the conceivable relationships that may exist amid the many physical and behavioral phenomena found in the universe (Giancoli, 2005; Hewitt, 2010; Leon, 1999). The term *science* is more commonly used to refer to the global activity of building a valid knowledge base. According to Francis Bacon, science is neither philosophy nor humanism, but is instead a process of discovery that leads to an accumulation of knowledge (Stutz, 2006). Knowledge may be defined loosely as the acquisition of information gained through sensory experience and/or investigation. Knowledge, accordingly, is expected to contribute to the reduction of uncertainty (Giancoli, 2005). In addition, the activity of science demands freedom of expression and association, a demand that makes allies of scientists, writers, and artists (Ferris, 2002). However, there are rules that govern the manner in which any knowledge base is built, and these rules also fall under the purview of science (Medawar, 1981; Schiavetti & Metz, 2002). Only to the extent that scientific guidelines for data acquisition are consistently adhered to can the acquired knowledge base validly contribute to a reduction of uncertainty.

The Structure and Philosophy of Science

Measurement and quantification are the trademarks of science (Hewitt, 2010). Science only embraces events that can be directly or indirectly observed and quantified. When and if measurement cannot be made, any subsequent knowledge base assembled as a result will be precarious and unsatisfactory at best.

Moreover, in modern science, argument by appeal to authority has little if any significance (Hewitt, 2010; Maxwell & Satake, 1997). Scientific investigations having the potential to add new knowledge to a contemporary knowledge base must inevitably build upon earlier work. Indeed, science, and the whole of civilization, represents a series of incremental advances, each building upon that which came before (Hawking, 2002; Medawar, 1981). To this end, science is a process that is intended to generate more than just a loose collection of facts. Science is expected to generate an organized, structured body of knowledge in much the same way that a random pile of building material (bricks, steel, wood, etc.) is organized to create a building. What is the mechanism that serves as a basic organizing principle in science? By the generation of theory, science provides the necessary blueprints that indicate how loose collections of facts can, and should, be organized into a coherent knowledge base (Stutz, 2006). However, once generated, theories must also be tested continuously to refine and update current or existing knowledge. Furthermore, new knowledge thus obtained must be disseminated, and the procedures governing the manner in which old and new knowledge is communicated also fall under the purview of science (Medawar, 1981; Schiavetti & Metz, 2002). In short, science provides a systematic way of thinking and behaving, resulting in the unrelenting acquisition, evaluation, and dissemination of knowledge. Hence, we arrive at the best description of this logical human activity, at times referred to as an extension of common sense (Medawar, 1981), and the term, *The Scientific Method*.

The Scientific Method: Philosophy and Practice

The Italian physicist Galileo Galilei (Portrait 1–1) and the English philosopher Francis Bacon (Portrait 1–2) are usually credited as the founders of the philosophy of the scientific method (Hewitt, 2010; Stutz, 2006). Most agree that at least five assumptions form the philosophical foundation for the scientific method. These basic philosophical assumptions are the following: the doctrine of empiricism; the practice of induction (inductive logic); the practice of deduction (deductive logic); the philosophy of determinism; and the attitude or mind-set of parsimony (Giancoli, 2005; Maxwell & Satake, 1997). However, for the scientist actively engaged in the practice of conducting investigations, the scientific method is not only a philosophy, but it is also a strategy that typically involves, but is not necessarily limited to, the following five procedural steps. The five procedural steps are organized from 1 to 6. The steps are presented below in a nonsequential manner at certain locations in the chapter in order to elucidate the subtle procedural differences that exist between single hypothesis-driven research and theory-driven research.

First (1A and 1B below): Ask a Scientific Question. This will require a careful and thorough review of the intended database. In most cases, the database refers to the scientific literature in a particular discipline, but only if that literature is composed of peer-reviewed scientific manuscripts published in high-quality, reputable journals. It then becomes important to rake through the

Portrait 1–1. Galileo Galilei (1564–1642). Modified and printed with permission. Wikimedia Commons, public domain.

Portrait 1–2. Francis Bacon (1561–1626). Printed with permission. Wikimedia Commons, public domain.

vast literature in order to separate that which appears to be known, from that which is clearly unknown. Only then is it possible to ask a relevant and testable question, a question in need of answering to which there seems to be no adequate or acceptable answer. With respect to scrutinizing a vast body of literature, a far less daunting task is to ask a scientific question based on the identified components (constructs) of a formal theoretical model. The process is made easier because questions relating to the separate constructs of theories give way to deductive logic, as described below.

Second (2A and 2B below): Formulate a Hypothesis. This is accomplished by using the existing database as a foundation for identifying all of the relevant variables (known and unknown). Once identified, the relevant variables are organized and categorized (labeled) in terms of which variables are potential antecedents (causes), which are potential consequents (effects), and/or which variables are correlates. The original scientific question is then restated (asked) in terms of the relevant and now categorized variables (experimental variables), in the form of a prediction (hypothesis) or a set of predictions (hypotheses). Formulating theory-driven hypotheses is also an easier task because predictions based on the separate constructs of theories also give way to deductive logic.

Third (3A and 3B below): Design an Experimental Method. The identified experimental variables are assigned operational terms, or are said to be operationally defined. Operational terminology includes expressions such as independent variable, dependent variable, control group/treatment, and/or

experimental group/treatment. A carefully designed outline or set of appropriate (experimental) procedures are then formulated for actually carrying forth the planned investigation. Investigations are therefore designed to test the plausibility of the original hypothesis or hypotheses.

Fourth (4 below): Report the Results, and fifth: (5A and 5B below) Discuss the Possible Significance and Interpretation of the Results. Finally (6 below), the scientific method is culled and summarized into the structure of a scientific manuscript. In the sections that follow, the first five of these strategic procedural steps that described the scientific method in practice, are integrated with the five philosophical assumptions (also provided above) that in total, defines the scientific method.

1A. Asking a Scientific Question: The Doctrine of Empiricism

As indicated above, it is important first, to ask a relevant and testable question that is in need of answering—a question to which there appears to be no adequate or acceptable answer. Prior to the formulation of a scientific question leading ultimately to a scientific inquiry, a significant amount of information gathering must, and generally does occur. Scientific questions are not posed in vacuums. Information that gives rise to relevant scientific questions and subsequently to sound research, must first be gathered and assembled from valid databases. Reputable databases (such as reputable journals) generally serve as a source of valid pre-existing knowledge. Reputable databases provide the very foundation upon which new scientific investigations are born. What separates a valid database from an invalid database as a source of pre-existing knowledge? Valid scientific databases (journals) only publish investigations that have strictly adhered to the doctrine of empiricism. What is meant by the term *valid*? In general, validity refers to the truthfulness or accuracy of a measure or of a conclusion, and in the sciences, many types of validity exist (Campbell & Stanley, 1966). Precise issues related to validity fall outside of the domain and purpose of the present chapter.

Empiricism Defined

Empiricism, simply stated, is the doctrine of observability. Empiricism as a philosophy asserts that knowledge must be gained through sensory experience. It is the doctrine that affirms that nothing can be said to exist until it is actually observed (directly or indirectly) to exist, and that it must be capable of being measured. In terms of science and the scientific method, empiricism is synonymous with unbiased observation and sound, accurate methods of measurement. Indeed, as indicated above, measurement and quantification are the trademarks of science, and science only embraces events that can be directly or indirectly observed and quantified. The doctrine of empiricism is therefore an essential characteristic of rigorous scientific investigation.

Evaluating the Database

Recall that prior to the formulation of a scientific question, a significant amount of information gathering must occur. This often involves a thorough review of information (prior knowledge) published in the intended database. Recall that the database refers to the scientific literature in a particular discipline, and that literature should be composed only of peer-reviewed scientific manuscripts published in well-respected journals. Hence, the basic requirement of empiricism provides the initial framework for judging the scientific merit of any reported phenomenon (Maxwell & Satake, 1997). Without even the fundamental requirement of empiricism, knowledge, or what would pass for knowledge in science, would be based largely on hearsay, speculation, superstition, mysticism, folklore, or unverified authoritarian pronouncements (Schiavetti & Metz, 2002). In the words of Francis Bacon, the pursuit of knowledge must not be blocked by the conventional wisdom of wishful thinking, looking for "proof" for what we already believe, or simply, ignoring information that does not please us (Stutz, 2006). Moreover, according to Bacon, the laws of physics, the laws of nature and all of the universe cannot be authentically investigated as long as there is an untested (unsubstantiated), preconceived, overarching, and therefore biasing concept of the universe already in existence (Stutz, 2006). Exactly what is and what is not implied by the use of the term *observation*?

Empiricism Versus Conventional Observation

Conventional observation is not what is implied by the term *empiricism* since the common, conventional kind of observation has no place in empirical science. Indeed, even Francis Bacon cautioned against too great a reliance on subjective sensations, arguing in favor of employing measurement instruments in the attempt to reduce or eliminate bias (Stutz, 2006). Therefore, the type of observation implied by the use of the term empiricism falls under the exacting rules that govern unbiased and valid research methods (Maxwell & Satake, 1997; Schiavetti & Metz, 2002). Consequently, empiricism embraces the types of observations made through the use of calibrated measurement devices and valid methodological procedures. While the subject matter of research methods and research design falls outside the scope and intent of the present chapter, it is important to state that empiricism in science adheres to sampling procedures that are also unbiased. Hence, empiricism also conforms to the inclusion of carefully designed control conditions, control subjects, or control groups for purposes of comparison and validation (Campbell & Stanley, 1966; Maxwell & Satake, 1997; Schiavetti & Metz, 2002).

Empiricism and the Need for Verification

Finally, empirical research must endure the scrutiny of scientific verification by others. The essential tenet of science is that each discovery or theory must be capable of being investigated, replicated, and verified by others, so that it can become a foundation upon which further work can stand (Stutz, 2006). Accordingly, all that passes for knowledge, and all that is worth knowing must be amenable to direct or indirect observation, employing accurate measuring devices and procedures that can be subsequently verified by others (Maxwell & Satake, 1997; Schiavetti & Metz, 2002). Issues relating to the reli-

ability (repeatability) of observations will not be addressed in the present context. Notwithstanding, most if not all scientific investigations share in common the assignment and the ultimate handling of variables.

2A. Formulating a Hypothesis: Identifying Relevant Variables

As indicated above, the empirical database provides a source and a foundation for identifying all of the relevant variables under consideration, prior to the formulation of a hypothesis. Related to empiricism is the fact that science is often engaged in the manipulation and observation (measurement) of variables. A variable may be defined as a measurable quantity that can vary or change under different circumstances (Schiavetti & Metz, 2002). Recall as well that once identified, the relevant variables need to be organized and categorized. In scientific practice, some variables are designated as antecedents, whereas other variables are destined to be consequents. As the name implies, a time-order relationship exists such that an antecedent variable is conceived as taking place prior to the occurrence of a consequent variable (Maxwell & Satake, 1997). Therefore, a scientific investigation may be defined as any set of procedures aimed at measuring or determining the influence or relationship of antecedent variables on consequent variables (Schiavetti & Metz, 2002). However, the real determinant of any particular variable's place or role in an investigation is the manner in which an investigator conceives that a meaningful relationship could or may exist, and/or the manner in which the investigator chooses to use the variable (Schiavetti & Metz, 2002). Once this has been established, it is then important that each variable of interest is defined in advance, according to the manner in which it is to be assigned, manipulated, measured, or controlled, and in short, defined by the way in which it is to be used (Maxwell & Satake, 1997). Then, the original scientific question may be restated in the form of a prediction (hypothesis) or a set of predictions (hypotheses) in the language of the experimental variables.

The term *hypothesis* may now be defined as a causal, correlative, or an otherwise inferential and testable prediction made with respect to potential relationships that may or may not exist between the variables in a particular investigation (Hempel, 1966; Hewitt, 2010; Maxwell & Satake, 1997). The term *inferential* is used here simply to mean that a relationship is presumed or is postulated to exist. Associated with the terms inferential, formulating a hypothesis, and actual statistical hypothesis testing, are probability estimates for making certain types of (statistical) inference errors. However, while issues related to inferential statistics in research are well beyond the scope and intent of the present text, the subject matter is briefly addressed below under the heading of "Reporting the Results: Hypothesis Testing." Notwithstanding, the simplest of causal relationships is one in which changes observed, or manipulations made in one variable are believed to be the direct cause of changes observed in a second variable. The simplest type of correlational relationship is one in which observed changes in one variable are associated, either directly or inversely,

with changes observed in a second variable, but neither variable is the direct cause of the changes observed in the other.

Single Hypothesis-Driven Versus Theory-Driven Research

In this chapter, we will occasionally find the need to differentiate between single hypothesis-driven (or single hypothesis-based) research and theory-driven (or theory-based) research. While useful conceptually, it should be kept in mind that the two strategic categories of investigation are not necessarily mutually exclusive. The two categories of investigation adhere to the same principles of empiricism and in practice are identical. However, theory-driven research often begins with several interrelated hypotheses. Each of the separate hypotheses often reflects a separate but related component (construct) of the theory. Hence, theory-driven research often requires that several theory-driven hypotheses be formulated.

Not every research question that is asked and not every hypothesis that is formulated will arise out of the necessity to test the separate components of a theoretical model. In many instances an investigator may simply want to find an answer to a relatively simple question. Based on the type of question posed, the investigator who designs and executes the one-shot, one-time single-hypothesis-driven investigation may or may not intend that the outcome, be it positive or negative, should serve as a means or impetus for generating further investigations. Correspondingly, the outcome of the one-time single-hypothesis-driven investigation, whether that outcome is positive or negative, may or may not warrant that additional investigations be conducted in the immediate future. Even so, one-time single-hypothesis-driven empirical investigations, if conducted properly, are often very useful in establishing valid experimental methods and valid but often disconnected, bits of empirical knowledge in a database.

3A. Designing an Experimental Method: Operationally Defining Variables

Having clearly stated a hypothesis (or even a set of hypotheses), a scientific investigation is then carefully designed so that it may address the specific question or set of questions that have been postulated (Hempel, 1966). This activity, in essence, will establish an initial foundation for the ensuing process of hypothesis testing. The use of *operationally defined* variables means that each of the separate components (variables) of any investigation should be defined with respect to, and in accordance with, the conditions under which each component is to be measured (Hempel, 1966; Stevens, 1958). In all experimental research, those variables designated as antecedents are often referred to as independent variables (Campbell & Stanley, 1966). Independent variables may also be called *active* variables, indicating that these variables are, in fact, manipulated (Schiavetti & Metz, 2002). Independent variables used as antecedents in experimental research tend to be continuous variables. Continuous variables exhibit precise and often quantifiable gradations between measures. Examples of continuous vari-

ables are variables such as drug doses, drug concentrations, current level, duration of exposure, temperature, lighting conditions, and so on (see Chapter 2). In experimental research, the variable that is designated as the consequent is referred to as the dependent variable (Schiavetti & Metz, 2002). A dependent variable is also an observable and measurable variable. The term *dependent* is an appropriate term since the assumption is made that any anticipated variance or change observed in the dependent variable is likely to have resulted from (or is dependent upon) manipulations that were made to the independent variable or variables (Campbell & Stanley, 1966). Dependent variables used as consequent variables in experimental research are often measured as relative changes in performance from a set of normative values, from a baseline, or from a control condition or control manipulation. Dependent variables may be continuous or categorical. Examples of continuous dependent variables might include learning performance, auditory discrimination performance, speech intelligibility performance, diadochokinetic rate, and motor performance. Examples of categorical dependent variables are the assignment of pass or fail; grades of A, B, C, or D; and judgments of acceptable or nonacceptable, hot or cold, and so on (see Chapter 2).

When operational definitions are used to transform vague concepts into concise, measurable operations, the communication that takes place in science is greatly enhanced (Maxwell & Satake, 1997). As a simple example, consider the category *severe hearing loss*. The concept of severe could vaguely refer to any hearing loss producing harsh consequences with respect to an individual's receptive communication. However, the accepted operational definition of severe hearing loss is customarily as follows: for any ear, an audiometric three-frequency pure tone average yielding values falling between 71 and 90 decibels (dB) in hearing level (HL). The concept of three frequency pure tone average could also be defined operationally as the average of the absolute thresholds obtained by air conduction at the audiometric frequencies, 500, 1000, and 2000 Hz. It is not difficult to see that the practice of operationally defining relevant variables can greatly reduce the likelihood of confusion and misunderstanding when communicating ideas (Maxwell & Satake, 1997). Issues that relate to the actual quantification of operational definitions are presented in Chapter 2.

Human Subject Groups

Slight alterations in independent-dependent variable terminology may arise in behavioral investigations involving groups of human subjects (Schiavetti & Metz, 2002). Sometimes the correct assignment of terms for the antecedent and the consequent variables is attribute and criterion variables. That is, rather than consisting of independent variables that can be directly manipulated, the antecedent variables under investigation may consist of subject attributes (Schiavetti & Metz, 2002). Human, and sometimes animal subjects may be chosen to participate in an investigation because they possess, as part of their history, certain known attributes that place them naturally into unique categories. The attributes in these subjects may be of particular interest to the investigator, though it may be impossible, improbable, or unethical to cause, create, or directly manipulate the attribute in the same manner that independent variables are manipulated. Examples of antecedent subject attributes would include gender, handedness, eye color, hair color, a particular animal strain, age range, autistic disordered, learning disabled, language delayed, diabetic, genetically altered, and so on (see Chapter 2).

In order to investigate the consequences of attributes used as antecedents, human subjects must be labeled along common attribute dimensions and placed into groups. It may then be necessary to create many separate groups based on the similarities or dissimilarities defined along particular attribute dimensions. When attribute variables are the antecedents, consequent variables such as measures of learning, of speech intelligibility, of speech articulation, of auditory discrimination, or of motor performance, and the like, are not formally thought of as dependent variables. Instead, they are often referred to as criterion variables (Schiavetti & Metz, 2002). It is then assumed that any observed variance or change in the consequent criterion variable in any particular group is likely to have resulted from the particular attribute present in the subjects within the group in question.

The Necessity for Formal Theory Construction

As indicated above, both the doctrine and the experimental practice of empiricism are essential for the establishment and creation of a valid database composed of large numbers of experimental observations. Indeed, that empiricism is a very important and immutable part of scientific research cannot be overemphasized. However, empiricism alone does not define all of science, nor does science advance by empiricism alone. Those who embrace the idea that empiricism alone will advance science, may succeed in supporting the establishment of valid experimental methods, but may also support the generation of many separate (but disconnected) bits of knowledge in a database. Nevertheless, when large numbers of observations in the form of separate investigations begin to accumulate in a database, as they inevitably will, an important next step, or "leap" in science, is to make sense of the information gleaned from the vast number of empirical observations. Unfortunately, empiricism alone provides no mechanism for systematically determining the overall relations that may exist between each bit of knowledge (Hempel, 1966). It also provides no mechanism for integrating knowledge from the databases of other scientific disciplines. Instead, it is only through the philosophical practice of inductive logic that the scientific method endeavors to organize a large accumulation of empirically based observations into the meaningful construction of a formal theory.

Formal Theory Construction: Inductive Logic (Induction)

Induction or inductive logic in science is a process of arriving at a conclusion, a generalization, or a theory, following an examination of many single observations or events. The inductive logic practiced in science (Medawar, 1981) is a logical extension of the common-sense inductive logic that is a part of all experiential human learning (Box 1–1). Induction, therefore, represents a logical process of reasoning that begins with particular or specific instances and concludes with a general theory or a set of principles (Hempel, 1966; Schiavetti & Metz, 2002). Some have suggested that induction represents a form of problem solving (Maxwell & Satake, 1997). Einstein emphasized the importance of what he called "free invention" of the mind, stressing the need for the creation of concepts, theories, and postulates from our own imagination, to then later confront these mental "constructs" with observation and experimentation (Lightman, 2002). This scientific method also specifies a pathway of events that are emphasized in this chapter. Put simply, this pathway includes but is not limited to, first beginning with observation, then advancing to induction, to theory, to deduction, and finally to additional experimentation.

The process of inductive logic begins with empiricism (Hempel, 1966) as indicated above. The scientific method (with its doctrine of empiricism) imposes certain requirements, restrictions, and rules that mandate the manner in which valid observations are to be made, recorded, analyzed, and reported, prior to the start of any empirical investigation. Following the gathering and examination of all of the relevant particulars (valid empirical observations), the induction process then advances to a level of reasoning in which separate factors, symbolic realities, or (hypothetical) constructs are assembled and integrated into a greater or generalized whole (Hempel, 1966). As indicated above, the theory-generating process of induction often requires an intellectual

---

Box 1–1. Simple Inductive Logic

Scientific inquiry is a human activity. It is perhaps not surprising, therefore, that the scientific method is a meticulous extension of what might otherwise be labeled conventional human reasoning or simply, ordinary common sense. Inductive logic has its basis in simple experiential learning. For example, a child raised in a family that keeps many dogs as pets will observe that each pet dog has four legs (specific instance). Without exception, each dog observed represents an object having four legs. In a logical attempt to simplify and categorize the world, inductive logic in this case leads to the generalization or general principle (general case or theory) that "all four-legged animals are dogs." Accordingly, when the child observes one of many canine pets in the home, the appropriate response is always "dog." However, if the child later observes a cat, a horse, a cow, or any other animate animal or inanimate model (as a toy), each of which has four legs, the child will probably also label the object as a dog. This universal labeling of all four-legged objects or animal archetypes as dogs will continue until the child learns, through additional experience, to refine and modify the original general principle (or theory) to "all four-legged animals are not dogs."

---

leap of faith (Hawking, 2002). The process represents a creative leap from the rigors of empiricism, to the derivation of a general theory, requiring a considerable degree of imagination and ingenuity on the part of an investigator (Hempel, 1966; Maxwell & Satake, 1997). This level of inductive reasoning not only requires a thorough familiarity with the current knowledge base in a particular discipline, but often requires an additional well-grounded familiarity with the current state of knowledge in other, related disciplines. Some investigators use the term *predictive knowledge* to mean the same as theory, and some have even suggested that induction bridges the gap between existing knowledge and predictive knowledge (Maxwell & Satake, 1997). However,

as indicated later in this chapter, the predictive power of a theoretical model may only be fully realized through the process of deductive logic. For the present, a simple block diagram illustrating the leap from observation to inductive logic, leading to the generation of a formal theory, is presented in Figure 1–1.

Definition of Theory in Science

As indicated in the preceding sections, the generation of theory is achieved by combining the fact-gathering activity of empiricism with inductive logic (Hempel, 1966). Recall that theory has been associated with the term *predictive knowledge*. Because of the potential predictive value of theory, some scientists believe that theory construction

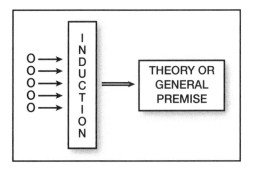

Figure 1–1. Inductive logic (Induction) and the construction of a formal theory. In the model, the arrows indicate the directional flow of events that begin with a series of separate empirical observations ("Os") on the far left. These observations represent experimental data obtained through investigations that employ the rules of empiricism. The arrows also indicate that the flow of events culminates in the formulation of a general premise or theory composed of hypothetical constructs, and is obtained only through the process of induction or inductive logic.

is the ultimate aim of science (Brody, 1970; Leon, 1999). It should again be made clear that the predictive power of theory is only as good as deductive logic and the formulation of hypotheses (see below), and the relative likelihood or probability of obtaining certain outcomes resulting from future investigations (Hempel, 1966; Maxwell & Satake, 1997). Therefore, in the present context, the use of the term *theory* should not be confused with the expression *hypothesis* which was defined previously. In common everyday speech, the word *theory* is often mistaken for *hypothesis*. Scientists, however, use the word *theory* in a manner that differs from its usage in familiar speech (Box 1–2). Hence, in scientific practice the two terms are not

---

Box 1–2. The Doctrine of Determinism

We can now extend the example of the concept "dog" as presented in Boxes 1–1 and 1–3. The original generalization, general case, principle, or theory stated that all four-legged animals or all four-legged animal archetypes are dogs. From the overall belief system presented in this example, one primary prediction (or hypothesis) derived through the process of deductive logic might begin with the general case and conclude with the following prediction: If I observe a single occurrence of what appears to be an animate (or even one inanimate) object having four legs, then the object should be labeled a dog.

Since the general case, principle, or theory, by definition, represents a lawful and orderly set of interrelated constructs, four-legged animal-objects observed yesterday, today, or in the future should be labeled as "dog." That is, the same four-legged object is not expected to change dramatically from one form (dog) to another (a chair), and certainly not in a random or haphazard manner, unless the general case, principle, or theory indicates that it should do so. The assumption of lawful, predictable, and stable observations in this particular case is an example of the doctrine of determinism.

synonymous (Hewitt, 2010). To be sure, well-conceived theories are expected to establish an organized, methodical, and logical structure to scientific thinking. Theory-driven hypotheses associated with theory-driven research are essential in providing a perspective that guides additional (future) scientific inquiry. Well-conceived theories also provide the organizing structure for communicating new facts as they emerge, enabling scientific investigators to explain newly acquired data (this point is discussed later in the chapter).

Once a well-conceived theory is formulated, it often develops into an orderly set of interrelated constructs (Schiavetti & Metz, 2002). Therefore, "theory" may be defined simply as any orderly set of well-defined and interrelated constructs. A construct may be defined as an abstraction, an idea, or a concept. Constructs have in the past been called, and are essentially the same as, *hypothetical constructs*. All of the separate components that go into a construct, and all of the factors that

constructs describe, are often called, for research purposes, variables (Maxwell & Satake, 1997). The well-defined concepts and components of any well-conceived theory are the factors that provide the organizing structure (i.e., the hypothetical constructs) to the theory. In essence, the hypothetical constructs that define a theory will ultimately determine the exact wordings of the theory-driven hypotheses that are ultimately formulated. The constructs of a simple theory are provided by the example in Box 1–3.

From Problem Solving to Problem Making

Induction and the building of theory represent only part of the creative philosophy of the scientific method. Science must also include a logical mechanism for testing the validity of theories that the inductive process has generated. Deduction (or deductive logic) is, in fact, the logical mechanism in science that is used to formally investigate the validity of theories (Hempel,

---

Box 1–3. The Simple Constructs of a Theory

Continuing with the simplistic example presented originally in Box 1–1, a child, through experience, endorses a general principle or advocates for the general case (or what would amount to a theory) that "all four-legged animals or animal archetypes are dogs." Having experienced a wide (or in this case, limited) variety of canine breeds in the home, the separate constructs of the general belief system held by the child in this particular example might be that independent of the size, shape, color, hair length, state of animation, behavioral disposition, length of tail, ear size, gender, and so forth, all of these animals have four legs and, therefore, they are all to be labeled as dogs. The separate components that go into the construct, such as the number of legs, the size, the shape, the color, and so forth, are, therefore, variables.

1966). Whereas inductive logic has been referred to as a process of problem solving, some embrace the idea that deductive logic represents a form of problem making (Maxwell & Satake, 1997).

1B. Asking Scientific Questions: Formulating Predictions Based on a Theoretical Model and the Role of Deductive Logic (Deduction)

Deduction has been described as the logical process of problem making. Like induction, the deductive logic practiced in science is a logical extension of common, everyday deductive reasoning, which is a component of all experiential human learning (Medawar, 1981). Inasmuch as the reasoning of induction began with particular or specific instances (empirical observations) and concluded with a general theory or set of principles, deduction begins with a general premise or theory. The theory may consist of well-organized principles and/or a set of laws (constructs) that are at least initially assumed to contain some degree of a priori validity. In actuality, a general theory reflects only a set of statements regarding the probable relationships that might exist amid the (hypothetical) constructs that comprise the theory itself (Hempel, 1966; Maxwell & Satake, 1997). Nevertheless, through deductive logic, the separate components (pieces or constructs) of the theory are used as a basis to ask (formulate) scientific questions or make predictions, that amounts to formulating a hypothesis, or in most cases, a set of hypotheses (Figure 1–2) prior to the acquisition of additional and specific empirical observations. Recall from above that the formulation

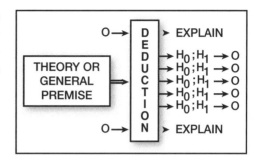

Figure 1–2. Deductive logic (Deduction) and the formulation of hypotheses. Deductive logic is used not only in the formulation of a question (*not shown*) that leads to a set of hypotheses, but is also used to explain observations. In the model above, the arrows indicate the directional flow of events that begin with a general premise or a theory. The general premise or theory is initially taken, at least temporarily, as the a priori truth, as each construct of the theory is tested empirically. Deductive logic is employed to ask scientific questions (*not shown*) that lead to the formulation of predictions. Predictions are represented by a specific set of hypotheses (H_0; H_1) prior to making experimental observations (Os). The "Os" represent scientific observations obtained through the rules of empiricism. The H_0 stands for the null hypothesis. The H_1 stands for the alternate hypotheses (see text for an explanation). Deductive logic is also used to explain a specific observation or behavioral occurrence once it has transpired as indicated at the top and the bottom of the deduction box.

of theory-driven hypotheses occurs in theory-driven investigations, and the hypothetical constructs that define a theory ultimately determine the exact wording, or the manner in which the theory-driven hypotheses are formulated. It must be re-emphasized, however, that hypotheses are only statements of probability, and the separate components (constructs) of any proposed theory must ultimately hold up to the doctrine of empiricism (Hempel, 1966). In this way, deductive logic is the philosophical mechanism utilized for setting up the necessary conditions that enable investigators to test the validity of theories that the inductive process has generated. Insofar as scientific research is concerned, the mental activity of deduction that began with a general theory ultimately concludes with the empirical observation of particular or specific instances.

2B. Formulating Theory–Driven Hypotheses

As indicated above, deductive logic leads to, and is very useful in formulating, in most cases, a set of hypotheses (see Figure 1–2) with regard to expected outcomes, based on the constructs of the theory. Once again, this is because the hypothetical constructs that define a theory will in essence ultimately define the theory-driven hypotheses that must be formulated.

Operationally defining (discussed earlier) the separate constructs of a theory is also very useful when formulating suppositions or conjectures through the process of deductive logic. In this respect the practice of generating operational definitions permits scientists to sharpen their level of communication when formulating theory-driven hypotheses. Hence, the term hypothesis may be extended and redefined as a causal, correlative, or an otherwise inferential and testable prediction made with respect to potential relationships that may or may not exist between the variables that define the (hypothetical) constructs in a particular theory (Hempel, 1966; Hewitt, 2010; Maxwell & Satake, 1997). In fact, many scientists believe that the primary reason for conducting scientific research is to investigate hypotheses in relation to the tenets (constructs) that define particular theories (Maxwell & Satake, 1997).

The Role of Determinism

Another philosophical assumption embedded in the scientific method is determinism. The doctrine of determinism plays an important role in the initial stages of formulating a set of hypotheses from any orderly set of interrelated constructs, which again, defines a theory (Schiavetti & Metz, 2002). The doctrine of determinism maintains that law and order exist in the natural universe (see Box 1–2). This doctrine may be contrasted with the philosophic position that natural events occur in a completely random fashion. Quantum mechanics (the science of atomic and subatomic particles) also maintains that predictability is inherently lacking in nature (Giancoli, 2005; Hewitt, 2010). However, even in subatomic "chaotic systems," there may exist patterns of regularity, and hence, "order" can often be found in "chaos" (Giancoli, 2005; Hewitt, 2010). Nevertheless, while quantum theory served to unify electromagnetism with the subatomic world of matter, distinctions between matter (mass) and energy disappear at this level (Stutz, 2006). The study of matter and energy at the atomic and subatomic level is at best difficult and exact measurements are impossible. This is because the very act of measurement directly affects what is being measured (Stutz, 2006). Thus, until a unifying theory of all matter can be discovered, it may well be the case that the doctrine of determinism applies entirely to the study of macroscopic events. Macroscopic events, therefore, refer to observations of mass and energy on a macro scale, which is considered by many to be more directly within the realm of sensory experience. These macro events would include behavior of whole organisms and, therefore, investigations not necessarily requiring the use of electron microscopes.

It therefore seems that logical and valid predictions, at least in the behavioral sciences, are more readily made when the initial premise upon which a prediction is built consists of a lawful and orderly set of interrelated constructs, or, simply, the exact definition of a theory (Schiavetti & Metz, 2002). Hence, assumptions of law and order in the constructs of theory give rise to predictions or simply to the formulation of theory-driven hypotheses.

3B. Designing Experimental Methods: Operationally Defining Theory Constructs

As before, beginning with a clearly stated set of hypotheses, a series of investigations are carefully designed to test the separate constructs of the theory. This activity serves as a foundation for the process of hypothesis testing. Any given construct within a particular theory or investigation must be defined according to the manner or the operations that are required to measure or to use the construct. In this way, a construct, a variable, or any other concept within a particular theory or investigation is said to be operationally defined (Campbell & Stanley, 1966; Hempel, 1966; Maxwell & Satake, 1997).

4. Reporting the Results: Hypothesis Testing

Reporting the results generally means, and is synonymous with, reporting the outcome of the inferential statistical data analyses that are, by and large, always performed in the behavioral sci-

ences. Recall that the term *inferential* means that a relationship is only presumed or is postulated (hypothesized) to exist. When performed, these analyses are directly related to the causal, correlative, or otherwise inferential and testable predictions that were formulated earlier in the investigation. Recall that a hypothesis was defined above as a causal, correlative, or otherwise inferential and testable prediction made with respect to potential relationships that may or may not exist between the variables in a particular investigation. Hence, performing inferential statistical analyses is synonymous with "hypothesis testing."

As briefly indicated above, hypothesis testing is also associated with the concept of "probability estimates" for making certain types of statistical inference errors. In this regard, inferential statistics are used in making decisions concerning the validity of apparent differences or relationships between the measureable variables observed as a direct outcome of an investigation. This is usually accomplished by examining the plausibility of the "null hypothesis (H_0)" and the probability (p) out of 100 possibilities, of committing a "Type I error." Simply and briefly put, the null hypothesis states that *no* differences (or relationships) exist between the mean (average) values of the different groups, conditions, or treatment levels. A Type I error is made when the investigator incorrectly rejects the null hypothesis in favor of the alternate hypothesis (H_1) which attests that differences (or relationships) *do* exist between the mean values of the different groups, conditions, or treatment levels. The probability of committing a Type I error is denoted by alpha (α), which is also called the level of significance (or level of confidence), and this value is usually set to a value (level) of 0.05, or at times to 0.01. Alternatively, a Type II error, denoted by beta (β), occurs when the investigator incorrectly fails to reject H_0 and instead rejects H_1.

Reporting the results additionally means visually summarizing any important, relevant, or noteworthy main effects and/or interactions or correlations. These are usually presented in the form of tables and/or graphically, using descriptive statistics. Descriptive statistics include, but are not limited to, the mean (group and/or treatment averages) and the standard deviation(s) from the mean(s). The standard deviation, by definition, is the square root of the variance, and the variance is defined as the mean of the sum of the squared deviations (of each data point) from the appropriate (group) mean value. Finally, it is often necessary to report, and to present, by table and/or by figure, instances where the results suggest that no observed changes occurred (i.e., no effect; no correlation) between the relevant variables under investigation.

5A. Discussing and Interpreting the Results: Evaluating Single Hypothesis–Driven Research

In the single hypothesis-driven research investigation, the empirically based observations reported in the results will either confirm or disconfirm the original hypotheses, expectations, or predictions upon which the investigation was originally conceived. That is, based on inferential statistical data analyses, an important goal of empirical research is to draw valid conclusions regarding the relationships (causal or otherwise)

that may or may not exist between the variables that have been under investigation (Hempel, 1966). Such information helps determine the direction that future scientific inquiry should take once the original formulated hypothesis has been shown to be either tenable or untenable. Statements regarding the significance or importance of the newly acquired data often mandate an additional course of action and decision making that ultimately impacts future investigations. As indicated earlier, the investigator who designs and executes the one-shot, one-time, single-hypothesis-driven investigation may or may not intend that the outcome, positive or negative, should serve as a means or impetus for generating further investigations. In the same way, the outcome of the one-time single-hypothesis-driven research investigation, be it positive or negative, may or may not warrant that additional investigations be conducted in the immediate future.

5B. Discussing and Interpreting the Results: Evaluating Theory–Driven Research

As with the single hypothesis-driven research investigation, empirically based observations reported in the results of a theory-driven research investigation will either confirm or disconfirm the original hypothesis, and/or set of hypotheses, expectations, or predictions upon which the investigation was originally conceived. However, because the theory-driven hypotheses that are formulated as a procedural part of theory-driven research investigations are in essence, the same (hypothetical) constructs that define the theory itself, these theory-driven hypotheses carry more weight than those that are formulated in single-hypothesis-driven investigations. Consequently, empirically based observations reported in the results of a theory-driven research investigation will, in addition, either provide support (verification), or lack of support (falsification) to the constructs that define the theory.

Recall that well-conceived theories can play a major role in helping to establish an orderly and logical structure to scientific thought. In addition, theory-driven hypotheses that are formulated during investigations of well-conceived theories are essential in providing a guide to future scientific inquiry. For these reasons, additional consideration and reflection will need to be given when discussing and interpreting the results of theory-driven investigations. These deliberations will need to address the manner in which the outcome of a theory-driven investigation should be interpreted relative to the original theory. Decisions will also need to be made at the conclusion of a theory-driven scientific investigation once the theory-driven hypotheses have been shown empirically to be either tenable or untenable. These decisions will determine the direction taken by future experimentation.

Providing Explanations and the Role of Parsimony

An explanation of the results will be needed at the conclusion of any investigation. In the single hypothesis-driven research investigation, once all the experimental events have occurred and all the data have been analyzed, explanations that are provided are often based on previous investigations, previous hypotheses, the current hypothesis, or possibly even unrelated conjectures. However, in theory-driven research, deductive logic is often the mental process involved when a general theory or a general set of principles is used to explain specific empirical outcomes. Deduction is also the same mental process that enables any individual to make sense of the world following the occurrence of natural events. Deductive reasoning begins with an all-encompassing generalization, a theory, or an explanatory model. The broad presuppositions of the theory are then utilized through deductive reasoning to explain a specific, or a set of observations, or behavioral occurrences after the events have occurred (Hempel, 1966).

In any explanation or discussion of the results, whether from a single hypothesis-driven or a theory-driven research investigation, an investigator must exercise a degree of caution and discretion. The cautionary discretion refers to the exercise and philosophical mind-set of parsimony (Maxwell & Satake, 1997; Schiavetti & Metz, 2002). Parsimony, in the present context, is another of the five philosophical assumptions of the scientific method, and it stands for prudence, caution, circumspection, restraint, and frugality of thought in any explanation. As an example, it is seldom stated following any series of investigations in the behavioral sciences, that the results "prove" the hypothesis to be true. Rather, it is stated that the experimental findings or analyses "are (or are not) consistent with" the original hypothesis (or hypotheses) that was originally stated and investigated (Campbell & Stanley, 1966; Giancoli, 2005). Hence, in the behavioral sciences, it is imprudent to use the term *proof*, and the use of such terminology should be avoided.

When explanations are provided at the conclusion of a single-hypothesis-driven research investigation, the doctrine of parsimony further mandates that the explanations be made using the least complex and/or least abstract descriptions possible. The same rules apply when explanations are provided at the conclusion of a theory-driven research investigation. Recall that well-conceived theories are expected to provide an organizing structure for communicating new facts as the facts emerge, enabling scientific investigators to better explain newly acquired data. However, cautionary discretion must especially be exercised when using an all-encompassing generalization or theory to account for, or otherwise explain a limited (small) set of observations. The investigator is to avoid ardent, overgenerous, overzealous, highly complex, or overly abstract explanations for simple occurrences, unless all of the simpler explanations have first been considered and/or systematically or experimentally ruled out (Box 1–4). Explanations are

---

Box 1–4. Explanations and Parsimony: Theory–Based Investigations

Using the same deductive reasoning that begins with the general case—all four-legged animals or animal archetypes are dogs—a simple explanation may be provided following either a planned or unplanned observation of a single occurrence of a four-legged animal or animal archetype.

For instance,

> [single observation]: The animal-object has four legs, what is it, and/or why?

> [general case]: All four-legged animals or animal archetypes are dogs.

> [explanation]: The animal-object observed has four legs, therefore it must be a dog.

Alternatively,

> [single observation]: Why does the observed animal-object have four legs?

> [general case]: All four-legged animals or animal archetypes are dogs.

> [explanation]: Because the observed four-legged animal-object must be a dog, it therefore must also have four legs.

also to be made with the fewest possible contradictions (Maxwell & Satake, 1997).

As William of Occam stated in the 14th century, "the assumptions introduced to explain a thing must not be multiplied beyond necessity." This statement, declaring the need for the frugality of thought (or parsimony), has become known as the "Occam razor" (Dirckx, 2005). Later, Isaac Newton (1642–1727) would be quoted as stating in his "Rules of Reasoning in Philosophy" that "we are to admit no more causes of natural things than such as are both true and sufficient to explain their appearances. . . . Nature is pleased with simplicity and affects and not the pomp of superfluous causes" (Hawking, 2002, p. 731).

In the example provided in Box 1–4, consider the single observation: Why does the observed animal-object have four legs? Employing the general case premise that all four-legged animals or animal archetypes are dogs, it would be imprudent to offer an explanation that the animal-object observed has four legs, but it really has two wooden legs and it is therefore posing as a dog, or the animal-object observed has four legs but it is not a real dog because its legs are magical, so it must be an alien dog-like creature from another world.

Confirmation and Support

Following an accumulation of numerous confirmatory empirical observations, decisions must then be made as to whether the available evidence is sufficient to lend support to the original theory. It should be emphasized that in science, every genuine hypotheses-test within a theory should be conceived as an attempt to falsify or refute the original theory (Popper, 1962). However, in the absence of unfavorable (disconfirming) evidence, continued instances of confirmation are normally taken to increase the overall support for the theory (Hempel, 1966). If a theory leads to logical predictions (stated in terms of specific hypotheses), and the results of the empirical investigations that follow indicate that the hypotheses are empirically tenable, then such evidence will begin to provide support to the original theory (Maxwell & Satake, 1997; Schiavetti & Metz, 2002).

Construct Validity

Once again, the statistical/empirical observations reported in the results of a theory-driven research investigation provide evidence that not only permits an evaluation (support or lack of support) of the hypotheses that generated the investigation, but evidence that also authorizes an evaluation of the (hypothetical) constructs that define the theory. "Theory" has been defined as an orderly set of interrelated, operationally defined (hypothetical) constructs. Therefore, it should be easy to understand that the term *construct validity* is synonymous with the expression "theoretical (or theory) validity" (Maxwell & Satake, 1997).

Construct validity is considered to be the most convincing form of validity. Recall that validity refers to the truthfulness, accuracy of a measure, or accuracy of a conclusion. In the present instance, it is used to indicate the accuracy and truthfulness of a theory. The greater the degree of construct validity that has been established, the greater is the evidence-based confidence that the constructs of a theory are actuality interrelated in a manner that is consistent with the manner suggested by the theory (Schiavetti & Metz, 2002).

Construct validity is usually established by the consistent accumulation of supporting evidence obtained from the results of many empirical investigations (i.e., quantity). These empirical investigations may be performed by the same or by different investigators employing the same, consistent operational definitions (Maxwell & Satake, 1997). Support for a theory continues to increase as long as empirical evidence is continuously brought together with theoretical considerations (Schiavetti & Metz, 2002). However, as additional support is obtained, the impact of any single finding will progressively diminish as the number of previously established confirmations continues to accumulate (Hempel, 1966). This diminishing-returns principle is especially true if the accumulation of confirmatory evidence consists exclusively of exact replications of the original investigation(s) that initially supported the theory.

Construct validity will be additionally strengthened by converging (corroborating) lines of supporting evidence from a diversity of scientific disciplines. It is highly desirable that a scientific theory accrues confirmation by "new evidence." New evidence refers to empirical observations that lead to knowledge that was not known or not taken into account when the original theory was formulated (Hempel, 1966). Hence, not only is the quantity of confirmatory evidence important, but the number of confirmations obtained from a diversity of investigations is equally, if not more, important in establishing construct validity (Popper, 1962). As the diver-

sity of confirmations is increased, the degree of support attributed to any single confirmation will be subsequently enhanced. When both the quantity and diversity of confirmations continue to accumulate, then the overall degree of construct validity obtained for a particular theory becomes a highly relevant issue (Hempel, 1966).

The greater the quantity and diversity of support for a theory, the greater will be the overall degree of construct validity for that theory, and the greater the likelihood that a particular theory may, in time, become a well-established principle or, perhaps, a general law (Campbell & Stanley, 1966; Hewitt, 2010). A general scientific law is a concise statement, often expressed in the form of an equation, which quantitatively describes a particular range of phenomena over a wide range of cases (Giancoli, 2005). In addition, and to reiterate a point made in the section above that addresses the principle of parsimony, it is imprudent in the behavioral sciences to use the term *proof.* The use of such terminology, such as in the statement, "the results of the present investigation prove the hypotheses and/or the theory to be true," should always be avoided. In place of such statements should be: "the results, effects or the changes observed in the present investigation are (or are not) consistent with the original set of hypotheses and therefore are (or are not) consistent with the original theory" (Campbell & Stanley, 1966; Giancoli, 2005).

Disconfirmation and Falsification

Any theory that cannot be refuted by any conceivable series of events is non-science or simply not science (Popper,

1962) and probably represents a common or shared superstition (or simply nonsense). From the above sections, it should be clear that a considerable amount of evidence must be amassed in order to establish construct validity. However, only a very limited number of disconfirming empirical observations are required in order to justify the decision that the available empirical evidence fails to support a theory (Hempel, 1966). If a lack of supporting evidence warrants falsification, science must be quite prepared to give up or modify previously accepted theories (Hempel, 1966).

Observed inconsistencies or "empirical anomalies" may at first be suppressed, because they conflict with what Thomas Kuhn (Kuhn, 1970) has called "normal science." Normal science refers to a research area, discipline, or knowledge base that is firmly grounded in one or more past scientific achievements. That established knowledge base is then recognized by a particular scientific community, over a significant period of time, as supplying the foundation for all future practice (Kuhn, 1970). Unfortunately, it may also be emphasized that normal science is often a matter of what has become accepted as politically correct. According to Kuhn, normal science is often not prepared to handle the inconsistencies that seem to compromise the current practice. Eventually the discrepant evidence may continue to appear in the literature until it is clear that a change in thinking is needed, a change in thinking that calls for a scientific revolution. Therefore, additional decisions are subsequently needed to determine whether disconfirming evidence is sufficient in magnitude to warrant either a complete abandonment of the original theory, or its modification (Kuhn, 1970). The decision-making process in science, beginning with a theory or general premise, is illustrated in Figure 1–3 and is simplistically described in Box 1–5.

The Scientific Method: Structure of a Scientific Manuscript

The scientific method in its entirety is best conceived as a research plan or a strategy. Research plans as a whole develop, progress, and evolve as a process, and this process is duplicated or recapitulated in the structure of a scientific manuscript. In order of their appearance, the sections include the abstract, introduction, method(s), results, discussion, and the references or list of citations. The abstract is a short, concise section that appears at the very beginning of a manuscript. Because the abstract represents a summary of the introduction, method(s), results, and discussion, the contents of the abstract will be addressed at the end of the discussion section review.

I. Introduction

The introduction of a scientific manuscript should provide the foundation, the rationale, and the justification needed for conducting an investigation. It should provide a statement of purpose, a research question(s) to be answered, and a hypothesis or set of hypotheses that have been formulated by rephrasing the original question(s) in operational terms. The introduction will also suggest a plan or an approach to answering the questions that have been asked and the hypotheses that have been formulated.

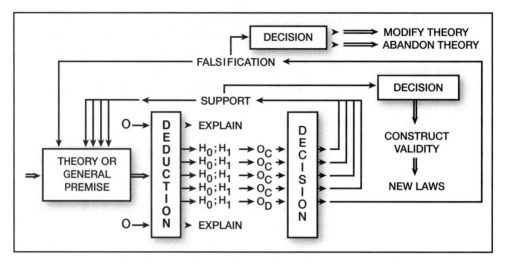

Figure 1–3. Hypothesis testing and decision making in science. In the model, the arrows indicate the directional flow of events that begin with a general theory that is subjected to deductive logic (deduction), as defined and described in the previous figure and in the text. In this model, theory-driven hypotheses (predictions) are formulated from the (hypothetical) constructs that define the theory. These are again represented as (H_0; H_1) and are formulated prior to making experimental observations (Os). Again, H_0 stands for the null hypothesis, and H_1 stands for the alternate hypotheses (see text for an explanation). The "Os" once again represent scientific observations obtained through the rules of empiricism. In the present model, the empirical observations may either confirm (OC) or disconfirm (OD) the original hypotheses or expectations upon which the theory-driven scientific investigation was based. An accumulation of confirmatory observations (OC) will require that a decision be made as to whether the evidence obtained lends support to the original theory, as suggested by the arrows. As more support is amassed for a theory, additional decisions are needed based not only on the quantity but also the diversity of the support. From this support, the overall degree of construct validity that has accumulated for the theory will be determined. The greater the quantity and the diversity of the support, the greater will be the degree of construct validity, and the greater the likelihood that a particular theory may, in time, become a well-established principle or perhaps, a general law (Hewitt, 2010). On the other hand, only one case of disconfirming evidence (OD) will necessitate that a decision be made as to whether the evidence fails to support (falsification) the original theory, as indicated by the arrows. In the case of falsification, additional decisions are subsequently needed to determine whether the lack of supporting evidence is sufficient to warrant that the original theory be completely abandoned, or that it only be modified.

The introduction of a scientific manuscript begins with a careful, thorough review of the most deliberately relevant and up-to-date scientific literature in the chosen database(s). The literature review found in the introduction is essentially a series of reported observations in which the subject matter of interest is clearly and unambiguously defined and operationally defined. All of the relevant variables of interest that are either known or unknown and are associated with the subject matter of interest are also identified and operationally defined. In terms of both the subject matter and each of the associated variables (when appropriate), the kinds of questions that should be addressed in the introduction are the following: what is it; how is it defined; how is it measured; how has it been defined and measured in the past; has it

Box 1–5. Simple Decision Making

The simplistic example presented in Boxes 1–1 to 1–3 may now be extended in order to demonstrate the decision-making process in science. The original general case, principle, or theory stated that all four-legged animals or all four-legged animal archetypes are dogs. Recall that the separate constructs of the general case in this particular example were that independent of the size, shape, color, hair length, state of animation, behavioral disposition, length of tail, ear size, gender, and so forth, having four legs is tantamount to application of the label "dog." Deductive logic would then yield the primary prediction (or hypothesis) taken from Box 1–3: If I observe a single occurrence of what appears to be an animate (or even one inanimate) object having four legs, then the object should be labeled a dog. Accordingly, the child in this example may observe several canine pets within and outside of their immediate surroundings, and the appropriate response is always, "dog." If in each instance, each of the observed objects with four legs is, in fact, a dog, then it is likely that the child will receive positive reinforcement following each occurrence, from an adult. The positive reinforcement would be interpreted in each case as confirmatory evidence, and therefore, additional support would be obtained for the original general premise (or theory).

Let us now suppose that in just one occurrence, the animal-object observed happens to not be a dog. In the one instance, the animal-object observed is, instead, feline (a cat). Therefore, following the response "dog," an adult either withholds positive reinforcement or administers negative reinforcement to the child. The observed animal-object had four legs, but the animal-object was not a dog. The possibility exists that the original hypothesis is untenable since the general premise upon which it was based, was itself unsound. Therefore, following one instance of disconfirming evidence, the validity of the original general premise (theory) would require re-evaluation. In view of the new evidence, one possibility would be to modify the general premise. This is accomplished by simply altering one word. The single word "all" in the general premise—all four-legged animals or all four-legged animal archetypes are dogs—can be replaced either with "not all" or "some." Over time, the general premise would encounter additional modification and refinement as the child is exposed to the vast array of other animals having four legs. Science progresses in the same manner.

been adequately defined and measured in the past; are changes or improvements needed in the way it has been defined or measured in the past; and if so, if such changes or improvements were made, what would be the impact of these modifications on the current state of knowledge? Hence, based upon what is presently known and/or what is presently not known, the next question that needs to be addressed is as follows: What needs to be investigated and what steps need to be taken immediately in order to correct the current problematic deficiency in the overall knowledge base? Having defined the problem, the original question that was asked may now be rephrased into the formulation of a testable hypothesis or a series of testable hypotheses, and placed into the introduction. Formulating theory-driven hypotheses as indicated above should be a relatively easy task since predictions based on the separate constructs of a theory easily give way to deductive logic. At or near the conclusion of the introduction, the methodological approach to answering the question(s) is briefly specified, and all throughout the introduction, previous investigations (observations) are generously cited as needed.

II. Method(s) Section

The overall experimental design of an investigation is what is found in the method section of a scientific manuscript. The method section represents the very heart of an empirical investigation. If the methods are poorly conceived or poorly implemented, it will be impossible to salvage any of the (invalid) data. The method section of a scientific manuscript is composed of subsections that will often include but will not be limited to the following: subjects, experimental design, instrumentation (equipment or apparatus), experimental procedures, and data analyses.

Subjects

If the subjects in the investigation are human, this section should include the numbers used, ages, genders, ethnicity if relevant, socioeconomic status if relevant, housing conditions if relevant, educational level if relevant, experience level and overall health when relevant, how subjects were chosen, included for investigation, eliminated or otherwise sampled, and group membership or experimental assignment should be included here as well.

If the subjects in the investigation are nonhuman, this section should include the numbers used, approximate ages (or weights), genders, species, strain, name and location of breeder, how subjects were chosen, included for investigation, eliminated, or otherwise sampled, housing and feeding conditions (i.e., circadian cycles), type of food, genotype if relevant, health status if relevant, and group membership or experimental assignment should be included here as well.

Experimental Design

If an experimental design subsection is included in the general method section of a scientific manuscript, it should specify, identify, and operationally define all the relevant antecedent and consequent variables. Antecedent variables will be composed of those that are directly or indirectly manipulated (independent variables, categorical variables), and those observed to vary that are not manipulated (predictor variables). Consequent variables will be composed of those that are observed (measured), that have quantities that will (vary) change either in combination with (predicted or criterion variables) or as a direct result (dependent variables, criterion variables) of changes (through manipulation), or due to differences (through category) attributed to the antecedent variables (i.e., the independent variables, categorical variables).

Instrumentation

Measurement devices are frequently utilized in scientific investigations, and they often take the form of electronic computerized instruments. A measurement device can also be a type of mechanical apparatus, a testing chamber, or any other form of nonhuman measurement tool. In the instrumentation section of a scientific manuscript, all such devices should be described in detail, including product names and model numbers. Steps taken to maintain machine calibration over the course of time and over the duration of each test session need to be addressed and implemented. The implementation and description of these calibration methods are likely to be found in the "Experimental Procedures" subsection.

An accurately calibrated measurement device helps to assure measurement reliability and internal validity. Reliability often refers to the accuracy and precision of a measurement. In the present context, however, reliability is more likely to be associated with stability of measurement, repeatability or reproducibility of measurement, or dependability of measurement over time. In the absence of measurement reliability, there can be no internal measurement validity. However, if an instrument is consistently inaccurate in its calibration, its use as a measurement tool may be reliable, but the invalid measures obtained from the instrument will pose a threat to internal validity. Additional steps that can be taken to assure and/or demonstrate the reliability of measurement devices include but are not limited to the following two procedures: test-retest (also known as intratest) reliability and intertest (also known as between-test) reliability. Once again, the implementation and description of these methods are likely to be found in the "Experimental Procedures" subsection.

A set of instructions given to the subject/participants is an instrument that is often used in scientific investigations involving human subjects. Instructions must be free of ambiguity and should therefore always be standardized. If the instructions given are inconsistent across subjects, measurement reliability is lost which threatens internal measurement validity. The implementation of methods having to do with the standardization of instructions administered to human subjects is likely to be found in the "Experimental Procedures" subsection.

The investigator/participants conducting the research represent yet another set of measurement instrument frequently utilized in scientific investigations involving human subjects. The investigator/participants in such studies often serve in the capacity of observers and data collectors. Hence, the observer/participants must also be viewed as a set of instruments whose calibration, for consistently maintaining a state of rational objectivity, is also subject to waxing and waning over time. Steps may be taken to assure and/or demonstrate the reliability of investigators/participants serving as measurement devices. These methods include but are not limited to the following two procedures: test-retest (also known as intrarater) reliability and interrater (also known as interobserver, between-observer, or interjudge) reliability. Once again, the implementation and description of these methods are likely to be found in the "Experimental Procedures" subsection.

The possible accumulation of intervening (confounding) variance resulting from "investigator/experimenter effects" on the performance of subjects must also be considered in many types of scientific investigations. Such effects are often referred to as experimenter or observer bias. In behavioral investigations, an investigator serving in the capacity of an observer and data collector is likely to have a vested interest in the outcome of the investigation. Hence, the investigator/participant might be unknowingly inclined, through their own behavior, to convey their expectations to the subjects. In doing so, the investigator/participants behavior toward the subject might unintentionally influence and bias the subject responses. When the possibility of experimenter bias exists, it is prudent to employ disinterested investigator/participant observers and data collectors. As before, the implementation and description of these methods is likely

to be found in the "Experimental Procedures" subsection.

Experimental Procedures

In general, this subsection will describe in detail how the investigation was conducted. This subsection may also be composed of additional subsections, as needed. Each step in the implementation of the procedures should be clearly stated and/or outlined in the order in which each step was performed. It is important that the experimental procedures are succinctly and unambiguously written in a manner that would enable other scientific investigators to conduct the same investigation. In this way, others may effortlessly replicate the results of an investigation.

This subsection will often integrate information described in the preceding subsections (see the "Instrumentation" subsection). For instance, and when appropriate, the procedures that are followed for subject selection, as well as the methods in which subjects are assigned to groups, can often be found in this subsection. This subsection often includes strategies for controlling (with control subjects or control conditions) unwanted sources of variance (confounding variables), as well as strategies used to account for, or otherwise control (by prevention) alternate sources of explanation due to errors in measurement. The possible contaminating effects of confounding variables may exist both in the design of the investigation and/or in the test environment. Such variables can threaten both the reliability and the internal validity of the results. For example, when possible, the experimental test environment should be consistent (the same) for each subject during all phases of testing. Within this regular and predictable test environment, there is an additional need to control for or otherwise eliminate any fluctuations occurring in temperature, noise levels, lighting, or any unnecessary distractions or disturbances.

Data Analyses

In this subsection there should be statements indicating an overall plan and a logical basis for the choice and type of inferential statistical analyses that will be performed on the data. It is also helpful in advance to indicate the alpha (α) level that has been chosen. Recall that the alpha level is also the level of significance (or level of confidence), or the probability of committing a Type I error, and this level is often set to a value of $p \leq 0.05$.

III. Results Section

As indicated above, results are reported and summarized for the relevant set of expectations that were formulated as a single hypothesis or as a set of theory-driven hypotheses. Results are summarized in sufficient detail, and in combination with reporting the outcome(s) of the inferential statistical data analyses that were performed in order to justify the conclusions that will be made in the discussion section. That is, the amount of detail summarized in the results should be relative and proportional to the volume of discourse that follows in the discussion section.

As indicated above, reporting the results includes visually summarizing the important main effects and/or interactions or correlations. These are usually summarized in the form of tables and/or

graphically, using descriptive statistics. Raw data from individual subjects is not reported in the results, except in those instances of single-case (time-series, quasi-experimental) investigations.

Missing data due to subject attrition should be reported in terms of frequencies or percentages. Results must also be summarized and presented, even when the data suggest that no changes were observed (i.e., no effect, no correlation) between the relevant variables. This is especially important in those instances where the results appear to be in direct contradiction to the original predictions and expectations.

Finally, discussing the implications of the investigation is a matter that is reserved for the discussion section. Explanations of the results that relate to the original predictions (hypothesis), or any direct statements related to the original theory or theory-driven hypotheses, do not belong in the results section. Furthermore, attempts interpreting the possible meaning of the results, once again, should not appear in the results section.

IV. Discussion Section

The discussion section is not simply a rehashing of the information provided in the results. Instead, it is the section in which the results are examined, evaluated, and interpreted. Interpretation in the present context implies that the meaning and the importance, or the lack of importance of the results, is made clear. It is also in the discussion section where inferences and conclusions about the results are drawn.

The discussion section may begin with a restatement and re-evaluation of the original hypothesis. Or, it may begin with a restatement and re-evaluation of the original theory and the theory-driven hypotheses that were formulated. The following kinds of questions are typically addressed in the discussion section: Do the results support the original hypothesis? Do the results fail to support the original hypothesis in favor of an alternative hypothesis? Do the results support the theory-driven hypotheses as well as the theory, or do the results fail to provide confirmation to the theory? Are the results of the present investigation consistent with what is currently known and accepted in the scientific literature? If so, how are the results similar?

If the results of the present investigation are inconsistent with previous investigations, how are they different and why might they be inconsistent? Statements that compare and contrast variations in the procedures, in the types of subjects sampled, in the methods used to control potential sources of bias and other threats to internal validity, or simply, those that contrast differences in the robustness of effects between investigations are all used to clarify the explanations that are made. Can the results of the present investigation be used to predict future outcomes? Can the results of the present investigation be used to generalize and to make statements relative to other populations, other theories, or other situations? The ease at which a set of results can be generalized to situations that are external to the immediate investigation is also an indication of the degree of external validity for the results.

There is an inclination in the discussion section to address the implications that the results have for future investigations, and/or for future clinical treatment possibilities. Statements as to the theoretical, practical, or clinical significance of the outcomes of the investigation often serve as the bases for these assertions. At the conclusion of the discussion section, additional statements address what questions remain unanswered, which problems remain unsolved, and what the next step or steps should be. This is usually followed by an additional statement addressing the direction that future investigations should take.

V. Abstract

As indicated above, the abstract appears at the very beginning of a research manuscript, even before the introduction. It is a highly condensed, concise, accurate, and sequentially composed summary of the entire manuscript. Journal publishers restrict the number of words that are allowable in the abstract, and word limitations can range anywhere from 100 to 250 words, maximum. The abstract usually begins with a statement of the problem to be solved, usually with two sentences that summarize the contents of the entire introduction. This is followed by two sentences that summarize the entire contents of the method(s), two or three sentences that summarize the entire contents of the results, and two or three more sentences that summarize the entire contents of the discussion. It is the shortest and most difficult section of the manuscript to write, and therefore, it takes the longest to write. For these reasons, it is usually the last section that is written even though it is the first section that is read.

VI. Reference Section

The complete citations of previous investigations that were referenced throughout the manuscript are found in the reference section. In most instances, these cited investigations represent the important work (empirical observations) of other scientific investigators. Because that work, in all likelihood, was essential in formulating the original foundation upon which the current investigation was conceived, the work of previous investigators must be properly acknowledged. References should provide an efficient way for the reader to locate all of the previous work that was cited in the manuscript. Therefore, the citations must be accurate, complete, and unambiguous. Each journal has its own stylistic requirements for the listing of the references in the reference section, as well as for the insertion of citations throughout the body of the manuscript.

Chapter Summary

- Science is defined as the observation, identification, description, experimental investigation, and theoretical explanation of natural phenomena.
- The scientific method is based on a foundation of empiricism, defined as the doctrine of observability. In science, empiricism refers to observations made under proper, exacting, and restrictive methodological rules.
- Empirical observations can only be obtained by conducting carefully designed and methodologically sound investigations.
- In the initial stages of any scientific discipline, a structured body of knowledge is built through a combination of empiricism and inductive logic.

- Inductive logic (induction) is defined as the logical process of problem solving in which particular or specific empirical observations are creatively integrated in order to formulate a general theory, or a general set of principles.
- Induction bridges the gap between existing knowledge obtained through empiricism, and predictive knowledge, otherwise known as theory.
- Theory was defined as an orderly set of interrelated constructs. Constructs are defined as concepts or components of a theory that are defined in terms of the operations that are used in their measurement.
- Theory provides the blueprint for scientific inquiry. The organization and structure furnished by theory suggest how loose collections of facts can and should be organized and interrelated into a coherent body of knowledge.
- Deductive logic (deduction) is defined as the logical process of problem making in which a general premise, a theory, or a set of laws or principles is used to make predictions or formulate a hypothesis or a set of specific hypotheses prior to the acquisition of specific empirical observations.
- Deductive logic is also the same mental process used to explain specific empirical facts once they have been observed.
- Hypothesis is defined as a causal, correlative, or inferential prediction made with respect to potential relationships between variables in a particular theory.

- Hypotheses are generated by deductive logic under an assumption of determinism, and are tested by empirical investigation.
- The doctrine of determinism maintains that law and order exist in the natural universe.
- Explanations must be made under the tenet of parsimony, which refers to the practice of avoiding highly complex, overly abstract explanations for simple occurrences, unless all simpler explanations have been considered and/or ruled out.
- Empirical observations resulting from carefully designed and executed theory-driven investigations are judged as relevant or irrelevant to any given set of hypotheses. The evidence obtained in this manner either confirms or disconfirms the original hypotheses or predictions upon which the investigation(s) was (were) originally conceived, and the theory upon which the hypotheses were formulated.
- The empirical evidence will reflect either positively or negatively on the theory from whence the theory-driven hypotheses were originally formulated.
- The overall degree of construct validity for a theory will be determined based on the accumulation of support or lack thereof. Construct validity (or theoretical validity) is evidence obtained in support of the hypothetical constructs of a theory.
- The degree of construct validity for a particular theory will increase as both the quantity and diversity of confirmatory evidence continue to accumulate.
- Far less accumulated disconfirming evidence (falsification) will warrant that the original theory be modified or completely abandoned.

Chapter 1 Questions

1. Define the following terms in reference to the philosophy of the scientific method: empiricism, inductive logic, deductive logic, construct, construct validity, determinism, and parsimony.

2. Define the following terms and indicate what information is required for each in reference to the pragmatics of the scientific method: asking a research question, formulating a hypothesis, designing a scientific method, reporting the results of the investigation, and discussing and interpreting results of the investigation.

3. Define the concept of theory. What important role (if any) does theory play in the advancement of science?

4. Differentiate between single hypothesis-driven research and theory-driven research.

5. Suppose you had never been exposed to the heat that is produced from a flame. Using the terminology presented, describe the series of logical steps that would transpire in the creation of a general rule or theory, beginning with repeated occurrences

(observations) of having your fingers burned by a hot match, a hot stove, a campfire, a fireplace, a branding iron, a soldering iron, a flat-iron, and a clothes iron.

6. In the example provided in question #5, how would you proceed to develop hypotheses to test your theory? Would it be easy or hard to establish construct validity? Are there any instances that might threaten to disconfirm the overall theory that you created?

References

Boring, E. G. (1957). *A history of experimental psychology* (2nd ed.). New York, NY: Appelton-Century-Crofts.

Brody, B. A. (1970). Explanation and prediction: Goals of the scientific enterprise. In B. A. Brody (Ed.), *Readings in the philosophy of science* (pp. 8–104). Upper Saddle River, NJ: Prentice Hall.

Campbell, D. T., & Stanley, J. C. (1966). *Experimental and quasi-experimental designs for research*. Chicago, IL: Rand McNally College.

Dirckx, J. H. (2005). *Stedman's medical dictionary for the health professions and nursing illustrated* (5th ed.). Baltimore, MD: Lippincott Williams & Wilkins.

Ferris, T. (2002). On the popularization of science. In S. W. Hawking, K. S. Thorne, I. Novikov, T. Ferris, & A. Lightman (Eds.), *The future of space-time* (pp. 153–170). New York, NY: W. W. Norton.

Giancoli, D. C. (2005). *Physics: Principles with applications* (6th ed.). Upper Saddle River, NJ: Prentice Hall.

Hawking, S. E. (2002). *On the shoulders of giants: The great works of physics and astronomy*. Philadelphia, PA: Running Press.

Hempel, C. G. (1966). Criteria of confirmation and acceptability. In E. Beardsley & M. Beardsley (Eds.), *Philosophy of natural science* (pp. 33–46). Upper Saddle River, NJ: Prentice Hall.

Hewitt, P. G. (2010). *Conceptual physics* (11th ed.). Upper Saddle River, NJ: Pearson Education.

Kuhn, T. S. (1970). *The structure of scientific revolutions* (2nd ed.). Chicago, IL: University of Chicago Press.

Leon, J. C. (1999). *Science and philosophy in the West*. Upper Saddle River, NJ: Prentice Hall.

Lightman, A. (2002). The physicist as novelist. In S. W. Hawking, K. S. Thorne, I. Novikov, T. Ferris, & A. Lightman (Eds.), *The future of space-time* (pp. 171–190). New York, NY: W. W. Norton.

Maxwell, D. L., & Satake, E. (1997). *Research and statistical methods in communication disorders*. Baltimore, MD: Williams & Wilkins.

Medawar, P. B. (1981). *Advice to a young scientist*. New York, NY: Harper & Row.

Popper, K. (1962). *Science: Conjectures and refutations*. New York, NY: Basic Books.

Schiavetti, N., & Metz, D. E. (2002). *Evaluating research in communicative disorders* (4th ed.). Boston, MA: Allyn & Bacon.

Stevens, S. S. (1958). Chapter 1: Mathematics, measurement, and psychophysics. In S. S. Stevens (Ed.), *Handbook of experimental psychology* (pp. 1–49). New York, NY: John Wiley.

Stutz, B. (2006). Introduction. In J. Langone, B. Stutz, & A. Gianopoulos (Eds.), *Theories for everything: An illustrated history of science from the invention of numbers to string theory* (pp. 8–17). Washington, DC: National Geographic Society.

Chapter 2

Measurement

The Greek philosopher Heracleitus (540–480 BC) wrote: "Nature loves to hide, and like the harmonics of a string, nature is susceptible to understanding, even measurement . . . "

Stutz, 2006, p. 237

Alphabetized Listing of Key Terms Discussed In Chapter 2

area

attributes

Briggsian logarithms

categorical variable

Celsius, Anders

Celsius scale (C)

centigrade (C)

centimeter

CGS-metric system

characteristic of a log

common logarithms

compliance

continuous variable

density

dynamic range of hearing

exponential notation

Fahrenheit, Daniel Gabriel

Fahrenheit scale(F)

frequency

foot-pound-second (fps) system

fundamental dimensions

gram

international system (SI)

interval scale

Kelvin scale

kilogram

length

logarithm (log)

Lord Kelvin

mantissa of a log

mass

measurement

measurement scales

meter

metric system

micron

MKS-metric system

Naperian logarithms

natural logarithms

nominal scale

ordinal scale

period

proportionality

qualitative variable

ratio scale

reciprocals

scientific notation

second

stiffness

tally

time

volume

weight

Measurement

Measurement is broadly defined as the assignment of numerals to objects or events according to rules (Hays, 1981; Speaks, 1999; Stevens, 1958). In the preceding chapter, the doctrine of empiricism mandated careful and precise measurements as an essential part of the scientific method. Furthermore, variables were defined in the last chapter as measurable quantities that vary or change under different circumstances, and operationalized concepts were defined as constructs. An operational definition in any scientific discipline requires that the measurement units of a particular construct be specified (Hempel, 1966). To satisfy this requirement, the basic (fundamental) physical dimensions used in physics and in hearing science (length, mass, and time) and their respective quantities (Halliday, Resnick, & Walker, 2011) require interpretation and clarification, as do their derivations. The measurement systems used to signify the scope and magnitude of the quantities representing length, mass, and time and their derivatives also require definition (Hays, 1981). According to Stevens (1958), the stature of a science is commonly measured by the degree to which it makes use of mathematics, though mathematics is not itself a science in the empirical sense, but a formal logical symbolic system. Notwithstanding, a perfect correspondence between mathematical measures and the empirical variables of the material universe will never exist. Hence, measurement is a relative matter. It varies in degree, type, and precision. The fact that numerals can be assigned under different rules requires different kinds of scales and different kinds of measurement (Hays, 1981). Therefore, the fit between mathematics and empirical variables is best, only to the degree that the dimensions and qualities of the events under investigation are measurable on well-founded scales (Hays, 1981; Stevens, 1958).

Measurement Levels (Scales of Measurement)

A clear understanding of the properties of the measurement scales that represent variables is important in any discipline. In general, not all observable measures share the same qualities, and not all observable measures retain properties amenable to formal mathematical operations (Hays, 1981). Therefore, in the sections that follow, four measurement scales are presented and arranged from the simplest to the most complex (i.e., nominal, ordinal, interval, and ratio), as originally defined by Stevens (1958).

Categorical Versus Continuous Variables

At this juncture it is appropriate to distinguish between a continuous variable, a categorical variable, and an attribute. An attribute is a property, a quality, a trait, or a characteristic (Hays, 1981). Examples of attributes are hair color, eye color, handedness, gender, animal, mineral, vegetable, or even personality type. Attribute variables (often called qualitative variables) may or may not require an observation that is dichotomous (Maxwell & Satake, 1997). A dichotomy may be defined as the existence of two mutually exclusive variable classes, such as male-female, right handed-left handed, yes-no responses, and so forth. Often, however, there are more than just two (dichotomous) categorical variable classes. In any case, each separate variable category will represent discrete, mutually exclusive, and exhaustive observations, with no quantifiable gradations between measures and no overlap of definitions (Hays, 1981). In other words, with categorical variables there are only a finite number of potential values that the variable can assume, and there can be no values that fall between any two categories on the scale (Box 2–1). Categorical variables are specified by name only, and they may be designated by the simple use of numerals (i.e., I, II, III; A, B, C, etc.).

In contrast to a categorical variable, a continuous variable may be measured along a continuum or dimension that reflects, at the very least, a rank ordering of values. The simplest example of a continuous variable employing rank ordering would be to assign certain attributes with the relativistic labels of first, second, third, fourth, and so forth. That is, continuous variables by definition exhibit quantifiable gradations between measures, even if the gradations are only relative, as observed in a rank ordering of attributes (see Box 2–1). When continuous variables are taken to their highest form, the possibility of even more precise numerical measures of gradation between each variable can exist. Furthermore, the best cases (or highest forms) of continuous variables may assume an infinite number of values between any two points on a scale. The use of the terms *categorical* and *continuous* will become clearer in the sections on measurement levels that follow.

Nominal–Level Measurement

The simplest form of measurement is, by definition, measurement generated when mutually exclusive categorical variables are employed. This is called nominal-level measurement (Hays, 1981). Examples of this type of measurement

---

Box 2–1. Categorical and Continuous Variables

Categorical Variables

> Examples: telephone numbers; social security numbers; male/female; normal/impaired; pass/fail; blue eyes/brown eyes; correct/incorrect; conductive hearing loss/sensorineural hearing loss/mixed hearing loss.

Continuous Variables

> Examples: mild/moderate/severe; first/second/third; Fahrenheit and Celsius temperature; sound frequency; sound intensity; speech intelligibility performance; diadochokinetic rate.

were provided under the heading "categorical variables" in Box 2–1. The term *nominal* means "by name only" and as such, the different values of the categorical variable(s) in question are nonoverlapping and are, therefore, discrete and mutually exclusive. The only property that may be applied to nominal-level measurement is differentiation based on identity (Maxwell & Satake, 1997; Schiavetti & Metz, 2002). Simply put, categories indicating differences may only be assigned a name or a label, with essentially no limitations on the number of separate categories that may be labeled. Inclusion within and the formation of mutually exclusive classes of objects or events are based on the demonstration of equality with respect to some trait or attribute (Hays, 1981; Stevens, 1958). That is, each member of each category is considered to be identical for purposes of nominal measurement (Maxwell & Satake, 1997; Schiavetti & Metz, 2002). Hence, individuals belonging to the same nominal category may be assigned together, to their own separate group, where they will be qualitatively classified as the same, but will be classified as qualitatively different from those falling into a different nominal category. Each nominally classified individual or observation is placed into only one class, making the classes or groupings discrete, mutually exclusive, and exhaustive (Hays, 1981). The only rule in nominal scales is as follows: Do not assign the same numeral to the different classes, or different numerals to the same class (Stevens, 1958).

Nominal-level measures are not amenable to formal mathematical operations and have little quantitative meaning (Hays, 1981). That is, the assigned labels do not and cannot specify the magnitude of the variable. For this reason, nominal-level measurement is considered quantitatively, to be the lowest, least powerful, and perhaps the crudest form of measurement scale. The following examples were provided in Box 2–1 under the heading "categorical variables": telephone numbers, social security numbers, designation of gender, and so forth. The only possible mathematical operation that may be performed with nominal-level data is to count the frequency of occurrence of members, objects, or measures falling into each mutually exclusive nominal category (Maxwell & Satake, 1997). This amounts to little more than tally taking (Schiavetti & Metz, 2002). For instance, the number of males and the number of females may be counted; the number of students who passed and the number who failed may also be counted. Taking a tally, however, is not sufficient to improve the quality and mathematical power of the nominal-level measurement. Therefore, tally-taking alone will not alter the "poor measurement or poor quantitative status" of nominal-level data.

Colors represent only a nominal level of measurement such that the labels for "color" (i.e., red, blue, green, yellow) consist of mutually exclusive categorical variables. Adding numbers to each color does not alter the data class and represents just another form of nominal-level measurement such that each assigned number consists of a mutually exclusive category. Hence, even the assignment of numbers to each color has no quantitative meaning. Also, labels used to signify "gender," whether they are female or male, also represent mutually exclusive categorical variables.

While nominal-level measurement has essentially no mathematical power, categorical variables that yield nominal-level measurement may be transformed into the crudest form of continuous variable. This transformation is usually accomplished by arranging or placing the categorical observations into a meaningful order, a meaningful continuum, or a meaningful dimension (Hays, 1981). If and when this is possible, the mathematical power of the measurement increases, and the quantitative status improves from that of nominal-level measurement to ordinal-level measurement.

Ordinal-Level Measurement

Ordinal-level measurement involves the ranking or logical ordering of categories based on the relative magnitude of a property, quality, or value of an attribute (Maxwell & Satake, 1997; Schiavetti & Metz, 2002). With an ordinal level of measurement, it may be said with certainty that if two measurements are unequal, then their true magnitudes must also be unequal. That is, if one measurement is larger than another, then its true magnitude must also exceed that of the other, but we cannot state by how much it is larger (Hays, 1981). The following examples of ordinal-level measurement were provided in Box 2–1 under the heading "continuous variables": mild/moderate/severe; first/second/third. Additional examples of categories arranged on a continuum that indicates more or less of a particular dimension would include hard/firm/soft, small/medium/large/larger/largest, short/regular/tall/taller/tallest, or freezing/cold/tepid/

hot/scalding. What each of these examples has in common is that each set of descriptors indicates continuous measurement along a common dimension. Therefore, the descriptors are not mutually exclusive, because each refers to a common attribute or dimension within a category. For instance, tall/taller/tallest could represent a rank ordering of descriptors according to the dimension of *relative height*. In a similar way, the descriptors cold/tepid/hot/scalding, are likely to represent a rank ordering based on the dimension of relative temperature. The rank ordering of categories along a meaningful dimension indicates "more or less" of a property, quality, or value of an attribute. Based simply on the relative magnitudes of the attributes under investigation, rank ordering may be easily accomplished without actually using calibrated measuring instruments. It is also possible to rank order mutually exclusive categories along a particular dimension or attribute. For instance, the categories men/women/children might be rank ordered from lowest to highest in terms of the attribute, vocal fold fundamental frequency. Hence, for measures made on this particular attribute, it turns out that men < women < children. On the other hand, for measures of vocal tract length or measurements of head size, the result would be such that men > women > children. Such rank ordering may also be accomplished using a series of descriptive "numerals" (whole number integers) beginning with 1. It could also be accomplished using a series of descriptive letters, beginning with "A." These descriptors might then be rank ordered, beginning with the greatest (or smallest) value, such that $1 < 2 < 3 < 4$; or $A > B > C > D$, respectively.

Rank ordering in this manner is a crude yet effective method of taking categorical variables and creating continuous and potentially quantifiable variables from them. In this way, it is understood that the categorical labels have now been assigned a numerical value that, in some meaningful way, reflects their rank ordering or relative amount, along a specified dimension. When a numerical quantity is assigned to some presumably meaningful attribute on the bases of rank, then it can be said that a level of quantifiable measurement has been established (Hays, 1981). Recall that measurement is defined as the assignment of numerals to objects or events, according to rules. Rank ordering is based on rules. Real measurement scales generally possess one, two, or all three of the following attributes: relative magnitude, equal intervals, and/or an absolute zero point. Therefore, the ordinal level of measurement allows for and acknowledges differences based on the identity of the category (as in nominal-level measurement), as well as the relative magnitudes of the differences in the attributes, objects, or events of the separate categories (Hays, 1981; Schiavetti & Metz, 2002).

Despite any clear advantages of ordinal-level measurement over nominal measurement, there are serious limitations to ordinal measurement scales. With ordinal-level measurement, the quantity of the intervals between ranked categories remains unspecified. That is, the actual value that corresponds to the difference between any two ranked categories of the attribute is not a fixed, linear measure. Instead, this difference is only a relative amount, and each relative interval between each ranked category will always vary by some unspecified magnitude (Hays, 1981). Consequently, using the previous example 1 < 2 < 3 < 4, the value of category 3 is not necessarily 3× that of the value of the category, or the attribute assigned with a 1. Likewise, if 1 > 2 > 3 > 4, the value of category 3 is not necessarily 1/3 that of the value of the category, or the attribute assigned with a 1.

In the example of color discussed above, numbers may be assigned to different colors in an attempt to represent preferences, with 1 assigned to red as the least preferred, 2 assigned to blue, 3 assigned to green, and 4 assigned to yellow as the most preferred. In this case, the original nominal (categorical)-level variables have been transformed into the crudest form of continuous variable, which is an ordinal scale. This is because the categories of "color" have now been assigned a numerical value that, in some meaningful way, reflects their rank ordering or relative amount along a specified dimension that we have called *preference*. Notwithstanding, while we can assume from such rank ordering that the color "blue" is preferred over the color "red" and that the color "green" is preferred over both "blue" and "red," we cannot state by how much each is preferred relative to the other. Knowing "how much" would require precise numerical knowledge of the intervals that separate each of the rank-ordered numbers.

Interval-Level Measurement

A vast improvement in mathematical power is achieved by the use of an interval level of measurement. Interval scales are linear and allow comparisons to be made based on categorical identity (as in nominal-level measurement), as well as on the relative magnitudes of the categories (as in ordinal-level measurement). However, interval scales possess three additional properties not found in the two previous measurement scales. Unlike ordinal scales of measurement: (a) the size of the interval between any successive units (or categories) of measure in an interval scale is a constant linear value that is always specified (Hays, 1981). The equal intervals found in an interval scale are created by the addition or subtraction of a constant base value to each successive value along the measurement scale. Therefore, the constant base value is also the precise value of the interval (Speaks, 1999). Hence, the interval between any two successive measurement units anywhere on an interval scale equals the interval between any other two units, independent of where on the scale the difference is computed (Schiavetti & Metz, 2002). Furthermore, (b) interval measurement scales employ continuous variables (Maxwell & Satake, 1997). As such, these variables are theoretically capable of assuming any numeric value, including fractional units of measure. Hence, these variables are not restricted to whole-number integers (Schiavetti & Metz, 2002). Finally, (c) interval measurement scales are characterized by an arbitrary value of "zero." The absence of a fixed or "true zero" point on the interval measurement scale indicates that when the value zero appears, it does not signify the complete absence of the attribute or quality, nor does this zero specify a true or absolute start-

ing point on the measurement scale (Hays, 1981; Maxwell & Satake, 1997; Schiavetti & Metz, 2002). The most common illustrations of interval scales of measurement are the Fahrenheit and Celsius temperature scales (Figure 2–1). Fahrenheit degrees (F°) usually refer to a temperature scale proposed in 1724 by, and named after, the Polish-born Dutch instrument maker and physicist Daniel Gabriel Fahrenheit (1686–1736). By this scale, water freezes at 32° and boils at 212°. The F° scale has been replaced by the Celsius (centigrade) degree scale (C°) in most countries, but it is still in use for nonscientific purposes in the United States. The Celsius scale is named after the Swedish astronomer Anders Celsius,(1701–1744), and by this scale, water freezes at 0° and boils at 100° (Stutz, 2006). In both of these temperature scales of measurement a value of zero does not signify the complete absence of the attribute temperature which in essence would be the complete absence of thermal energy. Because there is no absolute zero value in either of these scales, if the temperature yesterday was 30°, and it is 60° today, we cannot proclaim that it is twice as hot today as it was yesterday (Hays, 1981; Schiavetti & Metz, 2002). Such a computation would imply the existence of a ratio.

Still another example of an interval scale of measure is pH, which is a measure of the acidity or basicity of a solution. It is defined as the co-logarithm (or logarithm of the reciprocal) of the activity of dissolved hydrogen ions (H$^+$), or simply, protons. As illustrated in Figure 2–2, the level of H$^+$ is expected to be high when a solution becomes more acidic, and a pH of near zero is indicative

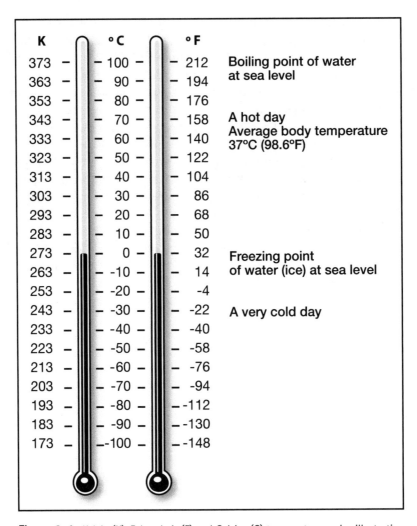

Figure 2–1. Kelvin (K), Fahrenheit (F) and Celsius (C) temperature scales illustrating the boiling and freezing points for water. Note that a temperature of 0°C or 0°F does not mean the complete absence of thermal energy. The Kelvin scale, however, does employ an absolute zero value (not shown).

of a very acidic solution, such as battery acid.

Finally, the many types of decibel (dB) scales that are discussed in the chapters that follow also represent examples of interval scales of measurement. This is because independent of whether the decibel is measured in terms of hearing level (dB HL) or sensation level (dB SL), both of which are discussed in Chapter 8, intensity level (dB IL) or sound pressure level (dB SPL), both of which are covered in Chapter 6, the value of zero dB does not signify the absence of sound. Instead, it will become clear in the subsequent chapters that a designation of zero dB should always be taken to indicate no change from the referent, or no change from the reference value.

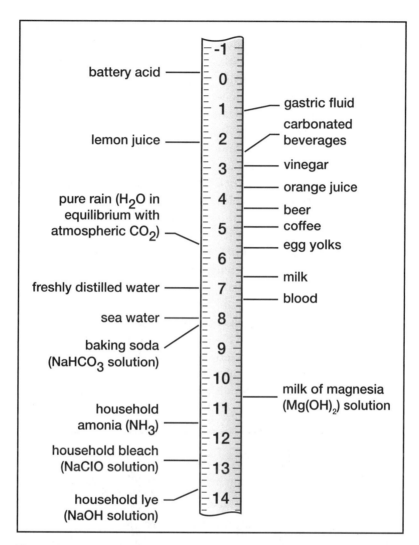

Figure 2–2. Measures of the pH of various solutions, from highly acidic battery acid (pH near zero) to distilled water (pH = 7), to household lye which is a very basic solution (pH near 14). The pH represents the logarithm of the reciprocal of the activity of dissolved hydrogen ions (H^+) or simply, protons. Printed with permission. Wikimedia Commons, public domain.

Ratio-Level Measurement

The highest degree of mathematical power is attained by the use of a ratio level of measurement. The ability to perform a greater number and greater complexity of mathematical operations contributes to the overall mathematical power of ratio measurement scales (Hays, 1981; Maxwell & Satake, 1997; Schiavetti & Metz, 2002). Mathematical transformations made with ratio-level data may be performed with the least amount of error. Therefore, the greater transformational invariance inherent within the ratio measurement scale contributes to its relatively higher suitability for use with powerful, parametric inferential statistics (Stevens, 1958).

Ratio measurement scales permit comparisons based on categorical identity (as in the nominal level of measurement), relative magnitude (as in the ordinal level of measurement), and the equality or linearity of intervals (as in the interval level of measurement). However, ratio-level measurement scales possess two additional properties not found in the three previous measurement scales (Maxwell & Satake, 1997; Schiavetti & Metz, 2002). The first is that unlike interval scales, the ratio scale of measurement has a fixed or true zero point that signifies the complete absence of an attribute or quality. This true zero point also specifies a fixed starting point of the measurement scale. Therefore, unlike the state of affairs that

exists with interval scales, if the length measurement of object A is 10 m and the length of object B is 20 m, it is quite permissible to state that object B has twice as much length as object A (Hays, 1981).

Unlike the Celsius and Fahrenheit scales, which are interval scales of measurement, the Kelvin scale (K), after William Thomson, First Baron Kelvin (or Lord Kelvin; 1824–1907), partially illustrated in Figure 2–2 and again in Figure 2–3, does incorporate an absolute zero. Lord Kelvin was a Scottish engineer, mathematician, and physicist (Gianopoulos, 2006). Zero degrees Kelvin corresponds to a total lack of thermal energy. Hence, as a scaling procedure, the Kelvin scale employs an absolute zero and is therefore not an example of an interval scale of measurement. The Kelvin temperature scale is instead an example of a ratio scale

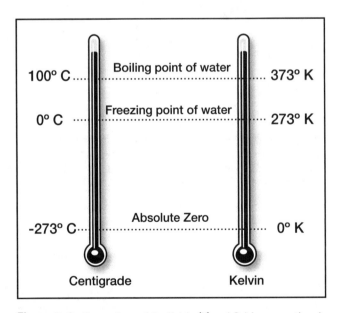

Figure 2–3. Comparison of the Kelvin (K) and Celsius or centigrade (C) temperature scales illustrating again the boiling and freezing points for water. Because the K scale is a ratio-level scale, a temperature of 0° K does correspond to a complete absence of thermal energy, and to −273 C.

of measure, and zero degrees Kelvin (the total lack of thermal energy) corresponds to a temperature of $-273°C$ or $-470°F$ (Stutz, 2006).

An important association also exists between interval scaling and ratio scaling. When differences are computed on measures made using an interval scale, those differences are computed and expressed using a ratio scale of measurement. In other words, the concept of a zero difference or zero distance does warrant the use of a fixed and nonarbitrary definition for zero, for measures originally computed on an interval scale (Hays, 1981). Second, since an absolute zero, and therefore, a fixed starting point, exists in a ratio scale, successive units of the measurement scale can be separated and specified by equal ratios or by equal proportions (Maxwell & Satake, 1997; Schiavetti & Metz, 2002). The ratios are created by the multiplication or division of a constant base value to each quantity along the measurement scale (Speaks, 1999). The constant base value, therefore, is also the precise value of the ratio. When any base value X is multiplied by itself n times, the n is referred to as an exponent where n is written in superscript to the right of the base as the standard expression X^n, which is also referred to as exponential notation. Therefore, it is important to remember throughout the text that any ratio scale of measurement is also an exponential scale of measurement (Speaks, 1999).

Summary

The ratio measurement scale permits whole numbers or fractions to be added, subtracted, multiplied, and divided. Most measures in physics and in hearing science involve ratio-level computations. As indicated in the chapters that follow, these will include measures that incorporate length, mass, time, and each of their separate derivatives. Examples of continuous variables with ratio-level measurement can be found in the determination of sound frequency, sound intensity, speech intelligibility performance, and diadochokinetic rate. A ratio measurement scale will also be put to use in calculations of the decibel, in which the logarithm of a ratio is used in the computation and transformation of acoustic intensity and/or pressure. A summary of the four measurement levels discussed in the text is presented in Table 2–1.

Exponential Notation and Scientific Notation

Exponents

As previously indicated, when a base value (X) is multiplied by itself n times, the n is the exponent that is written in superscript to the right of the base. This standard expression X^n is, therefore, referred to as exponential notation. Recall as well that exponential (ratio) scales by definition permit a greater number and greater complexity of mathematical operations over other types of measurement scales. In hearing science, the values that are often measured span extreme ranges. For instance, consider the range over which human hearing operates. From the lowest fractional amounts of either sound pressure or acoustic intensity required to produce a threshold response, to the upper limits of pressure or intensity that

Table 2–1. Summary Table of Measurement Levels

Scale	Properties	Examples
Nominal	Mutually exclusive categories	Gender
		Eye color
		Handedness
		Hearing loss type
Ordinal	Mutually exclusive categories	A < B < C < D
	Rank ordering	1 > 2 > 3 > 4
	Relative magnitudes	First, second, third, fourth
		Mild, moderate, severe
Interval	Mutually exclusive categories	Fahrenheit degrees
	Rank ordering	Celsius degrees
	Relative magnitudes	Decibel scales
	Linear equivalence of specified intervals	
Ratio	Mutually exclusive categories	Stimulus frequency
	Rank ordering	Stimulus intensity
	Relative magnitudes	Stimulus duration
	Linear equivalence of specified intervals	Air pressure
		Airflow
	Equivalence of specified ratios with a true zero point	Speech/word
		Intelligibility performance
		Kelvin degrees

can be tolerated with pain, the dynamic range (or ratio) of measurable values is vast. The dynamic range turns out to be 10 million to 1 for sound pressure (force/area), and about 100 trillion to 1 (power/area) for acoustic intensity (ANSI, 1996; Giancoli, 2005; Hewitt, 2010; Hirsh, 1952). The number 10 million is usually written 10,000,000, and the number 100 trillion is written as 100,000,000,000,000. It is clear that large numbers expressed in con-ventional notation (i.e., 10,000,000:1 and 100,000,000,000,000:1) are often cumbersome to use. There is also a greater chance for computational error when using conventional notation (Giancoli, 2005). Notice that the number 10,000,000 has seven zeros to the right of the 1. Notice also that the number 100,000,000,000,000 has 14 zeros to the right of the 1. Therefore, using exponential notation, the dynamic range over which human hearing operates can be rewritten as 10^7:1 for sound pressure. The same dynamic hearing range over which human hearing operates can be rewritten as 10^{14}:1 for acoustic intensity. The dynamic range may also be expressed with an upper limit of pressure or intensity that can be tolerated without pain, as 10^6:1 for sound pressure and 10^{12}:1 for acoustic intensity (Hirsh, 1952). Therefore, numbers expressed in this manner are less cumbersome to use and are less prone to mathematical error (Giancoli, 2005).

The advantage of using exponential notation over conventional notation also becomes clear when very small numbers are used in computations. For example, one of the reference values in the computation of decibels of acoustic intensity (or simply intensity level; dB IL) expressed, as power/area, is 0.0000000000000010 watts/cm² (Durrant & Feth, 2013). It is not difficult to understand that a number having a large aggregate of zeros would be cumbersome to work with in conventional notation (Giancoli, 2005). Notice that the whole number 1.00 appears 16 places to the right of the decimal point (i.e., 15 zeros separate the decimal point from the 1 in the number 0.0000000000000010. A simpler way to express this value is to raise the base number 10 to the exponential value of −16, or simply, to rewrite the entire reference value in exponential notation as: 10^{-16} watts/ cm² (Durrant & Feth, 2013).

To further illustrate the ease of using exponential notation, the calculation of dB IL can often require the use of yet another reference value, 0.0000000000010 watts/m². Once again, the ensemble of zeros in this number would be both cumbersome and difficult to work with in the absence of

error (Giancoli, 2005; Speaks, 1999). The number 10 in this case appears 12 places to the right of the decimal point (i.e., 11 zeros separate the decimal point from the 1 in the number 10). A simpler way to express this value is to raise the base number 10 to the exponential value of −12, or simply to rewrite the entire reference value in exponential notation as 10^{-12} watts/m² (Durrant & Feth, 2013).

Conversion of Conventional to Exponential Notation

Before proceeding with a description of computational rules involving mathematical operations with exponents, it will be useful to illustrate the process of converting exact integer multiples of 10 from conventional notation to exponential notation. Some useful steps for converting conventional integer multiples of 10 to exponents may be found in section A1 of Appendix A. Table A1–1 of Appendix A presents a summary of these rather simple conversions when exact integer multiples of 10 are used.

Working With Exponents

Considering the advantages in using exponential rather than conventional notation, it is not surprising that many of the computations encountered in hearing science will entail their use. Certain operating principles exist that relate to mathematical computations involving the use of exponents (Giancoli, 2005). Some of these basic principles will be of tremendous value in arithmetic computations of the decibel. Therefore, a review of some of the operating principles in the use of exponents is prerequisite to many of the sections that follow. Their description is left to section A2 of Appendix A. Students should find the operating principles in section A2 of Appendix A useful when working on Problem Sets 2–1 and 2–2 below.

Problem Set 2–1

1. Find:
   a) $10^{-3} \times 10^{7}$; b) $10^{-2} \times 10^{-7}$;
   c) $10^{2} \times 10^{8}$.

2. Find:
   a) $1/10^{-7}$; b) $1/10^{5}$; c) $106/10^{-10}$;
   d) $10^{-9}/10^{-10}$; e) $10^{-12}/10^{3}$;
   f) $10^{-7}/10^{-7}$.

3. Find:
   a) $(10^{10})^{2}$; b) $(10^{5})^{-3}$; c) $(10^{-8})^{-2}$;
   d) $(10^{-9})^{2}$; e) $(10^{0})^{3}$; f) $(10^{-4})^{0}$.

Problem Set 2–2

1. Convert the following exponential quantities to an equivalent conventional notation:
   a) 10^{-10}; b) 10^{10}; c) 10^{-5}; d) 10^{5};
   e) 10^{-1}; f) 10^{1}; g) 10^{0}.

2. Convert the following conventional quantities to an equivalent exponential notation:
   a) 100,000,000; b) 0.00000001;
   c) 1,000,000; d) 0.000001.

Scientific Notation

As indicated in the previous section, exponential notation allows very large and very small numbers to be represented with greater ease and less chance for error when compared to conventional notation. As shown in Table A1–1 of Appendix A, it is a simple procedure to convert numbers such as 10,000; 100,000; and 1,000,000 to exponential notation (i.e., 10^{4}; 10^{5}; and 10^{6}, respectively). However, not all quantities in physics or in hearing science can be expressed as exact integer multiples of the base 10. For instance, a wide variety of other numbers are also >1.00, such as 200,000 or 350,000. There are also many numbers that are <1.00, such as 0.00002. Numbers such as these require a less cumbersome method of expression that is also less prone to computational error (Giancoli, 2005).

Working With Scientific Notation

The method of choice when working with numbers other than those that happen to be exact integer multiples of the base 10 is to convert the numbers into scientific notation (Speaks, 1999). Any number, regardless of size, may be expressed in scientific notation. The conversion process is really quite simple because scientific notation is always used in combination with exponential notation. When utilizing scientific notation, any number can be translated into the product of a simpler number, called a coefficient (ranging from 1.000 to 9.999), and any base value (for our purposes, the base 10) that is raised to an exponential power (Speaks, 1999). Therefore, any quantity expressed as the product of a coefficient and a base that is raised to an exponential power, or simply,

$$[1.000 \text{ to } 9.999] \times 10^{x}$$

is a quantity that is said to be expressed in scientific notation (Hewitt, 2010; Speaks, 1999). Conversion from conventional to scientific notation can be accomplished with a few simple procedures (Speaks, 1999). These procedures are outlined in section A3 of Appendix A. The values expressed in exponential notation that were presented in Table A1–1 of Appendix A are again presented in Table A3–1 of Appendix A, alongside of their scientific notation equivalents. For example, 0.0000000001 rewritten in scientific notation is simply 1×10^{-10}, just as 10,000,000,000 expressed in scientific notation, becomes 1×10^{10}. Other numbers, such as 200,000; 350,000; or 0.00002 may also be expressed in scientific notation as 2×10^5, 3.5×10^5, and finally 2×10^{-5}, respectively. Additional examples of numbers that have been converted from conventional to scientific notation are also presented in Table A3–2 of Appendix A. The information provided in this section of Appendix A should be useful in answering the questions presented in Problem Set 2–3 found below.

Problem Set 2–3

1. Convert the following quantities into scientific notation:
    a) 246812; b) 2468.12; c) 24.6812;
    d) 0.246812; e) 0.00246812.

2. Convert the following quantities into scientific notation:
    a) 0.00001; b) 0.0001; c) 0.01;
    d) 10,000; e) 100,000,000.

In subsequent chapters such as in Chapter 6, scientific notation will be useful, if not essential, for transforming both large and small numbers into a convenient form prior to mathematical computation, conversion to logarithms, or conversion to metric equivalents. The advantage of using scientific notation will especially become obvious in com-

putations of the decibel. For example, one of the reference values in the calculation of decibels of sound pressure level (or dB SPL), expressed as force/area, is 0.00002 newtons/m². This value is often written in scientific notation as 2×10^{-5} newtons/m². Another reference value in the calculation of dB SPL, also expressed as force/area, is 0.0002 dynes/cm². Once again, this value is often expressed in scientific notation as 2×10^{-4} dynes/cm². Finally, the operating principles for the multiplication and division of values expressed in scientific notation may be found in section A4 of Appendix A. This information may be used in solving the equations found in Problem Set 2–4 presented below.

Problem Set 2–4

Use scientific notation:

1. Find:
    a) 800×50; b) $2,000 \times 0.005$
    c) 0.0005×0.032; d) 0.05×500;
    e) 500×25.05.

2. Find:
    a) $800 \div 50$; b) $500 \div 0.025$;
    c) $0.05 \div 0.0025$; d) $10,000 \div 0.5$;
    e) $3000 \div 0.06$.

Logarithms (Logs)

In the chapters that follow, logarithms will appear in decibel computations employing observed and reference quantities expressed either as power/area (i.e., dB IL) or as force/area (i.e., dB SPL). Therefore, in order to understand some of the basic concepts in hearing science, it is necessary to have a working knowledge of exponential notation, scientific notation, and logarithms. The rules that apply to computations involving logarithms are natural extensions of the previously discussed rules that applied both to exponential notation and to scientific notation (Giancoli, 2005).

Recall that any base value (X) may be multiplied by itself n times. Recall as well from a former discussion that when a base value is raised to an nth power exponent, and the exponent is written in superscript to the right of the base, the expression X^n is referred to as exponential notation. As shown previously, converting exact integer multiples of 10 from conventional notation to exponential notation is quite simple. Table 2–2 is now provided in order to illustrate the simplest kind of numerical conversion, first to exponential, and then to logarithmic equivalents (Tables 2–3 and 2–4). Note that the numbers provided in Table 2–2 are exact integer multiples of 10. For any exponent n, $X^n = Y$, where Y represents the equivalent value expressed in conventional notation.

Logarithms Defined

The base value 10 can be raised to any exponential value (n) as in 10^n, in order to obtain a conventionally expressed value Y. Moreover, any conventional value Y may be expressed in terms of the base value 10 raised to some exponential power (Giancoli, 2005). For any base value X raised to an exponential power n, such that X^n, if $X^n = Y$, and Y is the equivalent value expressed in conventional notation, then the logarithm to the base X (or $\log_x$) of the value Y is simply the exponent n of the base X, or

Table 2–2. The Simplest Kind of Numerical Conversion Is to Exponential Notation

If: $Y = X^n$		
Then:	Y	$= X^n$
	0.0001	$= 10^{-4}$
	0.001	$= 10^{-3}$
	0.01	$= 10^{-2}$
	0.1	$= 10^{-1}$
	1.00	$= 10^{0}$
	10	$= 10^{1}$
	100	$= 10^{2}$
	1,000	$= 10^{3}$
	10,000	$= 10^{4}$

Table 2–3. Exponential Values Presented in Table 2–2 Again Presented With Their Respective Logarithm Equivalents

Y	$= X^n$	$\log_x{}^Y = n$	$\log_x{}^n = n$
0.0001	$= 10^{-4}$	-4	-4
0.001	$= 10^{-3}$	-3	-3
0.01	$= 10^{-2}$	-2	-2
0.1	$= 10^{-1}$	-1	-1
1.00	$= 10^{0}$	0	0
10	$= 10^{1}$	1	1
100	$= 10^{2}$	2	2
1,000	$= 10^{3}$	3	3
10,000	$= 10^{4}$	4	4

Table 2–4. Logarithms Borrowed From Table 2–3 Expressed With a Decimal Point and Several Zeros That Follow

Y	$= X^n$	$\log_x{}^Y = n$	$\log_x{}^n = n$
0.0001	$= 10^{-4}$	-4.00	-4.00
0.001	$= 10^{-3}$	-3.00	-3.00
1,000	$= 10^{3}$	3.00	3.00
10,000	$= 10^{4}$	4.00	4.00

If: $X^n = Y$; then $\log_x{}^Y = n$

Example: If $10^5 = 10,000$; then $\log_{10} 10,000 = 5$

Example: If $10^{-5} = 0.00001$; then $\log_{10} 0.00001 = -5$

Therefore, the logarithm of any value expressed conventionally can be defined as the exponential power to which a base (usually 10) must be raised in order to obtain the conventional value itself (Giancoli, 2005). This additionally means that the log to the base X (or $\log_x$) of the equivalent value expressed in exponential notation is the exponential value of the base, or

If: X^n; then $\log_x X^n = n$

Example: If 10^5; then $\log_{10} 10^5 = 5$

Example: If 10^{-5}; then $\log_{10} 10^{-5} = -5$

Furthermore, it also follows that the log to the base X of any value expressed in exponential notation is equal to the $\log_x$ of the conventional equivalent of the value, or

If: $X^n = Y$; then $\log_x X^n = \log_x{}^Y$

Example: If $10^5 = 10,000$; then $\log_{10} 10,000 = \log_{10} 10^5 = 5$

Example: If $10^{-5} = 0.00001$; then $\log_{10} 0.00001 = \log_{10} 10^{-5} = -5$

Exponents/Logarithms of Whole Number Integers of 10

To further illustrate the relationship between exponents and logarithms, the exponential values presented in Table 2–2 are again presented in Table 2–3 with their respective logarithm equivalents. Note that for all values shown, the exponent n of the base X is not only the logarithm of X_n, but is also the logarithm of the equivalent conventional value, Y. Therefore, a logarithm is the same as an exponent (Giancoli, 2005; Speaks, 1999). In short, the logarithm of any number is the exponential value that the base 10 would need to be raised to, such that when it is, the value of interest would be the mathematical result. It should be noted that any number may serve as a base value for an exponent. There are, however, three base values most commonly used in physics. For instance, the number 2 (log2) is a commonly used base value, as is the number 2.718 (or e). Logarithmic computations made on numbers that use 2.718 as their base value (log$e$) are called natural or Naperian logarithms (Giancoli, 2005; Speaks, 1999). Throughout this text, the majority of logarithmic computations will be made on values having a base value of 10 (log10), as shown in Table 2–3. Logarithms that use 10 as a base are called common or Briggsian logarithms, and these are usually expressed in definitional or computational equations with the 10 omitted as the subscript to the term *log* (Giancoli, 2005; Speaks, 1999). Therefore, in the present context, the term log may appear in reference to the use of common logarithms with the understanding that the base value is always 10.

From Table 2–3, it can be observed that when a conventionally expressed quantity is an exact multiple of 10 (i.e., 0.1, 1.0, 10, 100, 1,000, etc.), the equivalent exponential expression of the same quantity will consist of a whole number integer exponent located to the right of the base. The whole number integer is also the logarithm of the quantity, and the log may be expressed with a decimal point and several zeros that follow (Giancoli, 2005). This simple point is illustrated in Table 2–4 using numbers borrowed from Table 2–3.

Problem Set 2–5

Find the common or Briggsian logarithm for each of the following:

a) 100,000; b) 1,000; c) 0.001; d) 0.0000001; e) 10^9; f) 10^4; g) 10^{-12}; h) 10^{-16}; i) 10^{-5}; j) 10^{xyz}; k) $10^{-x(y)}$.

Nonwhole Number Exponents/Logarithms

Obviously, not all of the values encountered in the sciences will be exact multiples of 10. For instance the numbers 2 through 9, 11 through 19, 21 through 29, and so forth, are not exact multiples of 10. Therefore, it may seem likely that the logarithms of such numbers will not simply consist of whole number integers. This is indeed the case. The base 10 may be raised to any value to obtain any quantity. That is, exponents are not restricted to whole number integers. Therefore, a log may be found for any value, and the log may well turn out to be a nonwhole number. This point is best illustrated in Table 2–5.

Recognize from Tables 2–4 and 2–5 that the logarithm of any number N consists of two parts. The first part is represented by a value located to the left of the decimal point. The second part is given by a value located to the right of the decimal point (Durrant & Feth, 2013; Speaks, 1999). Therefore, for any common logarithm,

$$\log \text{ of } N = X \cdot ABCDE$$

Table 2–5. Exponents Are Not Restricted to Whole Number Integers, and Logarithms May Be Nonwhole Numbers

The log of 1 = 0.00	since 10^0	= 1
The log of 2 = 0.301	since $10^{0.301}$	= 2
The log of 3 = 0.477	since $10^{0.477}$	= 3
The log of 4 = 0.602	since $10^{0.602}$	= 4
The log of 5 = 0.698	since $10^{0.698}$	= 5
The log of 6 = 0.778	since $10^{0.778}$	= 6
The log of 7 = 0.845	since $10^{0.845}$	= 7
The log of 8 = 0.903	since $10^{0.903}$	= 8
The log of 9 = 0.954	since $10^{0.954}$	= 9
The log of 10 = 1.00	since 10^1	= 10

such that the value represented by the X consists of a whole number integer (or sometimes zero) located to the left of the decimal point, and the value represented by A through E consists of a string of numbers (that are sometimes zeros) located to the right of the decimal point. Any nonzero string of numbers found to the right of the decimal point obviously represents a decimal value. Any zero or nonzero whole number integer X (in the first part of the log) that is located to the left of the decimal is called the characteristic of the log. Any zero or nonzero decimal value string A–E located to the right of the decimal (in the second part of the log) is called the mantissa of the log, or simply,

characteristic → X . ABCDE ← mantissa

↑

decimal point

Further clarification of computational procedures involving both the characteristic and mantissa of logarithms are left to Section B1 of Appendix B. Section B2 of Appendix B provides stepwise procedures for determining logarithms for a variety of types of numerical values, including decimals. Section B3 of Appendix B introduces antilogarithms (antilogs) and provides a series of logarithm tables (Tables B3–2, B3–3, B3–4, and B3–5). The negative logarithms of a small sample of decimal values are also provided in Table B3–6 of Appendix B. Finally, Section B3 of Appendix B presents several definitional and computational rules in the use of logarithms.

Problem Set 2–6

Identify the characteristic and the mantissa for each of the following:

a) 0.707; b) 70.07; c) 0.00007; d) 707; e) WX.YZ.

Problem Set 2–7

Using scientific notation and the log tables provided in Section B3 of Appendix B (Tables B3–1A–D), find the log of

a) 48; b) 57; c) 3,600; d) 770; e) 180; f) 850; g) 0.0085; h) 0.0044; i) 0.000078; j) 0.0046.

Problem Set 2–8

Using scientific notation and/or the log Tables B3–2 through B3–6 provided in Section B3 of Appendix B, find the log of

a) 0.48; b) 0.57; c) 0.36; d) 0.04; e) 0.18; f) 0.66; g) 0.78; h) 0.94; i) 0.27.

Measurement Systems

The Importance of Standard Units of Measurement

As indicated in Chapter 1, the rules that determine the manner in which scientific knowledge is communicated also fall under the purview of science. The expression of numerical quantities in the absence of standard units of measure is grossly inadequate in any scientific discipline, and would be unacceptable even in day-to-day transactions. It is imperative that standard units of measurement be specified along with the numerical values that represent the quantities expressed. The use of standard measurement systems can often provide safeguards against miscommunication. Their use also ensures that knowledge is conveyed in a manner that permits objective evaluation, a necessary condition for establishing validity and reliability. Therefore, out of necessity, science has adopted and uses a general standard system of measure (Hewitt, 2010).

Standard Measurement Systems

Three fundamental dimensions exist in physics. These dimensions are length, mass, and time (Halliday et al., 2011). It will become clear in the next chapter that each of the mechanical and acoustic quantities of interest to hearing science will be derived from quantities that represent these three fundamental dimensions (Hewitt, 2010). Several measurement systems have been used over the years to designate, measure, and standardize values representing these three fundamental physical dimensions.

The FPS System

The U.S. Customary System (USCS), formerly called the British System of Units (or the British Engineering System), is often used in the United States and in Burma as a standard system of measurement (Giancoli, 2005; Hewitt, 2010). The USCS or foot-pound-second (fps) measurement system is cumbersome to use and is not accepted internationally as a standard system of measurement. The USCS system employs the "foot" as the standard unit of length, and the "second" as the standard unit of time. A standard unit for "mass," unfortunately, does not exist in the USCS system.

Weight. The "pound" is used as the standard unit of weight or force (Dirckx, 2005) in the USCS system, and is often defined in terms of the standard kilogram. That is, the mass of an object that weighs one pound is equal to 0.4536 kilograms (Hewitt, 2010). However, weight is not a universal physical property because weight (unlike mass) varies with gravitational force. Weight, therefore, is not equal to mass, but it is related to mass. The weight of a body is the magnitude of the net force required to prevent the body from falling freely, as measured by someone on the earth (Halliday et al., 2011). Simply put, weight may be defined as a force placed upon an object due to the force of gravity.

Mass and Density

Mass may be defined, simply, as the amount or quantity of matter in any object (Hewitt, 2010). However, a less familiar definition is that the mass of a body is the characteristic that relates a force on the body to the resulting acceleration. That is, a physical sensation of mass can only be appreciated when one attempts to accelerate a body (Halliday et al., 2011).

As indicated above, weight and mass are not equal. While mass may be thought of as the overall quantity of matter contained in an object, density may be distinguished from mass as a measure of the compactness of matter. Density is used as an indication of how much mass occupies a given space (Halliday et al., 2011). Specifically, density is a measure of the amount of mass per unit volume or simply:

$$\text{Density} = \text{Mass/Volume}$$

The Metric System

The metric system that originated in France in 1791 is accepted internationally by the scientific community as a standard system of measure (Halliday et al., 2011; Hewitt, 2010). In the metric system, both large and small measurement units are defined as multiples of 10, from standard units of measure. This property, taken together with the fact that the metric system makes use of exponential and scientific notation, renders metric calculations in physics and in hearing science relatively effortless (Giancoli, 2005; Hewitt, 2010). The metric system is, therefore, the measurement system of choice in the study of hearing science.

In terms of length, the first international standard was the meter (m), which was established as the standard unit of length by the French Academy of Sciences in 1792 (Giancoli, 2005; Halliday et al., 2011). Based on an original definition for the meter, as "one-ten millionth of the distance from the earth's equator to either pole," the meter was more precisely defined in 1886 (Figure 2–4) as a distance marked off between two finely engraved marks on a bar of platinum-iridium alloy metal (Halliday et al., 2011; Hewitt, 2010).

In 1960, the meter was once again redefined as 1,650,763.73 separate wavelengths of the orange light that is emitted by the gas, krypton-86. In 1983 the meter was again defined by the 17th General Conference on Weights and Measures. Accordingly, the meter is the length traveled by a path of light in a vacuum, over an interval of 1/299,792,458 second; therefore, the speed of light (c) was defined as 299,792,458 m/s (Halliday et al., 2011). Stated in terms of the USCS (or fps) system, 1 meter is equal to approximately 39.37 inches, 3.28 feet, or 1.09 yards.

With respect to time, the standard unit of time in the metric system is the second (s). In conventional terms, 1 s is 1/60 of a min. In 1967 the 13th General Conference on Weights and Measures adopted a "standard" second based on the cesium clock. One second is defined as the frequency of radiation emitted by cesium-133 atoms as they pass between two particular states, or as 9,192,631,770 separate periods or oscillations of this radiation for a speci-fied wavelength (Halliday et al., 2011; Hewitt, 2010).

Finally, the standard unit for mass is the kilogram (kg). The kilogram is equal to 1,000 grams and is determined by the specific mass of a platinum-iridium alloy cylinder, 3.9 centimeters in height and in diameter, which by international agreement is defined as exactly 1 kg of mass (Halliday et al., 2011). The standard cylinder is kept and maintained by the International Bureau of Weights and Measures near Paris, France. Stated in terms of the USCS (or fps) system, 1 kg is equal to about 2.205 pounds (Giancoli, 2005; Hewitt, 2010).

The MKS Metric System. Currently, the most widely used measurement system is the Système International (SI) or International System (Halliday et al., 2011; Hewitt, 2010). In the SI system, the standard unit for length is the meter, the standard unit for mass is the kilogram, and standard unit of time is the second, as indicated in the previous section (Halliday et al., 2011). Therefore, the SI system of measures is also abbreviated as the MKS (meter-kilogram-second) metric system (Hewitt, 2010).

The MKS system of measures was formulated in order to designate, measure, and standardize values representing the three fundamental physical

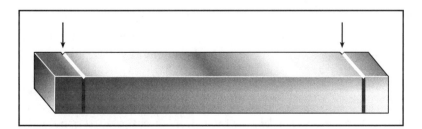

Figure 2–4. The meter may be defined as a distance of about 39.37 inches between and standardized by two finely engraved marks on a bar of platinum-iridium alloy metal.

dimensions of length, mass, and time. The MKS metric system is also the preferred measurement system in the field of physics (Hewitt, 2010). Hence,

Length, Mass, Time = SYSTEM

M(eter), K(ilogram), S(econd) = MKS

Length: One meter, which is the familiar quantity or standard unit of measure for the MKS system, may also be written in exponential notation as 10^0 meter. As previously indicated, both large and small measurement units in the metric system may be defined or derived from standard units of measure, as multiples of 10. Thus, additional multiples of the standard unit for length may be derived, and with each derivation, a different metric prefix will be applied to the new measure. It is important to note that the metric prefix and/or symbol that may be applied is also associated with a certain exponential value. The metric prefixes and symbols most often encountered in the study of hearing science are those that correspond to micro, milli, centi, deci, deca, and kilo. The exponential computations and metric prefixes are presented in Table C1–1 in Appendix C. For instance,

1000	(10^3)	meters =	
		1 kilometer	(1 km)
0.01	(10^{-2})	meters =	
		1 centimeter	(1 cm)
0.001	(10^{-3})	meters =	
		1 millimeter	(1 mm)
0.000001	(10^{-6})	meters =	
		1 micrometer	(1 μm)
		or 1 micron	(1 μ)

Therefore, 1,000 meters is 1 km, or by conventional standards, a little more than 6/10 of a mile. One-hundredth (1/100) of a meter is 1 cm. One-thousandth (1/1000) of a meter is 1 mm, and one millionth (1/1,000,000) of a meter is 1 μm or simply 1 μ.

Mass: One kilogram, which is the familiar quantity or standard unit of measure for the MKS system, is 1,000 grams, and may, therefore, be written in exponential notation as 10^3 grams. Hence,

1000 (10^3) grams =
1 kilogram (1 kg)

One gram (g) is the mass of one cubic centimeter (cc) of water at a temperature of 4° Celsius. One gram is also approximately 0.035 ounces. Hence, 1 kg is equivalent to approximately 35 ounces (i.e., 1,000 × 0.035) or 2.205 pounds in the USCS (or fps) system (Giancoli, 2005; Hewitt, 2010).

Time: One second, which is the customary quantity or standard unit of measure for the MKS system, may also be written in exponential notation as 10^0 s. Additional multiples of the standard unit for time may be derived. For instance,

0.001 (10^{-3}) seconds =
1 millisecond (1 ms)
0.000001 (10^{-6}) seconds =
1 microsecond (1 μs)

Simple Derivations of Length: Area and Volume. Complex quantities derived from length will be addressed in greater detail in the next chapter. However, simple derivations of MKS length, particularly area, need mentioning in the present context. In general, the unit of area is a square that has a standard unit of length as a side. The volume of an object refers to the space that it occupies, and the standard unit of volume is the space taken up by a cube that has a standard unit of length for its edge (Hewitt, 2010).

Area: The MKS unit of area is an essential component in MKS computations of the decibel and in MKS computations of pressure. The MKS unit for area is easily computed by squaring the MKS unit for length, which is the meter (Hewitt, 2010). Therefore, the squared meter (meter^2; m^2) is the MKS unit for area that is to be used in all MKS computations of the decibel and pressure.

Volume: The MKS unit for volume is easily computed by cubing the MKS unit for length, the meter. Therefore, the cubic meter (meter^3; m^3) is the MKS unit for volume (Hewitt, 2010). The m^3 is equal to 1,000 (10^3) liters, 10^6 milliliters (mL), or approximately 264.2 U.S. gallons. Therefore, a liter is also equal to approximately 0.26 U.S. gallons.

The CGS Metric System. There exists a second metric measurement system, called the CGS (centimeter-gram-second) system of measurement. Relative to the MKS system, the CGS system uses smaller metric units as standard values to designate and measure the three fundamental physical dimensions (Giancoli, 2005; Hewitt, 2010). For this reason, the CGS system is the preferred system of measurement in the field of chemistry. In the CGS measurement system, the standard unit for length is the centimeter, the standard unit for mass is the gram, and the standard unit for time is, once again, the second (Giancoli, 2005; Hewitt, 2010). Because the discipline of hearing science has no

officially adopted metric system, it will be important to understand and work with both the MKS and the CGS systems of measurement. Hence,

Length, Mass, Time = SYSTEM

C(entimeter), G(ram), S(econd) = CGS

Length: One centimeter (cm), which is the customary quantity or standard unit of measure for the CGS system, is one-hundreth (1/100) of a meter. This CGS standard for length may also be written in exponential notation as 10^{-2} meter.

Mass: One gram (g), which is the well-known quantity or standard unit of measure for the CGS system, may also be written in exponential notation as 10^0 gram. As previously indicated, a gram is approximately equal to the mass of 1 cc of water at a temperature of 4° Celsius, or 0.035 ounces (Hewitt, 2010). Additional multiples of the standard unit for mass may also be derived. For instance,

1,000	(10^3)	gram =	
		1 kilogram	(1 kg)
0.001	(10^{-3})	gram =	
		1 milligram	(1 mg)
0.000001	(10^{-6})	gram =	
		1 microgram	(1 μg)

Time: One second is the customary quantity or standard unit of measure for the CGS system. As indicated previously, 1 s may also be written in exponential notation as 10^0 s.

Simple Derivations of Length: Area and Volume. Simple derivations of CGS length, particularly area, once again require a word of mention in the present context.

Area: As was the MKS unit of area, the CGS unit of area is also an essential component in (CGS) computations of the decibel as well as in CGS computations of pressure. The CGS unit for area is easily computed by squaring the CGS unit for length, the centimeter (Hewitt, 2010). Therefore, the squared centimeter (centimeter^2 or simply cm^2) is the CGS unit for area that is to be used in all CGS computations of the decibel and pressure.

Volume: The CGS unit for volume is easily computed by cubing the CGS unit for length, the centimeter (Hewitt, 2010). Therefore, the cubic centimeter (centimeter^3; cm^3, or simply cc) is the CGS unit for volume. The cm^3 is equivalent to the milliliter (mL), or 10^{-3} L.

ships between measures or quantities are directly proportional, meaning that increases in the magnitude of one variable are associated with increases in the magnitude of a second variable. Similarly, a direct proportionality also pertains when decreases in the magnitude of one variable are associated with decreases in the magnitude of a second variable (Giancoli, 2005). An inverse proportion or an inverse relationship exists when two measurement variables are related in such a way that increases in the magnitude of one variable are associated with decreases in the magnitude of a second variable, or vice versa (Giancoli, 2005). A symbol that may at times be used to designate the concept of proportionality is a squiggly line, or simply "~" (Hewitt, 2010).

Proportionality

The investigation of relationships that exist between different quantities and variables is important, not only in the field of physics and hearing science, but in all of the sciences. It is often the case in scientific investigation or in the study of physical properties, that a given measurement variable or quantity will be found to be affected by one, by two, or by several different measurement variables (Giancoli, 2005). In hearing science, when one quantity affects other quantities, the appropriate expression often used to indicate such interdependence is to state that "the observed change in one measurement variable occurs as a function of changes in another (or other) measurement variable(s)." Throughout the text, it will become clear that some relation-

Direct Proportionality

For any two measurement variables or quantities X and Y, where ~ is often the symbol that indicates "is proportional to," the expression $X \sim Y$ is taken to mean that measurement variables X and Y are directly related or proportional. That is, any amount of change observed in variable X represents the same amount of change that may be observed in variable Y (Hewitt, 2010). It might also be stated that changes in X occur as a direct function of changes occurring in Y, or vice versa (Giancoli, 2005).

Example: the fundamental or best frequency ~ √stiffness (stiffness$^{1/2}$)

Or in words: the fundamental or best frequency of any object is directly proportional to the square root of the object's stiffness.

> Example:
> force ~ mass × acceleration

Or in words: force is directly proportional to the product of mass and acceleration.

> Example: $I \sim P^2$

Or in words: acoustic intensity is directly proportional to pressure squared.

Concepts such as the fundamental frequency, stiffness, mass, force, acceleration, acoustic intensity, and pressure are all important concepts that will be discussed in greater depth in the chapters that follow.

Inverse Proportionality

For any two measurement variables or quantities X and Y; if $X \sim 1/Y$, then variable X is inversely proportional to variable Y (Hewitt, 2010). Similarly, if $Y \sim 1/X$, then variable Y is inversely proportional to variable X. That is, any amount of change observed in variable X represents an inverse in the amount of change that may be observed in variable Y. We might also say that changes that occur in X vary inversely as a function of changes that occur in Y, or vice versa (Giancoli, 2005). In addition, it is often stated that if $X \sim 1/Y$, then quantities X and Y are reciprocals of each other.

> Example: stiffness ~ 1/compliance;
> compliance ~ 1/stiffness

Or in words: stiffness is inversely proportional to compliance, and vice versa.

> Example: frequency ~ 1/period;
> period ~ 1/frequency

Or in words: frequency is inversely proportional to period, and vice versa.

Both stiffness and compliance, as well as the relationship between frequency and period are important concepts that will be discussed in greater depth in the chapters that follow.

Chapter Summary

- Important issues relating to the matter of measurement in hearing science were discussed in Chapter 2.
- In this chapter, two broad classes of variables were defined: continuous and categorical variables.
- In this chapter, measurement scales were also defined as nominal, ordinal, interval, and ratio.
- Ratio scales, by definition, permit the greatest number and greatest complexity of mathematical operations over the other three types of scales.
- Nominal scales afford the fewest number and least complexity of mathematical operations over the other three scales.
- Exponential notation was introduced, and the operating principles of exponents were also defined.
- In this chapter, scientific notation was introduced as a method for solving problems involving logarithms.

■ In this chapter, measurement systems were introduced with an emphasis on the metric system. The basic components of the MKS and CGS metric systems are summarized below:

Length, Mass, Time = SYSTEM

M(eter), K(ilogram), S(econd) = MKS

C(entimeter), G(ram), S(econd) = CGS

■ In this chapter, metric prefixes important for working with and understanding quantities in hearing science were also provided.

■ In this chapter, the concept of proportionality was introduced together with an accepted symbol that designates proportionality ~. The terms directly proportional and inversely proportional were defined.

Chapter 2 Questions

1. What are the three fundamental dimensions found in physics? How are these three dimensions represented in the metric system(s) in terms of standard, quantitative units of measure?

2. Why are standard measurement systems necessary in science?

3. Define what is meant by the characteristic and the mantissa of the logarithm. What are the origins of the characteristic and the mantissa in the final logarithm?

References

American National Standards Institute (ANSI). (1996). *American National Standard specification for audiometers. ANSI S3.6-1996*. New York, NY: Author.

Dirckx, J. H. (2005). *Stedman's medical dictionary for the health professions and nursing illustrated* (5th ed.). Baltimore, MD: Lippincott Williams & Wilkins.

Durrant, J. D., & Feth, L. L. (2013). *Hearing sciences: A foundational approach*. Upper Saddle River, NJ: Pearson Education.

Giancoli, D. C. (2005). *Physics: Principles with applications* (6th ed.). Upper Saddle River, NJ: Prentice Hall.

Gianopoulos, A. (2006). The heavens. In J. Langone, B. Stutz, & A. Gianopoulos (Eds.), *Theories for everything: An illustrated history of science from the invention of numbers to string theory* (pp. 18–71). Washington, DC: National Geographic Society.

Halliday, D., Resnick, R., & Walker, J. (2011). *Fundamentals of physics* (9th ed.). Hoboken, NJ: Wiley.

Hays, W. L. (1981). *Statistics* (3rd ed.). New York, NY: CBS College-Holt, Rinehart & Winston.

Hempel, C. G. (1966). Concept formation. In E. Beardsley & M. Beardsley (Eds.), *Philosophy of Natural Science* (pp. 85–100). Upper Saddle River, NJ: Prentice Hall.

Hewitt, P. G. (2010). *Conceptual Physics* (11th ed.). Upper Saddle River, NJ: Pearson Education.

Hirsh, I. J. (1952). *The measurement of hearing*. New York, NY: McGraw-Hill.

Maxwell, D. L., & Satake, E. (1997). *Research and statistical methods in communication disorders*. Baltimore, MD: Williams & Wilkins.

Schiavetti, N., & Metz, D. E. (2002). *Evaluating research in communicative disorders* (4th ed.). Boston, MA: Allyn & Bacon.

Speaks, C. E. (1999). *Introduction to sound: Acoustics for the hearing and speech sciences* (3rd ed.). San Diego, CA: Singular.

Stevens, S. S. (1958). Chapter 1: Mathematics, measurement, and psychophysics. In S. S. Stevens (Ed.), *Handbook of experimental psychology* (pp. 1–49). New York, NY: Wiley.

Stutz, B. (2006). Life itself. In J. Langone, B. Stutz, & A. Gianopoulos (Eds.), *Theories for everything: An illustrated history of science from the invention of numbers to string theory* (pp. 231–303). Washington, DC: National Geographic Society.

Chapter 3

Basic Terminology for Hearing Science

It was discovered sometime during the sixth or seventh century BC, and then later in the writings of Galileo (Hawking, 2002, p. 474), that by halving the length of a string, the pitch generated when the string was plucked represented the pitch produced at one octave frequency higher (or at 2× the original frequency). The same ratio seemed to apply for the length of a pipe in a flute. The Greeks realized that they could further subdivide the octave by altering the lengths of resonating objects. The idea that sound could be described mathematically was one of a number of discoveries that led to the realization that natural phenomena, such as sound, could be subjected to quantitative analysis.

Stutz, 2006, p. 15

Alphabetized Listing of Key Terms Discussed in Chapter 3

acceleration	deceleration	Elemente der Psychophysik
acoustics	diffusion	
amplitude	directionality	energy
area	displacement	energy principle
average acceleration	distance	equilibrium
average speed	drag	equilibrium position
average velocity	drag, frictional	Fechner, Gustav Theodor
cells	$E = mc^2$	
compliance	Einstein, Albert	first law of thermodynamics
compression	elastic limit	fluid
condensation	elasticity	fluid friction
conservative force	electromagnetic	force
cycle		

force, frictional	motion	sensation
frequency	Newton, Sir Isaac	simple harmonic motion
friction	nonconservative force	
Galileo Galilei	peak amplitude	Slinky
hearing	peak-to-peak amplitude	speed
heat		speed of light
Helmholtz, Hermann von	pendulum	spring
	pendulum bob	spring constant
Hooke's law	perception	spring-mass system
Hooke, Robert	period	static equilibrium
inelastic	periodic	stiffness
instantaneous acceleration	physics	thermal energy
		time
instantaneous speed	plastic region	uniform circular motion
instantaneous velocity	psychoacoustics	
law of the conservation of energy	psychophysics	vector quantity
	radioactivity	velocity
length	rarefaction	vibration
light	rate	volume
machine	reciprocals	waveform
magnitude	restorative force	waves
mass	scalar quantity	work
mechanics	second law of thermodynamics	
Micrographia		

The Importance and Relevance of Physics to Hearing Science

Physics is the most basic of all the sciences. The subject matter of physics concerns the structure and activity of all that exists in the physical world. Broadly speaking, physics includes the study of matter, motion, force, and energy (Giancoli, 2005; Hewitt, 2010). Therefore, physics serves as a foundation for every other scientific discipline (Hewitt, 2010). The assertion that physics is central to the sciences is perhaps most evident in the hearing sciences. This is because matter, motion, and energy are central to hearing science.

In Chapter 2, length, mass, and time were introduced as fundamental dimensions in physics. Mechanical and acoustic measures of interest to hearing science also consist of the same fundamental dimensions of length, mass, and time, as well as their derived values. Some of the derived values include area and volume as indicated previously. Other derived values relevant to hearing science include force, power, pressure, and the basic elements of vibration, such as displacement, velocity, and acceleration. Hence, the relevance of physics to the hearing sciences cannot be overstated, and it should not be surprising that a considerable amount of attention will be paid to the physics (i.e., the physical basis) of sound throughout this textbook.

Physics and Energy

Physics is called upon in any description of the propagation (generation) or dissemination of sound. Energy, in all of its constituent forms, is a dominant element of study in physics, and energy is required to set any mass into vibration. When vibrations are created, they produce waveforms. Waveforms in general can take many forms. They may take the form of ocean waves, earthquake waves, electromagnetic waves as in light, radio waves, or heat, or waveforms may take the form of sound traveling through an elastic medium, such as air or water (Giancoli, 2005). Sound, like all other waveforms is a physical event defined by known physical laws. Vibration and the production of waveforms may be found at the source of any sound.

All waveforms, independent of their origin, transfer energy from one location to another; therefore, vibrations and waveforms involve motion. Energy is pivotal to any discussion of motion, because motion of any kind requires energy (Giancoli, 2005; Halliday, Resnick, & Walker, 2011). Hence, the pro-

duction of sound also requires energy, and energy is essential in any discussion of sound. The concept and definition of energy are introduced in the section that follows.

Energy

The term *energy* comes from the Greek *energia*, which means "in work" (Stutz, 2006). Those who live in civilized technological societies know the importance of energy. Most of the world invests considerable time, money, and political effort to obtain the fossil and the nuclear fuels that generate energy. Countless examples could be given to illustrate the many ways we use and depend upon energy. The concept of energy is also central to all of science. Energy binds molecules of matter together and is typically expressed in terms of its overall magnitude (Halliday et al., 2011; Hewitt, 2010). In biological systems, four types of energy are distinguished. The four types of energy consist of thermal, mechanical, chemical, and electrical energy. Biologic systems generate driving forces by altering the flow of substances and charges that cause energy to travel from one location to another (see Chapter 9). Other forms of energy also exist in the universe, such as nuclear energy, geothermal energy, solar energy, and light. Finally, there is sound, and sound also travels from one location to another (Giancoli, 2005).

Despite all the forms that energy takes and despite all that physicists claim to understand in connection with it, a clear scientific definition of energy is still difficult to provide. Moreover, while most individuals would agree that energy is central to their daily lives, it is likely that most people would find it difficult to provide a clear description of what energy is actually composed of (Halliday et al., 2011). The fact is that most of us observe energy only when it is transferred from one object to another, or when it is transformed from one form to another. For example, we experience energy in the form of electromagnetic waves such as heat and light from the sun. Energy is captured by plants that make up the food we eat, and we receive this energy through digestion (Hewitt, 2010). The sound that is produced by the application of a force to an object as it is set into vibratory motion also represents a reversible transformation or exchange of energy from one form to another. The two exchangeable forms of energy found in a vibrating mass will be discussed in detail in the next chapter.

Perhaps it is best stated that energy and matter make up the universe, but matter is substance, and energy is the "mover" of substance. That is, matter has mass and occupies space, but energy is usually conceived of as being more abstract than mass. Energy seems abstract because not only is energy a "thing," it is also a process (Hewitt, 2010). However, if energy is a "thing," then it must certainly have mass. Albert Einstein (1879–1955), who was awarded the Nobel Prize in Physics in 1921, linked energy with mass. Einstein (Portrait 3–1) reasoned that if energy is required to make mass, then energy must surely be released if mass disappears. Einstein first suggested that mass has the property of being convertible to other forms of energy, and in turn, energy has the attribute of convertibility to mass (Gianopoulos, 2006). The interconvertibility of mass and energy has been experimentally confirmed in

Portrait 3–1. Albert Einstein (1879–1955). Printed with permission. Wikimedia Commons, public domain.

countless instances (Giancoli, 2005; Hawking, 2002).

The now famous Einstein-Lorentz formula:

$$E = mc^2$$

where E = energy, m = mass, and c^2 is a conversion factor, is not only the formula for the conversion of mass into other types of energy, it also states that energy and mass are identical (Gianopoulos, 2006; Hewitt, 2010). This formula also states that mass increases exponentially as an object accelerates toward the speed of light (Stutz, 2006). Experiments have demonstrated that a small particle of matter, accelerated to 86% of the speed of light, yields twice as much mass as it does at rest (Hawking, 2002). Hence, even miniscule amounts of mass have the potential to yield enormous amounts of energy. Furthermore, what we commonly refer to as "radioactivity" represents mass in the process of being converted to energy (Stutz, 2006).

It is certain, therefore, that energy has mass and mass is energy. A change in the energy state of any object at rest should be accompanied by a change in its mass (Gianopoulos, 2006). For example, the filament of a lightbulb energized with electric current has more mass than when the light is switched off. A spring that is compressed or stretched has more mass than a spring at rest. Water that is heated has more mass than water that is not heated. However, the changes in mass given by these three examples would be so small they would be very difficult to measure (Giancoli, 2005; Hewitt, 2010). In the next chapter, we will see that objects set into vibration to produce sound will have a greater capacity to store and to manifest energy, provided that their mass is also relatively greater.

Energy Conservation and Work

Vibration, and the subsequent production of waveforms required to produce sound, involve the persistent reversible transformation of energy from one form to another in order to maintain motion, as indicated above. The two energy forms (potential and kinetic) will be addressed in detail in the following chapter. The point to be made presently is that energy is neither created nor destroyed. Instead, energy may be transformed from one type to another, and/or transferred from one object to another, but the total amount of energy in any system is always the same. That is, the total energy in a system is never increased nor decreased by any pro-

cess (Giancoli, 2005). The total energy in any system can change only by the amounts of energy that are transferred to or from the system (Halliday et al., 2011). This canon or principle of energy is called the law of the conservation of energy, and it was formulated by Hermann von Helmholtz (1821–1894) in his book (1847) *On the Conservation of Force* (Portrait 3–2). The law of the conservation of energy is also the first law of thermodynamics, stating that the energy that is made available for use in a system is equal to the energy that is inherently stored, or put into the system (Stutz, 2006).

Portrait 3–2. Hermann von Helmholtz (1821–1894) formulated (1847) the law of the conservation of energy. Printed with permission. Wikimedia Commons, public domain.

The energy principle is supported by countless experiments and no exception to this principle of energy (conservation) has ever been observed (Halliday et al., 2011; Hewitt, 2010). This law applies even as energy is converted from heat to mechanical energy, from chemical to electrical energy, from kinetic to potential energy, and would apply to gravitational, radiant, and nuclear energies as well (Stutz, 2006). Therefore, in terms of the concepts presented in Chapter 1, the law of the conservation of energy (the energy principle) is an example of a law having considerable construct validity.

The energy principle forms the basis for the continuous motion of a pendulum, and the continuous motion of a spring-mass system. It also forms the basis for the vibration of objects or substances involved in the production of sound following an applied force. In general, it forms the basis for and explains why any mass that is set into vibration by an applied force will continue (ideally) to vibrate over time. However, it is important in this context to note that not all forms that energy takes are compatible with motion or with vibration (Figure 3–1).

Energy, Work, and Machines

In the sections that follow, the motions of the pendulum and the motions of a simple spring-mass system will be used to illustrate principles that are important in any discussion of harmonic motion, and therefore, the propagation of sound. In addition to the illustrations presented in Figure 3–1, both the pendulum and the simple spring-mass system represent, and are also examples of,

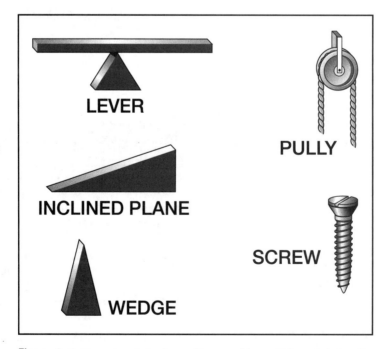

Figure 3–1. Examples of simple machines used to multiply and change the direction of forces.

simple machines. The law of the conservation of energy discussed above is the underlying principle behind every machine (Hewitt, 2010).

A machine may be defined as a device that is used for multiplying force (see Figure 3–1). Machines are also used for changing the direction of forces. It is also certain that machines perform work. However, a machine by itself cannot multiply energy and cannot multiply work (Hewitt, 2010). Work is accomplished when energy is transferred to or from an object by means of a force that acts on the object (Halliday et al., 2011). The use of the term *energy transfer* means that work is accomplished only if forces acting on an object result in a change in the motion (displacement) or in the energy state of the object that is acted upon.

In spite of the many ways that energy and work may be related, the traditional definition of energy has often been presented as "energy is the ability or the capacity to do work" (Hirsh, 1952). This, however, is an imprecise and somewhat invalid definition for all types of energy. That is, the energy associated with heat (friction or frictional drag) is often not available for work. Energy that is associated with friction and heat is not energy that is destroyed. Instead, the energy associated with friction and heat is simply energy that has been dispersed, and in that dispersed form, is "incompatible" with work. Nevertheless, for mechanical energy in the ideal absence of friction, the definition of energy that was provided, "energy is the ability or the capacity to do work," may be used to underscore the fundamental connection between energy and work (Giancoli, 2005). The concept of work, like the concept of energy, is expressed in terms of its magnitude only (Halliday et al., 2011).

Friction

The force of friction acts when the surfaces of solid objects slide or tend to slide over one another. When a net force is applied to an object to cause motion, an opposing force of friction (frictional force) will reduce the net force applied to the object (Hewitt, 2010). As illustrated in Figure 3–2, the direction of the frictional force always opposes the motion of an object. Thus, if an object is caused to move at a constant rate, a force equal to the opposing force of friction must be applied so that the two forces exactly cancel (Hewitt, 2010). For this reason, friction is a force that can be described both by its magnitude and by its direction. Friction is a sum of many forces that act between the surface atoms of one body and those of another body to oppose motion (Halliday et al., 2011). Therefore, friction is a force that opposes work.

The frictional force for solid objects does not change with the speed of the objects in contact, nor does it change with the amount of the area of contact shared by the objects. For example, the amount of friction between a tire and a road surface is nearly the same regardless of whether the tire is narrow or wide (Hewitt, 2010). Friction as a force is also not restricted to the surfaces of solid objects sliding over one another. Friction also occurs when objects travel through liquids or gasses. Liquids and gasses are collectively called fluids, but the term *fluid* may be applied to anything that flows. Fluid friction is often referred to as drag, or frictional drag (Halliday et al., 2011). When any

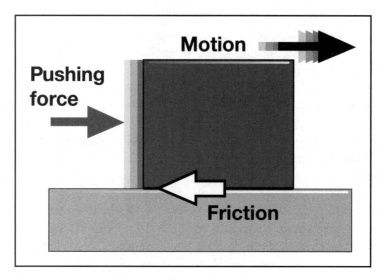

Figure 3–2. An applied net force produces displacement (motion), while frictional force opposes displacement and, therefore, opposes work. Copyright © 2014 Ron Kurtus, and School for Champions LLC http://www.school-for-champions.com/copyright.htm

object moves through a fluid, the object experiences a frictional drag force that opposes its motion (Halliday et al., 2011). Unlike the friction that exists between solid objects, frictional drag depends on the speed of the object and the area of contact between the fluid substance and the object (Hewitt, 2010). Therefore, objects that vibrate to produce sound in a fluid medium such as air will encounter a frictional drag force that opposes vibration. When an object in motion travels or vibrates through a fluid such as air, it may be said that the object "drags" through the air.

An object moving or vibrating through the air pushes air molecules out of its immediate path and causes air molecules in the regions immediately surrounding it to collide more frequently than would otherwise occur at random. When this occurs, the energy of motion of the object is transferred to the molecules of air, which then collide,

resulting in the production of vibration and the production of thermal energy. The object in motion is, by definition, transferring some of its energy to the molecules of air, and is therefore doing work. The energy that is transferred to the air has not been destroyed. However, if and when the total energy of motion is transformed in part to thermal energy, the transformation process cannot be reversed (Halliday et al., 2011). As a result, the energy of motion that is lost to heat and due to friction will no longer be available for the production of motion. This property is explained by the second part (Part 2) of the second law of thermodynamics (Stutz, 2006).

Motion, which includes the concepts of displacement, velocity, and acceleration, is considered to be a more useful form of work. If the force of friction is equal but opposite in direction to the force that is applied to produce motion, the net force acting on the object/substance will be zero, the net amount of displacement will also be zero, and the net work that is done or accomplished will henceforth be zero. In this case, energy is put to use, but no work is accomplished.

Conservative and Nonconservative Forces

For the present purpose, the principle of the conservation of energy discussed in the previous section works best with isolated mechanical systems. Isolated mechanical systems by definition exhibit no frictional forces. In an isolated system, a physical quantity such as mechanical energy will remain essentially unchanged during any process. The quantity of the mechanical energy of vibration in an isolated system is therefore said to be conserved for purposes of work (Hewitt, 2010). Hence, the law of the conservation of energy may be reworded as follows: "The total energy of an isolated system cannot change" (Halliday et al., 2011). An examination of the physics of motion for any mechanical system set into vibration is, therefore, greatly simplified when the only consideration is the conservative forces that cause the transfer of energy within the system. When friction or frictional drag is present, mechanical energy for purposes of work is not conserved. For this reason, and in relation to work, friction and frictional drag are called nonconservative forces (Halliday et al., 2011). In the sections that follow, both conservative and nonconservative forces will be considered in discussions of vibratory motion, of work, and of the production of sound. When friction or frictional drag is present, the energy of motion will, of course, be irreversibly

changed to heat. A closer examination of the relationship between two broad classes of mechanical energy (potential and kinetic) will also be provided in the next chapter.

Physics and Motion: An Overview

Motion is the enabler of the physical world, without which there would be no change in the universe (Stutz, 2006). The study of motion (also referred to as mechanics), with its related concepts of force and energy, has captured the interests of physicists from as early as the time of Aristotle, through the period of Isaac Newton, and into the present day (Giancoli, 2005; Halliday et al., 2011; Hewitt, 2010). Force and energy are also historical cornerstones within contemporary hearing science (Hirsh, 1952). Any substance or object having the properties of mass and elasticity may be set into vibratory motion by an applied force and by the utilization of energy. Since all known objects incorporate mass and elasticity, all known objects may be set into vibration. Therefore, by virtue of their capacity to vibrate, all known objects have the potential to produce sound. The concept of elasticity will be defined below.

Vibrations and Waves

A vibration can be described informally as a "wiggle in time" (Hewitt, 2010). Vibration is the property that makes the production, sensation, and ultimately the perception (audibility) of sound possible. A wiggle or a disturbance in both space and time has been loosely described as a wave (Hewitt, 2010). Vibrations produce waves, and waves, in turn, transport energy from one place to another. For example, when a small stone is thrown into a still, unmoving body of water such as a pond, the disturbance creates surface waves that move outward in all directions from the entry point of the stone, transporting energy from one place to another as illustrated in Figure 3–3. A vibration will be found at the source of any wave independent of the specific form the wave takes (Giancoli, 2005). The different types (shapes) of waves that exist for sound will be discussed in detail in Chapter 6. For the present, a wave (or a sound wave) may be described as a disturbance in both space and time that travels in an elastic medium (Hirsh, 1952), though not all waves require a medium through which to transmit. Electromagnetic waves such as light and radio waves travel at 186,000 miles per second and require no transmitting medium. Electromagnetic waves originate from discrete packets of energy called *quanta*, which are the minimum units of any physical entity involved in any interaction, and from which the term *quantum mechanics* is derived (Stutz, 2006). Waveforms of sound, however, cannot be transmitted in a vacuum (Halliday et al., 2011). Hence, sound propagation requires an elastic transmitting medium, and therefore sound can only be transmitted through a solid, a liquid, or a gas. Consequently, sound may be described as a propagated disturbance in a medium (Durrant & Feth, 2013). Vibrations transmitted through elastic media such as air, water, or steel produce sound waves that are likely to activate auditory and/or tactile sensory receptors in living organisms (Hirsh, 1952). Sound waves are, therefore, likely to be heard and/or tactilely experienced. It should be obvi-

Figure 3–3. Vibrations and subsequent surface waves produced in a fluid medium in response to an applied force.

ous that all of the physical concepts that manifest the properties of vibration and wave mechanics are intimately related to any discussion of sound.

Acoustics

The physical attributes of any waveform can be described and measured at different locations and at different times during the propagation of the waveform. A scientific analysis of the attributes and properties of sound can usually be found under the general heading of acoustics (Hewitt, 2010). Acoustics may be defined as the "science of sound" (Hirsh, 1952), though the term is derived from the Greek expression for "hearing" (Dirckx, 2005). The enormity of concepts that are encountered in the study of acoustics are firmly anchored in the realm of physics. Hence, acoustics also falls under the general domain of hearing science. Acoustics will be discussed in greater depth in Chapter 7.

Hearing

The term *hearing* in hearing science refers to the auditory sensation and cognitive perception of sound. Cognitive perceptions by definition fall under the umbrella of subjective and personal experience. Sound represents the type of physical energy that is capable of mechanically activating all of the nonneural peripheral components of the auditory system (see Chapter 10). It should not be surprising that physics terminology is essential to an understanding of the transfer of mechanical energy through all of the nonneural components of the peripheral auditory system. When the neural peripheral components of the auditory system become activated, an auditory neural sensation is sent to the central nervous system (see Chapter 10). Sound and the neural sensation of sound are, therefore, interdependent. However, concepts basic to physics are also required to characterize the principles of energy transfer through the peripheral and central nervous system components involved in hearing. The events involved in energy transfer across cell membranes also involve principles in physics and physiology that relate to substance diffusion (see Chapter 9) and charge flow (Irion, 2000).

Of particular relevance to physics and to auditory physiology is the potential energy created by ionic concentration gradients and subsequent electrical differences (voltage potentials) found across cell membranes (see Chapter 9). Potential energy is one of the important types of energy that will be defined in greater detail in the next chapter. For the present, and as indicated above, energy or material generally flows from regions of higher concentration or higher energy states, to regions of lower concentration or lower energy states, and the greater the potential (stored) energy, the greater will be the driving forces and the subsequent energy flow (Irion, 2000). This fact forms the basis for simple laws of diffusion. Physics also forms the basis for an understanding of how physical disorders of the auditory system often adversely modify the mass and stiffness, and therefore the resonating properties of auditory system components, and communication in general. The anatomy, physiology, neuroanatomy, and neurophysiology of the auditory system will be discussed in greater detail in Chapter 10.

Psychophysics and Psychoacoustics

By definition, all of our sensations/ perceptions are uniquely subjective, and each, whether it is somatosensory, visual, or auditory, falls under the heading of what may be defined as an individual, private, psychological experience. That is, all that we touch and all that touches us, all that we see, and all that we hear is uniquely personal to each of us. However, in spite of the totally subjective nature of our sensory experiences, it is still possible to develop fairly accurate measurement scales that help to define sensory experiences for purposes of comparison. In the previous chapter, measurement was defined as the assignment of numerals to events according to rules (Stevens, 1958). Discovering the orderly relationships that exist between the quantified linear physical attributes of stimuli and the scaling rules that determine the degree to which these physically quantified values correspond to nonlinear psychological experience is the subject matter of psychophysics.

Psychophysics as a discipline has historically existed as an outgrowth of sensory psychophysiology, a field of study found within the broader discipline of psychology (Boring, 1957). The events of interest in psychophysics are the sensations, and the systematic measurement and scaling of their magnitudes (Hirsh, 1952), and in no other branch of psychology has the "resort to measurement" been as deliberate as it has been in psychophysics (Stevens, 1958). The fit between linear mathematical measures of physical stimuli and nonlinear subjective, experiential variables such as sensations is valid only insofar as the experiential events under investigation (i.e., sensations) can be defined using well-established measurement scales (Hays, 1981; Stevens, 1958).

Gustav Theodor Fechner

Fechner (1801–1887) is credited as the founder of experimental psychology and for establishing the methodological foundations for the discipline of psychophysics. In 1834, Fechner (Portrait 3–3) was appointed professor of physics at the university in Leipzig, Germany. He later provided, with his publication in 1860 of *Elemente der Psychophysik*, methods that permitted the magnitude of a sensation to be computed from objective measurements of physical stimuli and responses (Boring, 1957; Hirsh, 1952).

In their purest form, sensations are characteristically thought of as immediate, direct, irreducible qualities or

Portrait 3–3. Gustav Theodor Fechner (1801–1887). Printed with permission. Wikimedia Commons, public domain.

attributes of a stimulus experience. Examples might include isolated experiences like loud, hard, heavy, color, and so forth. According to Fechner, sensations, unlike stimuli or responses, cannot be measured directly. All we can observe is whether a sensation is present or absent. We can also determine whether one sensation is greater than, equal to, or less than another sensation based upon an objective measure of the stimulus, and a behavioral response (Boring, 1957). The operational definition of the term *sensation* has become the designation of a response (Hirsh, 1952) such that the term sensation is often used to refer to the response of a sensory receptor to a stimulus. This means that any event or physical object that elicits a response must be considered to be an adequate or appropriate stimulus for that response. In other words, the concept of a sensation (stimulus) has become operationally defined for the sake of measurement, only in terms of the types of responses that may be elicited. Furthermore, the possibility that anyone could experience a pure or meaningless sensation devoid of interpretation (perception) is doubtful. Perceptions are subjective and personal. The concept of an objective perception would simply be a contradiction in terms.

The measurement of any sensory process, such as hearing for example, involves the establishment of relations between the responses made by individuals, and the stimuli that give rise to such responses (Hirsh, 1952). Actually, the term *perception* is often used in reference to an organized experience involving an aggregate of sensations. Perception also involves the combined integration of memories, the influence of past experiences, the attachment of significance or meaning, and judgment (Stevens, 1958), which are impossible to simply overlook. Perceiving is a cognitive process that involves knowing, understanding, organizing, naming, discriminating, analyzing, as well as responding.

As a branch of psychophysics, psychoacoustics deals with the quantified physical values associated with sound and the degree to which those physical values correspond to the scaling rules used to measure the psychological experience of sound that we often refer to as hearing. Of central interest in the study of psychoacoustics is the measurement and scaling of the subjective attributes associated with absolute and differential threshold, loudness, and pitch. Psychoacoustic measures of each of these subjective attributes are examined in Chapter 8.

Physics and Motion: Length, Mass, and Time

Three fundamental dimensions commonly investigated in physics and in hearing science were introduced in the preceding chapter. These dimensions are length (L), mass (M), and time (T) (Halliday et al., 2011). Each dimension is represented by a standard unit of measure expressed by the use of two metric systems. Recall that the standard measurement units in the MKS metric system are the meter (L), the kilogram (M), and the second (T). In the CGS metric system, the standard units of measure are the centimeter (L), the gram (M), and the second (T). Like energy and work, these standard units of measure often are expressed in terms of their magnitude only (or simply, by how much). However, each unit of measure may also be combined with other standard units through multiplication or division to generate more complex derived quantities (Halliday et al., 2011). Ultimately, derived quantities may be combined in a similar manner with other standard units to generate derived quantities that are even more complex. Thus, derived quantities that can be generated from the three fundamental dimensions can and will vary in their overall complexity (Giancoli, 2005; Hewitt, 2010). There are three basic components that are involved in any description of vibration. Each of the three components is derived from the concept of length. These basic components are displacement, velocity, and acceleration.

Derivatives of Length

Length may be defined as the linear distance or spatial magnitude between two points when the position of the two points is measured simultaneously (Giancoli, 2005). Recall that for any given object (mass), two simple derivatives of length may be computed. These derivatives of length are area and volume. When two quantities representing length for a particular object are known, the product of these two quantities is the area ($L \times L$, or simply L^2). More commonly, area is the product of length and width. When three quantities of length are known for a given object, the product of these quantities is volume ($L \times L \times L$, or L^3). In more common terms, volume may be defined as the product of length, width, and height. From the previous chapter, the

MKS units for area and volume were shown to be the squared meter (m^2) and the cubic meter (m^3), respectively. The respective CGS units for area and volume are the squared centimeter (cm^2) and the cubic centimeter (cm^3 or cc). As with measurements of length and distance, the two simple derivatives, area and volume, are expressed in terms of their magnitude only (Giancoli, 2005; Hewitt, 2010).

Displacement

Related to measures of length and distance is displacement. Broadly speaking, displacement is defined as a change in the position of a mass from one place or point to another place or point (Giancoli, 2005; Halliday et al., 2011). The distance that a mass is displaced is measured in standard units of length. Therefore, distance and displacement are both measured in terms of meters (MKS system) or centimeters (CGS system). However, a clear distinction is generally made between the total distance a mass has traveled and the actual amount of its displacement once a force has been applied.

Displacement and Equilibrium

The difference between distance and displacement may be illustrated with a simple example employing the relativistic concept of a starting point. Suppose an individual leaves home, walks 60 meters to the east, then turns around and walks (back) 40 meters to the west (Figure 3–4). The total distance traveled is 100 meters. This is because distance, like length, is measured only with respect to magnitude. Note that

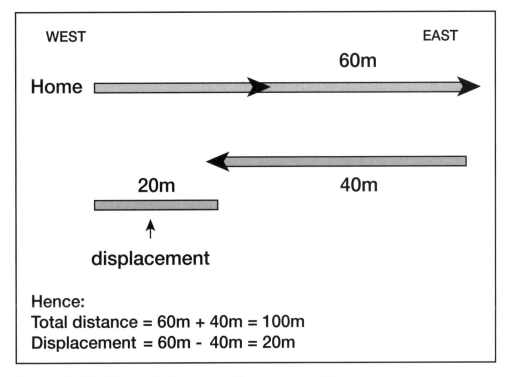

Figure 3–4. The differentiation between total distance and actual displacement.

the amount of displacement however, is only 20 meters, since at the end of the return trip the individual is only 20 meters from the starting point. The starting point or "home" in this particular case may be thought of as the point of equilibrium (see Figure 3–4). Therefore, unlike ordinary measures of length or distance, the concept of displacement is relativistic in that it retains the concept of equilibrium and is often quantified as a distance traveled relative to an arbitrary reference or starting point. Thus, displacement is a quantity that must be specified by both its magnitude and by its direction. Consequently, in broad strokes, displacement could be defined as any change from equilibrium in a specified direction (Giancoli, 2005; Halliday et al., 2011).

Equilibrium

In physics and in hearing science, equilibrium is often the reference or starting point for measures of displacement (Giancoli, 2005). Accordingly, a mass that has neither been displaced nor set into motion is at equilibrium. Hence, a mass that is at rest is at equilibrium. When referring to an object that is not moving, we might choose to use the term *static equilibrium* (Halliday et al., 2011) to signify that the object or mass is not in a dynamic (moving) state. For instance, a book resting on a table is in a state of static equilibrium. Even in reference to living systems, equilibrium is a condition in which a system remains constant without the utilization of energy (Irion, 2000).

If external forces acting in any direction on a mass are balanced by opposing directional forces, the mass is at mechanical equilibrium because the net force acting on the mass is zero (Hewitt, 2010). Therefore, equilibrium exists when the net sum of external forces acting on a mass is zero (Halliday et al., 2011). States or conditions of equilibrium also exist for objects that are in motion, though the term static equilibrium does not apply in such cases. For example, a compact disk (CD) that rotates at a constant, unchanging rate is at a state of equilibrium, and the laser beam that interacts with the CD does so in a frictionless manner. A hockey puck sliding across a frictionless surface at a constant rate of speed is also at a state of equilibrium, as are the rotating blades of a ceiling fan, if they are moving at a constant, unchanging rate of speed (Halliday et al., 2011).

Displacement (Motion) of a Pendulum

A pendulum consists of a mass (the pendulum bob) suspended from the end of a lightweight stalk or cable. The cable does not stretch, and its mass is negligible relative to the mass of the pendulum bob (Giancoli, 2005; Halliday et al., 2011). The lightweight cable that suspends the pendulum bob is suspended from above by its attachment to a pivot point as illustrated in Figure 3–5. Figure 3–6 illustrates arbitrary units of external force, as indicated by

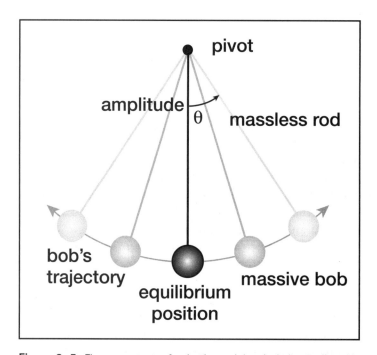

Figure 3–5. The components of a simple pendulum include an adjustable "bob" located at the end of a lightweight or massless rod or stalk that is itself attached to a fixed and frictionless pivot. Each displacement from the point of equilibrium (*shown by the dotted lines*) represents a measure of amplitude.

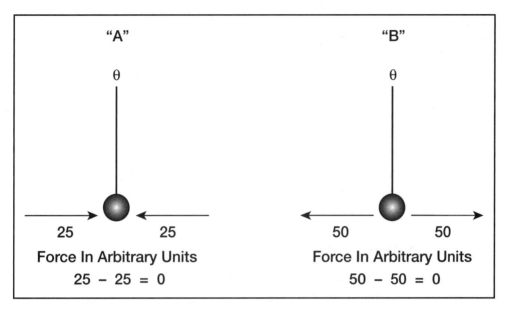

Figure 3–6. A balance of external (net) force. Each of the two pendulums shown is attached at a pivot point indicated by the θ. **A.** Pushing. **B.** Pulling. Force, defined simply as a pushing or a pulling, is applied equally but in opposite directions to the mass of each pendulum (the pendulum bob) as shown for the pendulums illustrated in A and B. When equal but opposing forces are applied in this manner, the net sum of the external forces acting on either pendulum mass is zero. Furthermore, in both cases, the pendulum does not move, displacement is zero, and there is no change from equilibrium.

a simple pushing (Figure 3–6A) or a pulling (Figure 3–6B), that act on the pendulum mass but are balanced by equal but opposing, pushing or pulling forces. The net sum of the external forces acting on the pendulum, in each case, is therefore zero. As illustrated in Figure 3–6A and Figure 3–6B, neither pendulum would move, and displacement would be equal to zero for both. Because the net external forces that are acting upon the mass of both pendulums are zero, both pendulums are at equilibrium.

When set into motion by a force applied in one direction, a pendulum will move at the pivot point of its stalk, as its bob is displaced from its point of equilibrium (see Figure 3–5). A pendulum will normally oscillate to and fro in this manner with a minimum amount of friction. The swinging motion of a pendulum will eventually cease. A small amount of friction acting externally on the pendulum will (if it exists) transfer energy away from the motion of the pendulum. This is precisely what friction and frictional drag force do. They transfer energy away from the motion of objects.

The external friction found within a pendulum originates from two sources. As the pendulum bob moves through the air, the bob encounters a frictional drag force that opposes the motion of the pendulum. Friction also acts on the pivot point of the pendulum stalk to oppose the motion of the pendulum. If the pendulum is to continue moving, the amount of energy loss in the pendulum resulting from friction and the frictional drag force will need to be compensated for by a constant applied force delivered to the pendulum (Halliday et al., 2011). The energy needed to apply a constant force to a pendulum is normally provided by the uncoiling of a mainspring that must be periodically wound, or it may be provided by the gravitational pull on a series of weights, as in a grandfather clock. In this way, the constant motion of a pendulum may be maintained by a constant applied force and the utilization of (potential) energy.

The Period of Motion of a Pendulum

Galileo (1564–1642) discovered that the time (in seconds) that it takes to execute just one complete back-and-forth cycle of displacement (called a period) for a pendulum depends on the length of the pendulum. The duration of the period of a moving pendulum does not depend on the pendulum mass, nor on the size of the arc through which the pendulum swings (Giancoli, 2005). The exact formula for the period of a simple pendulum for small arcs is as follows:

$$T = 2\pi\sqrt{l/g}$$

where T is equal to the period, l is equal to the length of the pendulum, and g is equal to the acceleration of gravity (Halliday et al., 2011; Hewitt, 2010). The term *acceleration* will be defined below. It is not difficult to see from the formula, however, that as the length (l) of the pendulum increases, the period (T) also increases. This is because the symbol for length (l) is in the numerator of the fraction. Therefore, the formula above indicates that for any pendulum set into motion, T is directly proportional to the square root of l, or simply: period (T) ~ $\sqrt{\text{length}}$ (l).

The Frequency of Motion of a Pendulum

In should be added that period (T) is equal to the inverse of the number of completed back-and-forth cycles of displacement that occur per unit of time (seconds), which is called frequency (f) or cycles per second, and vice versa (Giancoli, 2005; Hewitt, 2010). Thus, T and f are reciprocals.

Therefore,

frequency (f) = cycles/second
(cycles per second)

hence,

period (T) = 1/frequency (f)

and

frequency (f) = 1/period (T)

Since, for any pendulum set into motion,

period (T) ~ $\sqrt{\text{length}}$ (l),

therefore,

(T) and (f) are reciprocals

It then also follows that frequency (f) is indirectly (or inversely) proportional to the square root of the length (l) of the pendulum:

frequency (f) ~ $1/\sqrt{\text{length}}$ (l)

It is not difficult to see that as the length (distance of the bob from the pivot point) of the pendulum increases, the frequency or number of its cycles per second decreases, and as its length decreases, the frequency, or number of its cycles per second, also increases. The relationship between period, frequency, and bob distance from the pivot point of a pendulum is also illustrated in

Figure 3–7. The longer pendulum (with the greater bob-distance from the pivot point) exhibits a longer period and will swing back and forth less frequently in time (fewer cycles/second) compared to the shorter pendulum (with the lesser bob-distance from the pivot point that will exhibit a shorter period. For a pendulum clock, the speed and therefore the accuracy of the clock can be adjusted by simply sliding the pendulum bob up or down on the stem. Sliding the bob upward will cause the clock to gain time or run faster, and sliding the bob down will cause the clock to lose time, or run slower.

When the back-and-forth oscillations or vibrations of any object/mass repeat over the same path, as in the swinging motion of a pendulum, the motion is referred to as periodic motion (Giancoli, 2005; Halliday et al., 2011). The back-and-forth or to-and-fro periodic cyclic vibratory or oscillatory motion described for a pendulum in a small arc that begins with displacement, is often called simple harmonic motion (Halliday et al., 2011; Hewitt, 2010).

The Amplitude of Motion of a Pendulum

As a pendulum bob swings maximally to the left and to the right of its point of equilibrium, the magnitude of the distance that the pendulum bob is displaced on either side of equilibrium

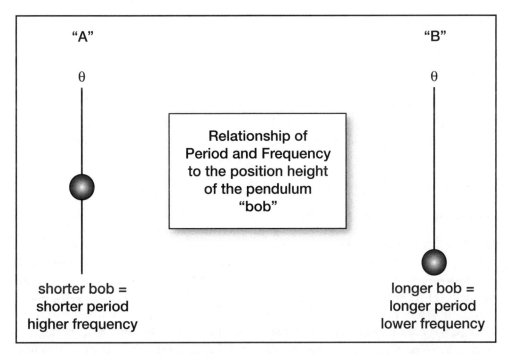

Figure 3–7. Period and frequency of motion of a pendulum. The pendulum shown in **B** is longer than the pendulum shown in **A** since the pendulum bob in **B** is farther from the pivot point of attachment θ. Since period (T) ~ √length (l), each cycle of the pendulum in **B** will take relatively longer in time to complete compared to each cycle of motion exhibited by the pendulum in **A**. Since frequency (f) ~ 1/√length (l), pendulum **B** with the longer length will swing back and forth less frequently than the shorter pendulum (**A**). The repetitious back-and-forth swinging of either pendulum over the same path is called periodic motion.

(in either direction) should, ideally, be equal in value. The maximum magnitude of displacement in either direction is measured in standard units of length, and is customarily referred to as the maximum amplitude of displacement (Giancoli, 2005). The direction of each maximum peak displacement is usually specified. The maximum peak of displacement in either direction is called the peak amplitude. In Figure 3–8, the peak amplitude to the left from equilibrium (E) to point a is represented by PA_1. This peak amplitude is equal in magnitude to the peak amplitude found to the right (from point E to b), or simply PA_2. Therefore, $PA_1 = PA_2$. The peak-to-peak amplitude represents the sum total magnitude of displacement in both directions ($PA_1 + PA_2$). Since $PA_1 = PA_2$, then the peak-to-peak amplitude (PPA) is simply 2× either of the separate peak amplitudes. Therefore, $PPA = 2 \times PA_1$ or $2 \times PA_2$, or simply PPA equals two times the peak amplitude. The greater the magnitude of displacement from equilibrium, the greater will be the amplitude. As with displacement, amplitude is also specified both by its magnitude and direction (Giancoli, 2005).

The Restorative Force in a Pendulum

Recall that the force of friction opposes motion, and friction or frictional drag are nonconservative forces. This means that when frictional forces are present, mechanical energy is not conserved. Energy is therefore converted to a form that is incompatible with work (Halliday et al., 2011). For simple harmonic motion to occur, an active force must exist that opposes displacement. This oppositional force on displacement must be proportional to the displacement of the mass from equilibrium and must also be a conservative force (Halliday et al., 2011; Hewitt, 2010). The conservative force that opposes displacement, which is also proportional to the displacement of the mass from equilibrium, is generally referred to as the restorative force (Giancoli, 2005). With a pendulum, the weight of the pendulum bob and therefore gravity (not elasticity) provides the restorative force that resists displacement, and moves the displaced pendulum in the direction of its original position of equilibrium once the maximum peak amplitude has been reached (Figure 3–9). Gravity, therefore, is a conservative restorative force (Halliday et al., 2011). The restorative force provided by weight and gravity is directly proportional to the pendulum's displacement. Hence, the vibratory, oscillatory, or swinging motion described for a pendulum is an example of simple harmonic motion (Hewitt, 2010).

The condition of *rest* represents a special case of motion, which is zero motion. For a pendulum, or any object set into vibration, the restorative force is zero at the precise point of equilibrium. This is true regardless of whether the object is in motion or at rest. If displacement is zero, then the restorative force must also be zero. A restorative force gradually increases proportionally in magnitude with any subsequent displacement from equilibrium, and reaches a maximum value when the amplitude of displacement is also at a maximum peak value, as illustrated in Figure 3–9.

A force consisting of a pushing or a pulling may be applied to any object. The

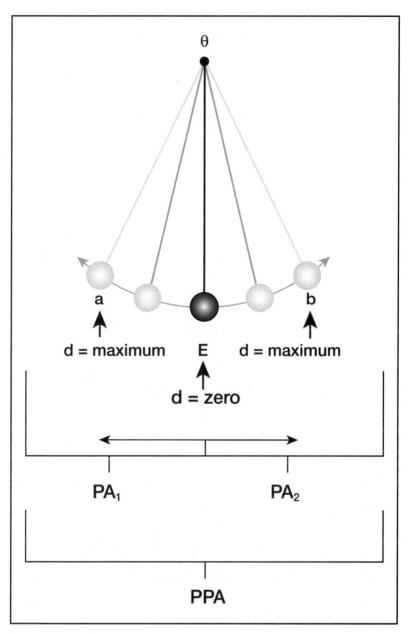

Figure 3–8. The peak and the peak-to-peak amplitudes of motion of a pendulum. From the point of attachment or pivot point (θ), the pendulum bob shown can be displaced maximally to the left (*a*) or maximally to the right (*b*) of equilibrium (*E*). Displacement (*d*) is zero at location *E* and maximum at locations *a* and *b*. The maximum displacement of the pendulum bob in either direction represents the peak amplitude (*PA*). For instance, the peak amplitude to the left (from point *E* to *a*) is represented by PA_1, and is equal in magnitude to the peak amplitude to the right (from point *E* to *b*), or simply PA_2. Therefore, peak amplitude PA_1 is equal in magnitude to peak amplitude PA_2. The peak-to-peak amplitude (*PPA*) is equal to the sum total magnitude of displacement in both directions ($PA_1 + PA_2$) or 2× the peak. Since $PA_1 = PA_2$, *PPA* is simply 2× either of the separate peak amplitudes (i.e., $2 \times PA_1$ or $2 \times PA_2$).

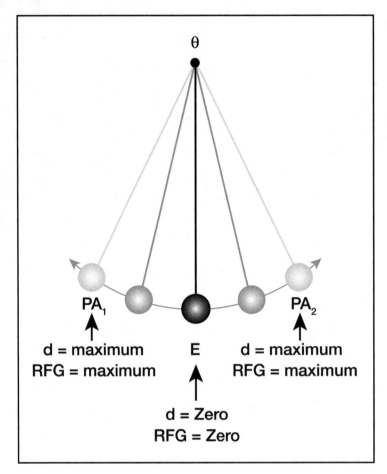

Figure 3–9. The restorative force of gravity in a pendulum. The conservative restorative force of gravity (*RFG*) for a pendulum is a force that opposes displacement. When displacement (*d*) is zero at the exact point of equilibrium (*E*), the *RFG* is also zero. Displacement gradually increases as the pendulum bob moves past *E*. As *d* increases, the *RFG* also gradually and proportionally increases. At each peak amplitude (*PA₁* or *PA₂*) where *d* is maximum, the restorative force of gravity (*RFG*) is also maximum.

force that is required to displace a pendulum, to distort a simple spring-mass system like a "Slinky," or even to distort the tines of a tuning fork, may be brief, regular, and/or repetitious. Recall that the pendulum bob changed its position in space when a force was applied, and did so without being physically altered in its shape or size. Often, however, an applied force will deform or otherwise distort a part or section of an object, producing temporary changes in the object's size, shape, or both. When this occurs, the object is not displaced in its entirety because the mass of the object is usually anchored to a fixed reference point. Nevertheless, the distortion of an object's shape that takes place in this manner represents yet another form of displacement (Giancoli, 2005). The amount and degree of the distortion, and therefore the displacement that results in this manner, depend on the arrangement and bonding of the atoms found in the material that is distorted. Whether the object returns to its original shape when the force is removed also depends on the type of material that is distorted (Hewitt, 2010). If an object that is distorted by force returns to its original shape when the external force is removed, then it can be made to vibrate.

Elasticity and the Restorative Force of Elasticity

Elasticity, like gravity, is an active conservative force that opposes displacement (Halliday et al., 2011). Elasticity is the property of matter that allows objects to temporarily change their shape or size, rather than fracture when a force is applied (Giancoli, 2005). The restorative force of elasticity is the property that produces a return of an object to its original shape once an external force is removed. Materials that do not resume their original shape after being deformed by a force are said to be inelastic. Examples of inelastic substances are clay, putty, and dough. Lead is also inelastic, because it is easy to permanently distort the shape of lead (Hewitt, 2010). Elastic materials are many and include rubber bands, air, water, and steel. However, for our purposes, the best illustration of elasticity in an object having the restorative force of elasticity is provided by a mechanical device known as a spring, or a simple spring-mass system. The elastic force of a spring was first discovered in 1660, and only later described in 1678

(Stutz, 2006) by the English scientist, inventor, and surveyor Robert Hooke (1635–1703).

Hooke's Law

Hooke's law (1678) states that the amount that an elastic mass can be distorted (strain) is in direct proportion to the force (stress) acting on the mass, but only for as long as the object has elasticity (Box 3–1). That is, Hooke's law only applies in the event that the external force that is applied does not stretch or compress the material beyond its elastic limit. According to Robert Hooke,

$$F \sim delta\ x$$

or the magnitude of the restorative force of elasticity (delta x), as indicated by the amount of change in length (stretch or compression), is directly proportional to the magnitude of the objects displacement from equilibrium, or simply, (F) the applied force (Hewitt, 2010). However, if an elastic material is stretched or compressed beyond its elastic limit, it will not return to its original shape. In this case, it remains distorted and enters into the *plastic region* (Giancoli, 2005). If it is stretched beyond its plastic region, it fractures. The plastic region, referred to as the yield strength of a material, is defined in physiology as the stress at which a material begins to deform plastically. This term yield strength is often used to describe the condition of bone at various stages of development or disease. Prior to the point of yield, the material will deform elastically and will return to its original shape when the applied stress is removed. Once the point of

Box 3–1. Robert Hooke (1635–1703)

Robert Hooke (1635–1703) was an English experimental physicist, born July 18 at Freshwater on the Isle of Wight. Hooke attended Oxford University and in 1655 was employed at Oxford as an assistant to the well-known physicist, Robert Boyle. Boyle later used Hooke's knowledge and skill in the construction of his air pump (Stutz, 2006). The famous English astronomer Edmond Halley and the famous British physicist Isaac Newton were also contemporaries of Robert Hooke, though Hooke was instrumental in the discovery of universal gravitation prior to its discovery by Newton. Hooke also collaborated with men like Christiaan Huygens, Antony van Leeuwenhoek, and the architect Christopher Wren (Stutz, 2006). Hooke was appointed professor of geometry at Gresham College in 1665, where he first suggested that the moon's craters were caused by internal volcanic activity or impact. He also stated his belief that fossil records held information about the earth's natural history (Gianopoulos, 2006). Additionally, in 1665 Hooke was the first to observe living tissue cells with the aid of a microscope, and gave them their name ("cells") in his most famous work, *Micrographia* (Langone, 2006). In 1666, Hooke originated the idea of using the pendulum as a measure of gravity and in 1672 discovered the phenomenon of light diffraction (Stutz, 2006). He also invented the first Gregorian reflecting telescope in 1674, described the planetary motions mathematically in 1678, and was the first to use the spiral (main) spring to regulate watches (Giancoli, 2005; Hewitt, 2010; Stutz, 2006). Unfortunately there are no accurate images of Robert Hooke. Historians claim that Sir Isaac Newton destroyed the only real images of Hooke that were in existence, and removed all references to Robert Hooke in his (Newton's) three books that form his landmark work, *Principia* (Hawking, 2002).

In 1660, Hooke discovered the first law of elasticity for solid objects, though his discovery was not made public until 1678 (Stutz, 2006). Simply defined, Hooke's law of elasticity stated that the amount that an elastic mass can be distorted (which he called strain) is in direct proportion to the force (which he called stress) acting on the mass, for as long as the object has elasticity. According to Hooke, the magnitude of the restoring force (a force that opposes displacement) of an elastic mass is directly proportional to the magnitude of displacement of the elastic mass from a point of equilibrium (Halliday et al., 2011). Increased stress beyond the elastic limit of the mass will permanently alter the shape of the object in question (Giancoli, 2005; Hewitt, 2010).

yield is passed, the deformation will be permanent and nonreversible. Shown in Figure 3–10 are two extremes of mass, stiffness (and therefore compliance) in two types of spring. Compared to the Slinky shown in Figure 3–10B, the heavy-duty spring in Figure 3–10A has considerably more mass and a great deal more stiffness.

Therefore, the amount of the restorative force will be greater in the heavy-duty spring compared to the restorative force exhibited by the Slinky, because a greater amount of net force would

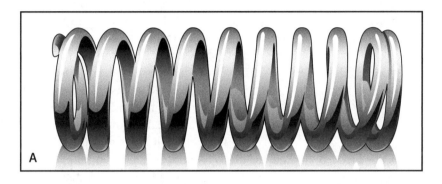

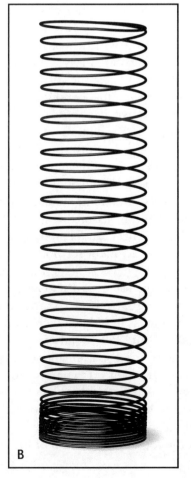

Figure 3–10. A. Heavy-duty spring characterized by high mass, high stiffness, and low compliance. **B.** A Slinky, characterized by low mass, low stiffness, and high compliance.

be required to displace the heavy-duty spring from equilibrium. The greater amount of force required to displace the heavy-duty spring is directly related to its much greater stiffness relative to much greater compliance found in the Slinky. When applied to a simple spring, Hooke's law also states that the restorative force delivered by a spring is proportional to the displacement of the free end of the spring from equilibrium when the spring is in a relaxed state (Halliday et al., 2011), or simply,

$$Fs \sim kd$$

where *Fs* is the force delivered by the spring, *d* is the amount of displacement of the free end of the spring from the point of equilibrium, and *k* is the spring (or force) constant. The spring constant *k* is a measure of the stiffness of the spring, such that the stiffer the spring, the larger the *k* value and the greater will be the force (the push or pull) delivered by the spring (restorative force or recoil) for a given amount of displacement (Halliday et al., 2011).

Displacement of a Spring-Mass System

Previously, displacement was defined for a free moving object as any change from equilibrium in a specified direction. Recall that when a force is applied to a simple spring-mass system (Figure 3–11), the distortion or deformation of the spring's shape represents still another form of displacement (Giancoli, 2005). When the external force is then removed from an elastic spring mass, the spring is often set into vibration. The vibratory or oscillatory

motion described for any elastic object that has been temporarily distorted is also an example of simple harmonic motion (Giancoli, 2005). As in the case of a pendulum, the distance that any spring can be displaced from its point of equilibrium will also be measured in standard units of length. Customarily these standard units of length are referred to as the amplitude of the vibration or oscillation. Furthermore, the time (in seconds) that it takes to execute just one complete back-and-forth cycle of displacement of a spring from (or around) its point of equilibrium is called the period of the vibration (Halliday et al., 2011). Figure 3–12A illustrates five hypothetical stages (I–V) in a single cycle of displacement for a pendulum, and the paralleling five stages in a single cycle of displacement for a spring with a mass attached at one end (a spring-mass system). At each of the five stages, the restorative force of gravity for the pendulum parallels the restorative force of elasticity for the spring-mass system.

At Stage I, both pendulum and spring-mass are at resting or static equilibrium, as indicated both by the vertical position of the pendulum and the location of the mass of the spring bisecting the vertical fragmented equilibrium line. Displacement for both pendulum and spring-mass at Stage I is zero. The restorative forces are also zero.

At Stage II, both pendulum and spring-mass have been displaced maximally to the left by an external force. The leftward displacement of the spring-mass has produced a compression of the spring such that the circular components that define the spring are concentrated into a small, condensed area. In terms of the total cyclic motion of the spring,

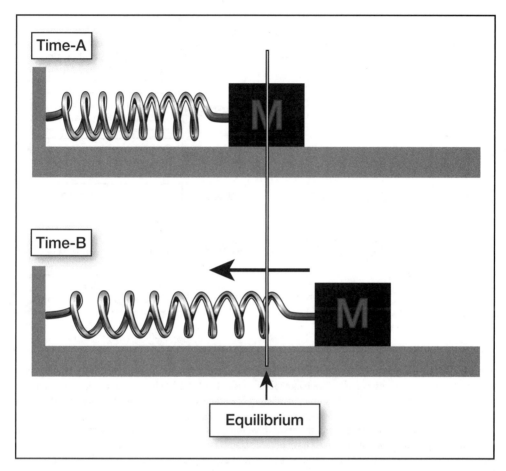

Figure 3–11. A simple spring-mass system where *M* indicates a mass. **A.** Time at which the spring-mass is at equilibrium. **B.** Time at which the spring-mass has been displaced (pulled) to the right of equilibrium. The arrow pointing to the left at Time **B** indicates the direction of the restorative force of elasticity. Modified with permission from David M. Harrison, Department of Physics, University of Toronto.

Stage II represents the compression or condensation phase of the cycle.

For both pendulum and spring-mass, Stage II also represents the peak amplitude of displacement. That is, displacement from equilibrium at this stage is at a peak value, as discussed previously. It must also be assumed that at Stage II, the external force that originally displaced both pendulum and spring has now been removed. According to Hooke's law, the magnitude of the restoring force of an elastic mass is directly proportional to the magnitude of displacement of the elastic mass from a point of equilibrium. Therefore, the restorative forces are maximum. Recall that gravity and elasticity are both active conservative forces that oppose displacement.

By Stage III a return of the pendulum and spring to the equilibrium position illustrated is the result of the restorative forces of gravity (for the pendulum) and elasticity (for the spring-mass system). Keep in mind that unlike the positions of

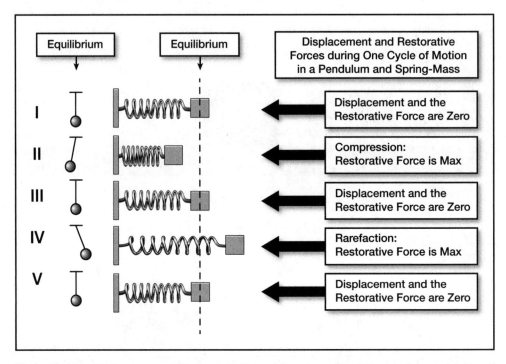

Figure 3–12A. Displacement and the restorative forces of gravity and/or of elasticity in a pendulum and/or spring-mass system, respectively. Five hypothetical stages (I–V) in a single cycle of displacement and the restorative force of gravity for a pendulum, paralleling five stages in a single cycle of displacement and the restorative force of elasticity for a spring-mass system. Stage I: both pendulum and spring-mass are at resting or static equilibrium. Displacement and the restorative forces for both pendulum and spring-mass are zero. Stage II: both pendulum and spring-mass have been displaced maximally to the left by an external force. This force produces a compression of the spring-mass, as well as the peak amplitude of displacement for both the pendulum and spring-mass. Displacement and the restorative forces are maximum. Stage III: the restorative force of gravity returns the pendulum to equilibrium, and the restorative force of elasticity returns the spring-mass to equilibrium, as both pendulum and spring mass are in motion. Therefore, at this brief instant in time, displacement and the restorative forces are zero. Stage IV: pendulum and spring-mass continue to move past equilibrium as both are displaced maximally to the right. This motion produces a stretching of the spring-mass representing the rarefaction phase of the cycle, as well as the peak amplitude of displacement for both pendulum and spring-mass. Displacement and the restorative forces are again at a maximum. Stage V: once again the restorative force of gravity returns the pendulum to equilibrium, while the restorative force of elasticity returns the spring-mass to equilibrium, as pendulum and spring-mass each complete one full cycle of symmetrical displacement. Displacement and the restorative forces are again zero.

either object at Stage I, during Stage III both pendulum and spring-mass are in motion. Therefore, the location of pendulum and spring-mass at Stage III is fleeting. Recall from an earlier discussion that states of equilibrium may also exist for objects in motion. Since pendulum and spring-mass are in motion at Stage III, the term *static equilibrium* does not apply, though by definition, displacement and the restorative force for either object is zero at this precise location.

As indicated in Figure 3–12A, the pendulum and spring-mass are expected to pass through the point of equilibrium shown at Stage III and then to advance to Stage IV. The forces that compel both pendulum and spring-mass to continue their displacement to Stage IV involve an energy transfer. The concept of energy transference, together with related terms such as inertia and momentum, will be the topics of Chapter 4.

At Stage IV, both the pendulum and spring-mass have been displaced maximally to the right due to factors found later in the text. The displacement of the pendulum and spring-mass to the right of equilibrium, to the position shown by Stage IV in Figure 3–12A, is intended to represent another maximum (peak) amount of displacement. Ideally, the peak amplitude observed at Stage IV equals the peak amplitude observed for the pendulum and spring-mass at Stage II. Together, the combined peak amplitude values observed at Stages II and IV represent the peak-to-peak amplitude of displacement for either the pendulum or spring-mass, as discussed earlier. At Stage IV, displacement and the restorative forces are again maximum.

Figure 3–12A also illustrates that the displacement of the spring mass to the right of equilibrium (Stage IV) has produced an expansion of the spring-mass. At Stage IV, the circular spring-like components that define the spring are spread out, separated, and stretched across a large area. Stage IV represents the noncompressed, rarified, or rarefaction phase of the cycle. The condition of the spring at this stage is in direct opposition to the compressed condition observed during Stage II, though it matters little whether the distortion (and therefore the displacement of the spring-mass) is caused by a pushing or by a pulling.

Hooke's law applies to the magnitude of the restoring force of an elastic mass that is displaced, regardless of whether the elastic mass is compressed or stretched. Because the restorative forces of gravity and elasticity oppose displacement, once again, the active conservative restorative force of elasticity that opposed displacement during compression at Stage II will return the spring-mass to a position of equilibrium during the rarefaction shown at Stage IV. The restorative force of gravity also returns the pendulum to equilibrium from Stage IV, as both pendulum and spring-mass move to Stage V.

Finally, Stage V represents the return of both pendulum and spring-mass to their starting point (Stage I) or equilibrium, as illustrated in Figure 3–6A. The return of both pendulum and spring-mass as shown by this stage defines one complete and symmetrical cycle of displacement. At Stage V, both displacement and the restorative forces are zero.

Figure 3–12B illustrates by histogram the relative amplitudes of displacement and the restorative forces of gravity and elasticity during the five stages (I–V) in a single cycle of motion for the pendulum and the spring-mass, as illustrated in Figure 3–12A. As illustrated, during Stages I, III, and V, displacement and both of the restorative forces are at their absolute minimum values (zero). During Stages II (compression) and IV (rarefaction), displacement and the restorative forces are at their maximum magnitudes. It should be emphasized that the relative magnitudes of displacement and the restorative forces fluctuate from maximum to minimum values along a continuum. Shown also in Figure 3–12B are the relative amplitudes of displacement and restorative forces at intermediate locations found exactly

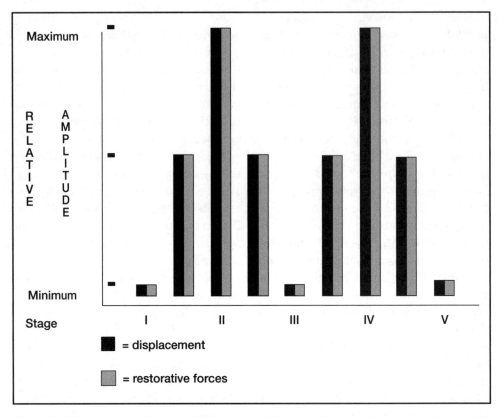

Figure 3–12B. Relative amplitudes of displacement and the restorative forces of gravity and/or of elasticity during each of the five stages for one cycle of motion illustrated by histograms. The relative amplitudes of displacement and the restorative forces of gravity and/or elasticity during the five stages (I–V) in a single cycle of motion for a pendulum and spring-mass. During Stages I, III, and V, displacement and the restorative forces are at their absolute minimum values (or simply zero). During Stages II (compression for the spring-mass) and IV (rarefaction for the spring-mass), displacement and the restorative forces are at their maximum magnitudes, as predicted by Hooke's law. Shown also are the relative amplitudes of displacement and the restorative forces at locations found exactly midway between each of the indicated stages. The magnitude of the amplitudes for intermediate locations will fall somewhere between maximum and minimum values.

midway between each of the labeled stages. The magnitudes of the amplitudes at each of these intermediate locations have values that fall between the maximum and the minimum.

Finally, as described for the pendulum, the number of whole cycles completed by the spring-mass over a 1 s duration of time is called the frequency of the vibration. Therefore,

$$\text{frequency } (f) = \text{cycles/second}$$
$$\text{(cycles per second)}$$

Also recall that period (T) and frequency (f) are reciprocals:

$$\text{frequency } (f) = 1/\text{period } (T)$$

and

$$\text{period } (T) = 1/\text{frequency } (f)$$

Therefore,

period (T) = 1/cycles/second

period (T) =

$$\frac{1 \times \text{second/cycle}}{\text{cycles/second} \times \text{second/cycle}}$$

Therefore,

period (T) =

$$\frac{\text{second/cycle or second(s)/cycle}}{1}$$

Thus,

period (T) = second(s)/cycle
(second(s) per cycle)

Hence, the time (in seconds) that it takes to execute just one complete back-and-forth cycle of displacement of a spring from its point of equilibrium is called the period. When and if the number of cycles/second decreases, the period (second/cycle) or time it takes to complete each one of those cycles will increase. If the frequency or number of cycles increases over time, the time it takes to complete each one of those cycles (the period of each cycle) will decrease. Since frequency and period are reciprocals, as frequency increases, period decreases; as frequency decreases, period increases.

Table 3–1 provides examples of select frequencies (cycles/second) and their respective periods (seconds/cycle). Note that in the majority of cases, period is most easily expressed

Table 3–1. Select Frequencies and Their Corresponding Periods

Frequency (cycles/second)	Period		
	$1/f$	Seconds	Milliseconds
1 Hz	1/1	1.00000	1000.000
2 Hz	1/2	0.50000	500.000
4 Hz	1/4	0.25000	250.000
10 Hz	1/10	0.10000	100.000
50 Hz	1/50	0.02000	20.000
100 Hz	1/100	0.01000	10.000
250 Hz	1/250	0.00400	4.000
500 Hz	1/500	0.00200	2.000
1000 Hz	1/1000	0.00100	1.000
2000 Hz	1/2000	0.00050	0.500
4000 Hz	1/4000	0.00025	0.250
8000 Hz	1/8000	0.000125	0.125
10,000 Hz	1/10,000	0.000100	0.100
20,000 Hz	1/20,000	0.000050	0.050

as so many milliseconds, or 10^{-3} seconds/cycle. Note also that as frequency is progressively increased, its reciprocal, 1/frequency (period), gets smaller. The relationship between frequency and period will be examined in greater detail in Chapter 5.

Derivatives of Length and Time

Distance and displacement have been described in terms of units of length. *Time* is customarily combined with units of length to arrive at the term *rate*. Rate is a term often encountered in physics and hearing science. Rate may be defined as a fixed ratio of time (measured per unit) between consecutive quantities, amounts, or degrees of a standard unit of measure (Giancoli, 2005).

Speed: Change in the Rate of Distance

As indicated previously, standard units of measure for length, mass, and time are expressed only in terms of their magnitude. Standard units belonging to each of these three physical dimensions are often combined through multiplication or division to generate more complex derived quantities (Giancoli, 2005). Any standard unit of measure or derivative (x) may be combined through division with the measurement unit for time (the second). When time is the denominator for any standard or derived unit of measure (x), such that

$$x \, / \, time(second)$$

then the ratio created should always be interpreted as a time-rate change in the numerator x. Hence, x/time is equal to a time-rate change in x. Simply put, x/second means that a predictable change in x occurs for each specified unit of time (i.e., per second). For instance, distance and time are combined through division in this manner to produce speed. Accordingly, a unit of distance divided by a unit of time is equal to speed:

$$speed = distance/time$$

Speed is equal to the time-rate change in distance (Giancoli, 2005; Halliday et al., 2011) or simply the rate of change per second of distance. Because speed indicates how fast a mass travels in any or all directions, speed is expressed only in terms of its magnitude. In general, the average speed of a mass is defined as the distance traveled along a path divided by the total time it takes to travel the distance. For example, if an automobile travels a distance of 240 km in 3 hr, the average rate of speed of the automobile is 80 km/hr, or simply

$$Average \ rate \ of \ speed =$$
$$distance \ traveled/time \ elapsed$$
$$= 240 \ km/3 \ hr = 80 \ km/hr$$

Speed is seldom if ever constant, and measures of the average speed fail to address fluctuations in speed that may occur at any given moment in time. Instantaneous speed is the speed of a mass computed at any moment or instant in time. Instantaneous speed may also be defined as the average speed taken over an infinitesimally short time interval (Giancoli, 2005). If speed is unchanging or constant, then the average speed and the instantaneous speed are the same value.

Finally, in everyday language, the term *speed* is often mistakenly used interchangeably with the term *velocity*.

In physics and hearing science, the terms speed and velocity are not equivalent, just as distance and displacement are not equivalent (Giancoli, 2005). Because speed is derived from distance, speed is devoid of direction. Velocity, however, is derived from displacement, and velocity retains the value of magnitude, as well as the value of direction. It may also be said that speed is the magnitude of velocity, with absolutely no reference to direction (Halliday et al., 2011).

Velocity: Change in the Rate of Displacement

Displacement, unlike distance, retains the concept of equilibrium and is therefore specified both by its magnitude and by its direction (Halliday et al., 2011). In science, displacement is often more important than distance (Giancoli, 2005). Because distance and displacement are conceptually different, a time-rate change in distance (referred to as speed) is also going to be conceptually different from a time-rate change in displacement. A time-rate change in displacement occurs when displacement and time are combined through division, resulting in the term *velocity* (Giancoli, 2005). Therefore, velocity is defined as the time-rate change, or simply the rate of change per second of displacement:

$$velocity = displacement/time$$

Furthermore,

$$displacement = velocity \times time/1$$

since

$$displacement = displacement/time \times time/1$$

and therefore,

$$displacement = displacement$$

Similar to measures of displacement, measures of velocity will include not only the concept of magnitude, but directionality as well (Halliday et al., 2011). Instantaneous velocity is the velocity of a mass computed at any moment or instant in time. Instantaneous velocity is also defined as the average velocity obtained over an infinitesimally short time interval (Giancoli, 2005). To be sure, if an object travels at a constant velocity, then its average velocity will be equal to its instantaneous velocity. For any object set into motion, the instantaneous speed and the instantaneous velocity will often have the same magnitude, if both are measured at the same instant in time. In addition, if velocity and speed are unchanging and constant, the average and/or instantaneous velocity will be equivalent to the average and/or instantaneous speed, provided only that there is no change in direction. In other words, when the direction of motion is not an issue, speed and velocity will correspond, and constant velocity will mean the same as constant speed, but of course, with no change in direction (Hewitt, 2003). For example, the commuter who travels 20 kilometers from home to work, followed by 20 kilometers on the return trip, has traveled a total distance of 40 kilometers. The commuter's average speed may be computed as 40 kilometers divided by the total commute time. Unequivocally, the average speed will be a value greater than zero. However, since the amount of displacement is zero, the commuter has essentially gone nowhere. Furthermore, the commuter's average velocity (displacement/commute time) is also equal to zero.

Velocity can be altered by changing speed, direction, or both (Hewitt, 2003). Changes in velocity may simply reflect how fast the direction or position of a moving object changes (Giancoli, 2005). For instance, an automobile racing on a circular track may be traveling at a constant speed, but its velocity is regularly changing because its direction is steadily changing (Hewitt, 2003). Uniform circular motion occurs for an object that moves at a constant speed through a circle. Although the speed is constant, the velocity is not. This is because speed is a scalar quantity (without a specified direction) and velocity is a vector quantity (for a specified direction). While speed may be constant, velocity through a circle is always changing.

Velocity may be expressed as meters/second (MKS system), centimeters/second (CGS system), or even miles/hour (USCS system). Velocity is the more appropriate term to use than speed when describing the vibratory, oscillatory, or the swinging motion characteristic of simple harmonic motion, because the directionality of the displacement may be specified. Velocity may remain constant and unchanging, but often it does not. Figure 3–13A illustrates again the five stages (I–V) in a single cycle of displacement, and the rate changes in displacement (velocity) for a pendulum, paralleling five stages in a single cycle of displacement and velocity of a spring-mass system.

At Stage I, both pendulum and spring-mass are at resting or static equilibrium, as indicated both by the vertical position of the pendulum and the location of the mass of the spring bisecting the vertical fragmented equilibrium line. Displacement and velocity are therefore zero for the pendulum and the spring-mass, at Stage I.

At Stage II (see Figure 3–13A), both pendulum and spring-mass have been displaced maximally to the left (compression for the spring-mass) by an external force that has been immediately removed. For pendulum and spring-mass, Stage II indicates that displacement (change from equilibrium) is at a maximum peak value. However, at this stage, velocity (the rate of change per second of displacement) is zero. Why is velocity at its minimum value at this location? The answer is because the motion of the pendulum or spring-mass in a given direction (left) has slowed to a halt. Why has this occurred? In the case of the spring-mass, recall that elasticity (and the restorative force) is an active conservative force that opposes displacement (Halliday et al., 2011). The farther the spring-mass deviates from equilibrium, the greater is the restorative force that opposes displacement. Therefore, the restorative force of elasticity slows the motion of the spring-mass when displacement is at its greatest value. In the case of the pendulum, gravity is also an active conservative force that opposes displacement (Halliday et al., 2011). As a general rule, whenever displacement is at a maximum value, velocity will be at an absolute minimum value.

At Stage III, both pendulum and spring-mass are moving. At the precise location of Stage III (equilibrium) shown in Figure 3–13A, displacement for pendulum and spring-mass is zero by definition. However, at Stage III, velocity (the rate of change per second of displacement) is at a maximum value.

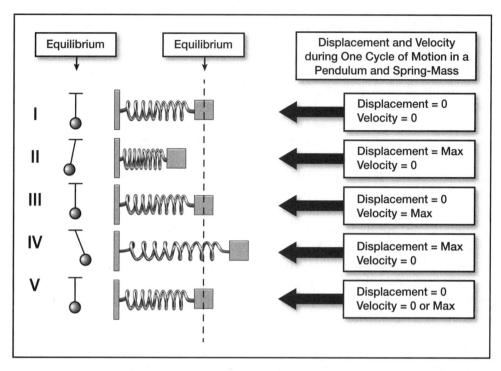

Figure 3–13A. Displacement and rate changes in displacement (velocity) in a spring-mass and pendulum. The five stages (I–V) in a single cycle involving displacement and the rate changes in displacement (velocity) for a pendulum, paralleling five stages in a single cycle involving displacement and velocity of a spring-mass system. Stage I: both pendulum and spring-mass are at resting or static equilibrium where displacement is zero and velocity is zero. Stage II: displacement to the left for both pendulum and spring-mass is maximum and velocity is zero. Stage III: both pendulum and spring-mass are in motion, displacement is zero, and velocity is at a maximum or peak value. Velocity is maximum and there are no restorative forces to oppose displacement or rate changes in displacement (velocity). Instantaneous velocity is also constant at this location for a fleeting instant in time. Stage IV: pendulum and spring-mass move past equilibrium as both are displaced maximally to the right. Displacement is at a peak value while velocity (rate of change in displacement) is zero. Stage V: once again displacement is zero, velocity is at zero if motion ceases, or velocity is at a maximum value if motion continues and instantaneous velocity is constant. Pendulum and spring-mass have each completed one full cycle of symmetrical displacement.

Why is velocity at its maximum value at this location? Because displacement is zero or near zero, the restorative force of elasticity (for the spring-mass) and of gravity (for the pendulum) are each at an absolute minimum value. Because the restorative forces of elasticity and gravity oppose displacement, at Stage III, no restorative forces exist to oppose displacement, or to oppose rate changes in displacement (velocity). The instan-taneous velocity at Stage III is maxi-mum but is also constant and there-fore unchanging, but only at the precise equilibrium point and only for a fleeting instant in time. As indicated in Figure 3–13A, pendulum and spring-mass will pass through equilibrium at Stage III and will then advance to Stage IV (rar-efaction for the spring-mass).

At Stage IV, both pendulum and spring-mass have again been displaced maximally to the right. Displacement of pendulum and spring-mass to the right of equilibrium during Stage IV indicates that displacement is again at a peak (maximum), as it was during Stage II. Velocity for both pendulum and spring-mass is also zero during Stage IV as the motion of the pendulum and spring-mass comes to a halt. This again is due to the increase in the restorative forces that oppose both displacement, and the rate changes in displacement. Both pendulum and spring-mass then move to Stage V (see Figure 3–13A).

At Stage V (equilibrium), displacement is zero and velocity is maximum and constant, just as described during

Stage III as long as motion continues. If motion ceases, velocity is again zero, as in Stage I. The eventual return of both pendulum and spring-mass to Stage V from the original starting point (Stage I) defines one complete and symmetrical cycle of displacement.

Figure 3–13B illustrates by histograms the relative amplitudes of displacement and velocity during the five stages (I–V) in a single cycle of motion for a pendulum and spring-mass, as presented in Figure 3–12A. During Stage I, displacement and velocity are both zero, because pendulum and spring-mass are not moving. During Stages II (compression for the spring-mass) and

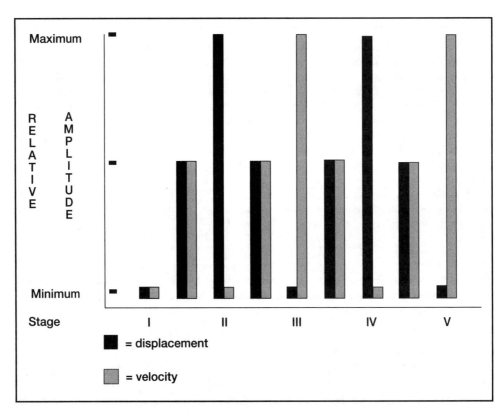

Figure 3–13B. Relative amplitudes in histogram form for displacement and velocity during each of the five stages for one cycle of motion as illustrated in Figure 3–13A.

IV (rarefaction for the spring-mass), displacement is at its maximum magnitude (amplitude). Because the restorative forces of gravity and elasticity that oppose displacement are also maximum during Stages II and IV (see Figure 3–12B), velocity will also be observed at its most minimum value (or zero) as the motion of the pendulum and spring-mass comes to a halt. During Stages III and V, both pendulum and spring-mass are in motion. Displacement at Stages III and V is equal to zero by definition, and the restorative forces that oppose both displacement and the rate changes in displacement (velocity) are also zero. Velocity, however, is maximum and is constant for a fleeting instant in time during Stage III (and during Stage V as long as the pendulum and/or spring-mass continue to oscillate). It should be noted that the relative magnitudes of displacement and velocity fluctuate from maximum to minimum values along a continuum. Shown in Figure 3–13B are the relative amplitudes of displacement and velocity at intermediate locations found exactly midway between each of the labeled stages. The magnitudes of the amplitudes for displacement and velocity at each of these intermediate locations have values that fall between the maximum and the minimum.

Acceleration: Change in the Rate of Velocity

Displacement was defined as a change or deviation from equilibrium in a specified direction. Velocity was defined as the rate (per second) of change in displacement (displacement/time), or a change in speed in a specified direction.

Velocity (displacement/time) like speed is seldom constant and often fluctuates over time. Acceleration is the term used to describe fluctuations or time-rate changes that often occur in velocity. Acceleration refers to motion that is changing both in speed and direction, and it specifies how rapidly the velocity of an object is changing (Giancoli, 2005). Acceleration exists when velocity and time are combined through division. Therefore, acceleration is defined as the time-rate change in velocity, or simply as the rate of change per second in velocity:

acceleration = change in velocity/time

Acceleration, therefore, is the rate at which velocity changes, or the change in velocity/time. The key to understanding acceleration is that acceleration always involves change (Hewitt, 2003). When direction is not changing, acceleration may be expressed as the rate at which speed changes, or

acceleration along a given path = change in speed/time

Average acceleration is defined as the change in velocity divided by the elapsed time taken to make the change or

average acceleration = change in velocity/elapsed time

Instantaneous acceleration may be defined as a very small change in velocity during a very short interval of time. When acceleration is held constant and displacement proceeds in a uniform direction, then both instantaneous and average acceleration are said to be equal (Giancoli, 2005; Hewitt, 2003). Also, by definition,

Since

acceleration = change in velocity/time

then

acceleration = displacement/time/time

or

$$\text{acceleration} = \frac{\text{displacement/Time}}{\dfrac{\text{Time}}{1}}$$

Hence,

acceleration = displacement/time^2

Additionally,

velocity = acceleration × time

since

displacement/time = velocity/time × time

and therefore,

velocity = velocity

Velocity indicates the rate at which the direction or position changes, and acceleration indicates the rate at which the velocity is changing (Giancoli, 2005). By strict definition, acceleration refers to any change in velocity over time, so acceleration applies to increases as well as to decreases in velocity. When the rate of change in velocity is positive or increasing, then the term acceleration may be used to mean an increase in acceleration. However, a negative rate of change in velocity (a decrease) is also, by definition, a rate-change in velocity. Often, negative rate changes in velocity are referred to as deceleration, though deceleration by definition is really a special case of acceleration, because both terms still refer to a rate-change in velocity (Hewitt, 2003). Hence, acceleration may be positive or negative. Acceleration always involves change (Hewitt, 2003), and when velocity is not changing and is constant, acceleration is zero (Giancoli, 2005). Figure 3–14A once again illustrates the five hypothetical stages (I–V) in a single cycle of displacement, together with rate changes in velocity (acceleration) for a pendulum, that parallel the same five stages in a single cycle of displacement and acceleration of a spring-mass system.

At Stage I, both pendulum and spring-mass are at resting or static equilibrium, as indicated both by the vertical position of the pendulum and the location of the mass of the spring bisecting the vertical fragmented equilibrium line. Displacement, velocity, and acceleration are therefore zero for pendulum and spring-mass at Stage I.

At Stage II, both pendulum and spring-mass have been displaced maximally to the left (compression for the spring-mass) by an external force that has been immediately removed. For pendulum and spring-mass, Stage II indicates that displacement (change from equilibrium) is at a maximum peak value. However, at this stage, acceleration, the rate change in velocity (the rate of change per second of velocity) is also at its maximum value. Why is acceleration at its maximum value at this location? The velocity of the pendulum and spring mass decreases (decelerates) as the motion of each comes to a halt. The motions of pendulum and spring-

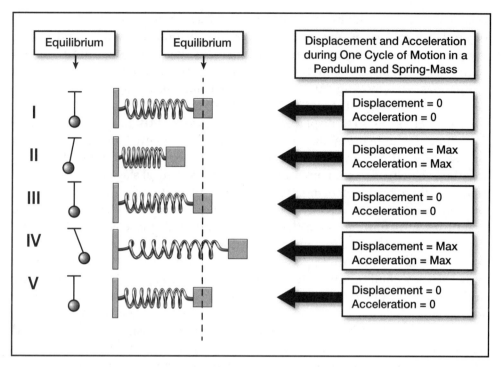

Figure 3–14A. Displacement and rate changes in velocity (acceleration) in a spring-mass and pendulum. Five stages (I–V) in a single cycle of displacement and the rate changes in velocity (acceleration) for a pendulum, paralleling five stages in a single cycle of displacement and acceleration for a spring-mass system. During Stage I, both pendulum and spring-mass are at resting or static equilibrium where displacement is zero and acceleration is zero. At Stage II, displacement to the left for both pendulum and spring-mass is maximum and acceleration is maximum because velocity and direction are both changing. At Stage III, both pendulum and spring-mass are in motion, displacement is zero, velocity is maximum and constant, and acceleration is zero for a fleeting instant in time. At Stage IV, pendulum and spring-mass move past equilibrium as both are displaced maximally to the right. Displacement and acceleration are again at their peak amplitude values. At Stage V, displacement is zero, velocity is maximum and constant, and acceleration is therefore zero as pendulum and spring-mass each complete one full cycle of symmetrical displacement.

mass will stop and change direction as the velocity of both increases (accelerates). Hence, the rate of change in the speed or velocity in a given direction of either the pendulum or spring-mass is the greatest, and the direction of motion of both is also changing maximally during Stage II. Why has this occurred? In the case of the spring-mass, elasticity opposes displacement. The farther the spring-mass deviates from equilibrium, the greater is the restorative force of elasticity that opposes displacement (Halliday et al., 2011). According to Hooke's law, the spring exerts a force (a restorative force) in a direction that is opposite to its displacement, and this restorative force acts to restore the spring to its original shape (Giancoli, 2005). Therefore, the motion of the spring-mass will change in direction. In the case of the pendulum, gravity opposes displacement (Halliday et al., 2011) and the restorative force of gravity acts to restore the pendulum to its point of equilibrium. Hence, the motion of the pendulum also changes in direction.

At Stage III, both pendulum and spring-mass are moving. At the precise location of Stage III (equilibrium) shown in Figure 3–14A, displacement for pendulum and spring-mass is zero by definition. However, at this precise location, velocity is maximum but constant, and therefore unchanging. Hence, the rate of change in velocity (acceleration) is zero, but only for a fleeting instant in time. As indicated in Figure 3–14A, pendulum and spring-mass will pass through equilibrium at Stage III and advance to Stage IV (rarefaction for the spring-mass).

At Stage IV, both pendulum and spring-mass have once again been displaced maximally to the right. Displacement of pendulum and spring-mass to the right of equilibrium during Stage IV indicates that displacement is at a peak (maximum) value, as it was during Stage II. Acceleration is also maximum during Stage IV, because the rate of change in velocity for pendulum and spring-mass is the greatest, and the direction of motion of both is also changing maximally, which is reminiscent of Stage II. The change in direction of motion for pendulum and spring-mass during Stage IV, is due once again to the restorative forces of gravity and elasticity, respectively. Both pendulum and spring-mass move to Stage V (see Figure 3–14A).

At Stage V, displacement is zero and acceleration is zero because velocity is maximum and constant (unchanging), just as described during Stage III, as long as motion continues. If motion ceases, acceleration together with displacement and velocity are each zero

in value, as in Stage 1. The eventual return of both pendulum and spring-mass to Stage V (equilibrium) from the original starting point (Stage I) defines one complete and symmetrical cycle of displacement.

Figure 3–14B illustrates by histograms the relative amplitudes of displacement and acceleration during the five hypothetical stages (I–V) in a single cycle of motion for a pendulum and spring-mass, as shown in Figure 3–14A. At Stage I, displacement and acceleration are zero, because pendulum and spring-mass are not moving. During Stages II (compression for the spring-mass) and IV (rarefaction for the spring-mass), displacement is at its maximum magnitude. During Stages II and IV (see Figure 3–14A) the motion of the pendulum and spring-mass comes to a halt as the motion of both changes direction. Therefore, the rate of change in velocity (acceleration) is maximum during these two stages. During Stages III and V, both pendulum and spring-mass are in motion and displacement is zero by definition. During Stages III and V, velocity is maximum and is constant (unchanging) for a fleeting instant in time, and therefore, acceleration must also be zero. It should be noted that the relative magnitudes of displacement and acceleration fluctuate from maximum to minimum values along a continuum. Shown in Figure 3–14B are the relative amplitudes of displacement and acceleration at intermediate locations found exactly midway between each of the labeled stages. The magnitudes of the amplitudes at each of these intermediate locations have values that fall between the maximum and the minimum.

Finally, Figure 3–15 illustrates and summarizes by histograms the relative

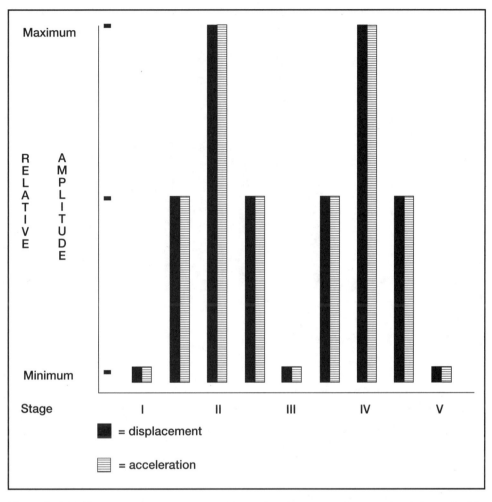

Figure 3–14B. Relative amplitudes in histogram form, of displacement and acceleration during each of the five stages for one cycle of motion as illustrated in Figure 3–14A.

amplitudes of displacement, velocity, and acceleration during the five hypothetical stages (I–V) in a single cycle of motion, as also shown previously in Figures 3–12B, 3–13B, and 3–14B. At Stage I, all three components are zero, because pendulum and spring-mass are not moving. During Stages II (compression for the spring-mass) and IV (rarefaction for the spring-mass), displacement and acceleration are maximum, and velocity is zero. During Stages III and V, both pendulum and spring-mass are in motion. For a fleeting instant in time, displacement and acceleration are zero, and velocity is maximum and constant (unchanging). The relative magnitudes of displacement, velocity, and acceleration fluctuate from maximum to minimum values along a continuum. Shown in Figure 3–14B are the relative amplitudes of each of the three elements at intermediate locations found exactly midway between each of the labeled stages. The magnitudes of each element at these intermediate

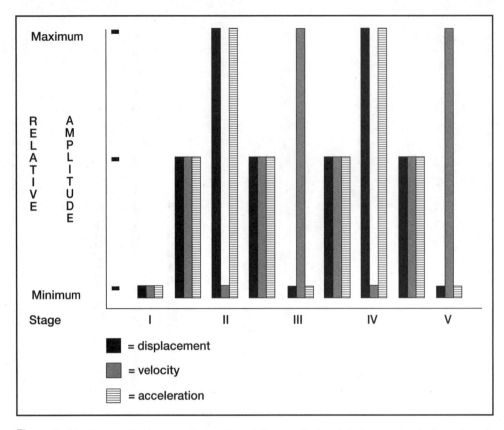

Figure 3–15. Summary in histogram form of the relative amplitudes of displacement, velocity, and acceleration during each of the five stages for one cycle of motion.

locations have values that fall between their maximum and their minimum values.

Chapter Summary

- In Chapter 3, the relevance and importance of physics to the hearing sciences was emphasized.
- This chapter emphasized that the generation of sound requires energy.
- Even though it is clear that energy is central to all of the sciences and is central to day-to-day living, an unambiguous definition of energy is difficult to furnish.
- According to Albert Einstein (1879–1955), energy has mass, and mass is energy; but the traditional definition of energy is that "energy is the ability or the capacity to do work."
- The law of the conservation of energy states that energy can be transformed from one type to another and from one object to another but the total amount of energy in any system is never increased nor decreased by any process.

- In this chapter, a machine was defined as a device that can multiply or change the direction of force as it performs work.
- When friction or frictional drag is present in any system, mechanical energy is lost and is not conserved. Therefore, friction and frictional drag are called nonconservative forces.
- If the energy of motion is transformed to thermal energy by friction or frictional drag, the transformation that occurs cannot be reversed. The energy of motion that is lost to heat will no longer be available for work.
- Psychophysics was defined in this chapter as a discipline that investigates the orderly relationships that exist between physical attributes like sound and the scaling rules that determine the degree to which these values correspond to psychological experience.
- Fechner (1801–1887) is credited as the founder of experimental psychology and for establishing the methodological foundations for the discipline of psychophysics.
- Acoustics was defined in this chapter as the "science of sound"; "hearing" refers to the auditory sensation and the cognitive perception of sound.
- Psychoacoustics was defined in this chapter as a branch of psychophysics.
- Vibrations produce waves, and waves transport energy from one place to another through a vibrating medium, making the production, sensation, and ultimately the perception (audibility) of sound possible.
- In this chapter, the three basic elements of vibration were defined as displacement, velocity, and acceleration.
- Displacement was defined in this chapter as a change in the position of a mass from one place or point to another place or point.
- Simple harmonic motion was defined in this chapter as uniform circular motion.
- The number of cycles per second of vibration during simple harmonic motion is referred to as *frequency* such that frequency = cycles/second.
- The time it takes to complete one cycle of vibration during simple harmonic motion is referred to as *period* such that period = (milli) seconds/cycle.
- Frequency and period are reciprocals such that 1/Frequency = Period and 1/Period = Frequency.
- Velocity was defined in this chapter as the rate of change in displacement (displacement/time).
- Acceleration was defined in this chapter as the rate of change in velocity (change in velocity/time).
- Equilibrium was defined in this chapter as the reference or starting point for displacement, and a mass that has not been displaced is at rest, or is at equilibrium.
- Equilibrium was also defined in this chapter as a condition in which a system remains constant without the utilization of energy.

■ Static equilibrium refers to objects that are not moving; mechanical equilibrium may exist in a moving object when the net sum of external forces acting on the object is zero.

■ Speed was defined in this chapter as the rate of change (time-rate change) in distance.

■ The simple harmonic motion of a pendulum was described in this chapter in terms of its displacement, its amplitude, its period, its frequency, and in terms of the restorative force of gravity.

■ Hooke's law states that the magnitude of the restoring force of an elastic mass is directly proportional to the magnitude of its displacement.

■ In this chapter, the simple harmonic motions of a pendulum and a spring-mass system were compared in terms of their displacement, velocity, acceleration, and the restorative forces of gravity and elasticity.

■ During simple harmonic motion, displacement and acceleration reach their maximum values when velocity is zero.

■ During simple harmonic motion, velocity is maximum and constant when displacement and acceleration are zero.

■ The restorative force of elasticity and gravity is maximum when displacement and acceleration reach their maximum values.

■ The restorative force of elasticity and gravity is zero at rest, or when velocity reaches its maximum value and is constant.

■ The restorative forces of elasticity and gravity are zero during states of equilibrium.

Chapter 3 Questions

1. What is the law of the conservation of energy? Who is credited for its formulation?

2. Differentiate between conservative and nonconservative forces.

3. Does Hooke's law apply to elastic or inelastic substances?

4. Why is a spring said to be elastic while putty is inelastic?

5. Can velocity be zero with maximum acceleration? Explain.

6. Can velocity be maximum with zero acceleration? Explain.

7. Can velocity be maximum with zero displacement? Explain.

8. Why is it that the massive explosions of stars in outer space produce no sound?

9. If you were elevated to the top of a mountain, would the altitude affect your ability to produce a loud yodel?

References

Boring, E. G. (1957). *A history of experimental psychology* (2nd ed.). New York, NY: Appelton-Century-Crofts.

Dirckx, J. H. (2005). *Stedman's medical dictionary for the health professions and nursing illustrated* (5th ed.). Baltimore, MD: Lippincott Williams & Wilkins.

Durrant, J. D., & Feth, L. L. (2013). *Hearing sciences: A foundational approach*. Upper Saddle River, NJ: Pearson Education.

Giancoli, D. C. (2005). *Physics: Principles with applications* (6th ed.). Upper Saddle River, NJ: Prentice Hall.

Gianopoulos, A. (2006). The heavens. In J. Langone, B. Stutz, & A. Gianopoulos (Eds.), *Theories for everything: An illustrated history of science from the invention of numbers to string theory* (pp. 18–71). Washington, DC: National Geographic Society.

Halliday, D., Resnick, R., & Walker, J. (2011). *Fundamentals of physics* (9th ed.). Hoboken, NJ: Wiley.

Hawking, S. E. (2002). *On the shoulders of giants: The great works of physics and astronomy*. Philadelphia, PA: Running Press.

Hays, W. L. (1981). *Statistics* (3rd ed.). New York, NY: CBS College-Holt, Rinehart & Winston.

Hewitt, P. G. (2010). *Conceptual physics* (11th ed.). Upper Saddle River, NJ: Pearson Education.

Hirsh, I. J. (1952). *The measurement of hearing*. New York, NY: McGraw-Hill.

Irion, G. (2000). *Physiology: The basis of clinical practice*. Thorofare, NJ: Slack.

Langone, J. (2006). The human body. In J. Langone, B. Stutz, & A. Gianopoulos (Eds.), *Theories for everything: An illustrated history of science from the invention of numbers to string theory* (pp. 73–145). Washington, DC: National Geographic Society.

Stevens, S. S. (1958). Chapter 1: Mathematics, measurement, and psychophysics. In S. S. Stevens (Ed.), *Handbook of experimental psychology* (pp. 1–49). New York, NY: Wiley.

Stutz, B. (2006). Introduction. In J. Langone, B. Stutz, & A. Gianopoulos (Eds.), *Theories for everything: An illustrated history of science from the invention of numbers to string theory* (pp. 8–17). Washington, DC: National Geographic Society.

Chapter 4

Application of the Basic Principles in Hearing Science

In a letter to Robert Hooke dated February 5, 1675, Newton wrote, "If I have seen further than others it is by standing upon the shoulders of giants" (Gianopoulos, 2006, p. 49; Hawking, 2002, p. 725). Perhaps Newton should have said, "I used the shoulders of giants as a springboard."

Hawking, 2002, p. XIII

Alphabetized Listing of Key Terms Discussed in Chapter 4

acceleration	force	joule
action	friction	Joule, James Prescott
atmospheric pressure	frictional resistance	kinematics
bar	Galilei, Galileo	kinetic energy
CGS metric system	geocentric	law of inertia
collisions	gravitational potential energy	laws of motion, Newton's
compliance	gravity	Leibniz, Gottfried Wilhelm
cycle	Halley, Edmond	
displacement	heliocentric	mass
dynamics	Hooke's law	mechanics
dyne	horsepower	Medicean stars
Einstein, Albert	Huygens, Christiaan	microbar
elastic collision	inertia	MKS metric system
energy	inertia, law of	momentum
erg	Inquisition	motion
first law of motion, Newton's	interactive forces	natural motion

net force	rate	stretching force (tension)
newton (of force)	reaction	
Newton, Isaac	recoil	support force
one atmosphere of pressure	reflecting telescope	telescope, Newtonian
	refracting telescope	third law of motion, Newton's
pascal (Pa)	restorative force	time
Pascal, Blaise	Rome, Holy Office of	vector quantity
pendulum	Rules of Reasoning, Newton's	vectors
peripatetics		velocity
Pope, Alexander	scalar quantity	violent motion
potential energy	scalars	watt
pounds per square inch (psi)	second law of motion, Newton's	Watt, James
power		weight
pressure	Slinky	work
Principia	spring-mass system	Wren, Christopher

A Brief Historical Account of Motion

The connection between vibratory motion and sound was introduced in the previous chapter. Historically, the study of motion, known also in physics as mechanics, has occupied the interests of scholars that have originated from the time of the ancient philosopher Aristotle (384–322 BC), up to and beyond the era of the eminent Albert Einstein (1879–1955). Today, a thorough understanding of motion remains an essential component within the study of contemporary hearing science. What follows is a brief historical account of Galileo Galilei (1564–1642) and Isaac Newton (1642–1727), both of whom made significant contributions that advanced the study of motion, and of hearing science.

Galileo Galilei (1564–1642)

Recall the image of Galileo (see Portrait 1–1) that was presented in Chapter 1. Galileo was born in Pisa, Italy, and became the foremost scientist of the early 17th century. He studied medicine and the philosophy of Aristotle at the University of Pisa from 1581 to 1584. At the age of 20, Galileo discovered the properties of the pendulum. As indicated in the previous chapter, Galileo demonstrated that the rate of harmonic motion of a pendulum is inversely dependent on its length. This discovery made accurate time-keeping possible. It is not known whether Galileo actually built a pendulum clock, though Christiaan Huygens (1629–1695) did build one more than ten years after Galileo's death (Giancoli, 2005).

In 1585, Galileo abandoned the study of medicine for research in mathematics (Hawking, 2002). His approach to science included idealization and simplification, the quantification of theories (operationism), the development of theories (induction) with testable hypotheses (deduction), and the completion of empirical investigations in order to test his predictions (or simply, hypothesis testing). For these reasons, Galileo is often called the "father of modern experimental science" (Hawking, 2002). In 1589 at the age of 25, Galileo became a professor of mathematics at the University of Pisa. From his experiments with falling and rolling objects, he developed the concept of *acceleration*. He demonstrated that for a given location on the earth, solid objects with different amounts of mass would fall to the earth at roughly equivalent speeds or with constant acceleration, provided the air resistance was equivalent, or zero, as in a vacuum. Galileo, however, could not explain why. This explanation would require the genius of Isaac Newton. Galileo additionally determined that objects forcibly set into motion by a push or a pull on a horizontal surface eventually come to rest due to a force, called "friction" and not "nature," as Aristotle had originally asserted. He also reasoned that if friction were completely removed, an object forcibly set into motion would continue to move indefinitely in a straight line with constant velocity, provided that no other force acted to alter its motion. Galileo coined the term "inertia," and inertia became central to Galileo's laws of motion. Hence, according to Galileo, the constant horizontal motion of an object was no less natural than the condition of rest. This way of thinking was in direct contradiction to the popularly held metaphysical philosophies of Aristotle. Hence, Galileo discredited the contemporarily held Aristotelian concepts of nature and motion and this led to the creation of a new vision of the universe (Gianopoulos, 2006). From his prudent observations and experimentation, Galileo helped advance a new worldview in which the affairs of the mind were separate from the affairs of matter. In turn, advocates of Aristotelian thinking (called Peripatetics) eventually forced Galileo to leave the University of Pisa. In 1592, Galileo became professor of mathematics at the University of Padua where he made significant discoveries in astronomy (Gianopoulos, 2006). Galileo built a refracting telescope that was an improvement on a design first proposed in 1610 by Hans Lipperhey (Hawking, 2002). His conclusions, based on his earlier observation in 1604 of a supernova, and his telescopic observations in 1610 of the moon, Jupiter, and the galaxy, were again in direct opposition to the prevailing philosophy of an unchanging universe, as put forth by Aristotle (Hawking, 2002).

In 1610 Galileo discovered and named the four brightest moons of Jupiter, which he called the Medicean stars (Hawking, 2002). Later he detected the phases of Venus, and the sunspots of the Sun. In total, Galileo's scientific conclusions gave credence to a heliocentric Copernican view of the cosmos

(Gianopoulos, 2006). By displacing the earth from the center of the universe, he was able to conclude that the earth and the heavens both operated under similar laws (Hawking, 2002). He attacked, with empirical evidence, the belief that mechanics and cosmology were separate subject matters. In 1616, officials of the Church, together with other Peripatetics, warned Galileo to abandon his belief in the Copernican view of the cosmos. In 1632, the Holy Office of Rome (The Inquisition) imprisoned Galileo for his published writings and confined him for an indefinite time to his villa in Florence (Gianopoulos, 2006; Hawking, 2002). Galileo remained there under house arrest in Tuscany, where he later died in 1642 (Giancoli, 2005; Hewitt, 2010).

Portrait 4–1. Isaac Newton (1642–1727). "Nature and nature's laws lay hid at night: God said, 'Let Newton be! And all was light.'" Written by Alexander Pope to describe Newton's gift to humanity (Hawking, 2002, p. 732). Printed with permission. Wikimedia Commons, public domain.

Isaac Newton (1642–1727)

Newton was born in Woolsthorpe, Lincolnshire, England, in the same year that Galileo died in Florence, while under house arrest (Gianopoulos, 2006; Hawking, 2002) (Portrait 4–1). At the age of 11, while attending grammar school, Newton discovered his particular talent for building clocks, sundials, and a working model of a windmill that was powered by a running mouse (Hawking, 2002). Newton led a rather solitary life (Gianopoulos, 2006), and much of Newton's adulthood was filled with episodes of harsh, vindictive attacks, not only against perceived enemies, but against friends and family as well. It has been speculated that Newton's achievements were the result of his vindictive obsessions and arrogance (Hawking, 2002). Beginning at the age of 19, and from 1661 to 1665, Newton attended Trinity College, which was part of Cambridge University (Gianopoulos, 2006). While at Cambridge, Newton studied the philosophy of Aristotle and Descartes, the science of Thomas Hobbs and Robert Boyle, the mechanics of Copernicus, the astronomy of Galileo, and the optics of Kepler (Hawking, 2002). While Newtonian mechanics has guided astronomers and scientists in their search for knowledge for more than 200 years, it was Newton's work with prisms and light (1704) (Portrait 4–2) that initially brought him fame (Gianopoulos, 2006). Newton was the first to use a prism to break a ray of light into a spectrum of colors. He then used a second prism to combine the colors back into white light (Stutz, 2006).

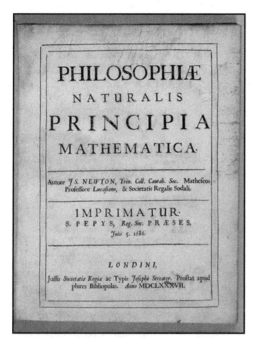

Portrait 4–2. Newton's mathematical principles of natural philosophy. Printed with permission. Wikimedia Commons, public domain.

Newton was a rationalist whose emphasis was often based on defining true mathematical notions, independent of observation (Gianopoulos, 2006). The British physicist Robert Hooke, the English astronomer Edmond Halley, the Dutch mathematician Christiaan Huygens, and the architect Christopher Wren were all contemporaries of Isaac Newton (Hawking, 2002). At the age of 23 (1665) Newton formulated his universal law of gravitation and later, from 1666 to 1667, developed the binomial theorem. The law of universal gravitation stated that all matter is mutually attracted with a force directly proportional to the product of their (individual) masses, and inversely proportional to the square of the distance between them. He was also able to use his inverse square law theory of

gravity to explain the elliptical motions of the planets and the rising and falling of the tides (Gianopoulos, 2006; Hawking, 2002). Newton invented the calculus (1666), though the differential and integral calculus developed by Gottfried Wilhelm Leibniz (1646–1716) in roughly the same period, is more commonly used by mathematicians and engineers. Nevertheless, Newton is still considered to be the father of infinitesimal calculus, mechanics and planetary motion, and theories of light and color. He secured his place in history by formulating the law of gravitational force and defining his three laws of motion (Hawking, 2002).

Newton, like Galileo, adhered to the heliocentric-Copernican view of the cosmos, and he viewed changes in the motion of a mass as originating from sources external to the mass, rather than representing internal activity within the mass (Hawking, 2002). In 1668, Newton developed (Stutz, 2006), constructed, and later made revisions (1671–1672) to the first reflecting telescope (Gianopoulos, 2006). Newton's original telescope was only 6 inches long and is still on display at the library of the Royal Society of London. His invention was the prototype for the design that later came to be called the "Newtonian telescope," a term that is practically synonymous with the reflecting telescope (Stutz, 2006). Newton became a mathematics professor at Cambridge in 1669 and was appointed the Lucasian Professor of Mathematics at Trinity College (in Cambridge) which is the same position held today by the renowned physicist Stephen Hawking (Gianopoulos, 2006). Extending the work of Galileo, Newton formulated his three laws of motion in his great work, the *Principia*

(Mathematical Principles of Natural Philosophy) which he published in 1687. Edmund Halley personally financed the publication of Newton's massive work as a masterpiece and a gift to humanity (Hawking, 2002). In his great work, Newton acknowledged his indebtedness to Galileo, while removing all references to the work of the man whom he considered to be his nemesis, Robert Hooke (Hawking, 2002). In his "Rules of Reasoning" (1687), he stated that, "We are to admit no more causes of natural things than such as are both true and sufficient to explain their appearances . . . " (Hawking, 2002). This statement is reminiscent of the rule of parsimony in science, as elaborated in Chapter 1.

The legacy that was left to us by Newton was his brilliant synthesis of Galilean terrestrial mechanics and Copernican-Keplerian astronomy. Newton was Knighted in 1705 by Queen Anne, and Sir Isaac Newton was buried in England's Westminster Abbey following his death in 1727 at the age of 85 (Gianopoulos, 2006).

Kinematics and Dynamics

In Chapter 3, mechanics was defined as the study of force, energy, and the relationship of both to the motion of objects. The study of mechanics may be divided into the two branches of kinematics and dynamics. Kinematics refers to the description and classification of how objects move. The stages of motion described and illustrated for the pendulum and the simple spring-mass system (i.e., displacement, velocity, and acceleration) in Chapter 3, illustrated

some of the subject matter of kinematics. Dynamics is concerned with the connection between force and motion and provides answers to why objects move as they do. Dynamics provided the foundation for the general law of the conservation of energy discussed in Chapter 3. The subject matter of dynamics also includes the driving forces related to energy that preserve and maintain the vibratory motion of a mass once the vibration has begun (Giancoli, 2005).

Inertia

What is the connection between force and motion? Aristotle asserted that a constant force is required to keep an object moving across a horizontal plane, because the natural state of any object is "rest." Aristotle, however, failed to recognize the property of inertia because he failed to imagine motion in the absence of friction. His failure impeded the progress of physics for nearly 2000 years (Hewitt, 2010). It took the genius of Galileo to postulate that an object slows down only if a force such as friction is exerted on the object. Accordingly, the force of friction is likened to any other force. That is, friction is like any other pushing or pulling that may act on an object. The major difference is that mechanical energy is not conserved when frictional drag is present. In a frictionless environment, Galileo reasoned that an object set into motion would travel indefinitely, and he coined the term *inertia*. Acknowledging his indebtedness to Galileo, and based largely on the foundation provided by his work, Isaac Newton formulated his three laws of motion. As indicated above, Newton published his three laws of motion in 1687 with his great work, the *Principia*.

Mass, Inertia, and Newton's First Law of Motion

In Chapter 3, mass was defined as the amount or quantity of matter in any object. Mass and energy were also said to be identical by the formula $E = mc^2$. Mass is "congealed" energy (Hewitt, 2010). The mass of a body was also defined as a characteristic that relates a force on a body to the resulting acceleration. In other words, a physical sensation of mass is appreciated only when one attempts to accelerate an object (Halliday, Resnick, & Walker, 2011). The information provided in the sections that follow corroborate the need to redefine mass, to that of a measure of the inertia within an object when

attempts are made to alter, in any manner, an object's motion.

In essence, Newton's first law of motion (Box 4–1), appropriately called the law of inertia, restated and redefined the property of inertia as initially proposed by Galileo. Recall that Galileo postulated that an object slows down only if a force, such as friction, is exerted upon it. The law of inertia describes an inherent property of mass that resists changes in motion. Inertia could also have been defined simply as a force that resists change. Objects at rest and/or those in motion together have in common the property of inertia. Why is it that objects exhibit inertia in the first place? It is because of their mass. Why do all objects share the property of inertia? It is because all objects have the property of mass. To the extent that an object has mass, the same object will also exhibit inertia. Mass may be redefined as a measure of the inherent inertia within an object. This is because the amount of an object's mass determines

---

Box 4–1. Newton's First Law of Motion (The Law of Inertia)

The law of inertia states that an object at rest tends to stay at rest and resists any change that might cause it to be set into motion. Hence, if a mass is at rest, it stays at rest. Likewise, a body (or mass) set into motion remains in motion and will resist forces that might slow it, speed it, or stop it. According to Newton, if an object is moving, it continues to move with the same magnitude and direction of velocity, unless it is compelled to change that state by forces impressed upon it (Hewitt, 2010). "Every body perseveres in its state of resting, or uniformly moving in a right line, unless it is compelled to change that state by forces impressed upon it." (Hawking, 2002, p. 743).

the extent to which the object will resist any force (any pushing or any pulling) that might cause a change in its existing motion. The greater the mass, the greater will be the inertia that must be overcome to produce a change in the motion of the mass. Hence, more massive objects require more force to set them into motion, to slow them, or to alter their direction of motion.

Problem Set 4–1

1. Place a card over the top of an empty water glass. Then, place a coin on the card. What happens to the coin if the card is quickly flicked off the glass without disturbing the glass itself? How can the actions of the coin be explained?

2. What explanation is there for being able to toss a ball into the air and catching it while also traveling in a high-speed commercial airplane?

3. Would a locomotive engine require more or less force to overcome its resting inertia as compared to a Slinky? Compared to a Slinky, would it take more or less force to get a locomotive to stop once it has started moving?

4. Is a sharp jerk more effective than a slow pull when attempting to tear off a paper towel or a plastic bag from a roll? Why?

5. Who first conceived of the concept of inertia, Galileo or Newton?

6. Why is it that a car headrest in an automobile helps guard against whiplash in a rear-end collision? Why is there forward motion of the passengers in an automobile when the brakes are applied suddenly?

Force

In Chapter 3, both conservative and nonconservative forces were discussed. Conservative forces included the restorative force associated with the spring-mass system, as well as the force of weight and gravity associated with the motion of a pendulum. Additional examples of conservative forces include electrical force, magnetic force, the force supplied by muscular contraction, the stretching force or tension provided by a spring-mass, and the support force, such as the kind afforded by a table or chair (Hewitt, 2010). In terms of mechanical systems such as those that produce simple harmonic motion and sound, potential energy can only be defined for conservative forces. The nonconservative, frictional (drag) force was also previously examined. In the chapters that follow, the mechanical forces of the middle ear, the hydraulic forces of the inner ear, and the driving forces generated by electrical and ionic concentration gradients within neurons will be explored. A formal definition of force will be important for a conceptual understanding of pressure, as pressure forms the basis for decibel (dB) measurements that are made with reference to sound pressure level (SPL). The concept of force is a very important building block for key principles in any discussion of hearing science.

Previously, force was defined informally as an external push or pull that is required to alter the motion of an object. An applied force and the utilization of energy may initiate or cause an unmoving object to move or to oscillate. Alternatively, a force that is applied may alter the existing motion or oscillation of an object. In addition, an applied force may temporarily distort the shape of an object that is fixed or anchored, but if the force is great enough, the fixed object may fracture or fall into pieces. Finally, force, and the utilization of energy, may ultimately produce no motion or change in the shape of a mass, whatsoever. In order to produce sound, force and energy utilization are unquestionably required to set an object, objects, or an elastic medium, into vibratory motion.

Force may be specified by both its magnitude and its direction (hence, it is a vector quantity), and when more than a single force acts on an object, the net force must be considered. As illustrated in Chapter 3 (see Figure 3–6), when the external forces acting in any one of several possible directions on a mass are exactly and evenly balanced by opposing forces, the mass is in mechanical equilibrium because the net force acting on the mass is zero (Hewitt, 2010). It then follows from Newton's first law that an object under the control of a single force cannot be in equilibrium (Hewitt, 2010). Mechanical equilibrium exists when the net sum of the external forces acting on a mass is zero. This is because equal but opposite forces will cancel (Halliday et al., 2011). In fact, Newton's first law of motion may be restated as follows: "If no net force acts on a body, the body's velocity cannot change, and therefore, the body cannot accelerate" (Halliday et al., 2011).

Mass, Acceleration, and Newton's Second Law of Motion

Like all physical properties, force is derived from the basic quantities of mass, length, and time. Newton's second law of motion (Box 4–2) defines the relationship that exists between mass, acceleration, and force:

$$\text{Acceleration} = \text{Force/Mass} \qquad (4\text{–}1)$$

Box 4–2. Newton's Second Law of Motion

Newton's second law of motion states that the acceleration (or the rate of change in velocity) of any body is directly proportional to the net force acting upon the body, and is inversely proportional to the mass of the body, or

$$\text{Acceleration (A)} = \text{Force (F)} \div \text{Mass (M)}$$

$$A = F/M$$

"The change of motion is proportional to the motive force impressed; and is made in the direction of the right line in which that force is impressed" (Hawking, 2002, p. 743).

According to Newton's second law of motion, acceleration is directly proportional to net force, or

$$\text{Acceleration} \sim \text{net force} \quad (4\text{–}2)$$

Therefore, if the net force acting on an object is zero, then acceleration is also zero, and the object may be said to be in mechanical equilibrium. Hence, net force is measured by the acceleration that it produces. Furthermore, the direction of the acceleration follows (or is in the same direction as) the net force acting on the object (Giancoli, 2005).

Newton's second law of motion also states that acceleration is inversely proportional to mass, or

$$\text{Acceleration} \sim 1/\text{mass} \quad (4\text{–}3)$$

This simply means that mass resists acceleration. Why might this be true? This is true because mass was also defined as the amount of inertia (inherent) within an object. Acceleration is the rate of change in velocity (Giancoli, 2005), and inertia, by definition, is a force that resists change. Newton's second law of motion also yields a formal definition for force. Solving for force, if

$$A = F/M$$

Then

$$M/1 \times A = F/M \times M/1$$

Therefore,

$$\text{Force (F)} = \\ \text{Mass (M)} \times \text{Acceleration (A)} \quad (4\text{–}4)$$

In words, the net external force (F) on a body is equal to the product of the body's mass (M) and the body's (A) acceleration (Halliday et al., 2011).

Hence, force is determined by the product of two factors, acceleration and mass. The formal definition for force: $F = M \times A$ may be used in place of the informal (push or the pull) definition given previously.

A Closer Examination of Force—I

In Chapter 3, displacement, velocity, and acceleration were defined as basic derivatives of length. Displacement is a change in the position of a mass, from one place or point to another place or point, and was measured in standard units of length (Halliday et al., 2011). Velocity is the rate of change (per unit of time) of displacement and acceleration is the rate of change (per unit of time) in velocity, or

$$\text{Velocity} = \text{displacement/time} \\ \text{and} \\ \text{Acceleration} = \text{velocity/time}$$

It was also shown in Chapter 3 that the equation given below follows from the above two equations:

$$\text{Acceleration} = \\ \text{displacement/time/time}$$

and therefore since

$$\text{Displacement/time/time} = \\ \text{displacement/time} \div T/1$$

then

$$\text{Displacement/time} \times 1/T \div T/1 \times 1/T$$

leads to Equation 4–5:

$$\text{Acceleration} = \text{displacement/time}^2 \\ (4\text{–}5)$$

It is now possible to formally specify the standard measurement units of force for both the MKS and CGS metric systems.

The MKS Metric Unit of Force

The metric system was introduced in Chapter 2. Recall that two separate metric measurement systems exist. The MKS metric system is the preferred measurement system in the field of physics. Recall that the discipline of hearing science has no officially adopted metric system. For this reason, it is important to represent a working understanding of both systems of measure as both are in use in the hearing sciences. Recall from Chapter 2 that the MKS metric system standard for length is the meter, the standard MKS unit for mass is the kilogram, and the MKS standard for time is the second; hence,

MKS SYSTEM

Length	Mass	Time
M(eter)	K(ilogram	S(econd)

The Kilogram–Meter/Second²: The Newton

Recall that Newton's second law of motion yielded the following formal definition for force:

$$\text{Force} = \text{mass} \times \text{acceleration} \quad (4\text{--}4)$$

Since

$$\text{Acceleration} = \text{displacement/time}^2$$

the formal definition for force may be rewritten as follows:

$$\text{Force} = \text{mass} \times \text{displacement/time}^2 \quad (4\text{--}6)$$

Employing the appropriate MKS units of measure in the above definition, the MKS definition of force may be expressed as

$$\text{Force} = \text{kilogram} \times \text{meter/second}^2$$

Therefore, the standard unit of force in the MKS metric system is the product of mass (kg) and length (m) divided by time² (sec²), and is often expressed as the

$$\text{Kilogram-meter/second}^2 \text{ (kg-m/sec}^2)$$

One kg-m/sec² of force is the amount of push or pull that is required to satisfy the criterion for one standard unit of force in the MKS system. It should be obvious from the above definition that one unit of force in the MKS system would require enough push or pull to accelerate a certain amount of mass across a particular distance, at a certain rate of motion In honor of Sir Isaac Newton, the kg-m/sec² unit of force in the MKS metric system was named the newton, or simply a newton of force.

Therefore,

$$1 \text{ newton} = 1 \text{ kg-m/sec}^2$$

The newton (kg-m/sec²) is the standard unit of force in the MKS metric system and is defined as that amount of force required to accelerate a mass of 1 kilogram, across a distance of 1 meter, at a rate of 1 second².

Force and Distance—I

The concept of work was briefly introduced in Chapter 3. Like the concept of energy, work is expressed in terms of its overall magnitude. It was informally stated that work is accomplished when energy is transferred to or from an object by means of forces (or a force) acting on the object (Halliday et al., 2011). In words, this means that work is accomplished only when a force applied to an object causes a change in the existing motion of the object, or a change in the energy state of the object. A force may also be applied to an object in the absence of work. For instance, if you were to push against a large stone wall, force is exerted, but no work is accomplished. If you were to stand stationary holding a heavy object in your arms, force is exerted, but work is once again, zero (Giancoli, 2005). Finally, borrowing from the example provided in Chapter 3 (see Figure 3–6), when external forces acting on a mass are balanced by opposing forces, and the net force acting on the mass is zero, the mass is in mechanical equilibrium and the amount of work is again, zero. Forces cancel only when they act on the same body or mass, or on the same system (Hewitt, 2010). This point is illustrated in Figure 4–1.

A formal definition of work is now presented. By definition, the quantity of work that is accomplished is given by the product of the distance that a mass is moved (or displaced), and the magnitude of the force applied, provided that the force is parallel to the displacement. Therefore, work may be expressed formally as Equation 4–7:

$$\text{work} = \text{force} \times \text{distance} \qquad (4\text{–}7)$$

The MKS Metric Unit for Work: The Joule

If, as indicated in the previous section, work may be defined by Equation 4–7,

then the standard unit of work in the M-K-S metric system may be defined as

$$\text{work} = \text{newton} \times \text{meter}$$

which is commonly expressed as the newton-meter or the joule.

Hence,   1 newton-meter = 1 joule

or   1 newton = 1 joule/meter

The joule of work is named in honor of the English scientist, James Prescott Joule (1818–1889) (Portrait 4–3). Joule believed that all forms of energy were the same, in that all forms were convertible—one into the other. Working closely with William Thomson, First Baron Kelvin (or Lord Kelvin, 1824–1907), Joule discovered that the rate of generation of heat by an electric circuit was proportional to the current squared, times the resistance. Joule fur-

Portrait 4–3. James Prescott Joule (1818–1889). Printed with permission. Wikimedia Commons, public domain.

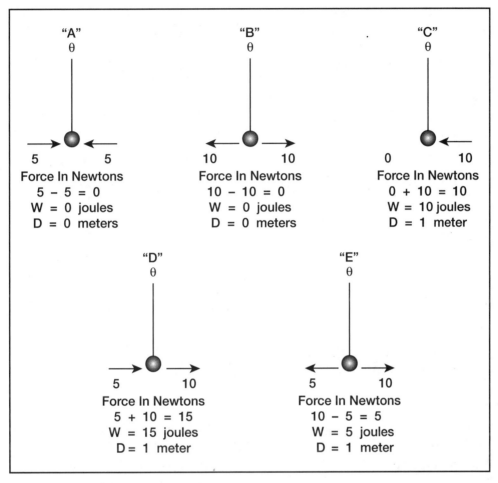

Figure 4–1. Net force and net work. Each of the five pendulums shown attach by the tops of their stalks at a pivot point. Assume in each case that each pendulum may be displaced by 1 m only. Force, defined in newtons, is applied equally but in opposite directions to the mass of each pendulum shown under **A** and **B**. When equal but opposing forces are applied, the net sum of the external forces acting on either pendulum mass is zero. For pendulums **A** and **B**, displacement (**D**) is zero, there is no change from equilibrium, and the net work (**W**) is equal to zero joules. In pendulum **C**, a force of 10 newtons is externally applied to one side only of the pendulum mass with a resulting displacement of 1 m to the left. Therefore, 10 joules of work are accomplished in pendulum **C**. In pendulum **D**, the result of unequal external forces of 5 and 10 newtons applied in the same direction will be additive. In this illustration, 15 joules of net work are accomplished with a displacement of 1 m to the right. Finally, when unequal external forces are applied in opposite directions to an object, the direction of displacement will favor the direction of the greater force. Hence, in pendulum **E**, 5 joules of net work are accomplished with a displacement of 1 m to the right.

ther established that the amount of work performed by a heat engine was proportional to the amount of heat lost in converting energy into work. Joule and Thompson were both convinced that their work on heat and electromagne-tism would eventually lead to a unified theory of energy. It was also during this time that Helmholtz was formulating his law of the conservation of energy (Halliday et al., 2011; Stutz, 2006). By definition, the standard unit of work in the MKS system is the joule, and 1 joule results when 1 newton of force is utilized in order to cause an object, having a mass of 1 kg, to move (or be displaced) at a rate of 1 sec², across a distance of 1 m. Therefore, 1 newton of force exerted across a distance of 1 m will accomplish 1 joule of work.

A Closer Examination of Force—II

Once again recall the equation below from Chapter 3:

$$\text{Acceleration} = \text{displacement/time/time}$$

and therefore, since

$$\text{Displacement/time/time} = \text{displacement/time} \div T/1$$

then

$$\text{Displacement/time} \times 1/T \div T/1 \times 1/T$$

leads to Equation 4–5:

$$\text{Acceleration} = \text{displacement/time}^2$$
$$(4–5)$$

The CGS Metric Unit of Force

As indicated in Chapter 2, the preferred system of measurement in the field of chemistry is the CGS metric system. Recall as well that the CGS metric system standard for length is the centimeter, the CGS standard for mass is the gram, and the standard CGS unit for time is once again, the second; hence,

CGS SYSTEM

Length	Mass	Time
C(entimeter)	G(ram)	S(econd)

The Gram–Centimeter/Second²: The Dyne

Returning now to Newton's second law of motion presented as

$$\text{Force} = \text{mass} \times \text{acceleration}$$
$$(4–4)$$

And considering Equation 4–5:

$$\text{Acceleration} = \text{displacement/time}^2$$
$$(4–5)$$

Equation 4–6 again follows as

$$\text{Force} = \text{mass} \times \text{displacement/time}^2$$
$$(4–6)$$

Employing the appropriate CGS measurement units in the above definition, the CGS definition of force may be expressed as

$$\text{Force} = \text{gram} \times \text{centimeter/second}^2$$

Therefore, the standard unit of force in the CGS metric system is the product of mass (g) and length (cm) divided by time² (sec²), and is often expressed as follows:

$$\text{gram-centimeter/second}^2 \text{ (g-cm/sec}^2)$$

One g-cm/sec² of force is the amount of push or pull that is required to satisfy the criterion for one standard unit of force in the CGS system. Once again, it should be obvious from the definition above that one unit of force in the CGS system would require enough push or pull to accelerate a certain amount of mass across a particular distance, at a certain rate of motion. The g-cm/sec² unit of force in the CGS metric system is called the *dyne*, or simply a dyne of force.

Therefore,

$$1 \text{ dyne} = 1 \text{ g-cm/sec}^2$$

The dyne (g-cm/sec²) is the standard unit of force in the CGS metric system and is defined as the amount of force required to accelerate a mass of 1 gram, across a distance of 1 centimeter, at a rate of 1 second².

Force and Distance—II

The concept of *work* was defined formally as the product of force and distance, or as Equation 4–7:

$$\text{Work} = \text{force} \times \text{distance} \qquad (4\text{–}7)$$

The CGS Metric Unit for Work: The Erg

Once again using Equation 4–7:

$$\text{Work} = \text{force} \times \text{distance} \qquad (4\text{–}7)$$

The standard unit of work in the CGS metric system may be defined as

$$\text{Work} = \text{dyne} \times \text{centimeter}$$

which is commonly expressed as the dyne-centimeter or the erg.

Hence,

$$1 \text{ dyne-centimeter} = 1 \text{ erg}$$

By definition, the standard unit of work in the CGS system is the erg, and one erg of work results when 1 dyne of force is utilized in order to cause an object, having a mass of 1g, to move (or be displaced) at a rate of 1 sec² across a distance of 1 cm. Therefore, 1 dyne of force exerted across a distance of 1 centimeter, will accomplish 1 erg of work.

Finally, when two or more forces act on an object, the net amount of work that is performed on the object is the sum of the "works" accomplished by the individual forces. The concept of net work is illustrated in Figure 4–1.

MKS and CGS Metric Units Compared: Force

It should be re-emphasized that force is derived from the three basic quantities of mass, length, and time:

M-K-S   kg-meter/second²
          = 1 newton

C-G-S   gram-centimeter/second²
          = 1 dyne

How do dynes of force compare with newtons of force? At a glance, it should be obvious that MKS units in general are much larger than CGS units of measure. Taking the definition of the dyne,

$$1 \text{ dyne} =$$
$$1 \text{ gram} \times 1 \text{ centimeter/second}^2$$

We may directly compare the difference in magnitude of 1 dyne with 1 newton by restating the definition of 1 newton in terms of grams and centimeters, using the rules outlined in Chapter 2, and the prefixes given in Table C1–1 of Appendix C. Hence,

$$1 \text{ newton} =$$
$$1 \text{ kilogram} \times 1 \text{ meter/second}^2$$

should be restated in terms of CGS measurement units as

$$1 \text{ newton} =$$
$$10^3 \text{ grams} \times 10^2 \text{ centimeters/second}^2$$

Therefore,

$$1 \text{ newton} = 10^3 \times 10^2 \text{ dynes}$$

Using the rules for obtaining the product of two exponential quantities with a common base, as outlined in Section A2 of Appendix A, the product of the two quantities is simply the common base raised to the sum of the separate exponential values. In words, we simply add the values of the exponents.

Therefore,

$$1 \text{ newton} = 10^{(3+2)} \text{ dynes}$$

$$1 \text{ newton} = 10^5 \text{ dynes}$$

$$1 \text{ newton} = 100{,}000 \text{ dynes}$$

Hence, the MKS newton is the larger unit of force. The newton is 10^5 or 100,000 greater than the CGS dyne of force.

MKS and CGS Metric Units Compared: Work

The MKS unit of work, like force, is also derived from the three basic quantities of length, mass, and time. Look again at Equation 4–7:

$$\text{Work} = \text{Force} \times \text{Distance}$$

$$\text{joule} = \text{newton-meter}$$

$$\text{joule} = 1 \text{ kg} \times 1 \text{ meter} \times 1 \text{ meter/sec}^2$$

Hence,

$$1 \text{ joule} = 1 \text{ kg-m}^2/\text{sec}^2$$

The CGS unit of work is also derived from the three basic quantities of length, mass, and time. Take Equation 4–7 again:

$$\text{Work} = \text{Force} \times \text{Distance} \qquad (4–7)$$

$$\text{erg} = \text{dyne-centimeter}$$

$$\text{erg} = 1 \text{ gram} \times 1 \text{ centimeter} \times 1 \text{ centimeter/sec}^2$$

Hence,

$$1 \text{ erg} = 1 \text{ g-cm}^2/\text{sec}^2$$

How do joules of work compare to ergs of work? Again, MKS units are expected to be much larger in magnitude than CGS units of measure. Take the definition of the erg:

$$1 \text{ erg} = 1 \text{ dyne} \times 1 \text{ centimeter}$$

We can directly compare the difference in magnitude of 1 erg of work with 1 joule. This can be accomplished by restating the value of 1 joule in terms of dynes and centimeters, using the rules outlined in Chapter 2 and the prefixes given in Table C1–1 of Appendix C.

Since

$$1 \text{ newton} = 10^5 \text{ dynes, and}$$
$$1 \text{ meter} = 10^2 \text{ centimeters}$$

it then follows that 1 joule can be restated in terms of CGS measurement units as

$$1 \text{ joule} = 10^5 \text{ dynes} \times 10^2 \text{ centimeters}$$

Therefore,

$$1 \text{ joule} = 10^5 \times 10^2 \text{ ergs}$$

Once again, the rules for obtaining the product of two exponential quantities with a common base states that the common base is raised to the sum of the separate exponential values. Once again, we can simply add the values of the exponents.

Therefore,

1 joule = $10^{(5+2)}$ ergs

1 joule = 10^7 ergs

1 joule = 10,000,000 ergs

10^{-7} joule = 1 erg

Hence, the MKS joule is the larger unit of work. The joule is 10^7 or 10,000,000 (ten million) times greater than the CGS erg of work.

Force and Area: Pressure

As indicated above, pressure forms the basis for decibel (dB) measurements that are made with reference to sound pressure level (SPL). Decibels measured in terms of SPL are a very important method of measuring the disturbance called "sound" in hearing science. Pressure may be defined as the amount of force per unit area, where force is understood to be acting perpendicular to the surface area. More simply stated, pressure is equal to force divided by area, as expressed by

$$\text{Pressure} = \text{force} \div \text{area} \qquad (4\text{–}8)$$

The MKS Metric Unit of Pressure

By definition, the standard unit of pressure in the MKS metric system is equal to 1 newton/meter² or

$$\text{Pressure} = \text{newton/meter}^2$$

In honor of the French scientist and mathematician, Blaise Pascal (Box 4–3 and Portrait 4–4), the MKS metric unit of pressure is also called the pascal, or

$$1 \text{ newton/meter}^2 = 1 \text{ pascal (Pa)}$$

Atmospheric pressure at sea level is also defined as

$$1.013 \times 10^5 \text{ newtons/meter}^2$$

or as 1.013×10^5 Pa

or   101.325 kPa

which is also defined as one atmosphere of pressure (Giancoli, 2005). In the British USCS (fps) system, one atmosphere of pressure is measured in pounds per square inch (psi) and is equivalent to 14.7 psi or

$$14.7 \text{ lb/inch}^2$$

In meteorology, there is also the unit of pressure defined as the bar (Giancoli, 2005), and by definition,

$$1 \text{ bar of pressure} = 10^5 \text{ newtons/meter}^2$$

or   1 bar = 10^5 Pa

or   1 bar = 10^6 dynes/centimeter²

and: 1 micro (10^{-6}) bar = 1 dyne/centimeter²

The CGS Metric Unit of Pressure

By definition, the standard unit of pressure in the CGS metric system is equal to 1 dyne ÷ centimeter² or

$$\text{pressure} = \text{dyne/centimeter}^2$$

Box 4–3. Blaise Pascal (1623–1662)

Blaise Pascal, a French religious philosopher, mathematician, and scientist, was born June 19, 1623, in Clermont-Ferrand. His father, Étienne Pascal, was a highly respected mathematician who devoutly took charge of Blaise's early education, which consisted mostly of ancient language studies. However, in spite of his father's attempts to keep Blaise away from the study of the sciences, Blaise taught himself geometry at the age of 12. In 1640, at the age of 16, Blaise Pascal published his book, *The Geometry of Conics*, which attracted the attention of the great mathematician, René Descartes. During the years between 1642 and 1644, Blaise Pascal conceived of and invented a calculating machine for his father. Pascal, however, is best known for his work in developing principles having to do with the pressure of liquids. Pascal's law or the first law of hydrostatics states that liquid contained in a vessel carries pressure equally in all directions (Stutz, 2006)—that is, when pressure is applied to the fluid in the confined space of a container, the fluid will pass the pressure equally to all parts of the container. Pascal's law is an important principle used in the design of hydraulic presses, hydraulic brakes, hydraulic elevators, hydraulic jacks and hydraulic lifts at service stations, vacuum pumps, and compressors. His experiments also led to his invention of the hypodermic syringe (Stutz, 2006).

Portrait 4–4. Blaise Pascal (1623–1662). Printed with permission. Wikimedia Commons, public domain.

MKS and CGS Units Compared: Pressure

Pressure, like force and work, is also derived from the three basic quantities of length, mass, and time. Therefore,

MKS

1 newton =	÷	meter² =	1 pascal
Mass Length Time²		Length²	

Hence,

$$1 \text{ Pa of pressure} = 1 \text{ newton/m}^2$$

or

$$1 \text{ Pa of pressure} =$$
$$(1 \text{ kilogram} \times 1 \text{ meter/second}^2)$$
$$\div \text{ meter}^2$$

In a similar way,

CGS

$$\begin{vmatrix} 1 \text{ dyne} = \\ \text{Mass} \\ \text{Length} \\ \text{Time}^2 \end{vmatrix} \begin{vmatrix} \div \end{vmatrix} \begin{vmatrix} \text{centimeter}^2 \\ = \text{Length}^2 \end{vmatrix}$$

and

$$\text{CGS pressure} = \\ (1 \text{ gram} \times 1 \text{ centimeter/second}^2) \\ \div \text{centimeter}^2$$

How does an MKS unit of pressure (pascal) compare to a CGS unit of pressure? Once again, MKS units are expected to be somewhat larger in magnitude than CGS units of measure. First, again consider Equation 4–8:

$$\text{Pressure} = \text{Force} \div \text{Area}$$

$$\text{MKS Pressure} = \text{newton} \div \text{meter}^2$$

$$\text{CGS Pressure} = \text{dyne} \div \text{centimeter}^2$$

and

$$1 \text{ newton of Force} = \\ 10^5 \text{ dynes of Force}$$

Second, since,

$$1 \text{ meter} = 10^2 \text{ centimeters}$$

Then,

$$1 \text{ meter}^2 = (10^2)^2 \text{ centimeters}$$

Using the rules for combining multiple exponents a and b with a common base (X), such that $(X^a)^b$, as outlined in Section A2 of Appendix A, the product of the two quantities is simply the common base raised to the product of the separate exponential values, or $X^{a \times b}$) Therefore,

$$1 \text{ meter}^2 = 10^{(2 \times 2)} \text{ centimeters}$$

and consequently,

$$1 \text{ meter}^2 = 10^4 \text{ centimeters}$$

Now, by restating the value of 1 newton in terms of an equivalent number of dynes, and restating meters^2 in terms of an equivalent number of centimeters using the rules outlined in Chapter 2 and the prefixes given in Table C1–1 of Appendix C, it may be logically surmised that the MKS unit of pressure

$$1 \text{ newton/meter}^2$$

is equal to

$$10^5 \text{ dynes}/10^4 \text{ (centimeter}^2)$$

Now we might ask just how many single CGS units of pressure (dyne/centimeter^2) are there in

$$10^5 \text{ dynes}/10^4 \text{ (centimeter}^2)$$

The rules for dividing two quantities, each consisting of a common base raised to a specified exponential value, as outlined in Section A2 of Appendix A, now becomes useful. The division of two quantities will simply be the (common) base raised to the difference of the separate exponential values found in the numerator and denominator, respectively. Accordingly,

$$10^5 \text{ dynes}/10^4 \text{ (centimeter}^2)$$

is equal to

$$10^{(5-4)} \text{ dynes/(centimeter}^2)$$

or simply

$$1 \text{ newton/meter}^2 = \\ 10 \text{ dynes/centimeter}^2$$

In conclusion, the MKS unit of pressure, the newton/meter^2 or pascal is 10 times greater than the CGS unit of pressure, known as the dyne/centimeter^2. Hence,

$$1 \text{ newton/meter}^2 \text{ (1 Pa)} = 10 \text{ dynes/centimeter}^2$$

The 10-fold difference between MKS and CGS metric units of pressure will be emphasized again in Chapter 6, when the reference pressure values employed in computations of decibels SPL are discussed.

Power

Energy has been defined as the ability or the capacity to do work, and work was defined as the transfer of energy from one object to another or the transformation of energy from one form to another. The definition of work, however, does not specify how quickly the work is performed. To determine how rapidly work is performed as a function of time, we again use the concept of "rate" that was introduced in Chapter 3. The rate at which work is achieved is called "power." Simple illustrations of power are provided in Box 4–4.

The unit of work in the MKS system was defined in the section above as the joule or the newton-meter. The unit of work in the CGS system was defined as the erg, or the dyne-centimeter. The concept of rate was introduced in Chapter 3. For any unit of measure x, a change in the rate of x may be specified as

$$x/\text{time(second)}$$

Recall from the previous sections that

$$1 \text{ joule of work} = 10^7 \text{ ergs of work}$$

Hence, power, the rate at which energy is transferred or transformed, or simply, the rate at which work is accomplished, may be defined as

$$\text{power} = \text{work/time} \qquad (4\text{–}9)$$

which translates to

MKS   joule/second or
             newton-meter/second

CGS 10^7 ergs/second or
             10^7 dyne-centimeters/second

In both the MKS and CGS systems, the unit for power is given a special name. The unit of power in both measurement systems is the watt.

Therefore,

    1 watt of power   =
    1 joule/second   =
    1 newton-meter/second

Also,

    1 watt of power   =
    10^7 ergs/second   =
    10^7 dyne-centimeters/second

Hence,

$$1 \text{ joule/second} = 10^7 \text{ ergs/second}$$

Making Sense of Power

The metric unit of power (the watt) was named in honor of the Scottish engineer, James Watt (1736–1819) (Portrait 4–5), who devised a way to specify

---

Box 4–4. Simple Illustrations of Power

Example A. Let us assume that a particular individual has the physical energy (i.e., strength) to carry a load of bricks up a flight of stairs. Depending upon their concern for how promptly the work is performed, they may choose either to walk or run up the flight of stairs. Regardless of whether they walk or run, the same amount of work will be accomplished in either case. The individual who chooses to walk may reach the top of the stairs before experiencing exhaustion. However, the individual who chooses to run may collapse from exhaustion well before reaching the top. In this example, the individual who decided to run was physically limited by the rate at which his or her body could transform chemical energy into mechanical energy. That is, the person was limited by the rate at which his or her body could perform work. The rate at which work is accomplished, is called *power*.

Example B. In the previous chapter, a machine was defined as a device that multiplies and/or changes the direction of forces. Machines also perform work. To keep an automobile moving, work must be performed by a machine to overcome the many forces of friction. Internal friction is produced by the motion of the numerous mechanical parts in an automobile, and external friction is caused by air resistance and the contact between tires and road surface. Machines such as automobile engines are limited by the rate at which they are able to do work. The rate at which work is accomplished is called power. The power rating (in horsepower) of an automobile engine refers to how much chemical (fossil fuel) energy can be transformed into mechanical energy per unit time. Actually, in the metric system, automobiles are rated in terms of kilowatts, and one horsepower is equivalent to 0.75 kilowatts (Hewitt, 2010). Automobiles having engines endowed with relatively more horsepower can deliver the same amount of work in less time compared to engines that are appraised with lower horsepower. In words, this means that a more powerful engine can accelerate the mass of an automobile at a much greater rate, relative to the less powerful engine. If you were to build an automobile to be used for competition, you would never consider equipping it with an underpowered engine.

---

the power of his newly developed and much improved steam engines.

We are probably most familiar with the use of the term *watt* as an indication of the rate at which a lightbulb filament changes electrical energy into light. The higher the specified watt-rating on a lightbulb, the higher will be the rate of

Portrait 4–5. James Watt (1736–1819). Printed with permission. Wikimedia Commons, public domain.

energy transformation per unit of time. Hence, a higher rate of energy transformation produces more light per second, resulting in a brighter illuminated bulb.

Recall from Chapter 2 that the poorly conceived British USCS or foot-pound-second (fps) measurement system employs the foot as the standard unit for length and the second as the standard unit for time. Recall that there is no measurement unit for mass in the fps system. The pound is used however, as the standard unit for force in the fps system. Since it is true, as expressed by Equation 4–7:

$$Work = force \times distance$$

It then follows that the unit of work in the fps may be defined as:

$$Work = pound \times foot$$

And therefore, given Equation 4–9:

$$Power = work/time$$

It also follows that the unit of power in the fps system may be defined as:

$$Power = foot\text{-}pound/second$$

Or simply, the ft-lb

James Watt determined experimentally that a healthy horse can work all day at an average rate of 360 ft-lb/sec. To provide a conservative estimate of the actual power of his steam engines (Giancoli, 2005), Watt multiplied this value by 1.5, which defined one horsepower as:

$$1 \text{ horsepower} = 550 \text{ ft-lb/second}$$

or

$$1 \text{ horsepower} = 746 \text{ watts of power}$$

$$1 \text{ horsepower} = 0.746 \text{ kilowatts of power}$$

Work and Energy Revisited: Types of Energy

Energy has been defined on several occasions as the ability or the capacity to do work. In a like manner and by definition, work is accomplished when energy is transformed from one form to another, or transferred from one object to another by means of a force (Halliday et al., 2011). Therefore, work is accomplished when force produces a change in motion or a change in the energy state of an object that is acted upon. In addition, units of work and units of energy are both defined by the joule. Sound represents waveforms created from the vibratory motion produced by the application of force to an object and/or medium. Because all waveforms transfer energy from one location to another, the production of sound and the subsequent waveforms that result, involves work. Hence, sound production represents both a transference and a transformation of energy, and therefore, the production of sound also involves work.

Some forms of energy were discussed in Chapter 3. These included thermal, chemical, electrical, solar energy, and light. Finally, there is sound and sound involves mechanical energy. Therefore, mechanical energy is of immediate interest to hearing science. For the present discussion, mechanical energy may take one of two forms, and these two forms are (a) mechanical potential energy and (b) mechanical kinetic energy, or some combination of both.

Potential Energy

Potential energy may be defined as energy that is stored for the purpose of work. Potential energy may also be defined in somewhat formal terms as energy that is associated with the arrangement of a system of objects (Giancoli, 2005). As such, potential energy belongs to a system of objects, and not to a single object alone. Hence, each object in a system will exert forces on the other objects within the same system (Halliday et al., 2011). Consequently, an object or mass may begin to store energy because of its relative position to some other object, objects, or substance (Hewitt, 2010). Some of

the most obvious examples of potential energy are given by the stored chemical energy found in fossil fuels and in electric batteries. The stored energy found within fossil fuel and batteries has the potential to do work and will deliver the work when and if the energy is liberated. Food is also a source of chemical potential energy. That is, the potential energy captured by the plants that constitute food is consumed by humans and other animals and becomes available through digestion (Hewitt, 2010). Other numerous examples of potential energy exist. For instance, mechanical elastic potential energy can be demonstrated in a bent bow, a stretched rubber band, a wound-up clock spring, and a pole vaulter's bent pole, just to name a few. In general, any object that exhibits a restorative force of elasticity, as introduced in Chapter 3, serves as a good example of a substance exhibiting mechanical potential energy.

Work and Potential Energy

Work, defined as the transfer of energy from one object to another, must be accomplished in order to load a mass with potential energy. The potential energy will remain stored within the mass until it is liberated, or transformed into another energy form. Until such time that the stored energy is liberated, we would conclude that the stored energy has only the potential to do work. The eventual transformation of potential energy into another energy form can occur slowly, rapidly, or may be postponed for some time. Once the transformation process begins, however, potential energy is changed for the purpose of work, with work being defined as the transformation of energy from one form to another. Work is once again accomplished as potential energy is slowly (or rapidly) transformed to another energy form.

It will be made clear in the sections that follow that potential energy that has been transformed is no longer referred to as potential energy. In addition, even though potential energy is always associated with a force, not all forces have potential energy (Halliday et al., 2011). As indicated above, potential energy can only be defined for conservative forces, especially in terms of mechanical systems that are known to be associated with simple harmonic motion. As introduced in Chapter 3, elasticity, like gravity, is an active conservative force that opposes displacement (Halliday et al., 2011). Frictional (drag) force, however, has no potential energy. Because frictional force is associated with motion only, it cannot be associated with potential energy. Because friction is a nonconservative force, mechanical energy is not conserved when frictional drag is present. More will be made clear regarding the conservation of mechanical energy in the sections that follow.

In Chapter 3, a basic mechanical device called a spring-mass system (Slinky) was discussed. A force applied initially to the spring-mass may produce a distortion in the shape of the spring. As indicated in the previous chapter, the distortion in the shape of any elastic object resulting from the application of an external force represents a type of displacement. The extent to which more or less force is required to deform an elastic substance (medium) or object is actually a measure of the elasticity inherent within the object or medium. When we consider the elasticity of any

object or medium, we must also consider the object's inherent stiffness and/or compliance.

Stiffness and Compliance

Recall from Chapter 3 that elasticity is the general property of matter that allows objects to temporarily change their shape or size, rather than fracture when a force is applied. Two aspects of elasticity are stiffness and compliance, such that

$$\text{stiffness} \sim 1/\text{compliance}$$

$$\text{compliance} \sim 1/\text{stiffness}$$

Stiffness and compliance are, therefore, reciprocals. Stiffness is inversely proportional to compliance, and vice versa. For an elastic substance, stiffness may be likened to a restorative force. Stiffness can be defined as a measure of the opposition to displacement, or distortion, per unit of force. Compliance has been defined as an indication of the amount of displacement, or distortion, per unit of force (Durrant & Feth, 2013). Therefore, MKS units of compliance may be described in terms of meters per newton, and CGS units of compliance may be described in centimeters per dyne. Now suppose that instead of a Slinky, a force is applied with the intent to distort a spring-mass system having a considerably greater amount of mass and stiffness, and very little compliance. As an example, one could easily imagine attempting to distort the shape of a coil spring. Stiff, massive coil springs are used in the suspensions of automobiles. It should be intuitively obvious that the coil spring would require a greater amount of force placed upon it in order to distort, relative to the Slinky. This is because the relatively greater stiffness of the coil spring would produce a large restorative force that would oppose displacement (Chapter 3), and its relatively greater mass would produce a large degree of inertia that would need to be overcome before it could be displaced.

As the more massive, stiff, and less compliant coil spring is progressively deformed past its resting shape, an increasingly greater amount of force would be required to continue to stretch or compress the coil spring to a value that more closely approximates its elastic limit. The greater the external force that is applied, the greater will be the distortion in the shape of the coil spring, up to the elastic limits of the spring. The more energy that is successively utilized, the more energy is gradually stored within the coil spring, and of course, the more work is progressively done in the process. The energy that is put to use to compress or stretch the spring-mass in this example would also closely approximate a restorative force that increasingly builds in opposition to the ever-increasing displacement of the spring-mass. Hence, in this instance, the greater amount of force required to distort the coil spring will be reflected in the greater amount of (potential) energy that is stored in the coil spring.

The restorative force of elasticity that was introduced in Chapter 3 is stored potential energy that assumes a relative value that would be expected from Hooke's law, that was also introduced in Chapter 3. The amount of stored potential energy is relative to the amount of external force that is put to use in order to distort the shape of the elastic object.

Hence, elasticity may be conceptualized as a property of matter that allows either a substance or an object (mass) to alter its shape and to store potential energy when an external force is applied. The potential energy is stored in the form of a restorative force that has the capacity to do work. If the restorative force of elasticity is great, then the greater will be the amount of work that can be accomplished once the elastic potential energy is discharged for purposes of work.

Computation of Potential Energy

Potential energy can be defined and computed for elastic substances. The definitional formula for elastic potential energy takes a somewhat different form than the equation that defines gravitational potential energy, as will be evident in the sections that follow. In order to stretch or compress a spring-mass by a given amount or distance x from its undistorted shape, a force (Fp) will be required that is directly proportional to x. If Fp is the force required to stretch or compress (or otherwise displace) a spring-mass to a distance x, and the spring constant or stiffness of the spring-mass is represented by k, then:

$$Fp = kx \qquad (4–10)$$

This equation would accurately define the potential energy in an elastic system at an instantaneous moment in time. It would also define the instantaneous potential energy in a spring-mass system stretched or compressed to a given distance x from its normal or resting shape (Giancoli, 2005). However, an average Fp would be needed to accurately compute the overall amount of elastic potential energy for a spring-mass that is progressively stretched from its resting state to a distance close to some arbitrary elastic limit. This is because the opposition to its displacement would continue to increase as the spring-mass approaches the elastic limit x. This means that the force required to displace a spring-mass from zero to kx when stretched (or compressed) to its maximum x is not a constant value and is expected to vary over the distance to x (Giancoli, 2005). If *Fav* is the average force required to stretch or compress a spring-mass over a distance, up to x, then the average force may be defined by

$$Fav = \frac{1}{2}\ kx$$

Because Equation 4–7 stated that

$$Work = force \times distance$$

It then follows that work is equal to

$$Force\ (\tfrac{1}{2}\ kx) \times distance\ (x)$$

Or simply,

$$Work = (\tfrac{1}{2}\ kx)(x)$$

$$(\tfrac{1}{2}\ kx)(x) = \tfrac{1}{2}\ kx^2$$

Therefore,

$$Work = \tfrac{1}{2}\ kx^2$$

It is of interest to recall that the MKS unit of work was defined as the joule. The MKS unit of potential energy, and every other type of energy, is also the joule (Halliday et al., 2011). Given that (potential) energy was defined as the ability or capacity to do work, it then follows that

$$Work = elastic\ potential\ energy \tag{4–11}$$

Or simply,

$$Elastic\ potential\ energy = \tfrac{1}{2}\ kx^2$$

The equation above states that elastic potential energy is proportional to the square of the amount of stretch or the square of the distance that the elastic mass is displaced (Giancoli, 2005).

Weight was defined as a force placed upon an object due to a dependence on gravity. When a mass is physically lifted above the ground, the potential energy stored within the mass will depend on the weight of the object and on the height that the object is elevated. In order to lift an object from the ground, force must be applied, energy must be utilized, and work must be done. The energy that is put to use to raise an object mass from the ground will be stored within the object as a restorative force. The restorative force that is supplied by weight and gravity is called gravitational potential energy, which is also stored potential energy (Halliday et al., 2011). By definition, gravitational potential energy is equal to the product of the weight and the vertical displacement of an object from the ground (height), or simply,

$$Gravitational\ potential\ energy = weight \times height \tag{4–12}$$

The energy that is put to use and the work that is required to vertically elevate a mass against gravity will be equivalent to a restorative force. Hence, gravitational potential energy may be conceived of as a restorative force that allows a substance or object mass to store potential energy. The potential energy provided by the restorative force of weight and gravity also has the capacity to do work. The amount of potential energy is equal to the work that must be accomplished against gravity in order to lift an object (Hewitt, 2010). It should be obvious from Equation 4–12 that lifting an object to a relatively higher elevation prior to its release also results in more energy that is stored. That is, the greater the vertical displacement of an object from the ground, the greater will be the gravitational potential energy within the object. This is because more energy would be utilized in lifting a mass to a relatively higher elevation, and therefore, more work would also be done in the process. The higher the object is lifted, the greater is the restorative force of gravity that increasingly builds in opposition to the ever-increasing vertical displacement of the mass. As a result, more work would/could be performed when the object is eventually released and the gravitational potential energy is transferred or transformed. Once again consider Equation 4–12:

$$\text{Gravitational potential energy} = \text{weight} \times \text{height}$$

And since work was defined by Equation 4–7 as

$$\text{Work} = \text{force} \times \text{distance}$$

it then follows that

$$\text{Gravitational potential energy} = \text{work}$$

It should be evident that the above equation is valid because weight is a force and height is equivalent to distance. Given the equation presented above, it would seem that (potential) energy really is, by definition, the ability or capacity to do work. The relationship between gravitational potential energy and work is further illustrated by the example provided in Box 4–5. Finally, as in the case of work, potential energy is generally specified by its magnitude only.

Active and Reactive (Interactive) Forces Associated With Potential Energy

Generally speaking, potential energy is always associated with a force, and force represents an interaction between different objects. A force on one object or substance is always exerted by some other object or objects, and it is impossible for an object to exert a force on nothing (Hewitt, 2010). As indicated previously, the restorative forces provided by weight, gravity, and elasticity represent potential energy. Potential energy represents a restorative force, and restorative forces in general oppose displacement, as initially introduced in Chapter 3. Recall from Chapter 3 that energy put to use to compress or stretch a spring-mass generates a restorative force that increasingly builds in opposition to the ever-increasing displacement of the spring-mass. For example, a force (Fp) that will be used to stretch or compress a spring-mass a given amount or distance x from its undistorted shape will need to be directly proportional to x. A force (Fp) applied to stretch or compress (or otherwise displace) a spring-mass to a distance x, where the spring constant or stiffness is also represented by k, could again be given by Equation 4–10:

$$Fp = kx$$

Box 4–5. Gravitational Potential Energy and Work

Suppose a large wooden stake needs to be driven vertically into the ground. The method chosen to perform this task might be to use the weight of an anvil attached to a pulley system, as a type of "pile driver." Prior to guiding and dropping the anvil onto the wooden stake, the anvil must be vertically elevated above the wooden stake. An anvil that is pulled to a higher vertical elevation in this manner would have relatively more potential energy to perform the task, compared to the same anvil pulled to a lower elevation. Why is this? Because the force that is required to pull the anvil to a higher elevation would be distributed across a greater distance. Therefore, the higher the anvil is elevated, the more work that is done, because Equation 4–7 states that

$$\text{work} = \text{force} \times \text{distance}$$

By the same reasoning, pulling the anvil to a relatively higher elevation prior to its release will result in (a) more gravitational potential energy, because by Equation 4–12:

$$\text{gravitational potential energy} = \text{weight} \times \text{height}$$

and (b) a greater potential to accomplish more work, because it is also true that

$$\text{gravitational potential energy} = \text{work}$$

Raising the anvil to a relatively higher elevation prior to its release would be a more effective strategy if one were to use the anvil to drive the wooden stake into the ground in this manner.

Recall from the above discussion that the equation shown above also defines stored potential energy in the spring-mass at any instant in time (Giancoli, 2005). The spring-mass itself exerts a force that is equal but in the opposite direction to the force (Fp) that has been applied. This opposing force is another name for the restorative force of elasticity or Fs. Hence, the restorative force may be defined by

$$Fs = -kx \qquad (4\text{–}13)$$

where the negative sign before the kx indicates that the restorative force is equal but opposite in direction to the original displacement force (Giancoli, 2005). With respect to gravitational potential energy, the higher an object is lifted, the greater is the restorative force of gravity that increasingly builds in opposition to the ever-increasing vertical displacement of the mass. In both of these instances, it is useful to think of the restorative force of elasticity and gravitational potential energy as examples of reactive or interactive forces (Halliday et al., 2011). It also happens that Newton's third law of motion relates well to interactive forces. To better understand the concept of potential energy, it is often useful to consider Newton's third law of motion, which is presented in Box 4–6. It is generally observed that when a force is actively applied to a mass, the mass always pushes or pulls back with a reactive force. For example, a force applied by an object or mass pushes or pulls on a spring-mass system (action), and the spring-mass system pushes or pulls on the object that applies the action force (reaction). A force applied by an object mass pushes or pulls on a pendulum bob (action), and the pendulum bob pushes or pulls on the object mass that applies the action force (reaction).

As indicated in Box 4–6, Newton's third law of motion states that whenever an object exerts a force on another object, the second object exerts an equal but opposite force on the first (Giancoli, 2005). The action and reaction pair of forces constitutes one interaction between two things (Hewitt, 2010). Simple examples of Newton's third law can be shown to exist in everyday situations (Giancoli, 2005; Hewitt, 2010). A hammer exerts a force on a nail, and the nail exerts an equal but opposite force on the hammer. Why is it then that the nail and not the hammer are both propelled forward? Newton's second law of motion indicates that an object's mass must also be considered in such a question. A hammer usually has much more mass than a nail, and Equation 4–1 states that

$$\text{Acceleration} = \text{force} \div \text{mass}$$

Hence, the acceleration of the nail is much larger than that of the hammer, owing to the much lower mass of the nail. As another example, a moving rocket exerts a strong force on the thrust gas produced by the rocket's engine, and the thrust gas exerts an equal but opposite force on the rocket, which propels the rocket. As a final example, walking along the ground requires exerting a horizontal force on the ground, as each foot pushes backward against the ground. The ground, in turn, exerts a horizontal and forward force on each foot, and we are propelled forward.

Box 4–6. Newton's Third Law of Motion

According to Newton's third law of motion, when two bodies interact, the force that is imposed on each body from the other of the two bodies is always equal in magnitude and opposite in direction (Halliday et al., 2011). Restated, for every action (active force) there is an opposite but equal reaction (reactive force). A reactive force as described by Newton is equal but in the opposite direction to an action force, and action and reaction forces always act on different bodies (Giancoli, 2005).

Recall the formula for Hooke's law ($Fs \sim kd$) presented in Chapter 3. In words, the magnitude of the restoring force (a force that opposes displacement, or Fs is directly proportional to the magnitude of the displacement of an elastic mass from a point of equilibrium d. The spring (or force) constant is once again represented by k. In essence, an active force (a push or pull) is applied to a spring-mass, and the spring-mass in turn pushes or pulls back with a reactive force that is equal, but in the opposite direction. A closer examination of Hooke's law reveals that it may actually represent a restatement of Newton's third law of motion. Finally, Newton's third law of motion, as well as Hooke's law are each consistent with the concept of simple harmonic motion. As indicated in Chapter 3, simple harmonic motion will occur provided that a restoring force is proportional to the amount of displacement from equilibrium. This condition is met, at least approximately, for most vibrations.

Making Use of Potential Energy

Potential energy is often associated with objects at rest. However, a more accurate appraisal is that potential energy is maximum only when an object is at rest. Hence, at any instant in time, potential energy will exist in relative amounts, from zero when velocity is maximum, to some maximum value at rest. This means that potential energy will exist in some measure, even in objects that are in motion, as long as the object's velocity is below the maximum. However, potential energy has significance only when it changes. That is, it has importance only when it is transferred or transformed to another

energy form, and work is performed (Hewitt, 2010). One of the kinds of energy into which potential energy is very often changed is kinetic energy, or the energy of motion.

Kinetic Energy

Suppose we apply a force to distort (by compressing or extending) an object that has an obvious degree of elasticity (like a spring-mass). Recall that the amount of an object's mass determines the extent to which an object resists forces that might cause a change in its existing motion (or in this case, an existing shape). Hence, depending on the mass and stiffness of any object, there will be more or less inertia to overcome and more or less energy expenditure to set any object into motion. Consequently, in order to temporarily alter the shape of the spring-mass, inertia must be overcome. When in fact the spring-mass becomes distorted, we can declare that energy was utilized, inertia was overcome, and work was done to temporarily distort the shape of the object. Similarly, if we apply a force against gravity to elevate a mass, energy is utilized, inertia associated with the object's mass must be overcome, and work will be done in order to elevate the object. In either example, where did the energy from the applied force go? As indicated in the preceding sections, the energy was stored in the object itself as elastic or gravitational potential energy.

Let us now continue with the same example. Suppose we were to remove the applied force against the restorative forces of elasticity and gravity. What if we were to release the compressed or expanded spring-mass and/or drop the object that had been elevated above the ground against gravity? What do we expect to occur if we were to do this? The answer is that we would probably expect part of the spring-mass and/or the whole elevated object to begin moving. We further anticipate that the part of the spring-mass that was displaced will move in a direction opposite to the direction that it was distorted. We also predict that the elevated object would move (drop) toward the earth, in a direction opposite to the direction it was lifted. However, in either case, this is not what would occur immediately. For a brief and infinitesimal moment in time, neither object would move. How can this be? Because the elastic and gravitational potential energy must first overcome the inertia that is inherent within each object before either object can move. Once again, depending on the mass and stiffness of each object, there will be more or less inertia to overcome with more or less energy expenditure required to set each object into motion. In order for the spring-mass and/or the elevated object to begin moving, the stored elastic and/or gravitational potential energy must begin a transformation to kinetic energy. How can we determine the approximate moment the transformation begins? The answer is, by direct observation. The transformation, which is gradual, begins when either object begins to move. Both the spring-mass and the elevated object will begin moving. Motion will be slow at first and will gradually increase in velocity over time. The gradual increase in velocity at any instant in time provides a relative index of the potential energy that has been converted to the energy of motion.

From the Greek word *kinetikos*, which means "motion" (Giancoli, 2005), kinetic energy is, by definition, the energy of motion. Kinetic energy is zero when an object is at rest. It can range from zero, as in a nonmoving object, up to a maximum value for an object in motion with a constant and maximum velocity. Hence, kinetic energy will be present in some measure as long as an object is in motion. When it is present, kinetic energy always takes on a non-negative value (Hewitt, 2010). A single universal formula may be used to define kinetic energy (Giancoli, 2005). For any object with mass whose speed or velocity is less than the speed of light, the equation states that kinetic energy is directly proportional to the product of half the object's mass and the square of the speed (or velocity) of the object, or simply

$$\text{Kinetic energy} = \tfrac{1}{2}\text{ mass} \times \text{velocity}^2$$
$$\text{or}$$
$$\text{Kinetic energy} = \tfrac{1}{2}\text{ mass} \times \text{speed}^2$$
$$(4\text{--}14)$$

Equation 4–14 states that when speed or velocity is doubled, both kinetic energy and the work that is accomplished will increase by a factor of 4 (Giancoli, 2005). A close examination of Equation 4–14 also indicates that if mass is doubled, kinetic energy is also doubled. This is an important point. Mass has also been defined as a measure of the inertia that is found within an object. The greater the object's mass, the greater is the object's inertia. Just as elasticity (i.e., stiffness and/or compliance) was defined as a property of matter that allows a substance or object (mass) to store potential energy, inertia may also be redefined as a property that enables an object to have kinetic energy. Consequently, the capacity for kinetic energy is directly dependent upon the mass of an object. It could also be stated that kinetic energy is "stored" in the motion of an object, due to its mass. Hence, both the potential and kinetic energy exhibited by any object are intimately dependent upon the inherent amounts of stiffness and mass, respectively, found within the object. From the above discussion it should be clear that potential and kinetic energy are not only interactive forces, they greatly determine the manner in which objects move. More important to hearing science, potential and kinetic energy determine the manner in which objects vibrate. Specifically, they influence the rate at which objects vibrate. In the chapters that follow, it will become clear that stiffness and mass, the same properties that control potential and kinetic energy, are the major determinants of the frequencies at which objects vibrate most efficiently, or best.

Work and Kinetic Energy

The net amount of work done on an object is equal to and is defined by the change in its kinetic energy (Giancoli, 2005). If an object's kinetic energy and speed (or velocity) remain constant, then the net amount of work done on the moving object is zero (Giancoli, 2005). This definition also signifies that if the net force exerted on a mass results in a change in its kinetic energy, then the change in kinetic energy is also equal to the net amount of work (Hewitt, 2010). Work may be defined once more as a change (delta) in kinetic energy (KE) or

$$\text{Work} = \Delta\text{KE} \qquad (4\text{--}15)$$

As in the case of work, kinetic energy is defined in terms of its magnitude only and therefore, kinetic energy is a scalar quantity.

Energy Conservation Revisited

According to the law of the conservation of energy previously discussed, the total energy, or the sum of all of the energies, in a system can be transformed and transferred (the definition of work), but the total amount of energy is never increased or decreased by any process (Giancoli, 2005). When a physical quantity remains unchanged during some process, that quantity is said to be conserved (Hewitt, 2010). At any given moment in time, the total energy (TE) in a system is equal to the sum of the potential energy (PE) and kinetic energy (KE) or

$$\text{TE} = \text{PE} + \text{KE} \qquad (4\text{--}16)$$

In previous sections of this text gravitational and elastic forces have both been referred to as conservative restorative forces (Halliday et al., 2011). Nonconservative friction and fictional drag force, by definition, transfers energy away from the motion of objects. Furthermore, energy was defined as the ability or the capacity to do work, and friction was defined as a force that opposes work. A closer examination of mechanical systems that produce harmonic motion and sound are greatly simplified when only conservative forces are taken into account, and nonconservative frictional drag is disregarded. What follows is a simple illustration of energy conservation minus friction or frictional drag forces. The force of gravity provides a simplistic opportunity to illustrate potential energy conservation in the absence of nonconservative frictional drag. The simplest way to visualize gravitational potential energy conservation is to use a falling object and real numbers expressed in joules of energy (Hewitt, 2010), as illustrated in Figure 4–2. This figure illustrates the actions of a circus pole diver prior to and after the diver has leaped from the top of a pole into a water bucket below. At the location marked with an *A* in the figure, the *TE* is equal to *PE*, since the diver has not yet jumped. At this location, motion is zero and *KE* is also equal to zero. At the locations shown that range from B to

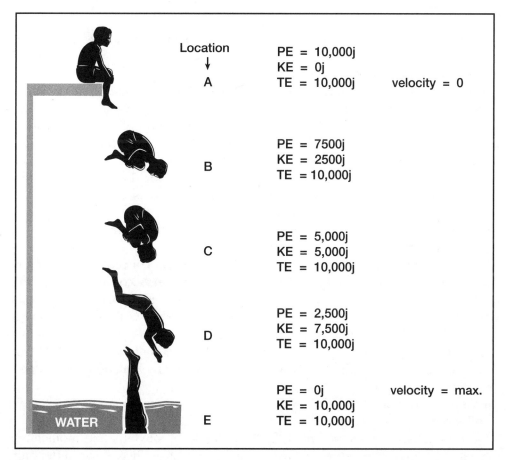

Figure 4–2. Conservation of potential energy. Free fall of a circus pole diver. At the top of the pole marked with an "A," the diver has a gravitational potential energy (*PE*) of 10,000 joules (*j*). The value 10,000j represents maximum *PE* and is also equivalent to the total energy (*TE*). This is because the diver is not moving at location "A," and kinetic energy (*KE*), which is the energy of motion, is zero. Also, recall that *TE* = *PE* + *KE*. At the locations *B* through *E*, the diver is in motion. At location B, the diver has fallen one fourth the distance to the water bucket below. Hence, one fourth of the *PE* (*TE*) has been transformed into *KE*. Note, however, at location "B" that the *TE* (*PE* + *KE*) remains constant. At location "C," half the *PE*, and at location "D," three fourths of the *PE* has been transformed to *KE*, yet *TE* remains constant at either location. Finally, at location "E," moments before the diver's motion is halted by the water contained in the bucket, all the *PE* has been transformed to *KE*, such that *KE* is maximum and is equivalent to the *TE*. The diver is also moving at a maximum velocity at location "E." Therefore, *PE* was conserved because it was transferred completely to *KE* as the diver fell toward the ground.

E, the diver is in motion. Note that at each successive location from locations B to E, there is no net loss or net gain in *TE*, and all that is changing are the relative values of *PE* and *KE*. At location E, the stored potential energy has been completely transformed, and all of the energy is kinetic, and therefore *KE* is also the *TE*. The diver at or near location E is also traveling at a maximum velocity. The illustration in Figure 4–2 indicates that potential energy is conserved because it is transformed totally into kinetic energy as the diver reaches the ground. Upon reaching the water, the *KE* of the pole diver (the *TE*) is transferred into the water.

The example of the pole diver is useful in illustrating a simple case of potential energy conservation. However, it does little to explain the energy conservation that gives rise to harmonic motion. Kinetic energy is also conserved and is quite often transformed into potential energy. For example, a hydraulic or wind-driven system that utilizes the kinetic energy of water or air, respectively, might be used to generate electrical energy that is stored as potential energy for later use. A hand-operated generator might also provide an example of kinetic energy conservation when it is used to produce and store electrical energy. However, the best illustration of potential and kinetic energy conservation occurring within the same system is still given by example in the simple pendulum and spring-mass systems.

Momentum

Before returning to a discussion of the pendulum and the spring-mass system,

another quantity that is conserved, according to the energy principle, is linear momentum. Momentum means inertia in motion (Hewitt, 2010). An object that is set into motion not only has kinetic energy, it also has the force of momentum. However, unlike the definition that was given for force, momentum is defined as the product of mass and velocity or by

$$\text{Momentum} = \text{mass} \times \text{velocity}$$
(4–17)

Momentum is usually specified both by its quantity and by its directionality, and the direction of the momentum is identical to the direction of the velocity. However, if directionality is not an important factor, then momentum may also be defined as

$$\text{Momentum} = \text{mass} \times \text{speed}$$

How does the concept of momentum relate to force? According to Newton's second law of motion, the net external force on a body is equal to the product of the body's mass and the body's acceleration (Halliday et al., 2011), or as expressed by Equation 4–4,

$$\text{Force} = \text{mass} \times \text{acceleration}$$

It should be obvious that momentum and force, as defined above, differ only in the use of the term velocity in the former and acceleration in the latter definition. Acceleration was defined in the previous chapter as a derived quantity equal to the rate of change in velocity. Velocity was defined as a derived quantity equal to the rate of change in displacement. Even though force and momentum are similar, they are in fact not the same. Momentum is defined primarily as the force of inertia and the kinetic energy in an object that has been set into motion by an external force. An MKS unit of momentum may be defined as

$$Momentum = kilogram\text{-}meter/second$$

$$Momentum = \\ (mass \times displacement/time)$$

And, of course,

$$Displacement/time = velocity$$

Predictably, momentum is relatively great in moving objects characterized by a relatively greater mass. Momentum is also greater in moving objects traveling at relatively higher velocities.

Changes in momentum occur when there are changes in mass. Momentum can also be changed following rate changes in velocity, or when there are changes in both mass and velocity. If mass remains constant, and rate changes in velocity occur, then by definition, acceleration occurs. Acceleration, however, is produced by a force. A force, defined as an external pushing or pulling acting on an object or system, may be used to alter the momentum of an object. Recall that the MKS unit of force, the newton, was defined as

$$1 \; newton = kilogram\text{-}meter/second^2$$

$$1 \; newton = \\ (mass \times displacement/time^2)$$

And, of course,

$$Displacement/time^2 = acceleration$$

Force can also be defined once again as a change in the rate of momentum, or

$$1 \; newton = momentum/time$$

The greater the net external force placed on an object, the greater will be the change in velocity, and hence, the greater is the change in momentum (Hewitt, 2010). Changes in momentum also depend on the duration of time over which a net external force is applied. A change (delta) in momentum may be defined as the product of force and time, or by

$$\Delta \; Momentum = force \times time \quad (4\text{--}18)$$

Momentum is maximal when kinetic energy is also at a maximum. Momentum is also maximal when velocity is maximum and unchanging. However, when the velocity of a moving object is constant, the object has zero acceleration. Therefore, since (Equation 4–4)

$$Force = mass \times acceleration$$

if velocity is constant, then

$$Force = mass \times zero$$

and hence,

$$Force = zero$$

The net force, by definition, is then equal to zero when velocity is maximum and constant. Also, when the net external force acting upon an object is in fact zero, the mass is in mechanical equilibrium by definition.

Collisions

Momentum and kinetic energy are transferred from one (elastic) mass to another when collisions occur in a system that contains particles having a similar elastic mass. These *elastic collisions* often occur with little or no loss (transfer) of energy away from the system (Hewitt, 2010). Elastic collisions involve objects that can recoil or bounce back without becoming permanently distorted, and they occur in the absence of heat generation. For instance, a sound wave represents an orderly change in the parts of a medium over space and time, resulting from the vibratory motion of an object (Durrant & Feth, 2013). When a disturbance such as sound is propagated in an elastic medium such as air or water, both momentum and kinetic energy are conserved. In order to illustrate the conservation of momentum, the collisions of a series of circular elastic masses are presented in Figure 4–3. As shown, the net momentum of a series of colliding objects of equal mass is unchanged before, during, and after the collisions (Hewitt, 2010).

The simple illustration of an elastic collision where kinetic energy and momentum are both conserved, as depicted in Figure 4–3, may also be illustrated by a common example. An example of energy conservation in elastic collisions is illustrated in the game of pool. The billiard balls used in this game each have an equal mass. In the game of billiards, a cue stick is used. With the cue stick, a force can be applied to the white unnumbered cue ball which is directed toward and strikes (collides with) any of several numbered stationary billiard balls. If the collision with one of the stationary billiard balls is

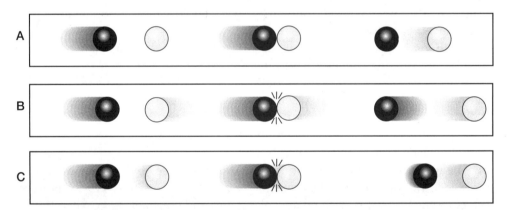

Figure 4–3. The conservation of momentum. Three examples of elastic collisions that might occur in elastic balls having an equal mass. In all three cases, momentum and kinetic energy are transferred from one ball to the other, and are, therefore, conserved. In Frame **A** the ball on the left (the darker ball) that is in motion, strikes the ball on the right (the lighter ball) that is at rest. During the collision, the darker ball transfers all of its kinetic energy to the lighter ball and then stops in its tracks. The lighter ball moves away in the same direction and with the same velocity as the darker ball on the left, prior to the collision. Frame **B** illustrates a head-on collision between two balls, one dark and one light. Both balls are in motion and are traveling at the same velocity. During the collision, each ball transfers its kinetic energy to the other. After the collision, each ball travels in the opposite direction from the collision, and with the same velocity. In Frame **C**, both balls (one dark and one light) are in motion and traveling in the same direction but moving at different velocities. Before the collision, the dark ball is traveling at a greater velocity than the lighter ball. During the collision, each ball transfers its kinetic energy to the other. After the collision, the darker ball moves in the same direction but with the same velocity as the lighter ball prior to the collision. The lighter ball moves in the same direction but with the same velocity as the darker ball prior to the collision.

direct and head-on, the momentum and kinetic energy of the cue ball can be transferred almost entirely to the numbered stationary ball. Of course, a very small amount of the energy is transferred away from the system (lost) in the form of an audible sound (Halliday et al., 2011). Nevertheless, with a direct collision, the cue ball stops dead in its tracks while the numbered billiard ball moves away in the same direction and with the same velocity as the cue ball prior to the collision (Giancoli, 2005; Hewitt, 2010).

The conservation of momentum and energy also applies to objects and media that are set into vibration. Recall that a force applied to an object does not always result in the elastic mass traveling off into oblivion, as shown in Figure 4–3. If the mass is anchored to a fixed reference point, the energy of motion following a collision will take the form of a vibration. When vibrations are created, they produce waveforms. As indicated in Chapter 3, all waveforms, independent of their origin, transfer energy from one location to another. The production of the kinds of waveforms required to produce sound involves the persistent and reversible transformation of energy from one form to another in order to maintain particle motion. However, inasmuch as waves can travel over large distances, the particles found within any transmitting medium (e.g., water or air) have only a limited amount of motion. The waves themselves are not particle matter. Instead, they represent oscillations that travel within matter, without carrying matter with them (Giancoli, 2005). The waveform carries energy through the medium and away from the source of the disturbance. Figure 4–4 illustrates

a series of longitudinally placed elastic particle collisions and the creation of waves as they might occur in the propagation of sound through an elastic medium, such as air or water. Note the development of successive areas of concentrated particle density followed by areas where particles appear to be widely dispersed, as the initial force (vibration) causes the consecutive displacement of the particles labeled *a* through *k*. It should be noted that each particle is displaced initially to the right. It then returns to equilibrium and is then displaced to the left. Cycles of motion for each particle are repeated over time in the same manner that has been described for the pendulum. In response to a vibratory force, each particle moves repeatedly around its point of equilibrium. Recall from Chapter 3 that successive areas that possess relatively higher particle density or concentration are called areas of compression. Successive regions where particle density is relatively lower are called areas of rarefaction.

The conservative restorative force of gravity for a pendulum was defined in Chapter 3 as a force that opposes displacement and was illustrated in Figure 3–9. We may now refer to this restorative force as gravitational potential energy. Potential energy represents a restorative force, and restorative forces in general oppose displacement. Note that Figure 4–5 is a modification of Figure 3–9 from the previous chapter, illustrating some of the principles that exist in a pendulum at rest. Figure 4–5 also illustrates some events that would take place while the pendulum is being loaded with energy by an external force, and its condition just before it begins to oscillate independently. As shown in particle name : a b c d e f g h i j k

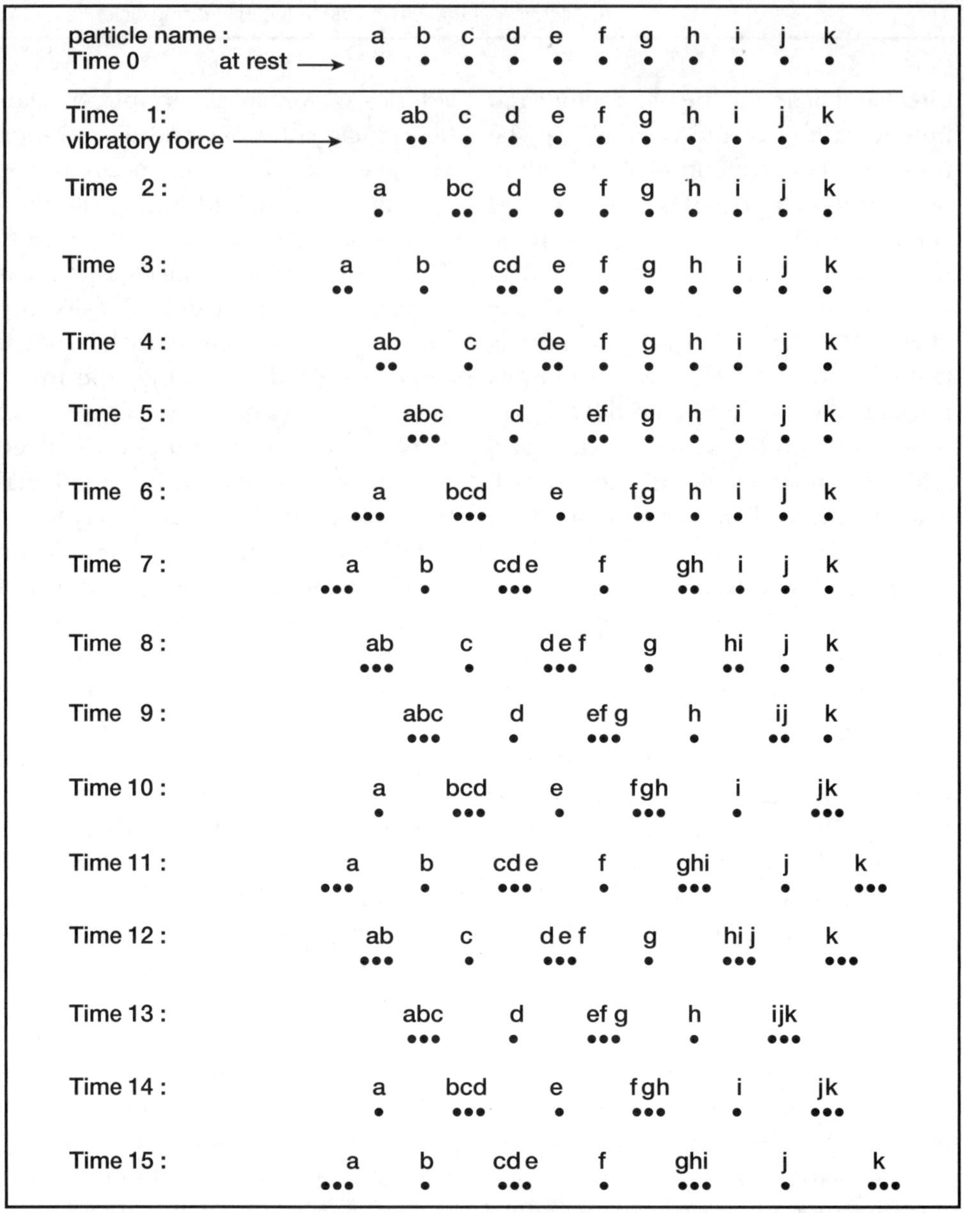

Time 0   at rest ⟶   • • • • • • • • • • •

Time 1:

vibratory force ⟶   ab   c   d   e   f   g   h   i   j   k

Time 2:   a   bc   d   e   f   g   h   i   j   k

Time 3:   a   b   cd   e   f   g   h   i   j   k

Time 4:   ab   c   de   f   g   h   i   j   k

Time 5:   abc   d   ef   g   h   i   j   k

Time 6:   a   bcd   e   fg   h   i   j   k

Time 7:   a   b   cde   f   gh   i   j   k

Time 8:   ab   c   def   g   hi   j   k

Time 9:   abc   d   efg   h   ij   k

Time 10:   a   bcd   e   fgh   i   jk

Time 11:   a   b   cde   f   ghi   j   k

Time 12:   ab   c   def   g   hij   k

Time 13:   abc   d   efg   h   ijk

Time 14:   a   bcd   e   fgh   i   jk

Time 15:   a   b   cde   f   ghi   j   k

Figure 4–4. Particle collisions in longitudinal sound wave propagation. Let particles *a* through *k* represent molecules or compounds of an elastic medium such as air or water. Sixteen consecutive moments in time are indicated to the left, beginning at Time 0 and ending at Time 15. Assume initially that the particles are evenly dispersed, are moving about in a random fashion, and are at rest at Time 0. At Time 1, a force in the form of a vibration (from an energy source) is applied in the direction of the arrow that is shown. Particle *a* is set into motion. It is initially displaced to the right and collides with particle *b* as indicated at Time 1. The collision of *a* with *b* sets *b* into motion at Time 2, as *b* collides with *c* and sets it into motion at Time 3. Note also that as each particle is displaced initially to the right, it returns to equilibrium and is then displaced to the left. Cycles of motion for each particle are repeated over time in a similar manner described for the pendulum. That is, in response to a force, each particle moves repeatedly around its point of equilibrium. Beginning at about Time 7, clear patterns of compression (***) and rarefaction (*) begin to emerge as the wave front travels from *a* to *k*. Finally, clear patterns of compression and rarefaction are established beginning at approximately Time 10 and continuing through Time 15. The successive waves of compression and rarefaction advance in a rightward direction, away from the force or the energy source that has produced the disturbance.

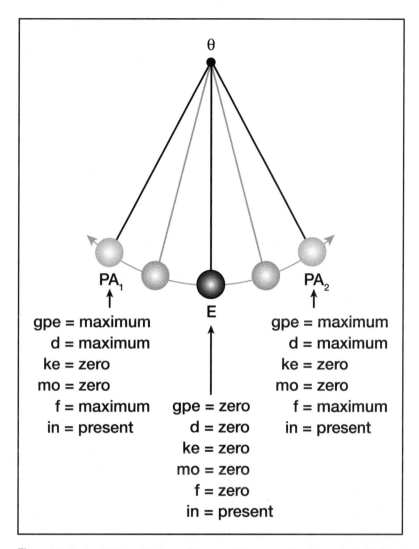

Figure 4–5. Loading a pendulum with energy. The restorative force of gravitational potential energy (*gpe*) illustrated is zero when displacement (*d*) is also zero at the exact point of equilibrium (*E*). Since the pendulum is not moving at Location E, kinetic energy (*ke*), momentum (*mo*), and net force (*f*) are also equal to zero. However, at this location, inertia (*in*) which is always present, will exert its influence if and when an attempt is made to change the existing (or lack of) motion in the pendulum. Suppose that an external force is applied to displace the pendulum bob, either to the right or to the left. After *in* has been overcome, *d* will gradually increase as the pendulum bob moves further away from *E*. As it continues to deviate from *E*, the *gpe* also gradually and proportionally increases. At the maximum peak of forced amplitude displacement (*PA₁* or *PA₂*), where *d* is obviously maximum, *gpe* is also maximum, and net *f* which is external, is also maximum. However, since the pendulum is not yet moving on its own, *ke* and *mo* are still equal to zero. At either extreme (*PA₁* or *PA₂*) when the external force is removed, *gpe* will then begin a slow transformation to *ke*, and the resistance to a change in motion, or simply *in*, which is always present, will exert its influence but will be overcome.

Figure 4–5, when displacement is zero at the exact point of equilibrium, gravitational potential energy is zero and net force is also zero. Since the pendulum is not moving, kinetic energy and momentum are equal to zero. However, while inertia (like mass) is always present, inertia will exert its influence at the point of equilibrium, if and when an attempt is made to change the existing (or lack of) motion in the pendulum.

> ## Changes in Energy, Force, and Momentum During Harmonic Motion

Looking at Figure 4–5, suppose that an external force is applied to displace the pendulum bob, either to the right or to the left. Inertia must first be overcome. Following this, displacement gradually increases as the pendulum bob moves farther away from equilibrium. As the pendulum bob continues to deviate from equilibrium, gravitational potential energy also gradually and proportionally increases and is stored within the pendulum as a restorative force. At the maximum peak of forced displacement (PA_1 or PA_2), gravitational potential energy is maximum, and the external force placed upon the pendulum is also maximum. Why is the external force maximum at this point? The farther from equilibrium an object is displaced, the greater is the restorative force that increasingly builds in opposition to the ever-increasing displacement of the mass. More external force is required as the degree of displacement, and opposition to the displacement, increases.

Since the pendulum at either of the extremes of forced displacement (PA_1 or PA_2) is not yet moving on its own,

kinetic energy and momentum are equal to zero. At the exact moment that the external force is removed from contact with the pendulum, the restorative force of gravitational potential energy will just begin its slow transformation to kinetic energy. A resistance to a change in motion (inertia), which is always present, will make its appearance. Inertia will be overcome, and a slow energy transformation will occur just as the pendulum slowly begins to move independently.

The manner in which potential and kinetic energy conservation occurs within the same system is still best illustrated by the use of a simple pendulum and spring-mass system. It was emphasized earlier that mechanical systems are better understood and greatly simplified when nonconservative frictional drag is disregarded. Friction only transfers energy away from the motion of objects. The presence of friction requires the need for constant compensatory external forces in order to maintain consistency in the oscillation of an object. If we consider only conservative forces, the total mechanical energy of a system neither increases nor decreases by any process. That is, the total energy of the mechanical system stays constant and is conserved (Giancoli, 2005). A discussion of the energy transformation of potential to kinetic to potential, and so forth, in the motion of the pendulum and spring-mass will therefore disregard nonconservative frictional forces.

Figure 4–6A illustrates once again five stages (I to V) in a single cycle of motion for a pendulum, paralleling the five stages described and illustrated in Chapter 3. In the first stage, labeled Stage I, the pendulum and the spring-mass are at static equilibrium. They are at rest and are not moving. Displace-

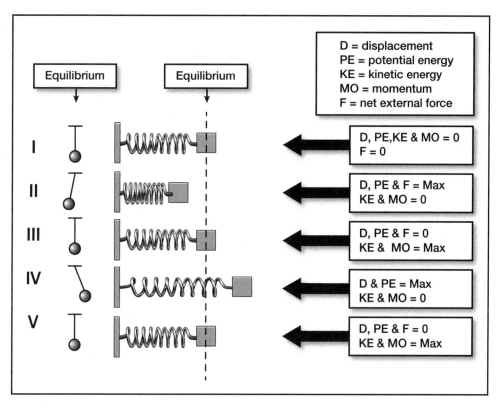

Figure 4–6A. Relationship between displacement, potential and kinetic energy, net force, and momentum in the motion of a pendulum and spring-mass system. Five stages (I through V) in a single cycle of motion for a pendulum are presented that parallel five stages in a single cycle of motion for a spring-mass system. Stage I: pendulum and spring-mass are at static equilibrium; displacement (*D*) and potential energy (*PE*) are zero. Inertia will resist motion and when an attempt is made to displace either object from rest. Stage II: pendulum and spring-mass are displaced (*D*) maximally to the left by an external force. The spring-mass is compressed. Potential energy (*PE*) and the net external force (*F*) are maximum. Kinetic energy (*KE*) and momentum (*MO*) are zero. Stage III: pendulum and spring-mass are in motion and pass through equilibrium. Displacement (*D*), potential energy (*PE*), and net force (*F*) are all zero. Kinetic energy (*KE*) and momentum (*MO*) are maximum. Stage IV: pendulum and spring-mass have traveled well past equilibrium, and are displaced (*D*) maximally to the right. The spring-mass is stretched. Potential energy (*PE*) is maximum and equal to the total energy in the system. Kinetic energy (*KE*) and momentum (*MO*) are zero. Stage V is identical to Stage III, as pendulum and spring-mass each complete one full cycle of symmetrical motion.

ment and potential energy are both zero. Inertia will also resist motion only if, at this stage, an attempt is made to displace either object from rest.

Suppose that at Stage I an external force is applied so that at Stage II the pendulum and spring-mass have been displaced maximally to the left by this external net force. As illustrated in Figure 4–6A, this force has produced a compression of the spring-mass. Both gravitational (for pendulum) and elastic potential energy are at their maximum values. External force is also maximum since the opposition to displacement is the greatest. Because the pendulum and spring-mass are not yet moving on their own, kinetic energy and momentum are also zero. The object or source of the external force that has pushed or pulled the pendulum and spring-mass to Stage II must now be removed from its contact with these simple machines. The moment that the external force is removed, the restorative forces of gravity and elasticity within pendulum and spring-mass, respectively, will begin their slow and gradual transformation to kinetic energy. Motion, however, does not begin immediately because of the resistance to changes in motion, known also as inertia. Once inertia is overtaken, which is almost instantaneously, the pendulum and spring-mass will begin their slow and gradual motion back toward equilibrium. As more of the stored potential energy is transformed into the energy of motion (kinetic energy), the velocity and momentum of the pendulum and spring-mass will also increase, until all of the potential energy has been transformed to motion. At Stage III, pendulum and spring-mass are in motion and are passing through (though only for a brief instant) the point of equilibrium. By definition, displacement, potential energy, and force are all equal to zero at this exact location. Kinetic energy is equal to the total energy and is maximum. Because instantaneous velocity is maximum (and constant) and acceleration is zero, momentum is also maximum at this exact location.

As pendulum and spring-mass continue to move just to the right of the exact point of equilibrium, kinetic energy will, at that moment, begin a slow and gradual transformation to potential energy. More and more of the energy of motion will be transformed into potential energy as pendulum and spring-mass continue to deviate farther to the right of equilibrium. As the rightward motion continues, velocity and therefore momentum in the pendulum and

spring-mass also gradually decrease. This is because the ever-increasing restorative force of potential energy is a force that opposes displacement. The transformation to potential energy will continue until all of the kinetic energy has been transformed—that is, when potential energy is equal to the total energy in the system.

At Stage IV, motion in the pendulum and spring-mass has been halted. Pendulum and spring-mass are now displaced maximally to the right of equilibrium. The displacement has produced a stretching of the spring-mass, as illustrated in Figure 4–6A. Potential energy is equal to the total energy in the system at this location. Motion has ceased because kinetic energy (the energy of motion) is zero. Momentum is also zero. The rate of change in velocity (acceleration) is, by definition, also maximum. Furthermore, the restorative force of potential energy, which has become maximal, has completely opposed any additional displacement to the right of equilibrium. The motion of pendulum and spring-mass will change direction as soon as the restorative forces in both can begin their slow transformation back to kinetic energy. Motion toward the direction of equilibrium, however, cannot begin immediately because of inertia. Once inertia is overtaken, which is almost instantaneously, the pendulum and spring-mass will begin their slow and gradual motion back toward equilibrium. As more of the stored potential energy is transformed into the energy of motion, the velocity and momentum of the pendulum and spring-mass will also increase, until all of the potential energy has been transformed to motion.

As shown in Figure 4–6A, the events that occur in Stage V are identical to those that have occurred during

Stage III. Gravitational and elastic restorative forces have returned the pendulum to the point of equilibrium by their transformation to kinetic energy. Kinetic energy and momentum are maximum, displacement and potential energy are zero, as pendulum and spring-mass each complete one full cycle of symmetrical motion. Though kinetic energy is equal to the total energy of the system at this point of equilibrium, once pendulum and spring-mass cross to the left of equilibrium, kinetic energy will once again begin a slow and gradual transformation to potential energy. In the ideal complete absence of friction, the pendulum and spring-mass should continue to oscillate indefinitely.

Figure 4–6B presents by histograms the relative amplitudes of potential energy, kinetic energy, and momentum during the five stages (I to V) in a single cycle of motion for a pendulum and spring-mass, as shown in Figure 4–6A.

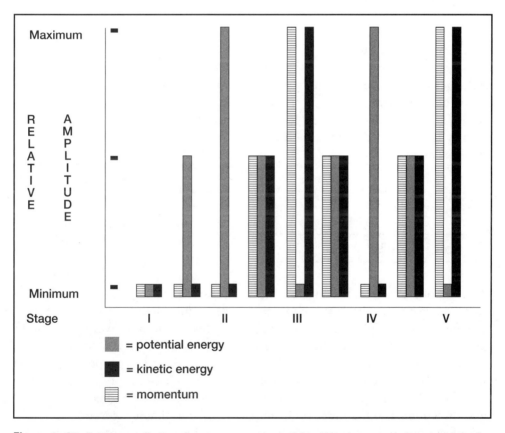

Figure 4–6B. Relative amplitudes of momentum and potential and kinetic energy during each of the five stages illustrated in Figure 4–6A for one cycle of motion. Shown in histograms are the relative amplitudes of potential and kinetic energy, and momentum during the five stages (I to V) in a single cycle of motion for a pendulum and spring-mass, as illustrated in Figure 4–6A. At Stage I pendulum and spring-mass are at rest. All three variables are zero. During Stage II (compression for the spring-mass) and Stage IV (rarefaction for the spring-mass), potential energy is equal to the total energy in the system. Kinetic energy and momentum are zero. During Stages III and V, kinetic energy is equal to the total energy in the system, momentum is maximal, and potential energy is zero. The magnitudes of the three variables at each of the intermediate locations fall somewhere between the maximum and minimum values observed at each of the labeled stages.

Recall that the total energy in a system *TE* is equal to the sum of the potential energy *PE* and kinetic energy *KE*, or Equation 4–16:

$$TE = PE + KE$$

Figure 4–6B indicates that at Stages II and IV, when pendulum and spring-mass are displaced maximally to the left or right, respectively, potential energy is equal to the total energy in the system. At these two stages of motion, kinetic energy (and momentum) are equal to zero, or

$$TE = PE + 0$$

At Stages III and V, momentum is maximum, displacement is zero, and potential energy is zero. However, kinetic energy is equal to the total energy in the system, or

$$TE = 0 + KE$$

Scalar and Vector Quantities

Throughout this text, reference has been made to the three fundamental dimensions of length, mass, and time, and to the physical quantities derived from them. In their description, many of these quantities were defined by measures that employed both magnitude and directionality. Quantities requiring clarification based not only on specifying how much, but also on the designation of in which direction, are called vector quantities, or simply vectors. Other quantities requiring clarification based on measurements made only in terms of overall magnitude, with no reference to directionality, are called scalar

Table 4–1. Table of Select Vector and Scalar Quantities

Scalars	Vectors
area	acceleration
energy	displacement
length	net force
mass	friction
speed	momentum
temperature	pressure
time	velocity
volume	
work	

quantities, or simply scalars. Table 4–1 presents a list of selected scalar and vector quantities that have been discussed in the text thus far.

Chapter Summary

- In this chapter, a brief history of motion was presented, together with the study of motion, known also as mechanics, was emphasized in Chapter 4.
- In this chapter, Newton's three laws of motion were presented: Newton's first law of motion redefined the property of inertia as initially proposed by Galileo.
- Newton's second law of motion stated that acceleration is inversely proportional to mass, and yielded the formal definition for force, as force = mass × acceleration.
- Newton's third law of motion stated that for any pair of bodies, a force that is imposed on one body of the pair is always equal

in magnitude and opposite in direction to the force imposed on the other body of the pair.

◾ In this chapter, MKS and CGS metric units of force were defined as the newton and the dyne, respectively.

◾ Work was defined as the product of the distance that a mass is moved (or displaced), and the magnitude of the force applied, provided that the force is parallel to the displacement, or simply, work = force × distance.

◾ In this chapter, MKS and CGS metric units of work were defined as the joule and the erg, respectively.

◾ Pressure was defined as the amount of force per unit area, where force is understood to be acting perpendicular to the surface area, or simply, pressure = force ÷ area.

◾ In this chapter, MKS and CGS metric units of pressure were defined as the newton/meter^2 or pascal (Pa), and the dyne/centimeter^2, respectively.

◾ Power was defined as the rate at which work is accomplished, or power = work/time.

◾ In this chapter, the MKS metric unit of power was defined as the watt.

◾ One watt of power in the MKS metric system is equal to one joule/second.

◾ In this chapter, the CGS metric unit of power was also defined as the watt.

◾ One watt of power in the CGS metric system is equal to 10^7 ergs/second.

◾ In terms of power: 1 joule/second = 10^7 ergs/second.

◾ In this chapter, potential energy was defined as energy that is stored for the purpose of work.

◾ In this chapter, instantaneous elastic potential energy was defined as kx where k indicates the spring constant or stiffness and x refers to the distance stretched or the elastic limit.

◾ Average elastic potential energy or ½ kx is proportional to the square of the amount of stretch, or the square of the distance that the elastic mass is displaced, such that elastic potential energy = ½ kx^2.

◾ Gravitational potential energy is equal to the product of the weight of an object and the vertical displacement of an object from the ground (height), or simply, gravitational potential energy = weight × height.

◾ At any instant in time, potential energy will take on a relative value and has significance only when it is transformed to kinetic energy.

◾ Kinetic energy has been defined as the energy of motion.

◾ Kinetic energy is directly proportional to the product of half an object's mass and the square of the speed (or velocity) of the object, or simply, kinetic energy = ½ mass × velocity^2.

◾ A change (delta) in the kinetic energy (*KE*) of a mass is also equal to the net amount of work that is accomplished, or work = ΔKE.

◾ At any given moment in time, the total energy *TE* in a system is equal to the sum of the potential energy *PE* and kinetic energy *KE*, or: TE = PE + KE.

- In this chapter, momentum was defined as inertia in motion, and as the product of mass and velocity or momentum = mass × velocity.
- Changes (delta) in momentum depend upon the amount and also the duration of the external force placed on an object, or momentum = force × time.
- In this chapter, the generation of vibrations and waveforms was described as a series of elastic collisions that transfer energy from one location to another.
- In this chapter, the simple harmonic motion of a pendulum and spring-mass system were compared in terms of their displacement, potential energy, kinetic energy, and momentum.
- Scalar quantities refer to terminology defined by measures involving magnitude only.
- Vector quantities are concepts that are defined with respect to measures of both magnitude and directionality.

Chapter 4 Questions

1. In a moving pendulum, when is momentum at its greatest value? Describe why.

2. In a moving pendulum, when is kinetic energy at its greatest value? Describe why.

3. In a moving spring-mass system, when is potential energy at its greatest value? Describe why.

4. If the total energy (TE) in a moving spring-mass system is 200 joules, and the potential energy (PE) is 50 joules, how many joules define the kinetic energy (KE)?

5. If the total energy (TE) in a nonmoving spring-mass system is 200 joules, how many joules define the potential energy (PE)? How many joules define the kinetic energy (KE)?

6. Explain why displacement, velocity, and acceleration are vector quantities.

7. In the pendulum and spring-mass systems, what is the relationship between displacement and potential energy? What is the relationship between displacement and kinetic energy?

8. How is Hooke's law similar to Newton's third law of motion?

References

Durrant, J. D., & Feth, L. L. (2013). *Hearing sciences: A foundational approach*. Upper Saddle River, NJ: Pearson Education.

Giancoli, D. C. (2005). *Physics: Principles with applications* (6th ed.). Upper Saddle River, NJ: Prentice Hall.

Gianopoulos, A. (2006). The heavens. In J. Langone, B. Stutz, & A. Gianopoulos (Eds.), *Theories for everything: An illustrated history of science from the invention of numbers to string theory* (pp. 18–71). Washington, DC: National Geographic Society.

Halliday, D., Resnick, R., & Walker, J. (2011). *Fundamentals of physics* (9th ed.). Hoboken, NJ: Wiley.

Hawking, S. E. (2002). *On the shoulders of giants: The great works of physics and astronomy*. Philadelphia, PA: Running Press.

Hewitt, P. G. (2010). *Conceptual physics* (11th ed.). Upper Saddle River, NJ: Pearson Education.

Stutz, B. (2006). Introduction. In J. Langone, B. Stutz, & A. Gianopoulos (Eds.), *Theories for everything: An illustrated history of science from the invention of numbers to string theory* (pp. 8–17). Washington, DC: National Geographic Society.

Chapter 5

Harmonic Motion

In 1633 Galileo wrote, "by steady or uniform motion, I mean one in which the distances traversed by the moving particle during any equal intervals of time, are themselves equal."

Hawking, 2002, p. 515

Alphabetized Listing of Key Terms Discussed in Chapter 5

0.707

$2\pi f$

$2\pi f m$

$2\pi r$

2π radians

$2r$

$s/2\pi f$

360°

acceleration

acoustic impedance

acute angle

amplitude

angle

angular frequency

angular velocity

aperiodic waveform

arc

Archimedes (287–212 BC)

best frequency

characteristic frequency

characteristic impedance (Z_c)

circle

circumference

complex signal

complex waveform

compression

condensation

cos

cosine

cosine wave

critical damping

cycle

damping

damping factor (d_f)

degrees (of phase)

density

diameter

displacement

driver

equilibrium

even-numbered harmonics

external auditory canal

first resonant frequency

forced vibration

formant frequencies

free vibration

frequency (f)

friction

frictional resistance

formant frequencies

fundamental frequency

harmonic frequencies

harmonic motion

harmonics

heavily damped

Helmholtz, Hermann von (1821–1894)

hertz (Hz)

Hertz, Heinrich Rudolph (1857–1894)

Hertzian waves

Hooke's law

hypotenuse

instantaneous amplitude

load

$\log_{10}$

$\log_e$

logarithms

Marconi, Guglielmo (1874–1937)

mass

mass dominated system

mass reactance

Maxwell, James Clerk (1831–1879)

mean

mean square amplitude

mho

natural frequency

natural logarithm

Newton's second law of motion

octaves

odd-numbered harmonics

ohm

overtones

partials

peak amplitude

peak-to-peak amplitude

period (T)

periodic motion

periodic waveform

phase

phase angle

phase lag

phase lead

projected circular motion

principle of resonance

pure tone

radian(s)

radius

rarefaction

rayls

reactance

rectangular wave

resistance (frictional)

resistance dominated system

resonance

resonant frequency

resounding

right angle

right triangle

root-mean-square (RMS) amplitude

simple harmonic motion

sin

sine

sine wave

sinusiod

sinusiodal motion

square wave

standard deviation

starting phase

statistics

stiffness

stiffness dominated system

stiffness reactance

theta (Θ)

trigonometry

tubes (half-wave resonating)

tubes (hollow)

tubes (quarter-wave resonating)

uniform circular motion

unit circle

variance

velocity

vocal tract

waveform

X_m

X_s

Y

Z

Z_A

Z_c

What Is Harmonic Motion?

In previous chapters, harmonic motion was described as the elementary "back-and-forth" or oscillatory motion found in the movements of a pendulum or in the motion of a simple spring-mass system. Harmonic motion begins with an initial force that is applied to a mass in order to produce temporary distortion or displacement. Subsequently, the oscillatory motion described for any elastic object that is merely distorted or displaced by an applied force was also used to illustrate harmonic motion. Although harmonic motion can include both simple and complex oscillatory motion, the term *simple* as introduced in Chapter 3 is a description of events that relate to a single rate of oscillation rather than to oscillations that might be expected to occur in a complex series of vibrations (Giancoli, 2005).

What Is Sinusoidal Motion?

The motion that occurs repeatedly over time and over the same path around a point of equilibrium was also described in the previous two chapters. The kind of motion that occurs in response to a displacing force was defined as periodic motion. Periodic motion is also harmonic motion, and harmonic motion is often described as sinusoidal motion. The motion of a simple harmonic oscillator set into vibratory motion by merely displacing its mass from equilibrium is purely sinusoidal in nature. Therefore, in order to develop the concept of periodic motion, it will be useful to begin the present discussion with the term *sinusoid*. Sinusoid comes from the concept and equation for the sine of a given angle, a concept that is borrowed from trigonometry.

Simplified Trigonometry

To begin with, Figure 5–1 illustrates a right triangle, *OQP*. A right triangle is a triangle having a right angle, and a right angle is any angle that is equal to 90°. The right angle in Figure 5–1 is labeled angle *Q*. The acute angle that is created by segments *OP* and *OQ* is also labeled with the symbol, theta (Θ). An acute angle is any angle that is less than 90°. Note also in Figure 5–1 that segment *OP* has been labeled the *hypotenuse* of the right triangle. The hypotenuse of any right triangle is, by definition, the side that is opposite the right angle; hence, it is also the longest side. Segment *OQ* is the side adjacent to the acute angle Θ, and segment *PQ* is the side opposite to the acute angle Θ.

What Is the Cosine (cos) and Sine (sin) of an Angle?

In the right triangle *OQP* shown in Figure 5–1, the ratios of the lengths of each of the sides can be described for any value of angle Θ. For instance, the ratio of the side adjacent to angle Θ to the hypotenuse may be defined as the cosine of angle Θ, or simply

$$\cos \Theta =$$
side adjacent to $\Theta \div$ hypotenuse
(5–1A)

or x/r

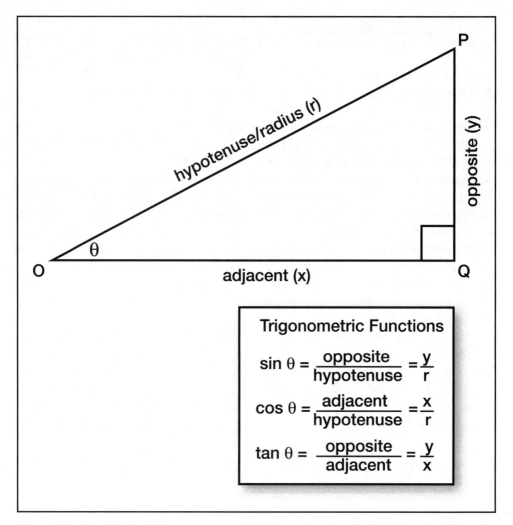

Figure 5–1. The right triangle.

Also, the ratio of the side opposite angle Θ to the hypotenuse is defined as the sine of angle Θ, or simply,

$$\sin Θ =$$
side opposite to Θ ÷ hypotenuse

(5–1B)

or y/r

Finally, the ratio of the side opposite angle Θ to the side adjacent to angle Θ is defined as the tangent of angle Θ, or simply:

$$\tan Θ =$$
side opposite Θ ÷ side adjacent to Θ

(5–1C)

or y/x

For our purpose, only the cosine and sine, and therefore, only Equation 5–1A and 5–1B will be considered for angle

Θ. Furthermore, the significance of the labels: radius (r), segment (x) and segment (y) in Figure 5–1 will also become clear in the section that follows.

Simplified Trigonometry and the Unit Circle

The right triangle OQP shown in Figure 5–1 may be placed into a unit circle as shown in Figure 5–2A. A unit circle is defined as a circle with a radius r, and the value of r is equal to 1. Note that the unit circle illustrated in Figure 5–2A is bisected by an x-axis and a y-axis and that the intersection of the x-axis and y-axis divides the unit circle into four equal quadrants, as additionally illustrated in Figure 5–2B.

The right triangle of Figure 5–2A is located within the quadrant bounded by the values corresponding to the positive x-axis and positive y-axis, as also

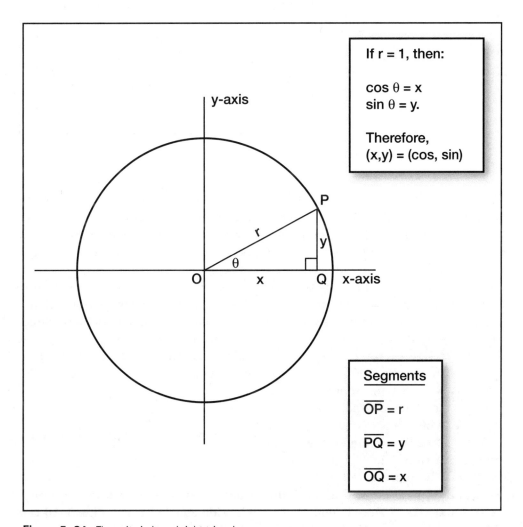

Figure 5–2A. The unit circle and right triangle.

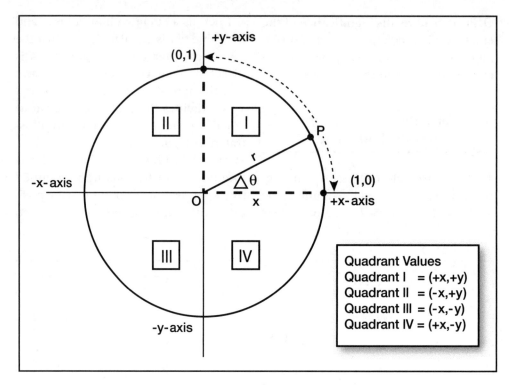

Figure 5–2B. The unit circle quadrants.

illustrated in Figure 5–2B. Note that in Figure 5–2B, the adjacent side (segment *OQ*) of the right triangle in Figures 5–1 and 5–2A is flush with the horizontal positive *x*-axis, and this side is labeled with an *x*. The segment *PQ* that is opposite to the angle Θ has been labeled with a *y* to indicate the *y*-axis value for a given point *P*.

In both figures, the origin *O* is the point of intersection of axes *x* and *y*. Note as well that the radius *r* of the circle is equal to the hypotenuse of the triangle, which is also equal to 1. Any point *P* along the circumference of the unit circle shown in Figures 5–2A or 5–2B may be represented as a coordinate (i.e., *x*, *y*) distance from both the *x*-axis and *y*-axis. The circumferences illustrated in Figures 5–2A and 5–2B

are defined as the curvatures forming the boundaries or contours of each unit circle. The location of any hypothetical point may be determined by the length of segments *x* and *y*, respectively.

Figure 5–2B makes the point clear that because radius *r* moves through the unit circle in a counterclockwise direction, with *r* = 1, and with an adjacent side equal to *x*, then Equation 5–1A may be restated:

Since:

$$\cos Θ = \text{adjacent/hypotenuse} = x/1$$

Then: $\cos Θ = x$

Similarly, with *r* = 1, and with the opposite side equal to *y*, Equation 5–1B can also be restated:

Since:

$$\sin \Theta = \text{opposite/hypotenuse} = y/1$$

Then: $\sin \Theta = y$

Note as well that the right triangle of Figure 5–1, shown again in Figure 5–2B, is located within quadrant *I* that is bound by the values corresponding to the (nonzero) positive *x*-axis and positive *y*-axis. Note as well that the remaining three quadrants are bound by values that correspond to negative *x*-values and positive *y*-values (Quadrant II), negative *x*-values and negative *y*-values (Quadrant III), and positive *x*-values and negative *y*-values (Quadrant IV). This distribution of values for each of the four quadrants is illustrated in Figures 5–2B and 5–2C.

Length and the corresponding amplitude changes in both of the segments *x* (cos angle Θ) and *y* (sin angle Θ) are observed as shape changes in the three right triangles shown (A, B, and C). These changes occur as a direct function of the counterclockwise rotation of radius *r* through the unit circle and are illustrated in Figure 5–2D.

Uniform Circular Motion

Simple harmonic or sinusoidal motion is often illustrated as uniform circular motion. Simple harmonic motion is the projection of uniform circular motion on a diameter of a circle, in which circular motion occurs (Halliday, Resnick, & Walker, 2011). As previously illustrated, uniform circular motion is best

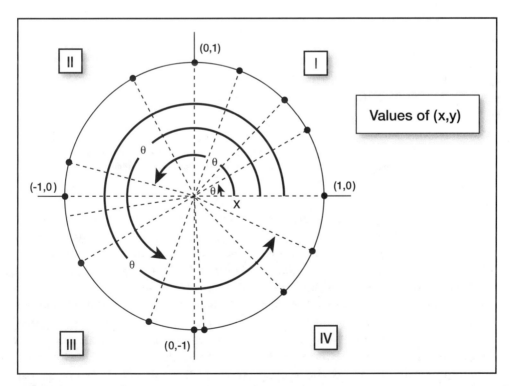

Figure 5–2C. (*X, Y*) Values associated with each of the four unit circle quadrants.

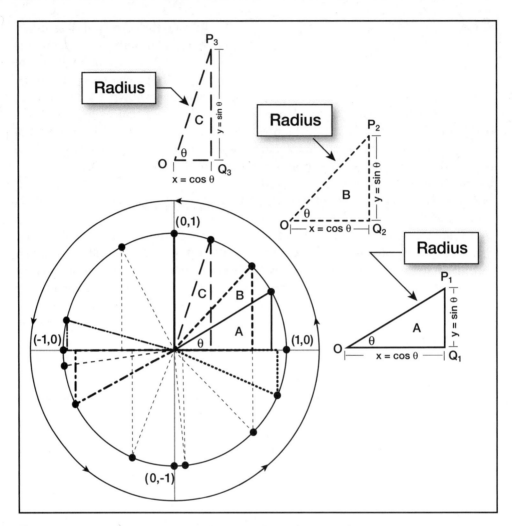

Figure 5–2D. Changes in the length of x (cos angle Θ) and y (sin angle Θ) as a function of uniform circular motion of a hypothetical radius shown in right triangles A, B, and C through a unit circle.

demonstrated by the counterclockwise rotation of a radius and a corresponding point P, around the circumference of a circle. The concept of sinusoidal or uniform circular motion was illustrated in Figures 5–2B, 5–2C, and 5–2D and is again illustrated in Figure 5–3A.

As illustrated in Figure 5–3A, changes in degrees of phase or phase angle for angle Θ also occur as the radius r, shown as the dashed line, is rotated counterclockwise around the point of

origin for all possible points P, through the complete 360° circumference for one cycle of a unit circle. Recall from Figures 5–2B and 5–2C that the sine function for angle Θ will always be a positive value when computed in Quadrants I and II and will take on negative values when computed in Quadrants III and IV. Furthermore, the cosine function for angle Θ will always be a positive value when computed in Quadrants I and IV and will take on negative val-

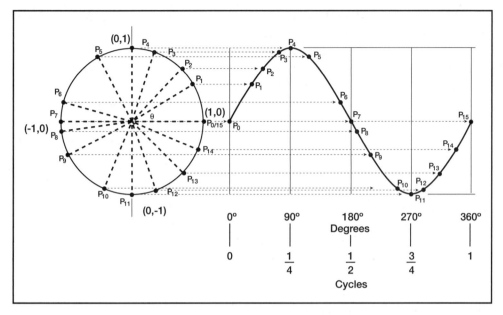

Figure 5–3A. Sine wave amplitudes for sin $\Theta = (y/r)$ across one cycle (360° of phase).

ues when computed in Quadrants II and III. It is also important to note that the starting point for sinusoidal motion (and for the sine wave) traditionally begins when radius r is flush with or equal to the positive x-axis and angle Θ is equal to 0°. At this starting point, the length (amplitude) of side y (at location P_0) is, of course, zero as illustrated in Figure 5–3A.

Hence,

If   angle $\Theta = 0°$

And $y = 0$

Where   sin $\Theta = y$

Then   sin 0° = 0.

Similarly, when radius r is flush with the positive x-axis and angle Θ is equal to 0°, side x (of the right triangle) assumes the value of radius (r), or simply the value of 1.

Hence,

If   angle $\Theta = 0°$

And $x = 1$

Where   cos $\Theta = x$

Then   cos 0° = 1.

When the rotation of radius r is directed away from the positive x-axis and toward the positive y-axis, which is the customary direction of rotation of radius r within the unit circle, segment y begins to assume larger quantities, while segment x begins to take on values that are less than 1. The counterclockwise rotation of radius r ensures that angle Θ will always hold a positive value.

As shown in Figures 5–2D and 5–3A, a continuous and progressive counterclockwise rotation of radius r toward the positive y-axis produces a progressive increase (toward 90°) in angle Θ, and a progressive decrease in the length of side x equal to values less than 1, eventually becoming zero (at 90°). The counterclockwise rotation toward 90° of radius r also produces a progressive increase in the height of side y which will take on values greater than 0, and eventually 1 (which is the length or height of radius r). This described stepwise, counterclockwise creation of different angles through Quadrant I (as well as through each of the quadrants) is also illustrated in Figure 5–3B. It is important to note that when radius r creates 45° of angle with the x-axis, or stated differently, when the radius reaches the halfway point of rotation within Quadrant I, the length (amplitude) of side y, and the length (amplitude) of side x at such a location will be equal. The lengths of both segments (X and Y) at the halfway point may be computed as an average (or mean), and in statistical terms, the mean of any set of values in a distribution is the midpoint between the two extremes. In this case, the extreme length values for either the X or Y segments in Quadrant I, are 0 and 1. The halfway point for either line segment may be computed as an average of the square of the two extreme lengths (amplitudes). A squaring of the two extreme lengths (0 or 1) permits mean length computations for any values, including those that involve negative numbers (such as when x or y = −1). However, having computed the mean of the squared lengths, the square root of the final average must then be performed in order to compensate for the initial squaring procedure. Therefore, the average length of Y or x may be computed as

$$1^2 + 0^2 \div 2$$

or $$(\tfrac{1}{2})$$

and $$\sqrt{\tfrac{1}{2}} = 0.707$$

Hence,

If   angle $\Theta = 45°$

And $\sin \Theta = y$

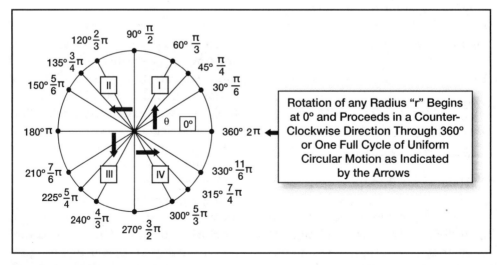

Figure 5–3B. A few of the many possible degrees of rotation of a radius within the four quadrants (I, II, III, IV) of a unit circle.

Where $\sin \Theta = 0.707$

Then $\sin 45° = 0.707.$

Furthermore,

If angle $\Theta = 45°$

And $\cos \Theta = x$

Where $\cos \Theta = 0.707$

Then $\cos 45° = 0.707.$

In Quadrant I, the continued motion of radius r eventually brings it flush with the positive y-axis, as indicated in Figures 5–3A–B and Figure 5–4. Therefore, when angle Θ equals 90° (or one quarter of 360°), side y of the triangle assumes the length of radius (r), or simply 1. The length of side x of the triangle would also be reduced to zero.

Hence,

If angle $\Theta = 90°$

And $y = 1$

Where $\sin \Theta = y$

Then $\sin 90° = 1.$

Furthermore,

If angle $\Theta = 90°$

And $X = 0$

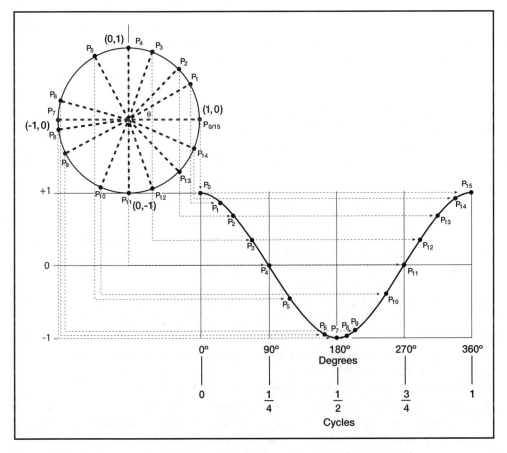

Figure 5–4. Cosine wave amplitudes for cos Θ = (X/r) across one cycle (360° of phase).

Where $\cos \Theta = X$

Then $\cos 90° = 0$.

To summarize, with respect to the counterclockwise rotation of a radius (r) through Quadrant I of a unit circle and the subsequent changes that accrue in angle Θ, for values (x, y) where (x, y) = (cos, sin), the following are true statements:

a. If angle $\Theta = 0°$ then $\cos 0° = 1$ and $\sin 0° = 0$, yielding P (1,0).

b. If angle $\Theta = 45°$ then $\cos 45° = 0.707$ and $\sin 45° = 0.707$, yielding P (0.707,0.707).

c. If angle $\Theta = 90°$, then $\cos 90° = 0$ and $\sin 90° = 1$, yielding P (0,1).

In actuality, the principles of sinusoidal motion and the continuous counterclockwise rotation of a radius apply as well to the separate coordinate locations found throughout all four quadrants within the unit circle. Keeping in mind that the starting point for sinusoidal motion commonly begins at the location in Quadrant I where the radius is flush with the positive x-axis, and where angle $\Theta = 0°$ at point $P(1, 0)$, it may be said that the positive x-axis serves as a reference for all subsequent determinations of angle Θ and for all measures of the degree of rotation of radius r, for each cycle of rotation.

Furthermore, it should be clear that the total distance in degrees that radius r can rotate within a circle is 360°, which defines one cycle of uniform circular rotation (see Figure 5–3B). Recall as well from Figure 5–2B that the sine function for angle Θ will always result in a positive value for phase angles computed in Quadrants I and II, and will take on negative values when angles are computed in Quadrants III and IV. Similarly, the cosine function for angle Θ will always result in a positive value for angular computations made in Quadrants I and IV and will take on negative values for angular computations made in Quadrants II and III (see Figure 5–2B). As indicated in Figures 5–2D, 5–3A, and 5–4, when radius r is flush with or equal to the negative x-axis, and the rotational degree of angle Θ corresponds to one half of 360°, or 180°, $P(x,y) = (-1,0)$. It can also be seen from these figures that if radius r is flush with and equal to the negative y-axis, rotational degrees correspond to three-fourths of 360°, or 270° where $P(x, y) = (0,-1)$. Finally, when radius r returns to and is once again flush with and equal to the positive x-axis after movement through a full cycle (360°) of rotation, $P(x, y)$ is once again equal to (1, 0). The sine and cosine values for each quarter of rotation of phase angle, together with the sines and cosines for the midpoint angles (or mean amplitudes) that fall between each of the quarter rotations, are presented in Table 5–1.

What Are Sine and Cosine Waveforms?

The Sine Wave

A sine wave is an example of a simple periodic waveform. Like the sine function in trigonometry from which it was named, where $\sin \Theta = y$ and $\sin 0° = 0$, the uniform projected circular motion that defines a sine wave begins at 0° where the amplitude of the waveform is also zero. The actual type of sound that is represented by a simple two-dimensional periodic sine wave signal

Table 5–1. Sine and Cosine Values at Each Quarter Rotation and Their Respective Midpoints

sin 0° = 0	sin 45° = +0.707
sin 90° = +1	sin 135° = +0.707
sin 180° = 0	sin 225° = −0.707
sin 270° = −1	sin 315° = −0.707
sin 360° = 0	
cos 0° = +1	cos 45° = +0.707
cos 90° = 0	cos 135° = −0.707
cos 180° = −1	cos 225° = −0.707
cos 270° = 0	cos 315° = +0.707
cos 360° = +1	

is a sound having only one resonating frequency or what is simply known as a *pure tone*. It will become clear in the sections that follow that not all periodic waveforms are sine waves, most if not all the periodic sounds encountered in the environment are not pure tones, and many environmental sounds are not even periodic (Chapter 6). Nevertheless, the sine wave is the simplest type of waveform because it represents the uniform projected circular motion of only a single radius through one hypothetical unit circle. In sum, a sine wave is so named because every point P specified on the sine wave waveform is derived from the sine function of angle Θ (sin Θ) which, at each angle, will always reflect the length of segment y, as radius r rotates counterclockwise, beginning at the positive x-axis of equilibrium, with 0° of phase.

Phase Angles for a Sine Wave

Because one full cycle of rotation of radius r is equal to 360°, the resulting single waveform is projected as a sine wave, defined as one cycle, having 360° of rotation, or 360° of phase per cycle (see Figure 5–3B). As stated in Chapter 3, the physical attributes of any waveform can be described and measured at different locations and at different times during the propagation of the waveform. Recall that a unit circle has a radius r that is equal to 1. Figures 5–3A and 5–5A illustrate the projected sine wave that is created as radius r sweeps through 360° of the unit circle. Traditionally, the sine wave begins with radius r placed flush with the positive x-axis, in quadrant I, where angle Θ is equal to 0° of phase. Therefore, 0° is the standard starting phase (angle) for the typical sine wave and for any point P that corresponds to (x, y) or (cos, sin). Hence, the notation $P(1,0)$ indicates that the amplitude (y) of the projected sinusoid waveform at 0° of starting phase is equal to zero. Note also that the sine wave with a starting phase of 0° intersects the equilibrium line (labeled with an E and an arrow in Figure 5–5A). The concept of equilibrium was introduced and discussed earlier in Chapters 3 and 4. Recall as well that equilibrium is often described as the reference or starting point for measures of displacement, such as those that include measurements of peak amplitude (Giancoli, 2005).

Phase Lead and Phase Lag for Sine Waves

As indicated in the previous section, 0° is the starting phase or phase angle for the typical sine wave. Also recall that the amplitude (y) of the sinusoid waveform at 0° of phase angle is equal to zero, because sin $\Theta = y$, angle $\Theta =$

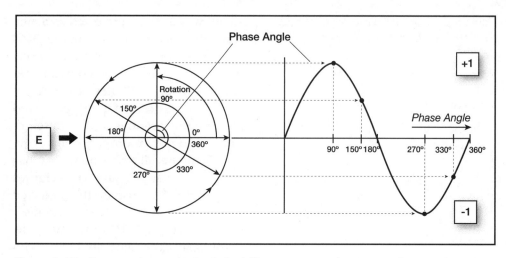

Figure 5–5A. Sine wave phase angles for sin θ = (*y/r*) across one cycle (360° of phase). Reprinted with permission from J. Angus and D. Howard (2006). *Acoustics and psychoacoustics* (3rd ed). New York, NY: Elsevier.

0° of phase, sin 0° = 0, and therefore, *y* = 0. In addition, a sine wave with a starting phase of 0° will always begin at the horizontal line referred to as equilibrium. This point is also illustrated in Figures 5–3A, 5–5A, and 5–5B.

When instantaneous comparisons are made between two or more sinusoidal waves, the phase angles observed at any point in time across the separate sine waves will not always be equal to zero. This is because there is no guarantee that two or more objects will be set into motion at the exact same moment in time, or that two or more components of a sound will begin their vibratory cycles at the same moment in time. Therefore, although 0° may be the phase angle at the initiation of any particular sinusoidal waveform, phase differences become relevant when comparisons are made between cycles generated by vibrating objects or components whose cycles begin earlier or later in time, relative to the other waveforms. Waveforms that commence relatively earlier in time are said to lead other waveforms in phase (phase lead). Conversely, those waveforms that are initiated relatively later in time are said to lag (behind) the phase of other waveforms (phase lag). Figure 5–5B illustrates four identical sine waves differing only with respect to their observed relative starting phases. Relative to the other sine waves that are shown, each of the four sine waves appears to begin at different starting phases, as indicated by the solid regions of each sine wave. Keeping in mind that we may begin observing a sine wave at any one of 360 possible degrees of phase angle, Figure 5–5B illustrates just four of the possible starting phases that might be observed at any moment in time. We may use (the starting phase of) sine wave A as the reference for meaningful phase comparisons between the other sine waves (B through D). Therefore, sine wave D is said to *lead* each of the other three sine waves (A through C) in phase. The amount of actual phase-lead illustrated by sine wave D will be determined relative to an assumed starting

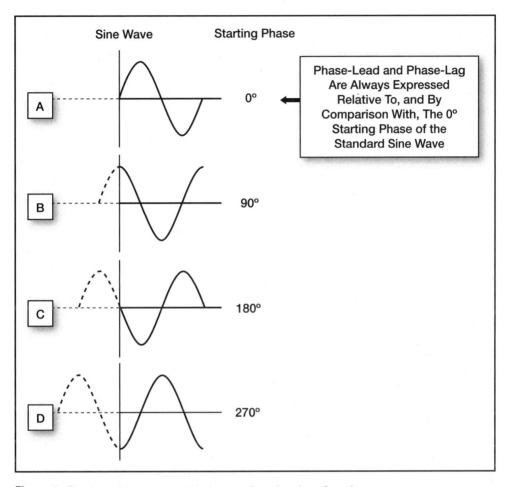

Figure 5–5B. Four of the many possible degrees of starting phase for a sine wave.

phase for all sine waves, which is 0°, as illustrated in sine wave A. This is, of course, because, by definition, all sine waves begin at 0° of phase. Therefore, sine wave D is said to lead sine wave A by 270°. Sine wave D, however, is said to lead sine waves B and C in phase by 180° and 90°, respectively. It can also be said that sine wave C leads sine wave B by 90° and that it leads sine wave A by 180°. Furthermore, sine wave B leads sine wave A by 90°.

By the same indication, sine wave A is said to *lag* each of the other three sine waves (B through D) in phase. Sine wave A lags sine waves B, C, and D in phase by 90°, 180°, and 270°, respectively. Sine wave B also lags sine wave C by 90°, and lags sine wave D by 180°. Finally, sine wave C lags sine wave D in phase by 90°.

The Cosine Wave

A cosine wave is also an example of a simple periodic waveform. Like the cosine function in trigonometry from which it was named, where $\cos \Theta = x$ and $\cos 0° = +1$, the uniform projected periodic circular motion that defines a cosine wave begins at 0° where the amplitude of the waveform is +1 (see Figure 5–4). The type of sound that is represented by a simple two-dimensional periodic cosine wave signal would be a pure tone, with the same shape and sound as a sine wave but distinguished by the fact that the 0° starting cycle begins at an amplitude of +1. Unlike the sine wave (see Figure 5–3A), the cosine wave (see Figure 5–4) is so named because every point P specified on the cosine waveform is derived from the cosine function of angle Θ (cos Θ) as radius r rotates counterclockwise. As before, radius r begins at the positive x-axis of equilibrium at a hypothetical point (P_0) at 0° of phase. As with the production of a sine wave, one counterclockwise cycle of rotation of radius r from the positive x-axis also produces continuous degree changes in angle Θ, ranging from 0° to 360°. For any degree of rotation of radius r, the amplitude of the projected cosine wave at any given location, from points P_0 to P_{15}, will always equal cos Θ, or simply, the value x, as illustrated in Figure 5–4. In sum, a cosine wave is so named because every point P specified on the cosine wave waveform is derived from the cosine function of angle Θ (cos Θ), which at each angle will always reflect the length of segment x, as radius r rotates counterclockwise, beginning at the positive x-axis of equilibrium, with 0° of phase.

Phase Angles (Lead and Lag) for a Cosine Wave

Similar to the sine wave, the cosine wave begins at the location where radius r is flush with the positive x-axis, in Quadrant I. At this location, angle Θ is of course equal to 0° of starting phase. Hence, like the sine wave, 0° is the starting phase (phase angle) for the typical cosine wave, and for any point P that corresponds to $(x, y) = (\cos, \sin)$. However, unlike the sine wave, a 0° starting phase does not place the projected cosine wave on an intersection with the line of equilibrium. Instead, the cos 0° is equal to the maximum length of the radius and is equal to the maximum amplitude for the unit circle. It is the equivalent length of radius r (or x). The notation $P(1, 0)$ indicates that the amplitude x of the projected cosine waveform at 0° of phase is equal to +1. When radius r is rotated counterclockwise so that it is flush with the positive y-axis (P_4), 90° of rotation of radius r have been completed (see Figure 5–4). However, the notation $P_4(0, 1)$ indicates that the amplitude x of the projected cosine waveform for 90° of rotation at point P_4 is equal to zero. Hence, cos 90° = 0, and the projected cosine wave at 90° of phase does in fact intersect the equilibrium line indicating zero amplitude displacement. Therefore, as described for the sine wave, 0° is the standard starting phase (angle) for the typical cosine wave and for any point P that corresponds to (x, y) or $(\cos, \sin)$. The notation $P(1, 0)$ indicates that the amplitude (x) of the projected sinusoid waveform at 0° of starting phase is equal to +1. Phase comparisons between cosine waves would be made in the same manner as those described above for the sine wave, with the amount of actual phase-lead or phase-lag determined relative to the assumed starting phase for all cosine waves, which is 0°. Caution should be practiced when attempting to make phase comparisons between a sine and a cosine wave. For example, it is inaccurate though tempting to assume that because 0° of phase angle is equal to zero amplitude (y/r) for the sine wave, and +1 amplitude for the cosine wave (x/r), that the cosine wave leads the sine wave in phase by 90°. This is absurd because in this example, both waves compared began at 0° of starting phase. Differences in amplitude that may exist between sine and cosine waves when examined for phase differences have little if any bearing on phase relations that may exist between the two.

Phase Relations Between Displacement, Velocity, and Acceleration During Harmonic Motion

Figures 3–7A, 3–8A, and 3–8C (Chapter 3) graphically illustrated the relative amplitudes of displacement, velocity, and acceleration during one cycle of simple harmonic motion. Recall that when displacement and acceleration are each at their absolute maximum amplitudes, velocity is at its minimum. Similarly, when velocity reaches maximum amplitude, both displacement and acceleration reach their absolute minimum amplitudes. The phase relations between the maximum and minimum amplitudes of the three derivatives of length (displacement, velocity, and acceleration) may be depicted with the use of sinusoidal waveforms, as illustrated in Figure 5–6. From the figure it becomes clear that when displacement is at maximum amplitude, velocity is zero. Therefore, displacement leads velocity by 90° of phase. Acceleration (the rate of change in velocity) is also at a maximum peak value (either plus or minus) when displacement is at a maximum value, and acceleration also leads velocity by 90°. Velocity lags both displacement and acceleration by 90°, as illustrated in Figure 5–6. Displacement and acceleration, however, are out of phase by 180°. That is, displacement

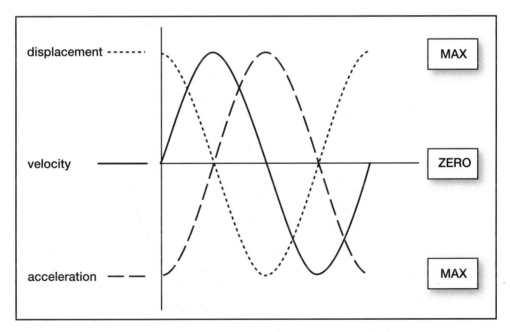

Figure 5–6. Phase relations in amplitude between displacement, velocity, and acceleration.

leads acceleration by 180°, and acceleration lags displacement by 180°.

Finally, it should also be noted that while displacement and acceleration are 180° out of phase with respect to their amplitudes, they do not, in fact, interact destructively by cancelling each other. Such an interaction, however, would be expected in the simple case of two sine waves or pure tone sounds, presented exactly 180° out of phase, and only if both had identical frequencies and amplitudes.

Peak Amplitude of a Sine Wave

Figures 5–3 and 5–5 illustrated that one cycle of the counterclockwise rotation of radius r from the positive x-axis produces continuous degree changes in angle Θ, ranging from 0° to 360°. For any degree of rotation of radius r, the amplitude of the projected sine wave, at any given location, from points P_0 to P_{15} (see Figure 5–3A) will always be equal to sin Θ, or restated, it will be equal to the length value of y. When radius r is rotated counterclockwise, to a position that is flush with the positive y-axis (P_4), the radius r has completed 90° of rotation. The notation $P_4(0, 1)$ shown in Figure 5–3A indicated that the length of segment y that was projected onto the sinusoid waveform at P_4 for 90° of rotation was equal to the maximum (peak) amplitude for a unit circle, or simply +1. This value (+1) is the equivalent length of radius r (or y). Therefore, the point P_4 with 90° of phase on the sine wave illustrated in Figure 5–3A may also be conceptualized as the *peak amplitude* for the projected sine wave. An illustration of the peak amplitude for a sine wave is again provided in Figure 5–7. The maximum

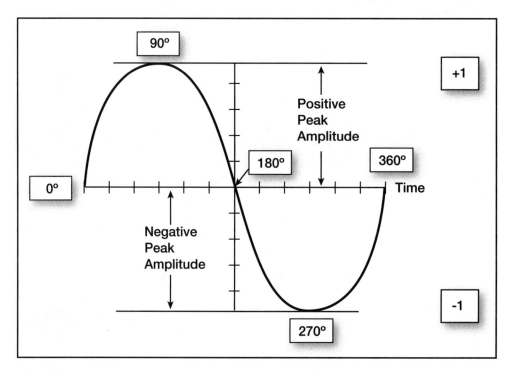

Figure 5–7. Peak amplitude of a sine wave.

peak of displacement from equilibrium, or peak amplitude, was discussed in detail in Chapter 3. Recall as well from Chapter 3 that amplitude is a vector quantity that may be specified both by its magnitude and by its direction.

Peak-to-Peak Amplitude of a Sine Wave

The peak-to-peak amplitude was also previously defined in Chapter 3 as the sum total magnitude of displacement from equilibrium in both the positive peak and negative (trough) directions. The peak-to-peak amplitude of a sine wave is illustrated in Figure 5–8A. In the previous Figure 5–3A, the peak-to-peak amplitude of the sine wave can also be conceptualized as the peak amplitude value at P_4, plus the absolute value ($|\,|$) of the peak amplitude at point P_{11}.

Using the references provided in Figure 5–3A, for any sine wave, peak-to-peak amplitude may also be defined as 2× the peak (P_4) amplitude. Therefore, for the illustrated sine wave of Figure 5–3A, the peak-to-peak amplitude is equal to

$$P_4 + |P_{11}| =$$
$$\text{peak-to-peak amplitude} =$$
$$+1 + |-1| =$$
$$\text{peak-to-peak amplitude} =$$
$$2 = \text{peak-to-peak amplitude}$$

Or simply,

$$2 \times P_4 = \text{peak-to-peak amplitude}$$
$$2 \times +1 = \text{peak-to-peak amplitude}$$
$$2 = \text{peak-to-peak amplitude}$$

Finally, the illustration in Figure 5–8B depicts two sine waves, each with the same starting phase and frequency (cycles/second) but differing only in their individual peak-to-peak amplitudes.

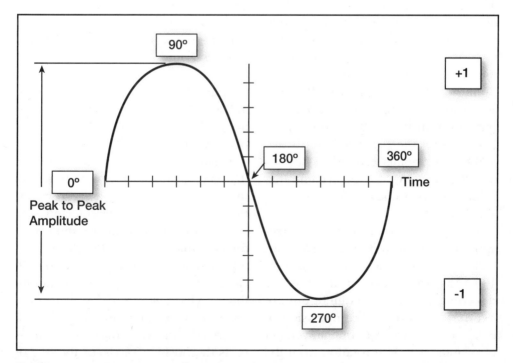

Figure 5–8A. Peak-to-peak amplitude of a sine wave.

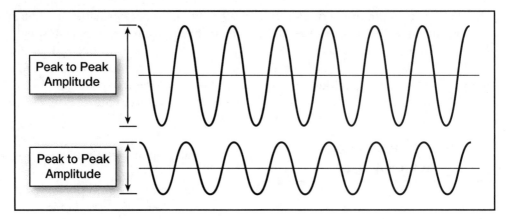

Figure 5–8B. Peak-to-peak amplitude differences for two sine waves having the same starting phase and frequency.

Compression and Rarefaction of a Sine Wave

As illustrated in Figures 5–3A, 5–3B, and 5–5A, the continued counterclockwise rotation brings radius r to the negative x-axis (P_7) after 180° of rotation (angle $\Theta = 180°$). Recall that the sin 180° = 0, and the notation $P_7 (-1, 0)$ for 180° of phase indicates that the amplitude y of the sinusoid waveform is equal to 0. That is, the projected sine wave once again intersects the line of equilibrium. Note that in Figures 5–3B, 5–5A, and 5–8A, the initial 180° of excursion (phase) from 0° to 180° represents a half-cycle of the projected sine wave and that the points marked as P_0 to P_7 (see Figure 5–3A) have been computed from positive values of y, where $y = \sin \Theta$.

The projected amplitudes corresponding to the initial positive 180° half-cycle of the sine wave (from 0° to 180°) that rise above (in the positive direction) the line of equilibrium are referred to as areas of compression or condensation. One-quarter movement of counterclockwise rotation from the negative x-axis brings radius r flush with the negative y-axis where rotational degrees correspond to 270°, or point P_{11} in Figure 5–3A. The notation $P_{11}(0, -1)$ in Figure 5–3A indicates that the amplitude y of the projected sinusoid waveform at P_{11} is again equal to the maximum value of radius r, but in a direction corresponding to the negative y-axis, or simply −1. This negative amplitude is also illustrated in Figures 5–5A, 5–7, and 5–8A. Because sin 270° = −1, and because amplitude is a vector quantity, the point P_{11} at 270° of phase in Figure 5–3A may be shown as a negative peak of displacement, or a negative peak amplitude.

Finally, radius r rotates to a position that is once again flush with the positive x-axis (at point P_{15} in Figure 5–3A. Both radius r and the projected sine wave amplitudes at this location have thus completed one full cycle of rotation, or 360°. The notation $P_{15}(1, 0)$ indicates that at 360° of phase, the amplitude y of the sinusoidal waveform is equal to 0, because sin 360° = 0. The projected sine wave once again intersects the positive x-axis, or the line of equilibrium, as illustrated in Figures 5–3A, 5–5A, and 5–8A. It is noteworthy that the added 180° of excursion, from 180° to 360°, or from points P_8 to P_{15} shown in Figure 5–3A, represents another half-cycle of the projected sine wave with a peak amplitude of –1 that was computed from negative values of y, where $y = \sin \Theta$. At location P_{15} in Figure 5–3A, a new cycle may be initiated, beginning once again at point P_0 with a 0° starting phase. The corresponding areas of the sine wave (see Figures 5–3A, 5–5, and 5–8A) located below the equilibrium line are referred to as areas of rarefaction. Corresponding areas of compression and rarefaction for a sine wave are highlighted in Figure 5–9.

Compression, Rarefaction, and Equilibrium

The periodic shape of the sine wave is often utilized in descriptions of particle or pressure displacement, as in the propagation of sound, or voltage displacement. Displacement was previously defined as a directional change in the distribution of particles, pressure, or energy around or away from a point of equilibrium in response to a force. For our purpose, each wave front generated during the propagation of sound may be conceived of as a series of repetitive particle or pressure displacements, all of which deviate from a condition of equilibrium. For the sine wave, all amplitude values that correspond to the initial half-cycle of rotation (from 0° to 180°) located above a line of equilibrium, are conceptualized as belonging to the area of compression or condensation, as discussed in Chapter 3. Because equilibrium may be understood to represent normal atmospheric pressure, areas of compression are typically illustrated with a positive (+) sign to denote a region of amplitude in which pressure is "greater than

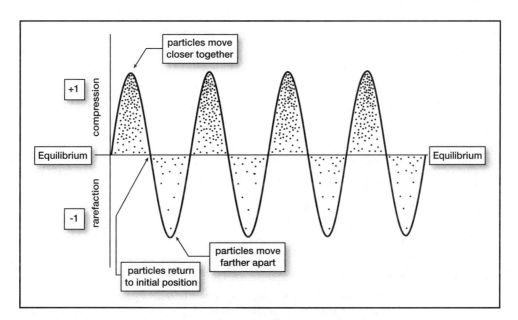

Figure 5–9. Areas of compression and rarefaction illustrated for a sine wave.

normal." Hence, when sine waves are applied to descriptions of vibratory motion or to sound propagation, areas of amplitude located above equilibrium are taken to represent waveform regions within the vibratory cycle that have relatively greater particle density, greater particle concentration, or higher pressure, as illustrated in Figure 5–9.

With respect to descriptions of vibratory motion involving particle or pressure displacement where amplitudes are associated with the second 180° half-cycle of rotation (from 180° to 360°) located below the line of equilibrium, all amplitude values that correspond to this second half-cycle are conceptualized as belonging to the rarefaction part of the sine wave (see Figure 5–9). Like compression, the concept of rarefaction was also discussed in detail in Chapter 3. Because equilibrium is understood to represent normal atmospheric pressure, areas of rarefaction are usually represented with a negative (–) to signify amplitude regions where pressure is less than normal. Therefore, sine wave areas located below the equilibrium line are characterized as regions within the vibratory cycle having relatively lower particle density, lower particle concentration, or lower pressure.

Root-Mean-Square (RMS) Amplitude

As indicated previously and as illustrated in Figure 5–10A, a sinusoidal waveform is composed of one waveform component representing a single frequency. Hence, the sine wave is often utilized to represent an auditory signal composed of a single tonal frequency, such as a pure tone. The pure tone, composed of a single frequency component, is the simplest of all auditory signals (see Chapter 6). Generally speaking, pure tones, and the periodic sinusoidal waveforms used to illustrate them, may exhibit very little fluctuation in their overall amplitude over time. Consequently, a measure of displacement, as reflected in the peak-to-peak amplitude, is often adequate to account for amplitude variations in sinusoids. By comparison, a complex waveform is, by definition, created by two or more signals that occupy the same space at

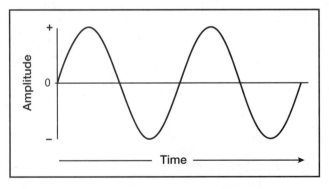

Figure 5–10A. A simple sine wave illustrates an auditory signal composed of a single tonal frequency (pure tone).

the same time. Hence, complex waveforms are composed of two or more constituent waveforms, by definition. A complex signal may, for instance, consist of two or more pure tones, producing a complex periodic waveform (see Chapter 6). A complex periodic waveform may also be generated by two or more complex periodic signals that are, by themselves, not pure tones. Additionally, and as illustrated in Chapter 6, not all complex signals are periodic. Each elemental constituent (component) within a complex signal often exhibits an autonomous frequency, starting phase, amplitude of vibration, and at times, a unique waveform morphology. The interaction of the constituent waveforms within a complex signal will not necessarily result in the overall production of a periodic waveform. Complex waveforms may also be aperiodic (not periodic). An aperiodic waveform is one whose waveform morphology shows no indication of periodicity over time. Instead, aperiodic waveforms often exhibit random versus regular repetitious variations in their waveform morphology (see Chapter 6).

Complex waveforms may exhibit periodic or aperiodic fluctuations in their peak or root-mean-square (RMS) amplitudes over time.

It will become clear in the sections that follow that the computation of the peak and/or the peak-to-peak amplitude as a measure of signal magnitude works well for signals and waveforms that are both simple and periodic, provided that their amplitudes are invariant over time. The computation of these two measures is, however, a far less useful measure or index of amplitude variation (or average amplitude) when applied to simple periodic nonsinusoidal, as well as complex periodic and/or complex aperiodic (nonperiodic) signals, especially when their instantaneous amplitudes vary over time. In such cases, the root-mean-square (RMS) amplitude is a measure that better reflects the overall power of a waveform (Durrant & Feth, 2013). As a simple example that demonstrates the necessity for RMS amplitude measurements, observe the two nonsinusoidal but simple periodic electrical square-wave pulse signals shown in Figure 5–10B. Both of the square-waves

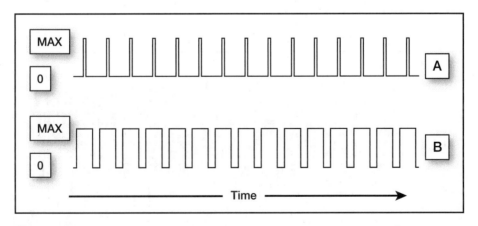

Figure 5–10B. Simple periodic nonsinusoidal square-wave electrical pulse signals.

shown in Figure 5–10B exhibit identical peak amplitudes yet differ in their overall amounts of energy. For any signal, energy exists only when the waveforms of the signal take on nonzero displacement values relative to equilibrium. Differences in the overall energy between the two electrical square-wave functions shown, as expressed by their RMS amplitudes, should be evident by the greater amount (duration) of nonzero waveform displacement in the square-wave function labeled with the letter B. The square-wave signal labeled with an A remains at a zero value for a longer duration of time compared to electrical square-wave B. The computed RMS amplitude would be greater for electrical square-wave function B, simply because each instantaneous peak in B is at maximum amplitude for longer durations of time during each cycle.

The complex periodic acoustic waveforms shown in Figures 5–10C and 5–10D serve as yet additional examples of waveforms requiring the use of RMS amplitude computations (Rosen & Howell, 2013). In each case, the instantaneous amplitudes of the complex periodic waveform of the vowel "ahhhh" /ɑ/ shown in Figure 5–10C, and especially the complex aperiodic waveform of the (sibilant fricative) consonant "shhhh" /ʃ/ (Figure 5–10D) will vary over time.

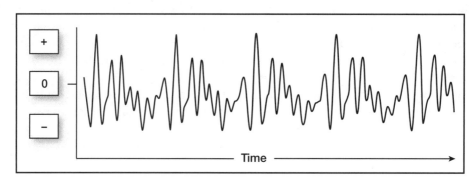

Figure 5–10C. Complex periodic nonsinusoidal waveform signal for the vowel "ahhhh" /ɑ/. Original source: Rosen, S., & Howell, P. (1991). *Signals and Spectra for Speech and Hearing.* ISBN: 0-12-597231-8. With permission from author.

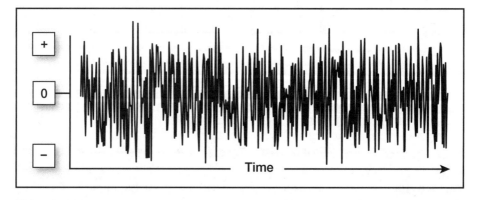

Figure 5–10D. Complex aperiodic waveform signal for the (sibilant fricative) consonant "shhhh" /ʃ/.

Therefore, the RMS amplitude is a measure that better reflects the overall power of such a waveform, and only a computed RMS amplitude could adequately describe the overall average peak-to-peak amplitudes of waveforms such as those found in speech signals, over time.

Computation of RMS Amplitude

Like computations of the (biased) sample variance (S^2) in the discipline of statistics, and its square root ($\sqrt{s^2}$ or S) which is commonly known as the sample standard deviation, the RMS amplitude for any waveform may be defined as the square root of the mean of a sample of squared instantaneous amplitudes, or deviations (i.e., compressions and rarefactions), from equilibrium. More simply put, it is the standard deviation (or square root of the mean of a sample of squared instantaneous amplitude deviations) obtained from a waveform (Durrant & Feth, 2013). RMS amplitude may be written as

$$\text{RMS amplitude} = \sqrt{\Sigma(X - M)^2 \div n}$$
$$(5\text{--}2)$$

or $\qquad [\Sigma(X - M)^2 \div n]^{\frac{1}{2}}$

where

$\sqrt{}$ = taking the square root of

$[\ ]^{\frac{1}{2}}$ = taking the square root of

Σ = summation

X = an instantaneous amplitude

M = the mean amplitude, equilibrium, or simply zero

$(X - M)^2$ = the squared amplitude deviations from the mean

n = the number of deviations that were squared

For most waveforms, the real or imaginary point of equilibrium represents zero amplitude. Hence, the average of the maximum positive (compression) and maximum negative (rarefaction) amplitude deviations across separate cycles for any signal will always be equal to zero, regardless of the true overall amplitude of a waveform. That is, the mean of the instantaneous amplitude deviations from above and below the point of equilibrium is always equal to zero. Furthermore, if the deviations were not squared, the sum of the unsquared (+) and (−) deviations from equilibrium would also be equal to zero. Because it cannot be the case that all waveforms have zero amplitude, the best solution, as in statistics, is to square both the positive and negative deviations, and then summate all of the now positive deviations from equilibrium, to obtain a meaningful, nonzero column of sample amplitudes that can be averaged. A sampling of instantaneous amplitudes might proceed in the manner illustrated in Figure 5–10E, where each of the six sample values (amplitudes) is assigned the prefix $+A_x$ or $-A_x$.

RMS amplitude is, therefore, computed in a nearly identical manner as the computation of the descriptive statistic known as the (sample) standard deviation ($\sqrt{s^2}$ or S), defined as the square root of the sample variance (s^2), which is easily computed for any sample set of numbers. In summary, to compute RMS amplitude using the written form of Equation 5–2:

1. (a) Subtract the mean (zero) from each instantaneous positive (compression) and from each negative (rarefaction) deviation

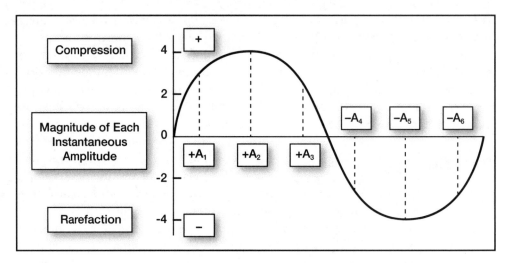

Figure 5–10E. Sampling of instantaneous amplitudes for the computation of the RMS amplitude of a sine wave.

of interest, in the sample of peak amplitudes. (b) Square each instantaneous positive (compression) and each negative (rarefaction) deviation of interest, in the sample of amplitudes.

2. Now add the squared deviations together or simply summate the squared values.

3. Take the mean of the squared deviations by simply dividing by n, which is the (biased) number of deviations that were originally squared in the sample. This is the mean square amplitude that is equivalent to the statistical measure of a (biased) sample variance, or s^2.

4. Take the square root of the mean of the squared deviations (i.e., the square root of the biased sample variance) to compensate for the overinflated (variance) values created by the initial but necessary squaring process. This then yields the RMS amplitude, which is equivalent in measure to a

biased sample standard deviation, in statistics.

RMS Amplitude of a Sine Wave

As in the statistical computation of standard deviation, the RMS amplitude for a complex waveform is likely to require the assistance of a computer. However, the actual computation of RMS amplitude may be illustrated in a simplified form for one complete cycle of any sinusoidal waveform. This measure is easily obtained for sine waves because such waveforms exhibit symmetrical and invariant deviations above and below the point of equilibrium. For example, consider the sinusoid presented in Figure 5–11A. If the peak (or maximum) amplitude value of this sinusoid is set to four arbitrary units (with a peak-to-peak amplitude of 8) then RMS amplitude may be computed (see Table 5–2) employing the six instantaneous amplitudes provided, together with the steps that were outlined above when using Equation 5–2. Each observation X in the

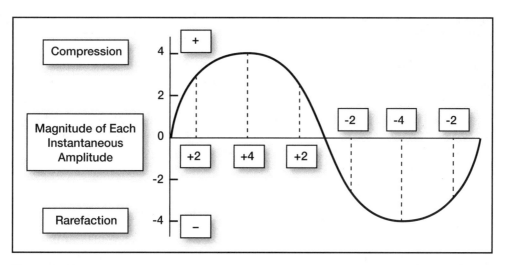

Figure 5–11A. Quantities used in the computation of RMS amplitude for a sine wave (Table 5–2) based on Figure 5–10E.

Table 5–2. Computation of RMS Amplitude for a Sine Wave Using Equation 5–2 ($[\Sigma(X - M)^2 \div n]^{1/2}$) and Based on Values Provided in Figure 5–11A

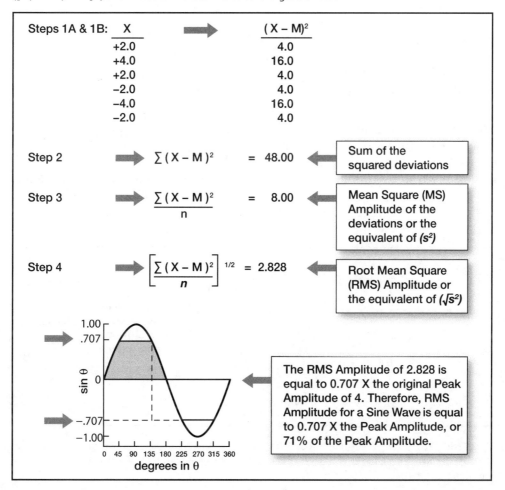

183

equation in Table 5–2 represents any one of the six instantaneous amplitudes for $+A_x$ or $-A_x$ that were illustrated in Figures 5–10D and numerically represented in Figure 5–11A. Computation of RMS amplitude in Table 5–2 therefore begins with Steps 1a and 1b. As indicated in Table 5–2, the RMS amplitude for a sine wave with a peak amplitude value of 4 is equal to 2.828. The computed RMS amplitude value of 2.828 is actually 71% (0.7070) of the original peak amplitude of 4. That is, 0.707 times the original peak amplitude of 4 is equal to the RMS amplitude of 2.828.

It so happens that if the peak amplitude value of the sine wave illustrated in Figure 5–11A had been set to five arbitrary units, then the computed RMS amplitude would have been equal to 3.535. The RMS amplitude value of 3.535 is also 71% (0.7070) of this new peak amplitude of 5. For any peak amplitude value of a sine wave, the computed RMS amplitude value is always 71% (0.7070) of whatever the value of the peak amplitude happens to be. Because we are able to assume invariance in the amplitude of a simple

sine over time, the RMS amplitude of one cycle of any sine wave would be sufficient to define the average amplitude for the entire sine wave over time, which is therefore calculated simply by multiplying:

$$0.7070 \times \text{the peak amplitude}$$

Or the equivalent,

$$0.3536 \times \text{the peak-to-peak amplitude}$$

In general and as summarized also in Figure 5–11B,

1. For any peak amplitude (P):

   RMS amplitude is equal to $0.7070 \times P$.

2. For any peak-to-peak amplitude (PP):

   RMS amplitude is equal to $0.3536 \times PP$.

Relationship of RMS Amplitude to the Unit Circle

Recall that in a unit circle, the maximum amplitudes of +1 and −1 are equiva-

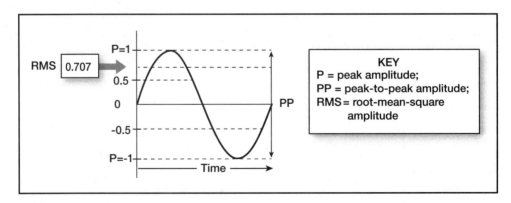

Figure 5–11B. Summary illustration of peak (P), peak-to peak (PP), and the RMS amplitude of a sine wave. Because the peak amplitude of a sine wave is equal to 1, the RMS amplitude of a sine wave must also be equal to 0.707.

lent to the length of segment y and that each is derived from the sine function of angle Θ (sin Θ), such that

$$\sin 90° = +1$$

$$\sin 270° = -1$$

It was also shown that

$$\sin 0° = 0$$

$$\sin 180° = 0$$

$$\sin 360° = 0$$

In statistical terms, the mean of any set of values in a distribution represents the best estimate of any value that can be found in that sample distribution of values, or in the case of the sine wave, the mean amplitude represents the midpoint between the two amplitude extremes. For the unit circle, the mean of the two amplitude extremes of +1 and −1 (represented as the midpoint of sine 90° and sine 270°) is, of course, zero, or equilibrium, as indicated above. Nevertheless, the mean of each +1 peak amplitude and −1 peak amplitude for a unit circle can be determined in the following manner using the following rules. Note that the combination of +1 and −1 actually represent a peak-to-peak (or 2 × peak) amplitude for the unit circle.

1. Square each instantaneous positive (compression) and each negative (rarefaction) deviation.
2. Divide each of the squared deviations by two (since both peak amplitudes combined actually represent the peak-to-peak amplitude) and add the products of the squared deviations together.

3. Take the mean of the squared deviation products by simply dividing by n, which is the number of deviations that were originally squared.
4. Take the square root of the mean of the squared deviation products.

Step (1)

$$(\text{compression}) \ 1^2 + (\text{rarefaction}) \ -1^2$$
$$= 1.00 \text{ and } 1.00$$

Step (2)

$$(\tfrac{1}{2} \times 1.00) + (\tfrac{1}{2} \times 1.00) = 1.00$$

Step (3)

$$1.00 \div 2 = \tfrac{1}{2} \text{ or } 0.5$$

Step (4)

$$\sqrt{0.5} = 0.7070$$
$$\uparrow$$

Root Mean Square (RMS) Amplitude of the Unit Circle

Hence, for the unit circle,

RMS amplitude = 0.7070

Alternatively, the mean of the zero amplitude observed at equilibrium and at each of the maximum amplitudes of +1 or −1 is equal to 0.5 and −0.5, or simply on half of each of the peak amplitudes. For a sine wave, each of the midpoints for each of the peak amplitudes (+1 or −1) is reached twice during each half-cycle of rotation. The mean of each peak amplitude of compression, and peak amplitude of rarefaction for a sine wave, can be determined in the following manner using the rules listed below:

1. Square each instantaneous positive (compression) and each negative (rarefaction) deviation.
2. Multiply each of the squared deviations by two (since each is reached twice during each half-cycle of rotation) and add the products of the squared deviations together.
3. Take the mean of the squared deviation products by simply dividing by n, which is the number of deviations that were originally squared.
4. Take the square root of the mean of the squared deviation products

Step (1)

$$(\tfrac{1}{2})^2 \text{ or } (0.5)^2 + (-\tfrac{1}{2})^2 \text{ or } (-0.5)^2$$
$$= 0.25 \text{ and } 0.25$$

Step (2)

$$(2 \times 0.25) + (2 \times 0.25) = 1.0$$

Step (3)

$$1.0 \div 2 = \tfrac{1}{2} \text{ or } 0.5$$

Step (4)

$$\sqrt{0.5} = 0.7070$$
$$\uparrow$$

Root Mean Square (RMS) Amplitude of the Unit Circle

To be sure, in the simple case of the unit circle where the peak amplitude is equal to 1 arbitrary unit, the RMS amplitude is simply 0.7070×1. This point may again be demonstrated. Figure 5–11B can be used to illustrate that the RMS amplitude of any sine wave

generated by the movement of a radius through a unit circle is always equal to $0.707 \times$ the peak amplitude (which is always 1), or is simply equivalent to 0.707. To begin with, Figure 5–11B illustrates a sine wave with peak and half-peak amplitudes that we can describe as sample values of interest. There are peak (P) amplitudes at 1 and at –1. Also shown are the two positive half-peak amplitudes, each at +0.5, and the two negative half-peak amplitudes, each at –0.5. Hence, there are six sample values of interest in total. Once again, using the written form of Equation 5–2,

1. Square each instantaneous positive (compression) and each negative (rarefaction) deviation of interest, in the sample of amplitudes. This yields the six (positive squared) values of 0.25, 1.0, 0.25, 0.25, 1.0, and 0.25.
2. Now add the squared deviations (squared values) together or simply summate the (six in this case) squared values. Therefore, $0.25 + 1.0 + 0.25 + 0.25 + 1.0 + 0.25 = 3.00$.
3. Take the mean (or average) of the squared deviations (squared values) by simply dividing by n, which is the number (six in this case) of deviations that were originally squared in the sample (of original amplitude values). Hence, $3.00 \div 6.00 = 0.5$.
4. Take the square root of the mean of the squared deviations to compensate for the overinflated (variance) in the values that was created by the initial but necessary squaring process. Hence, $\sqrt{0.5} = 0.7070$.

The RMS amplitude of a unit circle may also be represented as the average number of degrees between equilibrium, and each quarter rotation of radius r, or simply, the mean of each $90°$ of rotation, beginning at $0°$. The quarter rotation degree markers are listed below as sine wave locations A through D. Hence, the mean number of degrees between the angles presented on the left of the equal sign, computes to

$$0° + 90° = 45° \qquad \text{(A)}$$

$$90° + 180° = 135° \qquad \text{(B)}$$

$$180° + 270° = 225° \qquad \text{(C)}$$

$$270° + 360° = 315° \qquad \text{(D)}$$

As indicated previously in Table 5–1, the sine of each of the mean number of degrees in each quarter cycle rotation (listed) is also equivalent to 71% of the peak amplitude in each instance, because

A $\sin 45° = 0.7070$

B $\sin 135° = 0.7070$

C $\sin 225° = -0.7070$

D $\sin 315° = -0.7070$

What Are Radians?

Inasmuch as angles of motion are customarily measured in degrees, the mathematics of circular motion may also be computed using radians as standard units of angular measurement. The radian is a way to express the angle Θ (or theta) of a unit circle in terms of the curved distance (arc) traveled between two points along the circumference of a circle. The two points that determine the length of this arc segment are defined by the locations where the horizontal x-axis segment (line of equilibrium) and the radius r intersect the outer perimeter of the circle. Recall that at the onset of rotational motion, angle Θ begins at $0°$ where radius r is flush with and equal to the horizontal x-axis segment. As radius r rotates counterclockwise, the distance between the two points—the point of inter-section of radius r with the outer perimeter of circle, and the point of intersection of the fixed equilibrium line (horizontal x-axis segment) with the outer circle perimeter—gradually increases, as will be illustrated in Figure 5–12B. If and when the length of the arc defined by the intersection described above reaches a value (in length) equal to the length of radius r, then one radian of angular rotational measure has been reached or has been defined for angle Θ. However, in order to better understand radians, it is important first to review some basic properties of circles, as illustrated in Figure 5–12A.

Diameter and Circumference

To begin with, the diameter of a circle is usually defined as a line segment that passes through the center of the circle. The diameter, therefore, divides the circle into two equal halves (Figure 5–12A). The diameter is also defined as twice the length of the radius (r), or simply

$$\text{diameter} = 2r$$

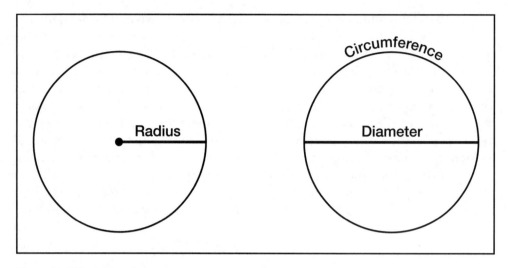

Figure 5–12A. Radius, diameter, and circumference of a circle.

The circumference of any circle may be thought of as a curved spherical arc that defines the outer boundaries of the circle, as well as the distance or length around the circle. It was the Greek mathematician Archimedes (287–212 BC) who initially determined that the circumference for any circle may be computed by taking the product of a constant value π (3.14159265) and the circle's diameter, or simply,

$$\text{circumference} = \pi \times \text{diameter}$$

where $\pi = 3.14159265$

since $\text{diameter} = 2r$

Hence, $\text{circumference} = \pi 2r$

or   circumference = $2\pi r$ or 2π (radians)

Therefore, for a unit circle whose radius r is equal to 1, the circumference is equal to $2\pi r$, where

$$2\pi r = 6.283$$

It is also noteworthy that the value π is, by definition, always equal to the circumference of a circle divided by the circle's diameter, or

$$\pi = \pi 2r/2r$$

Radians of Angles

In order to further introduce radians, it is now important to look at Figure 5–12B. Note that radius r and the side adjacent to angle Θ, or simply side x, are both equal in length. Therefore, radius r and side x may be said to represent two separate radii. Note also that side x intersects the perimeter of the circle at point S, and radius r intersects the circle perimeter at point P. As radius r is rotated counterclockwise, an arc SP is created, whose length is defined by the intersection of these two radii with the perimeter of the circle at points S and P, as illustrated in Figure 5–12B. It should be obvious that as radius r is rotated counterclockwise, point P moves progressively away from point S and arc SP increases in

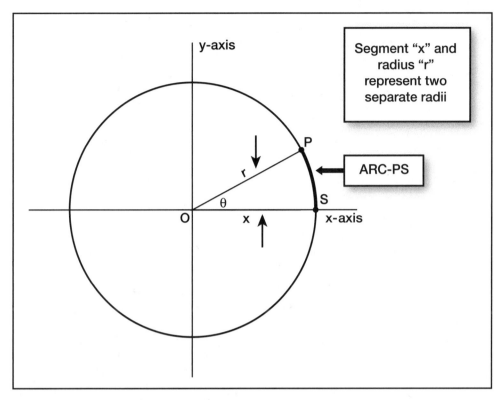

Figure 5–12B. Arc-*PS* created by the intersection of radius *r* and segment *x* with the outer perimeter of a unit circle.

length. When arc *SP* reaches a length that is equal to the (fixed) length of radius *r* (as discussed above), then angle Θ is exactly equal to 1 radian by definition. Therefore, a radian is a unit of angular measurement formed at the center (Θ) of a circle. Angle Θ is equal to one radian when an arc (*SP*) whose length is delineated by the intersection of two radii with the perimeter (circumference) of the circle is equal to the length of radius *r*. Hence, angle Θ may generally be specified in radians, such that

$$\text{Angle Θ in radians} = \text{arc length} \div \text{radius length}$$

$$(5\text{–}3A)$$

or in the present example,

Angle Θ in radians =
Arc *SP* ÷ radius *r*

For any unit circle with a radius $r = 1$ and Arc $SP = 1$;

where

Angle Θ in radians = arc *SP*/radius *r*

and   Angle Θ in radians = 1/1

then   Angle Θ = 1 radian

In summary, for any angle Θ, 1 radian of angular measure exists: when the two radii, consisting of a radius *r*, a side *x*, and an arc (*SP*) that is delineated by the intersection of the two radii (*r* and *x*) with the outer perimeter of a circle are all equal in length.

Hence,

Angle Θ = 1 radian

when

radius r = (side x) = arc SP

How Many Radians Are There in A Unit Circle?

The arc length that is created by a full cycle of rotation through a complete circle would, of course, consist of the entire length of the circumference. Recall that the equation for the circumference of a circle is $2\pi r$. This means that a full circle has an arc length that is equal to $2\pi r$ (the circumference). Hence, restating the general equation presented as Equation 5–3A above for the unit circle,

Angle Θ in radians =
arc length ÷ radius length

where for a complete unit circle,

Arc length = $2\pi r$

Then, for a complete unit circle

Angle Θ in radians = $2\pi r/r$

or

Angle Θ in radians = 2π

Therefore,

one circle = 2π radians

or

one unit circle = 6.283 radians

Radians and Degrees: Both in a Unit Circle and for a Sine Wave

Radians are also related to degrees in a unit circle and are related to sine waves in the following ways. The relationship between a few of the possible degrees of rotation of radius r and the corresponding number of radians is illustrated in Figures 5–12C and 5–12D.

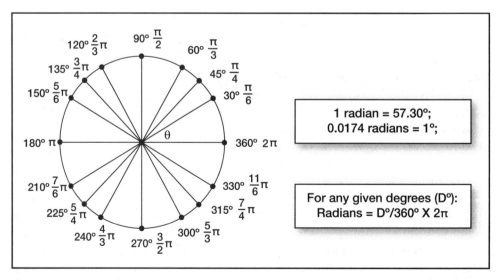

Figure 5–12C. A few of the many possible degrees of rotation of a radius within a unit circle with corresponding radians.

Figure 5–12C is a slight modification of Figure 5–3B presented earlier. Figure 5–12D also illustrates the relationship between degrees, cycles, and radians in two cycles of a sine and cosine wave. Recall that one full cycle of radius r in a complete circle consists of 360° of rotation. Since,

$$2\pi \text{ radians} = \text{degrees in one circle}$$
$$(5\text{–}3B)$$

then $2\pi \text{ radians} = 360°$

and $1 \text{ radian} = 360°/2\pi$

since $2\pi = 6.283 \text{ radians}$

Therefore,

$$1 \text{ radian} = 360°/6.283$$

Consequently,

$$6.283 \times 57.30° = 360°$$

Hence, $1 \text{ radian} = 57.30°$

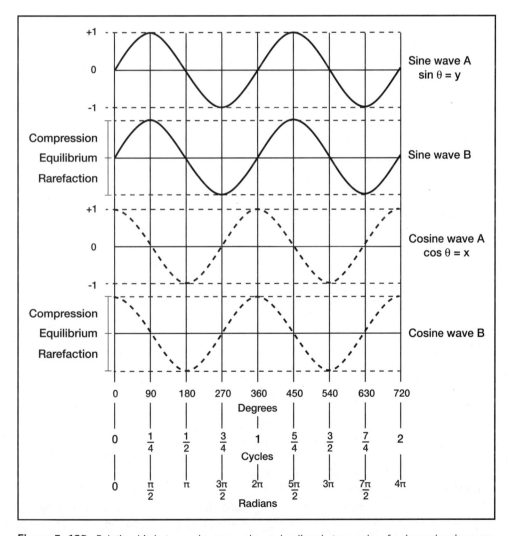

Figure 5–12D. Relationship between degrees, cycles, and radians in two cycles of a sine and cosine wave.

also $2\pi \div 360°$ radians = $1°$

Therefore,

0.0174 radians = $1°$

Computing Radians for Unit Circles and Sine Waves

What follows are examples of some simple methods used to convert the degrees in a unit circle or in a sine wave into radians, followed by methods that could be used to verify the conversion. Looking again at Figures 5–12C and 5–12D, it becomes clear that because 90° corresponds to one quarter of a full cycle (¼ × 360°), it is evident that 90° also corresponds to (¼ × 2π) radians, or simply,

$2\pi/4$ radians

or $\pi/2$ radians = $90°$

Since

$2\pi/4$ radians = $\pi/2$ radians

Furthermore, since

$\pi/2 = 1.5707$

and   1 radian = $57.30°$

then

$\pi/2$ radians = $1.5707 \times 57.30°$

since $1.5707 \times 57.30° = 90°$

then $\pi/2$ radians = $90°$

Figures 5–12C and 5–12D also illustrate that 180° corresponds to one half of a full cycle (½ × 360°). Therefore, 180° should also correspond to ½ × 2π radians, or simply,

$2\pi/2$ radians = $180°$

since $2\pi/2$ radians = π radians

and $\pi = 3.1415$

also   1 radian = $57.30°$

then

π radians = $3.1415 \times 57.30°$

and $3.1415 \times 57.30° = 180°$

Therefore,

π radians = $180°$

As a final example, Figures 5–12C and 5–12D also illustrate that 270° corresponds to three quarters of a full cycle (3/4 × 360°). Therefore, 270° should correspond to (3/4 × 2π) radians, or simply,

$6\pi/4$ radians = $270°$

since

$6\pi/4$ radians = $3\pi/2$ radians

and $3\pi/2 = 4.712$

also   1 radian = $57.30°$

then

$3\pi/2$ radians = $4.712 \times 57.30°$

and $4.712 \times 57.30° = 270°$

Therefore,

$3\pi/2$ radians = $270°$

As a general rule, to convert degrees into the radians illustrated in Figures 5–12C and 5–12D, for any given number of degrees of interest ($D°$),

1. Determine what fractional part of 360° the number of degrees of interest ($D°$) represents, or simply, state the ratio: $D°/360°$.
2. Reduce the numerator and denominator in the $D°/360°$ ratio by finding the common divisors in both, and multiply the final ratio (fraction) by 2π.

Mass and Stiffness in Opposition

To produce harmonic motion, a force in the form of a pushing or a pulling is applied to an elastic object at rest. In order to apply a force, energy must be utilized, work must be accomplished, and inertia must be overcome as discussed in previous chapters. For a simple harmonic oscillator, the amount of force that is initially delivered will be proportional to the amount of displacement that initially occurs.

The restorative force of elasticity will also be proportional to the object's displacement from equilibrium as postulated by Hooke's law. The initial pushing or pulling on a spring-mass or pendulum results in a maximum or peak amplitude of displacement in either one direction or the other. How is it that the properties of displacement and acceleration are in direct phase opposition to each other during simple harmonic motion, as illustrated in Figure 5–6?

The Role of Mass

To begin with, every object is composed of relative amounts of mass and relative amounts of stiffness. Recall that mass is a measure of the inertia within an object and by definition, the inertial force that is afforded by mass is a force that resists or opposes change, like changes in displacement. Acceleration was previously defined as the rate of change in velocity, and according to Newton's second law of motion, acceleration is inversely proportional to mass such that

$$Acceleration = force/mass$$

Therefore, it may be stated that mass (inertia) resists acceleration (changes in velocity) as well as velocity (changes in displacement). Mass and inertia also resist displacement if the object has not yet been displaced, as by definition, displacement constitutes a change from equilibrium.

The Role of Stiffness

Elasticity was previously defined as the general property of matter that allows objects to temporarily alter their shape or size when a force is applied. Compliance was defined in Chapter 4 as an indication of the amount of displacement or distortion per unit of force, whereas stiffness was described as a measure of the opposition to displacement or the opposition to distortion, per unit of force (Durrant & Feth, 2013). Hence, stiffness and compliance were said to be reciprocals. Stiffness was also defined as the restorative force of elasticity that is directly proportional to displacement, such that

$$F \sim \text{delta } x$$

This definition was also provided by Hooke's law, which may also be written as

$$F \sim -kx$$

in which k, the spring constant, corresponds to stiffness. The negative sign before the spring constant indicates that the direction of the spring force is always opposite to the direction of the displacement of the free end of the spring (Halliday et al., 2011). The restorative force of stiffness also resists displacement in an elastic object that has been displaced. As an object gradually reaches its maximum displacement, the restorative force of stiffness or gravity also gradually builds in opposition to the displacement. The restorative force will eventually bring the object to a halt, but in order to do this, the restorative force must first overcome inertia. In addition, once the object has been halted, the restorative force must again overcome inertia in the maximally displaced object, to initiate movement in the opposite direction, or in a direction (back) toward equilibrium. Therefore, opposition exists between stiffness and mass in an object set into vibratory motion. This opposition exists because the restorative force opposes displacement, whereas mass favors displacement. Conversely, stiffness promotes rate changes in velocity (acceleration), and mass opposes acceleration in an object set into vibratory motion. Hence, with each cycle of harmonic motion, the restorative force of elasticity and acceleration are in perpetual phase opposition to the inertial force of mass and displacement, as illustrated previously in Figure 5–6. The balance between the two forms of opposition will always depend upon the relative amounts of mass and stiffness inherent within a given vibrating system.

Relation to Sound

How do the fundamental trigonometric functions addressed above relate to the physics of sound? Periodic, harmonic, and sinusoidal motion has been defined in terms of uniform circular motion. A body in uniform circular motion moves about the circumference of a circle at a constant speed, or through a constant number of degrees of rotation per second (Hirsh, 1952). Recall from Chapters 2 and 3 that the *second* is the standard unit of measure for time in both the CGS and MKS metric systems. The concept of time is also a fundamental physical dimension used in physics (Halliday et al., 2011) as well as in hearing science. Recall also that the term *rate* was defined as a fixed ratio of time (measured per unit) between consecutive quantities, amounts, or degrees of a standard unit of measure (Giancoli, 2005). The property of time, therefore, may be used to bridge the gap between basic trigonometric functions and physics, and therefore, between trigonometry and the waveform properties of sound.

Frequency and Period Revisited

Hertz

In Chapter 3, the number of completed back-and-forth cycles or oscillations of displacement of a pendulum, a spring-mass, or a sine wave occurring per unit of time (per second) was simply called the number of cycles per second, or the frequency (f) of vibration. In honor of the German physicist (Box 5–1 and Portrait 5–1) Heinrich Hertz (1857–1894),

Box 5–1. Heinrich Rudolph Hertz (1857–1894)

Hertz was born in Hamburg Germany on February 22, 1857. Hertz abandoned the study of engineering which he had prepared for in his earlier years, and did so in favor of physics, which he turned to at the age of 20. Hertz discovered that he was more interested in learning the laws of nature than in applying them. He therefore set off to study physics at the University of Berlin under the very eminent scientist, Hermann von Helmholtz. Helmholtz (1821–1894) was a distinguished physicist and physiologist and was instrumental in helping to establish the field of experimental psychology (Boring, 1957). Beginning in 1833, and during much of his career, Hertz also devoted considerable effort and attention to the theoretical study of electromagnetic waves as put forth by the Scottish physicist James Clerk Maxwell (1831–1879). In one theory, Maxwell unified all the phenomena of electricity and magnetism (Giancoli, 2005) and proposed that light was an electromagnetic wave. Maxwell measured the speed of light and proposed that light was simply electromagnetic radiation that vibrated within a particular frequency range (Hewitt, 2010). Hertz set out to test Maxwell's prediction that many kinds of electromagnetic radiation exist in nature (Stutz, 2006). The discoveries in electromagnetic theory that made Hertz famous occurred from 1885 to 1889, when he was professor of physics in the Karlsruhe Polytechnic. In 1888, Hermann von Helmholtz encouraged Hertz to compete for a prize in electromagnetics that was being offered by the Berlin Academy of Sciences. As a result, Hertz was able to establish strong and clear confirmation for Maxwell's theory (Giancoli, 2005). Hertz was able to demonstrate, beyond doubt, that light waves and electromagnetic waves are identical. Hertz determined that these electromagnetic radio waves, called Hertzian waves at the time, could be reflected and refracted like heat and light waves, and that these Hertzian waves seemed to move at the speed of light (Stutz, 2006). Hertz was appointed professor of physics at the University of Bonn in 1899 and remained there until his death in 1894. The idea that electromagnetic waves could be produced and could be made to travel through space introduced the possibility of new avenues for communication. Hertz's work eventually caught the attention of the inventive genius of the Italian physicist, Guglielmo Marconi (1874–1937) who developed the "wireless" telegraph (Giancoli, 2005). Initially, Marconi was able to send and receive radio telegraph waves across a distance of a mile and a half, and by 1901, was successfully transmitting across the Atlantic (Stutz, 2006). Others used the results of Hertz's work to develop what we know presently as the radio, the television, and radar. His work also led to the discovery in 1895 of x-rays as described by the German physicist and Nobel Laureate, W. K. Röntgen (Hewitt, 2010; Stutz, 2006).

Portrait 5–1. Heinrich Rudolph Hertz (1857–1894). Printed with permission. Wikimedia Commons, public domain.

the term *hertz* (Hz) is the special name that is also synonymous with frequency, and with cycles/second. Hence, the unit of frequency is the Hz. For example, frequencies of 250, 500, 1000, 2000, 4000, or 8000 cycles/second may be expressed as 250 Hz, 500 Hz, 1000 Hz, 2000 Hz, 4000 Hz, or 8000 Hz. Likewise, frequencies of 250, 500, 1000, 1500, 2000, 2500, 3000, and so forth, cycles/second may be referred to as 0.25 kHz,

0.5 kHz, 1 kHz, 1.5 kHz, 2 kHz, 2.5 kHz, 3 kHz, and so forth.

Recall as well from Chapter 3 that the amount of time it takes to complete just one full cycle of displacement of a pendulum, a spring-mass, or a sine wave, is called a period. It was also stated that the period of pendulum vibration was directly proportional to the square root of the pendulum length, and that the frequency of pendulum vibration was inversely related to the square root of the pendulum length. The period of a cycle can range from seconds (which is rare) to fractions (thousandths) of a second (which is common). Period (T) was also stated to be equal to the inverse of frequency (f), making T and f reciprocals.

Consequently,

$$period\ (T) = 1/frequency\ (f)$$

and

$$frequency\ (f) = 1/period\ (T)$$

The relationship between frequency and period for six *audiometric* frequencies is shown in Table 5–3 borrowed from the computations of frequency and period of Table 3–1. The relationship between frequency and period is also illustrated in Figure 5–13A using 1 second as the unit for time, and in

Table 5–3. Frequency and Period for Six Audiometric Frequencies, Borrowed From Table 3–1

Frequency (cycles/second)	Period		
	1/f	Seconds	Milliseconds
250 Hz	1/250	0.00400	4.000
500 Hz	1/500	0.00200	2.000
1000 Hz	1/1000	0.00100	1.000
2000 Hz	1/2000	0.00050	0.500
4000 Hz	1/4000	0.00025	0.250
8000 Hz	1/8000	0.000125	0.125

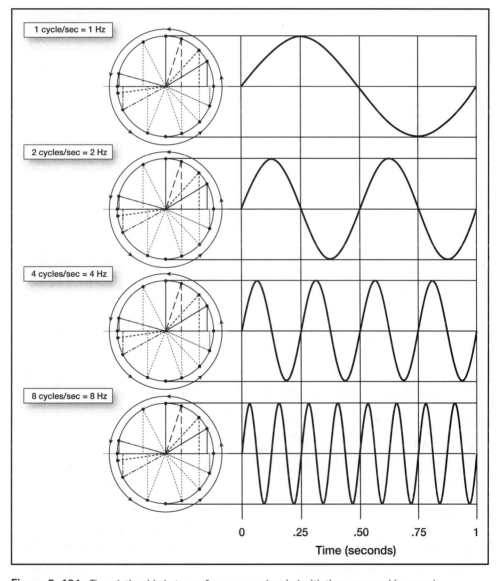

Figure 5–13A. The relationship between frequency and period with time measured in seconds.

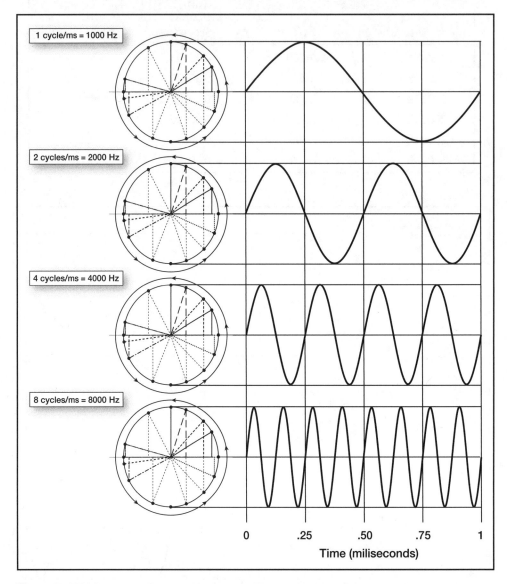

Figure 5–13B. Relationship between frequency and period with time measured in milliseconds.

Figure 5–13B, using 1 millisecond as the unit for time. Finally, Figure 5–13C illustrates the relationships between radians, phase, period, and peak amplitude for two cycles of a sine wave. An easy method that may be used to compute frequency from period, or period from frequency is illustrated below with Equations 5–4A and 5–4B.

1. If the period (*T*) is known, and frequency (*f*) is unknown, then

$$1000 \div T \text{ (in msec.)} = f \text{ (in Hz)}$$
(5–4A)

2. If the frequency (*f*) is known, and period (*T*) is unknown, then

$$1000 \div f \text{ (in Hz)} = T \text{ (in msec.)}$$
(5–4B)

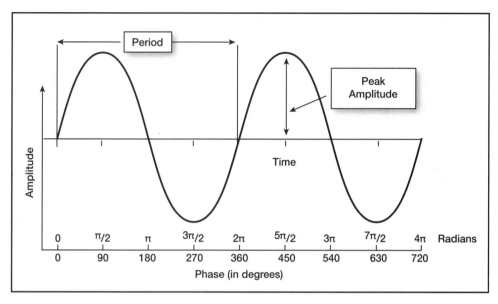

Figure 5–13C. Relationships that exist between radians, phase, period, and peak amplitude for two cycles of a sine wave.

Mass, Stiffness, Frequency, and Period

The relationship between mass and stiffness and their effects on frequency and period can also be formalized with the following equation:

$$\text{period } (T) = 2\pi \, [m \div k]^{1/2}$$
$$(5\text{--}5A)$$

$$\text{frequency } (f) = 1/2\pi \, [k \div m]^{1/2}$$
$$(5\text{--}5B)$$

where

m = mass

k = the spring constant or stiffness

$[\ ]^{1/2} = \sqrt{\ }$, or the square root

Looking at Equations 5–5A and 5–5B (Giancoli, 2005), it is clear that an increase in mass (m) results in an increase in T but also results in a de-crease of f. Furthermore, an increase in stiffness (k) produces a decrease in T and a subsequent increase in f. Consequently, based exclusively on inherent amounts of stiffness and mass, two basic and relative predictions can be made in terms of the natural rate of vibration (or the fundamental frequency) for any object. These predictions are as follows: (a) If the inherent stiffness of the displaced object is proportionally greater than the object's inherent mass, the inertial force of mass will be overcome relatively quickly, and the movement of the object will be halted relatively sooner in time, when displacement is maximum. This will enable both displacement and acceleration to reach their maxima at a faster rate. The lower inertial force also means that the transfer of potential energy to the energy of motion (kinetic energy) in the halted, and maximally displaced object, should also occur at a more rapid rate. Hence, there will be less mass to oppose acceleration and more stiffness to oppose displacement. The greater degree of restorative force under these conditions is also favorable to a more rapid acceleration. Therefore, the vibrating object with a relatively greater degree of stiffness should oscillate naturally at a faster rate. (b) If the inherent mass of the displaced object is proportionally greater than the object's inherent stiffness, the inertial force will dominate the restorative force, and the movement of the object will be halted relatively later in time when displacement is at a maximum. Hence, in this case, both displacement and acceleration reach their maxima at a slower rate. The greater inertial force also means that the transfer of potential energy to kinetic energy in the halted and maximally displaced motion of a vibrating object, occurs at a slower rate. Hence, there is more mass to oppose acceleration, and there is less stiffness to oppose displacement. The greater degree of inertia is also favorable to greater displacement. The vibrating object with a relatively greater degree of mass should oscillate naturally, at a slower rate. To summarize, higher frequencies and shorter periods are associated with greater acceleration and greater stiffness. Lower frequencies and longer periods are associated with less acceleration and greater mass. Stiffness and mass determine the frequencies at which objects (or media) will vibrate.

Free Vibration and Resonance

If an object (mass) is suddenly disturbed by a force, or if it is simply displaced from equilibrium and allowed to oscillate freely, the mass will vibrate best or most efficiently at one specific frequency. The single frequency that represents the natural rate of vibration of the mass is often called the natural, best, and at times, even the (first) resonant frequency. Most often it is called the *fundamental frequency*. The statement that a mass vibrates best or most efficiently at one frequency should be taken to mean that relatively little effort (minimum force) will be required to initiate and maintain vibratory motion (Durrant & Feth, 2013) and to obtain a large resonating amplitude at that one particular special (fundamental) frequency. The fundamental frequency reflects, or is characteristic of, the object's inherent properties of mass and stiffness. The term *characteristic frequency* has also been applied to this one special frequency that is strictly determined by the combined amounts of stiffness and mass inherent within the object set into vibration. In free vibration, the instrument that delivers the external disturbance or the displacing force (the driver) does not itself transmit its own unique frequency of vibration to the mass that has been set into resonance (the load). The natural, resonant, or fundamental frequency of vibration is strictly determined by the stiffness and mass that are inherent within the object mass (the load). Furthermore, free vibration is often used together with the energy principle introduced in Chapter 4 to describe the singular, natural rate of vibration at which an object would resonate ceaselessly in a frictionless environment. As previously discussed, an understanding of harmonic motion and sound is greatly simplified when nonconservative frictional drag (resistance) is disregarded.

Therefore, as introduced in Chapter 4, free vibration in the absence of friction produces vibration at the fundamental frequency, such that the total energy *TE* in the mass is equal to the sum of the potential energy *PE* and kinetic energy *KE*, or

$$TE = PE + KE$$

It should be easy to conceptualize that at any given moment in time, potential and kinetic energy reciprocally interact at a rate that corresponds to the lowest and most frequent rate at which natural resonance occurs—that is, the lowest natural rate of vibration which is known as the fundamental frequency.

Angular Velocity/Angular Frequency

It has been stated that an object such as radius *r* that moves within a unit circle at a constant speed will undergo uniform circular motion. Although the magnitude of the velocity of this rotation may remain constant, the direction of the velocity is continuously changing as radius *r* moves through 360° of rotation. A change in the direction of velocity of any object constitutes a "rate of change in the velocity" of that object, just as a change in the magnitude of velocity constitutes a rate of change in velocity.

Recall from Chapter 3 that acceleration is a vector quantity that represents motion that is changing both in speed and in direction. Therefore, an object such as a radius, revolving in a unit circle at a constant speed, is continuously accelerating. For our purposes, the time-rate change in angle Θ may be defined for the unit circle, and for uniform circular motion in general. The

time-rate of change in angle Θ (Θ/sec) is also equal to the rate at which radius *r* rotates through 360° of the unit circle, and this is equal to $2\pi f$ (Halliday et al., 2011).

Recall that the term *f* stands for cycles/second, or frequency. Both Θ/sec and $2\pi f$ are defined as the angular velocity, angular frequency, resonant frequency, or fundamental frequency. Therefore,

$$2\pi f = \Theta/\text{sec}$$

$$2\pi f = \text{angular velocity} \quad (5\text{--}6)$$

$$2\pi f = \text{angular frequency}$$

$$2\pi f = \text{fundamental frequency}$$

Fundamental Frequency

Recall the relationship described above between mass and stiffness and the effects of both on frequency, as stated in Equation 5–5B:

$$\text{frequency } (f) = 1/2\pi \, [k \div m]^{\frac{1}{2}}$$

Multiplying each side by 2π results in

$$2\pi \, (f) = 1/2\pi \, (2\pi) \, [k \div m]^{\frac{1}{2}}$$

or $\qquad 2\pi f = [k \div m]^{\frac{1}{2}}$

Equation 5–6 indicated that $2\pi f$ represents angular velocity, angular frequency, and the natural, first resonant, or fundamental frequency of vibration (Halliday et al., 2011). It is clear that for any mass, the first resonant or fundamental frequency ($2\pi f$)

a. is directly proportional to the square root of stiffness:

$$2\pi f \sim \sqrt{s}$$

b. is inversely proportional to the square root of mass

$$2\pi f \sim \sqrt{1/m}$$

For instance, if stiffness is increased by a factor of 9:1, $2\pi f$ will increase by a factor of 3:1. If mass is increased by a factor of 9:1, $2\pi f$ will be reduced to one third (3:1). If stiffness is increased by a factor of 16:1, $2\pi f$ will increase by a factor of 4:1. If mass is increased by a factor of 16:1, $2\pi f$ will be reduced to ¼ (4:1). So, as a practical example, if the fundamental frequency for a vibrating mass were 200 Hz, and its stiffness were increased by a factor of 4:1, then its fundamental frequency would also increase by a factor of 2:1 (or the square root of 4) to a fundamental frequency of 400 Hz. If instead, the mass of the 200 Hz resonating object were to increase by a factor of 4:1, then its fundamental frequency would decrease by a factor of 2:1 (or the square root of 4) to a fundamental frequency of 100 Hz (Speaks, 1999).

Friction, Damping, and Resistance

As indicated in Chapter 3, friction is encountered in the natural realm of free-vibrating objects. Any object that vibrates in a fluid medium such as air will encounter a frictional drag force that opposes vibration. Consequently, any object-mass set into free vibration will not vibrate indefinitely. The motion of an object-mass will be damped. Therefore, free vibration is really damped sinusoidal vibration. Damping occurs when the presence of friction (the frictional force) causes the motion of a vibrating object to be reduced. For-

mally stated, when the motion of an oscillator is reduced by an external force, such as friction, the oscillator and its motion are said to be "damped" (Halliday et al., 2011). The properties of damping are, however, not always negative. For instance (sensory), outer hair cells located in the inner ear serve a significant role in hearing, such as in frequency tuning that eliminates and helps prevent frequency and pitch distortion, due to their all-important damping properties.

Though the amplitude of the waveform of any oscillating mass at its maximum resonance may be significantly reduced by damping, the expression of the first resonant or fundamental frequency itself should not be significantly affected, though it may be somewhat affected (Durrant & Feth, 2013). If it is at all affected, damping will tend to slightly lower the frequency of oscillation from that of the fundamental. This can be illustrated by the spectral envelope for the waveform shown in the upper section (panel) of Figure 5–14A. The upper spectral envelope and waveform illustrate an exponential decay of vibrations due to the effects of a moderate degree of damping. The lower spectral envelope and waveform (lower panel) illustrate the rapid exponential decay of vibration due critical damping (see below).

Damping, or friction, which is also known as (frictional) resistance, generally results in a wasting (but not the destruction) of energy, such that kinetic energy is converted to heat. Once kinetic energy has been converted to heat, the energy of motion can no longer be used for work. Figure 5–14B illustrates degrees of damping for five damping factor levels where damping

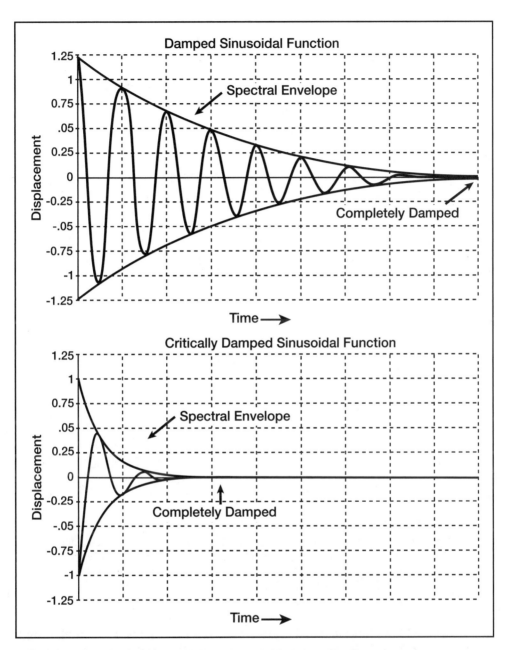

Figure 5–14A. Upper spectral envelope (*upper panel*) illustrates a moderately damped sinusoidal oscillation. Lower spectral envelope (*lower panel*) illustrates a critically damped sinusoidal oscillation.

(d_f) is defined as the natural logarithm or $\log_e$ of the ratio of amplitudes (A_1/A_2) for any two consecutive cycles of vibration (Speaks, 1999). Unlike base ten logarithms ($\log_{10}$), common logarithms or natural logarithms ($\log_e$) use a base e where e is a constant value approximately equal to 2.718281828. In any vibrating system, the duration of vibrations is directly related to the magnitude

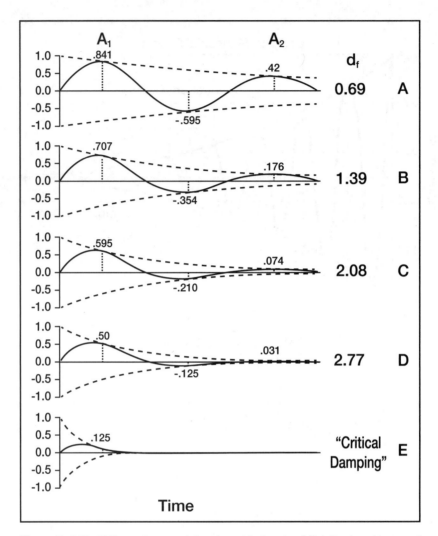

Figure 5–14B. Different degrees of damping with damping (d_f) defined as the natural log ($\log_e$) of the ratio of amplitudes (A_1 and A_2) for any two consecutive cycles of vibration. The damping ranges from 0.69 to 2.77 (A to D), to critical damping (E). $\log_e$ = 2.718281828. Reprinted from C. E. Speaks (1999), with permission.

of the applied force and inversely proportional to the level of damping. In a low-damped system, depending upon the magnitude of the force applied, the duration of vibrations can be relatively long, such as in the case of a hand-held tuning fork (Speaks, 1999). In a highly or heavily damped system, friction causes the resonances to fade away or decay very quickly, and in a system that is critically damped, resonances

cease before the completion of a single (symmetrical) cycle. Good examples of critically damped systems are the normally functioning shock absorbers in well-made automobiles.

The real world provides examples of objects that are set into free vibration, whose resonating amplitude is diminished in real time by frictional drag. One example is a large bell with an internal clapper, tilted so that the weight of the clapper strikes the bell's inner surface. The bell vibrates at its resonant or fundamental frequency by the application of the force provided by the clapper, but the resonances diminish with time. Also, a modest amount of force is usually only required to set a tuning fork into vibration at the particular fundamental frequency for which it was designed to resonate. The fundamental frequency of any vibrating object is strictly determined by the particular and relative amounts of stiffness and mass inherent within the object.

Forced Vibration

If an object mass is to be set into a continuous state of vibrating motion, energy must be continually applied to compensate for the damping effect of frictional resistance. This is because free vibration cannot continue indefinitely as long as there is friction. As long as vibrations are produced within an air or water medium rather than in a vacuum, there will always be friction. For all practical purposes, all vibrating motion (free or forced) will eventually be impeded by frictional resistance. In the case of a pendulum, if the pendulum is to continue moving (oscillating), the amount of energy loss in the pendulum resulting from friction and a frictional drag force will need to be compensated for by a constant applied force, delivered to the pendulum (Halliday et al., 2011). Friction mostly acts at the support point of a pendulum, transferring energy away from the motion of the pendulum. As indicated in Chapter 4, the presence of friction requires the need for the application of constant compensatory external forces in order to maintain consistency in the oscillation of an object. In forced vibration, the instrument that delivers the external disturbance or the displacing force (the driver) often, though not exclusively, transmits its own unique frequency of vibration to the mass that has been set into resonance (the load) (Durrant & Feth, 2013).

The two angular frequencies that are associated with a system undergoing forced vibrations are: (a) the fundamental or natural angular frequency of the system (the load) that is the fundamental frequency at which the "load" would vibrate if suddenly disturbed and allowed to vibrate freely, and (b) the angular frequency of the external driving force (the driver) that is causing the driven oscillations (Halliday et al., 2011). At the natural, best, first resonant, or fundamental frequency of the load, oscillations occur with the greatest amplitude in response to the least amount of force, provided that the driving force, and the proper rate of stimulation is delivered by the proper driver, at or near the fundamental frequency of the load that is to be set into vibration. When the frequency of the force vibration from a driver matches the natural or fundamental frequency of the object (load) that is to be set into motion, a dramatic increase in the amplitude of vibration occurs in the load. This phenomenon is often called *resonance*, which means *resounding* or *sounding again* (Hewitt, 2010). The *principle of resonance* states that when a periodically vibrating force is applied to an elastic system (the load), the elastic system will be forced to vibrate (resonate) and will initially vibrate under forced vibration at the frequency of the force that is applied by the driver. The nearer the frequency of the applied force is to the natural frequency of the elastic system (the load), the greater will be the resulting amplitude of vibration in the elastic system, or load (Speaks, 1999). Forces applied in excess, or at frequencies that are significantly different from the fundamental frequency of the load, often create unnatural and/or unwanted resonances at other frequencies. How might excess force alter the vibratory properties of a load? Recall from earlier discussion, Newton's second law of motion. For any object set into motion where mass is a constant, if net force is increased, acceleration is also increased.

$$Acceleration = force\ /\ mass$$

Hence, acceleration is directly proportional to the net force acting upon an object and is inversely proportional to the mass of the object. Recall as well that higher frequencies and shorter periods are associated with greater amounts of acceleration. A possible outcome arising from the application of too much force by the driver is not only the generation of the fundamental frequency, but in addition, the generation of progressively higher frequencies that exhibit progressively lower amplitudes. These added frequencies are called *harmonics*.

Harmonics

The *fundamental* frequency of resonance (f_0) refers to the basic, the essential, the primary, or the first natural frequency of resonance. When a load is driven to produce harmonic frequencies and the production of harmonics is linear, then the fundamental frequency will not only be the lowest frequency (or resonance) generated, it will also exhibit the greatest amplitude requiring the least amount of effort. Therefore, harmonic frequencies are natural reso-

nant frequencies, and the lowest resonant frequency is, of course, the fundamental frequency or the first resonance.

Recall that by definition, a complex waveform is created when two or more signals that differ in frequency, occupy the same space at the same time. Hence, complex waveforms are composed of two or more constituent (basic) waveforms and the generation of harmonics, by definition, creates a complex waveform that may or may not be periodic (or exhibit periodicity). By definition, when linear harmonics (as in a harmonic series, discussed in Chapter 6) are generated, they can often be defined as integer whole number multiples of the fundamental (f_0) frequency. Hence, for any given starting (or fundamental) frequency (f_0), the first harmonic of that frequency (f_1) is equal to $1 \times (f_0)$, the second harmonic (f_2) is equal to $2 \times (f_0)$, the third harmonic (f_3) is equal to $3 \times (f_0)$, the fourth harmonic (f_4) is equal to $4 \times (f_0)$, the fifth harmonic (f_5) is equal to $5 \times (f_0)$, the nth harmonic (f_n) is equal to $n \times (f_0)$, and so on. To illustrate, Table 5–4A presents six audiometric fundamental frequencies (f_0) together with the first five of their respective harmonics $(f_1$ through $f_5)$. Note that in each case, the first harmonic (f_1) is equal to the fundamental frequency (f_0). In addition to describing the derivation or production of a complex tone from a single fundamental frequency, harmonics also offer a linear method for scaling frequency. The term *partials* is often encountered in reference to harmonics. When all of the harmonics are integer multiples of the fundamental frequency, as illustrated in Table 5–4A, then the terms *harmonics* and *partials* are synonymous.

Finally, the term *overtone* is used to describe the components of a complex signal, composed of the fundamental frequency (f_0) and first harmonic (f_1), where the production of an additional second harmonic in the complex signal (f_2) is referred to not necessarily as the second harmonic but as the first overtone of the fundamental. Hence, the third harmonic (f_3) is also referred to as the second overtone, and so on (Speaks, 1999). Overtones are the (upper) partials that exist above the fundamental frequency.

Octaves

Another linear method for scaling frequencies is by the doubling or the halving of frequencies, beginning, once again, at an initial or fundamental frequency (f_0). Octaves (O) are often defined as multiple products of two and the fundamental frequency ($2 \times f_0$), where for any given starting (or fundamental) frequency (f_0), the first octave (O_1) of that fundamental or initial frequency is equal to $2 \times (f_0)$; the second octave (O_2) is equal to $2 \times 2 \times (f_0)$; the third octave (O_3) is $2 \times 2 \times 2 \times (f_0)$; the fourth octave ($O_4$) is $2 \times 2 \times 2 \times 2 \times (f_0)$; the fifth octave ($O_5$) is $2 \times 2 \times 2 \times 2 \times 2 \times (f_0)$; the nth octave (O_n) is $2^n \times (f_0)$; and so on. To illustrate, Table 5–4B presents six audiometric fundamental frequencies (f_0) together with the first five of their respective octaves (O_1 through O_5). Note that the audiometric frequencies used for hearing evaluations consist of the first five octave frequencies of (or beginning at) the lowest frequency consisting of 250 Hz.

Table 5–4A. Harmonics for Six Audiometric Fundamental Frequencies

f_0	f_1	f_2	f_3	f_4	f_5
250 Hz	250 Hz	500 Hz	750 Hz	1000 Hz	1250 Hz
500 Hz	500 Hz	1000 Hz	1500 Hz	2000 Hz	2500 Hz
1000 Hz	1000 Hz	2000 Hz	3000 Hz	4000 Hz	5000 Hz
2000 Hz	2000 Hz	4000 Hz	6000 Hz	8000 Hz	10,000 Hz
4000 Hz	4000 Hz	8000 Hz	12,000 Hz	16,000 Hz	20,000 Hz
8000 Hz	8000 Hz	16,000 Hz	24,000 Hz	32,000 Hz	40,000 Hz

Table 5–4B. Octave Frequencies for Six Audiometric Fundamental Frequencies

f_0	O_1	O_2	O_3	O_4	O_5
250 Hz	500 Hz	1000 Hz	2000 Hz	4000 Hz	8000 Hz
500 Hz	1000 Hz	2000 Hz	4000 Hz	8000 Hz	16,000 Hz
1000 Hz	2000 Hz	4000 Hz	8000 Hz	16,000 Hz	32,000 Hz
2000 Hz	4000 Hz	8000 Hz	16,000 Hz	32,000 Hz	64,000 Hz
4000 Hz	8000 Hz	16,000 Hz	32,000 Hz	64,000 Hz	128,000 Hz
8000 Hz	16,000 Hz	32,000 Hz	64,000 Hz	128,000 Hz	256,000 Hz

Odd and Even Harmonics

At times, not all of the integer multiples of the fundamental frequency are produced during forced vibration, and attention is given to the production of odd-numbered harmonics (e.g., f_1, f_3, f_5, f_7) often with the subsequent can- cellation of even-numbered harmonics (e.g., f_2, f_4, f_6, f_8). Of particular interest to hearing (and speech) science are the harmonic resonances produced by hollow tubes during forced vibration, specifically, tubes that are open at one end and are closed at the other, as illustrated in Figure 5–15, column A. Such tubes are

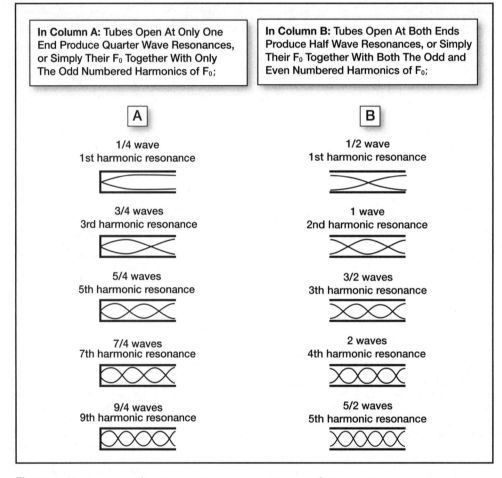

Figure 5–15. Resonances (fundamental frequencies and harmonics) generated by tubes that are opened at one end (*column A*) compared to those resonances generated by tubes that are opened at both ends (*column B*). Tubes opened at one end (*column A*) produce quarter-wave resonances such that at the fundamental frequency (f_0), only one quarter of the incident and reflected sinusoidal wave of the f_0 will fit into the tube. Harmonics are then created with the addition of odd-numbered fractional quarter-wave components of the f_0 waveform as they resonate within the tube. Tubes opened at both ends (*column B*) produce half-wave resonances such that at the fundamental frequency (f_0), only one half of the incident and reflected sinusoidal wave of the f_0 will fit into the tube. Harmonics are then created with the addition of both even-numbered and odd-numbered fractional half-wave components of the f_0 waveform as they resonate within the tube.

called *quarter-wave resonating*, for reasons that will be discussed in Chapter 7. Tubes such as these are located both in the external auditory canal and in the vocal tract, and, together with their fundamental frequencies (f_0), produce harmonics only at the odd integer multiples of their fundamental frequency. Some of the odd-numbered harmonics generated by the vocal tract (f_1, f_3, f_5) are commonly referred to as formant frequencies (e.g., the first, second, and third, respectively). On the other hand, tubes that are open at both ends are called *half-wave resonating* and generate both even and odd integer harmonics of their fundamental frequencies (Figure 5–15, column B). Finally, resonating tubes closed at both ends generate only the even integer multiples of their fundamental frequency. An explanation for the generation/cancellation of certain harmonics in the various tubes discussed will be provided in Chapter 7.

Impedance: Frictional Resistance and Reactance

Impedance, composed of the combined complex effects of frictional resistance and reactance (see below) can be defined informally as any "opposition to the flow (of energy)." What types of substances flow? Water flows, air flows, electricity flows, and vibratory motion should also be conceived of in terms of "energy flow." Impedance is symbolized by the letter "Z". Frictional resistance, reactance, and impedance are all measured in ohms, designated with the Greek symbol as Ω.

In Chapter 3, friction and frictional drag were defined as nonconservative forces with respect to mechanical energy. Friction in the real world is always present and is unavoidable. The presence of friction, therefore, necessitates constant compensatory applied external forces in order to maintain consistency in the forced vibratory oscillation of an object. Recall that a small amount of friction acting externally on a vibrating object transfers kinetic energy away from the motion of an object. This transference of energy usually takes the form of heat. As indicated above, all vibratory motion (free or forced) will eventually be impeded by frictional resistance. For the present, we signify frictional resistance as R.

Recall that mass and stiffness are properties of all matter, and that relative amounts of each determine (a) how much potential and/or kinetic energy the object can store during harmonic vibration; (b) the rate of transformation (transference) between these two forms of energy; and (c) the fundamental frequency at which the object vibrates best, which is strictly determined by mass and stiffness and the rate of transference between potential and kinetic energy. From the discussion above that dealt with harmonics, it should be clear that during forced vibration it is quite possible to drive an oscillating object into vibratory frequencies that differ from the fundamental frequency. As indicated above, in forced vibration, the instrument that delivers the external disturbance or the displacing force (the driver) often, though not exclusively, transmits its own unique frequency of vibration into the mass (the load) that has been set into vibration (Durrant & Feth, 2013). A load is often driven (by the driver) to produce not only the fundamental frequency (f_0), but harmonic frequencies of the fundamental frequency of the load, or even other, or added frequencies that are transmitted by the driver. As the frequency of the applied force (the driver) increasingly deviates from the fundamental frequency of the load, forcing the load to vibrate at frequencies that progressively deviate from the natural, or fundamental frequency of the load, there is a progressively increasing amount of opposition to the forced vibration that develops within the load (Durrant & Feth, 2013). This opposition to forced vibration that occurs within the load, is called reactance.

There are two types of reactance. There is the opposition to vibration that is associated with the inherent mass of the object-load (mass reactance), and there is the opposition to vibration that is associated with the inherent stiffness of the object-load (stiffness reactance). Restated, the two fundamental properties of an object-load, mass and stiffness, that also determine the fundamental frequency of the particular object-load, are the same two properties that will oppose (or react to) any attempt to vibrate an object-load at frequencies that deviate from its fundamental frequency (f_0). Reactance should be thought of as a type of "behavior" or a kind of "protest" exhibited by the physical attributes of mass and stiffness. As such, mass ≠ mass reactance, and stiffness ≠ stiffness reactance, but relative changes in the amounts of mass and/or stiffness, and/or a forced alteration in the natural frequency of vibration in an object-load by a driver force can and often will evoke either of the two types of reactance in the load.

During harmonic motion, the two reactance types are 180° out of phase with each other, just as displacement

and acceleration were shown (illustrated) in Figure 5–6 to be 180° out of phase. Ignoring the individual starting phases and observing only the peak amplitudes of each component, Figure 5–16A illustrates that the reactances, in both of their forms, are also 180° out of phase, because

1. Acceleration (a change in the rate of velocity), is inversely proportional to the mass (inertia) of an object. Mass not only opposes acceleration, but it also generates mass reactance (X_m), and X_m is in-phase with acceleration. In addition, X_m is frequency dependent.

2. Displacement, on the other hand, is directly proportional to the restorative force of elasticity, a force that opposes displacement. Hence, displacement is inversely proportional to stiffness. Stiffness opposes displacement, just as mass opposed acceleration. Stiffness is the physical property directly responsible for not only the restorative force of elasticity, but also for stiffness reactance (X_s), and X_s is in phase with displacement. Furthermore, X_s like X_m, is also frequency dependent.

3. Frictional resistance (R) as illustrated in Figure 5–16A is in-phase with velocity. The X_m that is in-phase with acceleration leads resistance (and velocity) in terms of phase, by 90°. The X_s that is in-phase with displacement lags resistance (and velocity) in terms of phase, by 90°. Unlike X_s and X_m, R is a property that is independent of frequency.

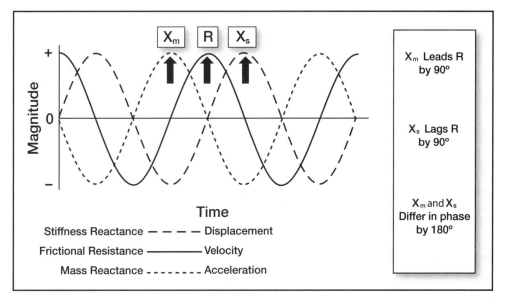

Figure 5–16A. Peak amplitude phase relations between stiffness reactance (X_s) and displacement, mass reactance (X_m) and acceleration, and frictional resistance (R) and velocity.

As illustrated in Figure 5–16A, the two reactance types are 180° out of phase with each other. Therefore, for any given frequency of oscillation, when X_s and X_m are equal in magnitude, they will cancel, and the amount of net reactance following this cancellation should be zero. Stated again, when both their magnitudes are equal, X_s and X_m cancel because, like displacement and acceleration, X_s and X_m are 180° out of phase with each other (Figure 5–16A). When are the magnitudes of X_s and X_m equivalent? When an object is vibrating at its natural, first resonant, or fundamental frequency, $X_s = X_m$. Otherwise, the total reactance in a system will be determined by the square of the difference between the two reactances, or $(X_m - X_s)^2$ as indicated in the sections that follow.

Recall from an earlier discussion that $2\pi f$ represents (a) angular velocity; (b) angular frequency; and (c) the natural, first resonant, or fundamental frequency of vibration (Halliday et al., 2011). Hence, the expression f_0 should mean the same as $2\pi f$. Mass reactance then is the product of angular velocity (or the fundamental frequency) and mass. Mass reactance is equal to $2\pi fm$ which is also equal to X_m. Stiffness reactance is equal to stiffness divided by the angular velocity (or the fundamental frequency). Therefore, stiffness reactance is equal to $s/2\pi f$ which is also equal to X_s.

Impedance, symbolized by the letter Z, can now be formally defined as the square root of the sum of the square of frictional resistance (R) and the square of the difference between the two reactances (X_s and X_m). Impedance can be expressed formally as

$$Z = \sqrt{[R^2 + (2\pi fm - s/2\pi f)^2]}$$

or

$$Z = [R^2 + (2\pi fm - s/2\pi f)^2]^{1/2}$$

or

$$Z = \sqrt{[R^2 + (X_m - X_s)^2]}$$

or

$$Z = [R^2 + (X_m - X_s)^2]^{1/2}$$

It should be noted that the type of opposition to the flow of energy or to vibratory motion that is afforded by the two reactance types can be distinguished from the type of opposition afforded by frictional resistance. Frictional resistance, as indicated earlier, dissipates kinetic energy. Opposition to the flow of energy (Z) afforded by the total reactance will take the form of a temporary energy storage within either the potential or kinetic energy of the vibrating mass (Durrant & Feth, 2013).

In addition, impedance that is measured in ohms may be expressed as $Z = $ Force/Velocity, or in MKS units, such that 1 ohm is equal to the force of 1 newton/meter/second (Durrant & Feth, 2013). Hence, Z, measured in ohms, represents a ratio of the force required to set otherwise immobilized particles of a substance in a sound-transmitting medium such as air or water into motion at a relative magnitude of velocity. When the overall acoustic impedance of a vibrating mass is high, the greater opposition to forced vibration will require a greater amount of net force from the driver because the transfer of energy from driver to load in this case is poor. Greater energy expenditure by the driver will be required in order to sustain forced vibratory motion. The more remote the driving frequency is from the natural, fundamental, or first resonant frequency of the load, the greater will be the impedance and the poorer will be the transference of energy.

Closer Examination of Mass Reactance

Examination of the formal definition for mass reactance ($2\pi fm$ or X_m) indicates the following, for any object that is set into vibratory motion as indirectly illustrated in Figure 5–16B:

1. Any increase in frequency (f) will produce a corresponding increase in $2\pi fm$. For each/any octave increment in frequency, $2\pi fm$ also increases by a factor of 2:1. For any object set into vibration at the fundamental frequency, any attempt to increase the rate of vibration will be met by opposition expressed as a reduction in amplitude, owing to the vibratory object's mass.

2. Any increase in mass (m) will produce a corresponding increase in $2\pi fm$. For any object set into vibration at the fundamental frequency, any attempt to maintain an unchanging, steady rate of vibration while increasing the amount of mass will be met by opposition expressed as a reduction in amplitude, owing to the vibratory object's mass. This is because adding mass to a vibrating object will decrease the natural, first resonant, or fundamental frequency of that object.

3. Frequency and mass are (therefore) directly proportional to $2\pi fm$.

Closer Examination of Stiffness Reactance

Examination of the formal definition for stiffness reactance ($s/2\pi f$ or X_s) indi-

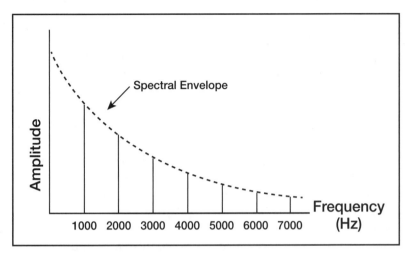

Figure 5–16B. The effects of mass reactance on the amplitudes of both even-numbered and odd-numbered harmonic frequencies. Recall that for any object set into vibration at the fundamental frequency, any attempt to increase the rate of vibration will be met by opposition, owing to the vibratory object's mass, and the effects of mass reactance ($2\pi fm$). In the figure, the fundamental frequency (f_0) is 1000 Hz. With the production of each progressively higher harmonic, beginning with the second harmonic (i.e., $2 \times f_0$), observed amplitudes at each harmonic will also be progressively lower due to the increased opposition to vibration provided by $2\pi fm$. In this example, the lowest amplitude can be observed at the seventh harmonic or 7000 Hz.

cates the following for any object that is set into vibratory motion:

1. Any decrease in frequency (f) will produce a corresponding increase in $s/2\pi f$. For each/any octave decrement in frequency, $s/2\pi f$ also increases by a factor of 2:1. Hence, for any object set into vibration at the fundamental frequency, any attempt to decrease the rate of vibration will be met by opposition, owing to the vibratory object's stiffness.

2. Any increase in stiffness (s) will produce a corresponding increase in $s/2\pi f$. For any object set into vibration at the fundamental frequency, any attempt to maintain an unchanging, steady rate of vibration while increasing the amount of stiffness will be met by opposition, owing to the vibratory objects stiffness. This is because adding stiffness to a vibrating object will increase the natural, first resonant, or fundamental frequency of that object.

3. Frequency is (therefore) inversely proportional to $s/2\pi f$. Stiffness is also directly proportional to $s/2\pi f$.

Closer Examination of Impedance

The formal definition for impedance was given by

$$Z = [R^2 + (2\pi fm - s/2\pi f)^2]^{\frac{1}{2}}$$

For any object that is set into vibratory motion, an examination of the formula for impedance indicates the following:

1. When $2\pi fm = s/2\pi f$,
   a. The total magnitude of impedance will be equal to frictional resistance or

   $$Z = R$$

   b. The object that is set into forced or free vibratory motion is vibrating (only) at its first resonant or fundamental frequency ($2\pi f$).
   c. Z is at its lowest possible value and the vibratory system is said to be *resistance dominated*.

2. When $2\pi fm > s/2\pi f$,
   a. The total magnitude of impedance will be equal to frictional resistance plus mass reactance, or

   $$Z = R + 2\pi fm$$

   b. The object that is therefore set into forced vibratory motion is not vibrating exclusively at its first resonant or fundamental frequency ($2\pi f$).
   c. The object that is set into forced vibratory motion is in fact vibrating at frequencies that are "higher" than the fundamental frequency ($2\pi f$).
   d. The vibratory system is said to be "mass dominated."

3. When $2\pi fm < s/2\pi f$,
   a. The total magnitude of impedance will be equal to frictional resistance plus stiffness reactance, or

   $$Z = R + s/2\pi f$$

   b. The object that is set into vibratory motion is not vibrating exclusively at its first resonant or fundamental frequency ($2\pi f$).
   c. The object that is set into forced vibratory motion is in fact vibrating at frequencies that are "lower" than the fundamental frequency ($2\pi f$).
   d. The vibratory system is said to be "stiffness dominated."

Admittance

Impedance was informally defined as any opposition to the flow (of energy). Admittance may be defined informally as "any facilitation to the flow (of energy)." Admittance is defined as the complex sum of conductance, which is the reciprocal of resistance, and susceptance, which is the reciprocal of reactance (Durrant & Feth, 2013). Admittance is the reciprocal of impedance. Recall that units of resistance, reactance, and impedance are measured in ohms. Admittance is measured in mhos, which obviously appears to be the reciprocal of the spelling of ohms. Recall as well that impedance was expressed as "Z." Admittance may be expressed as Y or as Z^{-1}. Hence,

$$Y = Z^{-1}$$

or

$$Y = 1/Z \text{ and } Z = 1/Y$$

The closer the driving frequency is to the natural, first resonant, or fundamental frequency of the load, the lower will be the impedance, the greater will be the admittance, and the greater will be the transfer of energy from the driver to the load.

Therefore,

$$Y \text{ is maximum when } Z = R$$

In addition, low amounts of damping (frictional resistance) increase admittance, as illustrated in Figure 5–17.

Impedance Mismatch

When an attempt is made to transfer the vibratory energy of a sound from one medium or object (driver) to another medium or object (load) during forced vibration, there is the possibility that vibratory energy will be lost in the transfer. The loss of energy in the transfer can be attributed to differences in mass and in the overall elastic properties between the driver and load. In the case of sound-propagating media, differences in density and, at times, differences in the speed at which sound is transmitted through separate types of media may also contribute to a loss of energy transfer. Vibratory energy that is lost in the transfer between driver and load is said to be lost due to an impedance mismatch. Lost energy for the most part will either be reflected away from the second object or medium (load), or it will be converted to heat by absorption (see Chapter 6). Media that transmit sound often vary in their composition, from solid to liquid to gaseous. Depending upon the media type, the density of the particular media can be defined in terms of mass (in kilograms or grams) divided by derivatives of length (meters or centimeters; square meters or square

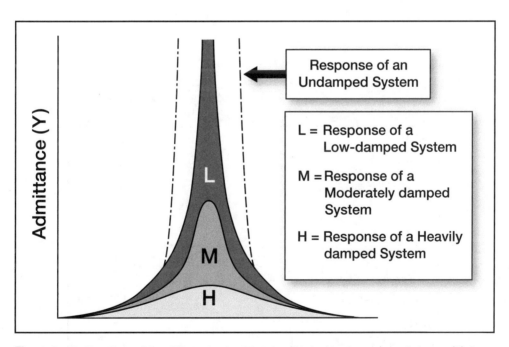

Figure 5–17. The effects of four different levels of damping (frictional resistance) on admittance (*Y*) shown on the ordinate. The response of an undamped system is illustrated by the hash marks. *L* = the response of low amounts of damping, *M* = the response of moderate amounts of damping, and *H* = the response of high or heavy amounts of damping.

centimeters; cubic meters or cubic centimeters). The stiffness of media may be defined in terms of force/area or simply the definition of pressure (e.g., newton/m² or dyne/cm²) (Durrant & Feth, 2013). An impedance mismatch between two media may be defined as a mismatch of either the characteristic impedances or of the acoustic impedances between the respective media.

Characteristic Impedance

The proportion of energy that is transferred or lost from one medium to another can be computed in either of two ways, using two analogous units of measure for comparison. One way is to compute the separate characteristic impedances of the two media (Durrant & Feth, 2013). Just as vibratory objects have natural, first resonant, or fundamental (characteristic) frequencies and reactances as a direct result of mass and stiffness, vibratory media also have characteristic impedances resulting from their separate physical compositions. The fundamental physical properties of a particular medium will determine the speed at which sound will propagate in that medium. The characteristic impedance (Z_c) for a medium may be defined as

$$Z_c = [\text{density of the medium}] \times [\text{the speed of sound } (c) \text{ in the medium}]$$

or simply by

$$Z_c = \text{density} \times c \qquad (5\text{--}7)$$

Characteristic impedances for particular media, measured in units called *rayls*, are presented in Table 5–5.

Table 5–5. Table of Characteristic Impedances

Material	Density (kg/m³)	Speed of Sound (m/s)	Rayls (Z_c)
Solids			
Aluminum	2700	6420	1.73×10^7
Iron and steel	7800	5941	4.63×10^7
Granite	2700	6000	1.62×10^7
Liquids			
Fresh water (20°C)	998	1482	1.48×10^6
Seawater (20°C)[a]	1025	1522	1.56×10^6
Fresh water (0°C)	917	1402	1.29×10^6
Gases			
Air (20°C)	1.21	344	4.16×10^2
Helium	0.18	965	1.74×10^2

[a]At 3.5% salinity.

Source: Giancoli, 2005; Halliday et al., 2011.

In Table 5–5, MKS values are presented in scientific notation for Z_c defined as the product of the density (kg/m³) and the (c) speed or velocity of sound (meters/second) for a given material media. Using the computed rayls of characteristic impedance, the proportion of transmitted sound energy (T) between two media Z_a and Z_b may also be predicted by the following equation (Durrant & Feth, 2013):

$$T = 4Z_bZ_a \div [Z_b + Z_a]^2 \quad (5–8)$$

Acoustic Impedance

The computation of the number of rayls of characteristic impedance for comparisons of energy transference between media is analogous to the computation and comparison of the acoustic impedances of two media. The acoustic impedance (Z_A) of a medium is measured in ohms (rather than rayls) and may be defined (Hamill & Price, 2014) as the square root of the product of density and elasticity or simply,

$$Z_A = [\text{density} \times \text{elasticity}]^{1/2}$$

Using the computed ohms of acoustic impedance, the proportion of transmitted sound energy (T) between two media may be predicted by the following equation (Hamill & Price, 2014):

$$T = 4r \div (r + 1)^2$$

where

T = the proportion (%) of energy faithfully transmitted;

r = the ratio of the acoustic impedance differences between the two media, measured in ohms.

It should be obvious from both of the above equations that an impedance mismatch often exists and a subsequent loss of energy often occurs when an attempt is made to transfer sound energy between two or more sound-propagating media, independent of the direction of the energy transfer.

Chapter Summary

- In this chapter, harmonic motion was defined as sinusoidal motion and was also defined as uniform projected circular motion or periodic motion.
- From trigonometry, both the sine and cosine functions for an angle formed by a radius within a unit circle were defined, and the relevance of both functions to harmonic motion and to the amplitudes of sine and cosine waveforms, was also emphasized.
- In this chapter, one cycle of uniform circular rotation for a sine or cosine wave was defined as 360° of phase angle.
- In this chapter, the terms *phase lead* and *phase lag* for standard sine and cosine wave functions were introduced and defined with examples.
- In this chapter, phase relations between displacement, velocity, and acceleration were introduced and the relevance of their phase relations to resonance was emphasized.
- In this chapter, the terms peak, peak-to-peak, and root-mean-square (RMS) amplitude were

defined and examples were given for their computation, together with illustrations of each.

- In this chapter, the analogy between the computation of RMS amplitude and statistical computations of variance and standard deviation was introduced and emphasized.

- The terms *compression* and *rarefaction* for sinusoidal waveforms were also defined with illustration.

- In this chapter, the concept of simple versus complex waveforms was introduced.

- In this chapter, the trigonometric concept of radians, as the curved distance or arc of the distance traveled by a radius within a unit circle, was introduced and defined using examples and illustrations.

- In this chapter, computational methods for converting unit circle and sine wave degrees into radians were introduced with illustrations.

- In this chapter, the inverse relationship of mass and inertia on rate changes in velocity (acceleration), and the opposition of mass to stiffness, which favors acceleration, were emphasized with respect to the overall rate of vibratory motion for an object.

- In this chapter, the antagonistic relationship between mass and stiffness, and their effects on the rate of transfer of potential to kinetic to potential energy during vibratory motion, was emphasized.

- In this chapter, the antagonistic relationship between mass and stiffness on the rate of vibratory motion was formally defined with respect to frequency measured in cycles/second (or hertz), and the reciprocal of frequency, which is period, was also revisited.

- In this chapter, free vibration was defined with respect to the natural, first resonant, or fundamental frequency of vibratory motion, both without, and in connection with, the concept of frictional resistance, or damping.

- The concept of free vibration was also defined as damped sinusoidal vibration, and the concept of forced vibration was defined with respect to driver and load, damping, reactance, overall impedance, and relative to the production of harmonics.

- In this chapter, the principle of resonance was introduced and this principle states that when a periodically vibrating force is applied to an elastic system the elastic system will be forced to vibrate and will initially resonate under forced vibration at the frequency of the force that is applied by the driver.

- In this chapter, the concepts of harmonics, partials, and octaves were defined, and the terms half-wave and quarter-wave resonances were introduced as a precursor to an in-depth discussion in Chapter 7.

- In this chapter, impedance was defined informally as an opposition to the flow and was defined formally as the complex interaction between frictional resistance and the interaction of the two separate types of reactance.

- Impedance, which is measured in ohms, was also defined in terms of force and velocity where 1 ohm is equal to 1 newton/meter/second or force per unit velocity.
- In this chapter, the phase relations between frictional resistance, mass reactance and acceleration, stiffness reactance and displacement, as well as the frequency-dependency of the two reactance types were discussed in detail with illustration.
- The two reactance types were defined in terms of angular velocity or angular frequency (or fundamental frequency), all of which were defined.
- The impact of changes in frequency, mass, and stiffness on each of the two reactance types, and on the total impedance within a vibrating body, was discussed in detail.
- In this chapter, the terms resistance-dominated, mass-dominated, and stiffness-dominated systems were introduced and defined.
- In this chapter, the term *admittance* was introduced as the reciprocal of impedance and was defined as the complex sum of conductance and acoustic susceptance, and is measured in mhos.
- Impedance mismatch was also introduced to account for the loss of vibratory energy during forced vibration, owing to differences that often exist between the driver and the load with respect to their separate mass and elastic properties.

- In this chapter, characteristic impedance was defined as the inherent property of any particular type of solid, liquid, or gaseous vibratory media due to the physical composition (i.e., the product of density and the speed of sound in the media) of the particular vibratory media.
- Characteristic impedance for a particular medium was defined using the equation Z_c = density × (C), where C represents the speed of sound in a particular medium and is measured in rayls.
- In this chapter, acoustic impedance was defined as an inherent property, analogous to the characteristic impedance, of any particular type of solid, liquid, or gaseous vibratory media, resulting from the physical composition (i.e., the square root of the product of density and elasticity) of the particular vibratory media.
- Acoustic impedance for a particular medium was defined using the equation Z_A = [density × elasticity] and unlike the characteristic impedance, is measured in ohms.

Chapter 5 Questions

1. Define harmonic motion and provide examples.

2. Define the following: right triangle; the sine value of any

angle; the cosine value of any angle.

3. What is the sine of 0°, 45°, 90°, 135°, 180°, 225°, 270°, 315°, 360°?

4. What is the cosine of 0°, 45°, 90°, 135°, 180°, 225°, 270°, 315°, 360°?

5. Using the terms radius, unit circle, sin Θ, 360°, and amplitude of *1*, describe why the name "sine wave" is assigned to descriptions of uniform circular, harmonic, or periodic vibratory motion.

6. Describe the phase relations (phase-lead versus phase-lag) between three sine waves, each with a starting phase of 45°, 90°, and 180°, respectively.

7. In the sine wave shown in Figure 5–18A, identify the area of compression, identify the area of rarefaction, locate the region of equilibrium, compute the peak amplitude, and compute the peak-to-peak amplitude. What

is the starting phase of this sine wave?

8. Define in words exactly what root-mean-square (RMS) amplitude is, and to what sample statistic it is analogous.

9. Of what significance to trigonometry, and to the computation of the RMS amplitude for a sine wave, is the number 0.707?

10. For the sine wave shown in Figure 5–18B, compute the RMS amplitude.

11. Define the following: circumference, radius, radians, diameter, $2\pi r$, $\pi 2r/2r$, and arc length.

12. In a unit circle: 1 radian is equal to how many degrees? 2π radians is equal to how many degrees? 1° is equal to how many radians?

13. What happens to period as frequency gets higher? What happens to frequency as period gets longer?

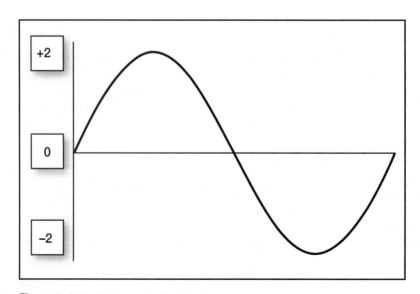

Figure 5–18A. Sine wave for Question 7.

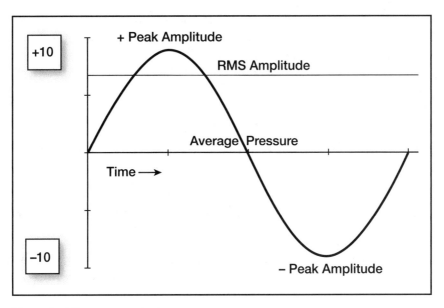

Figure 5–18B. Sine wave for Question 10.

14. What is the relationship between mass and stiffness in the definition of $2\pi f$? What does $2\pi f$ designate, or stand for?

15. Distinguish between a low-damped system and a heavily damped system and provide examples for each.

16. Distinguish between harmonic notation and octave notation.

17. How do the expressed resonances differ, when comparing quarter-wave resonating tubes to those resonances generated by half-wave resonating tubes?

18. Define the phase relationship between $2\pi fm$ and $s/2\pi f$. When are the values for both equal? When do the values for both cancel?

19. Define *impedance*. What does Z stand for? In what units of measure is Z evaluated? What is the reciprocal of Z? In what units of measure is Z^{-1} evaluated?

20. What does R stand for? At what particular frequency does $Z = R$ exclusively? State the formal definitional equation for Z.

21. What is Z composed of when an object is made to resonate at frequencies below its natural, first resonant, or fundamental frequency?

22. What is Z composed of when an object is made to resonate at frequencies higher than its natural, first resonant, or fundamental frequency?

23. What is Z composed of when an object is made to resonate at its natural, first resonant, or fundamental frequency exclusively?

24. What are the two factors that increase $2\pi fm$? What factor increases and what factor decreases $s/2\pi f$?

25. Define the term *impedance mismatch*. State the equation that defines the characteristic impedance for a medium, and indicate the units of measure.

26. State the equation that defines the acoustic impedance for a medium, and indicate the units of measure.

References

Angus, J., & Howard, D. (2006). *Acoustics and psychoacoustics* (3rd ed.). New York, NY: Elsevier.

Boring, E. G. (1957). *A history of experimental psychology* (2nd ed.). New York, NY: Appelton-Century-Crofts.

Durrant, J. D., & Feth, L. L. (2013). *Hearing sciences: A foundational approach*. Upper Saddle River, NJ: Pearson Education.

Giancoli, D. C. (2005). *Physics: Principles with applications* (6th ed.). Upper Saddle River, NJ: Prentice Hall.

Halliday, D., Resnick, R., & Walker, J. (2011). *Fundamentals of physics* (9th ed.). Hoboken, NJ: Wiley.

Hamill, T. A., & Price, L. L. (2014). *The hearing sciences* (2nd ed.). San Diego, CA: Plural.

Hawking, S. E. (2002). *On the shoulders of giants: The great works of physics and astronomy*. Philadelphia, PA: Running Press.

Hewitt, P. G. (2010). *Conceptual physics* (11th ed.). Upper Saddle River, NJ: Pearson Education.

Hirsh, I. J. (1952). *The measurement of hearing*. New York, NY: McGraw-Hill.

Rosen, S., & Howell, P. (1991). *Signals and systems for speech and hearing*. New York, NY: Academic Press.

Rosen, S., & Howell, P. (2013). *Signals and systems for speech and hearing* (2nd ed.). Leiden, The Netherlands: Brill.

Speaks, C. E. (1999). *Introduction to sound: Acoustics for the hearing and speech sciences* (3rd ed.). San Diego, CA: Singular.

Stutz, B. (2006). Matter and energy. In J. Langone, B. Stutz, & A. Gianopoulos (Eds.), *Theories for everything: An illustrated history of science from the invention of numbers to string theory* (pp. 146–229). Washington, DC: National Geographic Society.

Chapter 6

The Measurement of Sound

In the latter part of the 17th century, Robert Boyle (1627–1691) concluded that for sound to exist, there must be a material medium . . .
Durrant & Feth, 2013, p. 58; Halliday, Resnick, & Walker, 2011, p. 413

Alphabetized Listing of Key Terms Discussed in Chapter 6

$2r$	anechoic chamber	binary digital code
$2\pi r$	anti-aliasing filter	Blackman-Harris windowing function
3 dB down point	anti-imaging filter	
–3 dB/octave	Archimedes	Blackman-Nuttall windowing function
$4\pi r^2$	atmospheric pressure	
absolute threshold	audio-frequency signal	Blackman windowing function
absorption	baffle	
absorption coefficient	band-limited noise	broadband noise
acoustic clicks	band-pass filter	Brownian motion
acoustic intensity (I)	band-reject filter	bulk modulus (of elasticity)
algorithm	band-stop filter	calibration
aliasing	bandwidth (Δf)	capacitor
amplitude distortion	bar	capacitance
amplitude envelope	barrier	carbon microphone
amplitude modulated (AM)	behavioral threshold	carrier frequency
	bel	carrier wave
amplitude response	Bell, Alexander Graham	center frequency
amplitude spectrum	Bell Telephone Company	ceramic microphone
analog dither		characteristic impedance (Z_c)
analog signal	bidirectional microphones	
analog-to-digital		circumference

clicks

complex sound

complex waveform

compression

condenser microphone

consonance

consonants

crystal microphone

cubic difference tone

cut-off frequency

damping

decibel (dB)

dB (A)

dB (B)

dB (C)

dB IL

dB SPL

denominator

density

diameter

diffraction

diffuse sound-field

digital signal

digital signal-processing (DSP)

digital-to-analog

direct current (dc) pulse

dissonance

distortion

distortion product otoacoustic emission (DPOE)

dynamic microphone

dynamic range of hearing

echoes

elastic modulus

electret microphone

energy density

erasable programmable read-only memory (EPROM)

external auditory (ear) canal

fast Fourier transformation (FFT)

filter

Fourier analysis

Fourier, Jean Baptiste Joseph

Fourier series

Fourier synthesis

free sound-field

frequency

frequency distortion

frequency domain

frequency-limited noise

frequency modulated (FM)

frequency response

fundamental frequency

gated dc pulse

gated sinusoid

Gaussian distribution

Gaussian noise

half-power point

Hamming windowing function

Hanning windowing function

harmonic

harmonic distortion

high-pass filter

ideal filter

imaging distortion

impulse response

incident wave

inductor

inner ear

intensity level (IL)

inverse square law

isotropic propagation

law of reflection

level-per-cycle (LPC)

light

lightning

line spectrum

linear distortion

linear system

linear time-invariance

linear windowing function

longitudinal waves

low-pass filter

magnetic microphone

main lobe

mass

material media

medium

microbar

microphone

middle ear

missing fundamental frequency

moving-coil microphone

narrow-band acoustic tone burst

narrow-band noise

noise

noise survey

nondirectional microphones

nonlinear distortion

nonlinear system

nonlinear windowing function

notch-filter

nulls

numerator

Nyquist frequency

Nyquist theorem

Occupational Safety and Health Administration (OSHA)

octave-band

octave-band filter

octave bandwidth

odd harmonics

Ohm's law

omnidirectional microphones

one atmosphere of pressure

organ of Corti

overall bandwidth

otoacoustic emission

outer hair cells (OHCs)

overall level

Parzen windowing function

pass band

peak clipping

period

periodicity

periodicity pitch

piezoelectricity

pink noise

piston phone

plane wave

plateau

plateau duration

point source

power

power spectrum level

pressure

pressure microphones

pressure spectrum level

primary frequencies

propagated disturbance

pure tone

radius

ramping

rarefaction

ratio

real filter

rectangular pulse

reference values

reflection

rejection rate

residue pitch

reverberant field

reverberations

ribbon microphone

rise-fall time

Rochelle salt crystals

roll-off rate

saturation

sawtooth wave

shadow region

side lobe (side band)

simple waveform

sine (cosine) envelope windowing function

sinusoidal wave

sound

sound-field

sound level meter (SLM)

sound pressure level (SPL)

speech noise

speed of sound in air

speed of sound in water

spectral bandwidth

spectral density

spectral envelope

spectral nulls

spectral splatter

spectrum (spectra)

spectrum level

sphere

spherical point source

spherical wave

spherical wave front

square wave

standard normal distribution	transducer	voltage
stop band	transfer function	volume density
surface area of a sphere	transient distortion	vowels
	transmission	Walsh windowing function
system	triangular wave	
telephone trade	type 0 SLM	warble tones
third-octave-band	type 1 SLM	waveform
threshold	type 2 SLM	wave front
thunder	unidirectional microphones	weighting networks
time analysis	unit bandwidth	white noise
time domain	variable-reluctance microphone	wide-band noise
tone burst	velocity microphones	windowing function
total harmonic distortion (THD)	virtual pitch	work
		zero decibels (0 dB)

Sound Defined

Sound is the stimulating phenomenon (or stimulus) that psychologically gives rise to an auditory neural sensation, and to an auditory perception. However, as indicated in the previous chapters, sound is also a physical entity that is governed by physical laws. Sound may best be defined (physically) as a disturbance in particle or in pressure displacement, producing longitudinal wave fronts of compression in all directions (Halliday et al., 2011). A wave front may be defined as that particular set of molecules in a sound-transmitting medium where each propagated wave has maximum amplitude. In essence, the wave front is the crest of the wave. While the energy carried by a total waveform is distributed throughout, it is convenient to consider the wave front as carrying most of the energy. A careful examination of all sound-producing phenomena always reveals the existence of motion within, or the motion of, some type of physical medium. As indicated previously (see Chapter 4), vibration and the production of waveforms (wave fronts) are found at the source of any sound, as sound travels from one location to another (Giancoli, 2005). Vibrations that occur in physical matter produce waves, and waves, in turn, create alternating changes in particle and/ or pressure density that transport the energy of vibration from one place to another within the material medium. In Chapters 4 and 5, these alternating and successive changes in particle and/ or pressure density were called areas of compression and rarefaction. The vibration of physical matter, with the ensuing creation of regions composed of compressions and rarefactions, is the property that makes the production, the sensation, and ultimately the perception (or conscious audibility) of sound possible.

In addition, sound is only propagated (created, generated, transmitted) in an elastic or compressible medium, like a gas, a liquid, or a solid substance. Recall from Chapter 3 that sound is never and can never be transmitted in a vacuum. Air, water, and other material substances are composed of matter, and therefore, air, water, and other physical substances can be made to vibrate (resonate). Material media such as air, water, and other physical matter have elasticity, they are compressible, they have mass, and they can therefore propagate sound. There can be no sound if there is no disturbance in the distribution of the particles or in the pressure density of the matter that defines the medium in which a sound-creating vibration is found to be present. If there is no physical matter to compress and expand, there can be no sound (Hewitt, 2010). As first introduced in Chapter 3, sound may be described as a propagated disturbance in the density of an elastic material medium (Durrant & Feth, 2013; Hirsh, 1952).

Recall from Chapter 2 that density is an indication of how much mass occupies a given space (Halliday et al., 2011), such that density is a (scalar) measure of the amount of mass per unit volume, which is also called the "volume density" of a particular medium, or simply

$$Density = mass/volume$$

And therefore

$$Mass = density \times volume$$
$$(6–1A)$$

As indicated in Chapter 4, the air that surrounds us exerts an atmospheric pressure of about 15 lb/square inch (PSI), and this pressure is directly related to the (volume) density, or mass per unit volume or air (Halliday et al., 2011; Hirsh, 1952). Sound may be transmitted through the air, but it may also be transmitted through solids or through liquids. It happens that sound does not travel as efficiently in air as it travels in these other, more dense media. The greater density of the atoms contained within liquids and solids enable these materials to respond quickly to the motions (displacements) of adjacent atoms in response to sound, enabling a more efficient transmission of waveforms, with little loss of energy. As we will also see, sound travels about four times faster in water than in air, and about 15 times faster in steel, than in air.

Recall from Chapter 3 that the restorative force of elasticity (and sometimes gravity) is a force that resists displacement. Recall as well that if an elastic material is stretched or compressed to values that exceed its elastic limits, the material will not return (not be restored) to its original shape. Because both stiffness and mass determine the frequencies at which objects or media vibrate (see Chapter 5), it may be of interest to ask, what are the limiting properties of mass? It also happens that the mass (or the density) of a medium also responds to the compressive effects of pressure. Recall from Chapter 4 that pressure = force/area, and that mass also resists displacement through the property of inertia. It was even suggested (see Chapter 4) that mass might be redefined as a measure of the inherent inertia that exists within a material substance. If a material medium is subjected to the compressive forces of pressure, the density of the material increases. Why is this? As the material matter within a medium is subjected to forces that generate pressure (pressure = force/area), the mass per unit volume (or area) will increase as the volume (or area) decreases from the compressing effects of force. Volume density was, after all, defined as a measure of the amount of mass per unit volume.

Now consider Equation 6–1A from above:

$$Mass = density \times volume$$

It should also be clear from Equation 6–1A that in order for mass to remain constant (which it must) with increasing amounts of compressive force, as density increases from the addition of more force, volume, consequently, must also decrease. When a material medium is subjected to inward forces from all sides, the volume of the material will actually decrease by some fractional amount (Halliday et al., 2011). When forces are applied in order to generate waveforms in a seemingly noncompressible media such as a solid or a liquid, there is an upper limit to the compressibility of solids, and an upper limit to the compressibility of liquids. This is because both kinds of substances are less compressible, owing to the fact that their atoms/molecules are more tightly coupled to neighboring matter (Halliday et al., 2011).

The bulk elastic properties of a material medium will determine how much the medium will compress under a given amount of external pressure. The ratio of the change in pressure to the fractional amount (or degree) of vol-

ume compression, is called the "bulk modulus of elasticity" of the compressible material. That is, the bulk modulus (B) is the property that determines the extent, or the upper limit, to which a medium can change in volume (compliance), when pressure is applied. The term *modulus* means a type of standard. The ratio of the change in pressure to the degree, to the upper limit, or to the fractional amount of volume compression, is called the bulk modulus of the material (Giancoli, 2005), or

$$B = \frac{\Delta P}{\Delta V / V_o} \qquad (6–1B)$$

where ΔP is a measure of the change in the pressure of a substance when a force is applied, that then leads to the change in volume; ΔV is the change in volume that is proportional to the original volume V_o, and to the increase or change in pressure, ΔP. Bulk modulus is a measure of an opposition to compression (pressure) and therefore an opposition (as in elastic compliance) to the changes that occur in the volume of the compressed medium (Halliday et al., 2011). Values of the bulk modulus for various materials are provided in Table 6–1. Units of measure of the bulk modulus are often expressed as units of pressure (force/area). The MKS unit for pressure, expressed as force in newtons (N) divided by area, expressed as meters² (m^2), was introduced in Chapter 4. Scientific notation was introduced in Chapter 2 and is also reviewed in Appendix A. The bulk modulus (MKS) pressure values are presented (see Table 6–1) in scientific notation for each type of material listed (Giancoli, 2005; Halliday et al., 2011). Recall as well from Chapter 4 that one N/m² of

Table 6–1. Various Materials and Their Bulk Modulus Pressures

Material	Bulk Modulus (B) (N/m^2)
Solids	
Cast Iron	9.0×10^{10}
Steel	1.6×10^{11}
Brass	8.0×10^{10}
Aluminum	7.0×10^{10}
Marble	7.0×10^{10}
Granite	4.5×10^{10}
Liquids	
Water	2.2×10^9
Alcohol (ethyl)	1.0×10^9
Mercury	2.5×10^9
Gases	
Air, H_2, He, CO_2	1.0×10^5

Source: Giancoli, 2005; Halliday et al., 2011.

pressure is also equivalent to 1 pascal (Pa) of pressure.

As for terrestrial-dwelling animals such as humans, it should be recognized that the air we breathe consists of minute amounts of mass that move in response to forces, in a manner that is not unlike the movements that have been described in previous chapters for the pendulum and spring-mass system. Environmental air may be conceptualized as an infinite harmonic oscillator lacking a finite shape, as sounds are transmitted through the same medium in which we live and breathe. As illustrated in Chapter 4 (see Figure 4–4), it is only the wave that advances in response to a disturbance, and not the advancement of the individual particles of mass that comprise the mate-

rial medium. It is the energy within the waveform that moves, and therefore, it is the energy that advances through the medium (Durrant & Feth, 2013). Sound, therefore, represents the transfer of energy through an elastic medium (Speaks, 1999). Finally, the random kinetic movement of air molecules resulting from resting levels of thermal agitation is often referred to as Brownian motion (Hewett, 2010). However, unlike the random movement of air, sound is deliberate, not random, and sound propagation represents the production of predictable and not random waveform patterns.

The preceding chapters described many of the physical properties that define sound propagation, and those descriptions were aided by the use of the pendulum and the spring-mass. In Chapter 5, it was shown that the waveforms generated by a sound source can be illustrated in two dimensions with the help of a small measure of trigonometry and the use of simple sinusoidal waveforms. The sinusoid is often used to represent the (simplest) type of sound. The simplest type of sound is composed of only one frequency component, or, by definition, the simplest type of sound is called a pure tone. The pure tone was also defined in Chapter 5. Two-dimensional sinusoidal illustrations are also useful in many descriptions of complex sounds, consisting, by definition (Chapter 5) of two or more separate frequency (pure tone) components existing in the same space at the same time. Many of the sound waves that may be defined in this manner (e.g., simple, complex, periodic, aperiodic) will be illustrated in this chapter.

Amplitude, frequency/period, phase, compression, and rarefaction are all working terms that have been used consistently throughout Chapters 3 through 5. These are working terms that will also be used in descriptions of sound throughout Chapters 6, as well as throughout Chapters 7 and 8. Amplitude was introduced in Chapter 3 in reference to both the pendulum and spring-mass system to describe the peak and peak-to-peak excursions, as well as the relative amounts of displacement, velocity, and acceleration that occur during uniform cycles of motion. In Chapter 4, amplitude was again called upon in reference to the relative amounts of potential energy, kinetic energy, and momentum that exist in both pendulum and spring-mass systems during uniform cycles of motion. In Chapter 5, peak and peak-to-peak amplitudes were again revisited with respect to the excursions of sinusoidal waves, and the root-mean-square (RMS) amplitude was introduced. Frequency and period were introduced in Chapter 3 in reference to both the pendulum and spring-mass system to describe the regular and repetitious rate of movement that occurs during uniform cycles of motion. In Chapter 5, frequency and period were revisited with respect to sinusoidal waveforms, and the impact of frequency on the reactive properties of impedance was introduced. The hertz (Hz), the fundamental frequency (f_0), as well as harmonic and octave frequencies were each introduced in Chapter 5 as well. Compression and rarefaction, introduced in Chapter 3 in reference to the movements of both the pendulum and spring-mass system during uniform cycles of motion, were again called upon in Chapter 4 in reference to potential energy, kinetic energy, and the momentum that exists in both

pendulum and spring-mass systems during uniform cycles of motion. In Chapter 4, compression and rarefaction were also used to describe the longitudinal particle collisions (see Figure 4–4) that occur in the creation of waveforms of sound in an elastic medium such as air. In Chapter 5, the concepts of compression and rarefaction were once again employed in reference to the peak and peak-to-peak amplitudes of sine waves and in the computation of the RMS amplitude. Finally, the concept of phase angle was introduced in Chapter 5.

It will become clear in this chapter that amplitude, frequency/period, and phase are the main parameters of sound that must always be determined in order to completely specify and measure the sound stimulus. Hence, the focus of this chapter will be with the measurement of sound and will primarily emphasize these three main parameters. To begin, an important and initial consideration has to do with the actual physical measurement of amplitude. A discussion of sound (acoustic) intensity and sound pressure, leading to a definition of decibel (dB) scales of sound measurement, will require a brief review of some of the basic terms covered in previous chapters. Therefore, the first place to begin when discussing the measurement of sound is with an understanding of acoustic intensity.

Work, Power, and the Watt Revisited

In Chapter 4, the quantity of work accomplished was defined as the product of two components: the distance that a mass is moved (or displaced) and the magnitude of the force applied, provided that the force is parallel to the displacement. Therefore, work was expressed formally as

Work = force × distance
(displacement)

It then followed that the MKS metric unit for work, as defined in Chapter 4 was

work = newton × meter

which was expressed as the

newton − meter

or, the   joule

hence,

1 newton − meter = 1 joule

Therefore, and by definition, 1 newton of force exerted across a distance of 1 meter, will accomplish 1 joule of work, as indicated in Chapter 4.

It was also stated that the standard CGS metric unit of work, as defined in Chapter 4, was

work = dyne × centimeter

which was expressed as the

dyne − centimeter

or, the   erg

hence,

1 dyne − centimeter = 1 erg

Therefore, and by definition, 1 dyne of force exerted across a distance of 1 centimeter, will accomplish 1 erg of

work, as indicated in Chapter 4. Also recall that

1 joule = 10^7 ergs

In Chapter 4, power was defined as the rate at which energy is transferred or transformed, or simply, the rate at which work is accomplished, and therefore, power was defined as

Power = work/time

which translates to

MKS   Power = joule/second

or

CGS   Power = 10^7 ergs/second

Recall that in both the MKS and CGS systems, the unit for power was the watt.

Therefore,

1 Watt of power = 1 joule/second

also,

1 watt of power = 10^7 ergs/second

Hence,

1 joule/second = 10^7 ergs/second

Acoustic Intensity (I)

Acoustic intensity is defined as power divided by area, or

Acoustic intensity (I) = power/area
(6–2)

Since the unit of power is the watt (which is 1 joule/second or 10^7 ergs/

second), acoustic intensity or I may be defined as the rate at which work is performed, as the power (or energy per unit time) is transported across the unit area of the wave front, perpendicular to the direction of the flow of energy (Durrant & Feth, 2013; Giancoli, 2005). The manner in which the acoustic intensity of sound varies as a function of the distance of a sound from a real energy source, is often a complex issue, and will be discussed in the next section. Let us first assume that a sound source emits waveforms through a material medium, isotropically. Isotropic propagation means that the sound is transmitted with equal intensity in all directions (Halliday et al., 2011). If this condition is met, the wave is said to be a spherical wave or a spherical wave front because, as the sound wave moves outward from a central point source (also called a spherical point source) location, the energy it carries is equally spread over an increasingly larger area (Giancoli, 2005). This area that contains

the sound waves can be likened to, and may be defined as, the surface area of a sphere. Recall from Chapter 5 that it was Archimedes (287–212 BC) who initially determined that the circumference for any circle is computed by taking the product of the constant value π (3.14159265) and the circle's diameter (2 × the radius r), or simply,

$$\text{Circumference} = \pi \times \text{diameter}$$

where $\pi = 3.14159265$

since $\text{Diameter} = 2r$

Hence, $\text{Circumference} = \pi 2r$

or $\text{Circumference} = 2\pi r$

It was also Archimedes who determined that every point in a sphere surface is equidistant from the fixed point at the center of the sphere, and that particular distance just happens to be equal to the length of the radius r (Figure 6–1A). Hence, the surface area of a

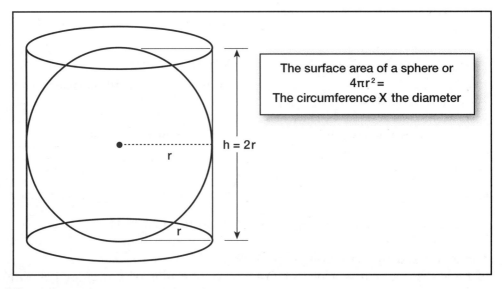

Figure 6–1A. Measuring the surface area of a sphere.

sphere with radius r is defined as the circumference $(2\pi r) \times$ the diameter $(2r)$, and therefore,

The surface area of a sphere is equal to

$$2\pi r \times 2r \qquad (6\text{–}3)$$
$$\text{or}$$
$$4\pi r^2$$

Inverse Square Law

What happens to a finite amount of acoustic intensity (power) or the "energy density" of a sound wave that originates from a point source, as the wave progressively propagates outward in all directions, and with equal power? As indicated above, this finite amount of sound wave energy would be consecutively and progressively spread (dissipated) over an increasingly larger surface area as a spherical wave. Let us assume as before that the sound wave is propagated from its point source with equal power in all directions and that it is propagated through an ideal environment (an ideal material medium). Such an ideal medium would have uniform dimensions, it would be spatially unlimited in all directions, and it would contain no obstacles, barriers, or physical conditions that would affect the basic characteristics of the propagated sound wave. The type of ideal medium described above characterizes one definition of a *free soundfield*, or a *free-field*, which will be covered in this chapter. If these conditions are met, the outward isotropic expansion of the spherical wave front from a (central) point source could be likened to the three-dimensional surface area of an expanding soap bubble

as was originally (Speaks, 1999) and later suggested by others (Durrant & Feth, 2013). Figure 6–1B illustrates in three dimensions a hypothetical wave front that is represented visually by the expanding surface area of a soap bubble. The outwardly expanding wave front (soap bubble surface) is shown arising from a central point source with equal amounts of power propagated in all directions, as illustrated by the insertion of several radii (r). Recall from Figure 6–1A and Equation 6–3 that every point in a sphere surface is equidistant from the fixed point at the center of the sphere, and that the distance from the center point to the sphere surface is also equal to the length of radius r. Therefore, in Figure 6–1B it should be understood that each r arises from a central point source and extends to the spherical surface of the bubble (the hypothetical wave front), and that each conceivable r shown in the illustration should also be equal in length.

As the outward isotropic expansion of the wave front continues, r also increases equally in length in all directions. Recall that acoustic intensity, the energy carried by a sound wave, was defined previously (Equation 6–2) as power that is distributed over a given area or I = power/area. The area covered by the expanding wave front will progressively increase in size as the square of the distance, as its distance progressively increases from the point source of origin. Hence, the intensity of the sound wave would certainly be expected to decrease in both power and in amplitude with an increasing amount of distance from that point source. It is, of course, a familiar observation that the greater the distance that one is positioned from the source of a sound, the

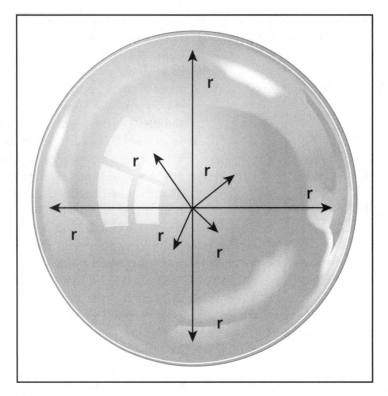

Figure 6–1B. The three-dimensional expansion of a wave front within the area of a bubble. Shown is the hypothetical isotropic expansion of a wave front from a point source using an expanding soap bubble surface as an analogy. Each radius (*r*) is equal in length.

less loud, the lower the magnitude or the less intense is the auditory experience of that sound source. As the area that is covered by a sound wave steadily increases in size with an increase in distance, the energy density (or *I*) of the sound wave will also decrease. This relationship for a spherical waveform is defined by the inverse square law:

The Inverse Square Law

$$I = P/4\pi r^2 \qquad (6\text{--}4)$$

where P = power (watts), and $4\pi r^2$ = the surface area of a sphere, as defined above in Equation 6–3. It should be obvious from Equation 6–4 that each time the radius increases by some value, the surface area of the sphere also increases by the square of that value. This point is also illustrated in Figure 6–1C.

It happens that the acoustic intensity (*I*) of a waveform at any observed wave front location (*d*) is inversely proportional to the square of the relative distance of that observed waveform front from the original sound (point) source, or simply,

I is proportional (~) to $1/d^2$
from the point source

where d = a given distance from a point source in which the expanding surface

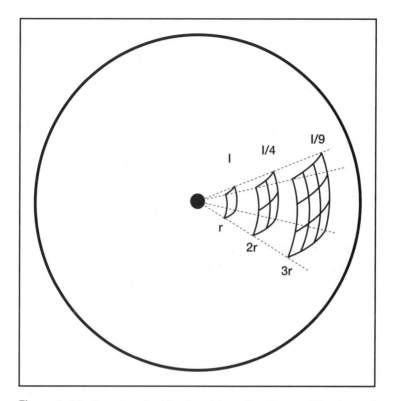

Figure 6–1C. The outward unidirectional expansion of a sound from a sound (point) source demonstrating the inverse square law. Illustrated is the hypothetical expansion of the surface area of a sphere covered by a wave front in one direction from a point source for a given intensity (*I*). At two times the distance (2*r*) and at three times the distance (3*r*), the area expands to four and to nine arbitrary units, respectively. The intensity also decreases inversely as the square of each distance.

area of a sphere may also be represented by radius (*r*).

Hence,

$$I \sim 1/r^2 \qquad (6\text{--}5)$$

Loosely defined, and as illustrated in Figure 6–1C, a twofold increase (2*r*) in the distance from a sound source results in a $1/2^2$ decrease, or a decrease to one fourth (¼) of the original level of the acoustic intensity *I*. A threefold increase (3*r*) in the distance from a sound source results in a $1/3^2$ decrease, or a decrease to one ninth (⅑) of the original level of the acoustic intensity,

and so forth. In Figure 6–1C, also note that at a twofold distance from the point source, the surface area of the wave front increases by a factor of 2^2, or by four arbitrary units. At a threefold distance, the surface area of the wave front increases by a factor of 3^2, or by nine arbitrary units. What would be the predicted intensity and the area of distribution of the wave front at a fourfold distance from the sound source? A fourfold increase (4*r*) in the distance from a sound source results in a $1/4^2$ decrease, or a decrease to one-sixteenth (¹⁄₁₆) of the original level of the acoustic intensity, and the surface area of the wave front would increase by a factor of 4^2, or by 16 arbitrary units.

Quantifying Acoustic Intensity

Threshold and Absolute Threshold

What is a threshold? A threshold is usually defined as the least amount or level of an environmental stimulus, in this case sound, that can be detected, on the average, by an individual or by a group of individuals, in the absence of any other environmental sounds. What is an absolute threshold? The term *absolute* refers for the most part to the kind of (absolute) threshold response that is expected from the listener. The absolute presence or absolute absence of the perceived stimulus is determined by the listener at each moment, as indicated by the responses that are provided by the listener. It is important to note that the method of presentation of the sound, the instructions given, and the methods used to determine or measure an absolute threshold for any particular individual or group must also be specified. Therefore, with respect to acoustic intensity and/or sound pressure, an absolute threshold represents the least amount or quantity that is required in order for a sound to be perceived or identified, on the average, by a given individual or group. The concept of threshold and absolute threshold will be covered in much greater detail in Chapter 8. However, it is noteworthy that in the present context, threshold as defined is based strictly on a behavioral response to a particular stimulus or set of stimuli. This means that auditory threshold judgments made on the part of the listener are subjective in nature. Hence, obtaining an absolute auditory threshold response requires that a subject is (a) able to perceive the sound, (b) physically able to respond at any moment to the sound by confirming behaviorally either its presence or its absence (in absolute terms), and (c) consciously willing or behaviorally disposed to respond to the sound. As a rule, auditory sensitivity is inversely related to auditory threshold. Lower auditory thresholds are correlated with greater levels of auditory sensitivity, and vice versa. How much acoustic intensity (or watts of power) is actually required for a threshold response? In terms of the upper limits for sound, how much acoustic intensity can be tolerated with or without pain?

Recall Equation 6–2:

$$\text{Acoustic Intensity } (I) = \text{Power/area}$$

As reviewed earlier in Chapter 4 and in the above sections of the present chapter, power is defined as the watt for both the MKS and CGS metric systems. Area was also defined in Chapter 2 as the MKS square meter (m^2) or the CGS square centimeter (cm^2). The acoustic intensity value that is close to the average (across human subjects) auditory threshold for a 1000-Hz pure tone is 10^{-12} watts/m^2 (MKS), or its CGS equivalent 10^{-16} watts/cm^2 (Hirsh, 1952; Moore, 2012). These two threshold quantities for acoustic intensity not only provide starting or reference values that help define the range of human hearing, but they also serve as reference values for computations of the *bel* and for the *decibel* (dB), discussed later in this chapter.

As indicated in Chapter 2, the dynamic range of acoustic intensities over which human hearing operates is vast. From the lowest fractional amounts of acoustic intensity required to produce a threshold response, to the upper limits of intensity that can be painfully tolerated, or tolerated without pain, the dynamic range (or ratio) of measurable values is large and is linear. For acoustic intensity (power), the dynamic range, extending to a level that is tolerated with pain, turns out to be about 100 trillion to 1 (Hewitt, 2010; Hirsh, 1952; Moore, 2012), or a ratio of 10^{14}:1. On the other hand, the dynamic range expressed with an upper limit of acoustic intensity that may be tolerated without pain is 10^{12}:1 or 1 trillion to 1 (Hirsh, 1952). The MKS range for acoustic intensity would therefore extend from the approximate threshold value of 10^{-12} watts/m² to an upper (painful) value of 10^2 watts/m², or to an upper limit without pain of 1 watt/m². The CGS acoustic intensity range would also extend from the threshold value of 10^{-16} watts/cm² to an upper painful value of 10^{-2} watts/cm² or, to an upper limit without pain of 10^{-4} watts/cm² (Hirsh, 1952).

Newtons (N), Dynes, and Pressure Revisited

In Chapter 4, units of force for both the MKS and CGS systems were defined as

MKS

$$kg\text{-meter/second}^2 = 1 \text{ newton}$$

CGS

$$gram\text{-centimeter/second}^2 = 1 \text{ dyne}$$

In addition, 1 newton = $10^3 \times 10^2$ (or simply 10^5) dynes, or, in words, 1 newton is equal to 100,000 dynes.

Pressure was also defined in Chapter 4 as the amount of force per unit area. Pressure is therefore equal to force divided by area or

$$Pressure = force/area$$

Recall as well from Chapter 4 that the standard unit of pressure in the MKS metric system is the

$$newton/meter^2$$

and that

$$1 \text{ newton/meter}^2 = 1 \text{ pascal (Pa)}$$

Also introduced in Chapter 4 was the standard unit of pressure in the CGS metric system:

$$dyne/centimeter^2$$

Also recall from Chapter 4 that 1 dyne/centimeter² in some instances has been referred to as

1 microbar (μbar) or 10^{-6} bars and that 1 bar = 10^6 dynes/centimeter²

It was additionally recognized in Chapter 4 that the MKS unit of pressure is 10 times greater than the CGS unit of pressure:

$$1 \text{ newton/meter}^2 \text{ (1 Pa)} = 10 \text{ dynes/centimeter}^2$$

Quantifying Pressure

The MKS sound pressure value that is close to the average human auditory threshold for a 1000-Hz pure tone is

$$0.00002 \text{ newtons (N)/ m}^2$$

which is also expressed in scientific notation as

$$2 \times 10^{-5} \text{ N/m}^2$$

Since 1 newton/m² = 1 pascal of pressure, it also follows that the MKS sound pressure value that is close to the average human auditory threshold for a 1000-Hz pure tone may be expressed as 0.00002 pascals (Pa), or in scientific notation as 2×10^{-5} Pa. However, this notation is seldom used. Instead, a zero is added in the negative sixth decimal place of 0.00002 Pa resulting in the equivalent value of 0.000020 Pa, or in essence, 20×10^{-6} Pa. This value is commonly expressed as 20 micro Pa or more conveniently as 20 µPa.

The CGS equivalent sound pressure value that is close to the average human auditory threshold for a 1000-Hz pure tone is

$$0.0002 \text{ dynes/cm}^2$$

which is also expressed in scientific notation as

$$2 \times 10^{-4} \text{ dynes/cm}^2$$

Once again, as with the two threshold quantities for acoustic intensity presented above, these three threshold quantities for sound pressure provide not only starting or reference values that help define the range of human hearing, but will also serve as reference values for computations of the bel and the decibel (dB).

Similar to acoustic intensity, the range (ratio) over which human hearing operates beginning with the lowest fractional amounts of sound pressure required to produce a threshold response, to the upper limits of sound pressure that can be painfully tolerated or tolerated without pain, is large and linear. For sound pressure, the dynamic range expressed with an upper limit that may be tolerated with pain happens to be about 10 million to 1 (Hewitt, 2010; Hirsh, 1952; Moore, 2012), or a ratio of 10^7:1. On the other hand, the dynamic range of pressure expressed with an upper limit that may be tolerated without pain is 10^6:1 or 1 million to 1 (Hirsh, 1952). The MKS dynamic range for sound pressure would therefore extend from an approximate threshold value of 2×10^{-5} newtons/m² to an upper value with pain, of 2×10^2 newtons/m², or to an upper limit without pain of 2×10 newtons/m².

The MKS dynamic range equivalently expressed in pascals of pressure extends from a value of 20 µPa to an upper value tolerated with pain of 200,000,000 µPa, or to an upper pressure value tolerated without pain of 20,000,000 µPa. In words, this range extends from a threshold of 20 µPa, to 200 million µPa tolerated with pain, or up to 20 million µPa tolerated in the absence of pain. These values may also be expressed in scientific notation as dynamic ranges extending from a threshold value of 2×10 µPa to an upper value of 2×10^8 µPa tolerated with pain, or 2×10^7 µPa tolerated without pain.

Finally, the CGS dynamic sound pressure range would extend from the threshold value of 2×10^{-4} dynes/cm² to an upper value tolerated with pain, of 2×10^3 dynes/cm². The upper limit of pressure tolerated without pain, is 2×10^2 dynes/cm². As with the dynamic ranges of acoustic intensities listed above, the ranges of pressure quantities will again be revisited in discussions of the decibel in the sections that follow.

Relationship Between Intensity (*I*) and Pressure (*P*)

The relationship between intensity and pressure may be defined by the following equation, where pressure is squared and is placed into the numerator and the characteristic impedance of the particular medium is placed into the denominator (Hirsh, 1952):

Intensity (power/area) =

$$\frac{\text{Pressure}^2 \text{ or (force/area)}^2}{\text{Density (mass/volume)} \times \text{speed of sound (distance/time)}}$$

Recall from Chapter 5 that the characteristic impedance: Z_c = [density of the medium] × [the speed of sound (*c*) in the medium]

or simply,

$$Z_c = \text{density} \times c$$

can be measured in units called *rayls*, as presented for various media in Table 5–5. This relationship is simplified in Equation 6–6 affirming that acoustic intensity (*I*) is proportional or roughly equivalent to pressure squared (*P²*) and that pressure (*P*) is proportional, or roughly equivalent to the square root of acoustic intensity ($\sqrt{I}$):

$$I = P^2 \qquad (6\text{–}6)$$
$$P = \sqrt{I}$$

Threshold and Upper Limit Values for Intensity and Pressure

The relevance of Equation 6–6 to computations of the bel and the decibel will also become clear later in this chapter. Provided that the necessary conversions are performed, MKS absolute threshold values for both intensity and pressure are computationally equivalent, as are CGS absolute threshold values for intensity and pressure. In a similar way, MKS upper limit values for both intensity and pressure are also computationally equivalent, as are CGS upper limit values for intensity and pressure. Each of these threshold and upper limit values, together with their respective dynamic ranges, are summarized in Tables 6–2A and 6–2B. Table 6–2A illustrates intensity and pressure upper limits and dynamic ranges tolerated with pain. Table 6–2B illustrates the same upper limits and dynamic ranges for intensity and pressure that may be tolerated without pain.

Acoustic Intensity Level (IL) and Sound Pressure Level (SPL)

As indicated in the sections above and in Chapter 2, the dynamic range of acoustic intensity (and sound pressure) over which human hearing operates is large and linear. When applications were made to the hearing sciences, the representation of this large linear range of human hearing turned out to be very cumbersome to work with and necessitated the use of a more compressed scale of measurement (Hirsh, 1952). Once again, and as illustrated in Tables 6–2A and 6–2B, the dynamic range of human hearing represents a ratio of 100 trillion to 1 (10^{14}:1) for acoustic intensity that extends to a level that is tolerated with pain, or 1 trillion to 1 (10^{12}:1) for an upper limit that is tolerated in

Table 6–2A. Summary Table of MKS and CGS Average Threshold, Upper Limit Values Tolerated With Pain and Dynamic Ranges for Intensity and Pressure

	MKS Average Threshold	CGS Average Threshold	MKS Upper Limit	CGS Upper Limit	Dynamic Range
Intensity	10^{-12} watts/m^2		10^2 watts/m^2		10^{14}:1
		10^{-16} watts/cm^2		10^{-2} watts/cm^2	10^{14}:1
Pressure	2×10^{-5} N/m^2 (or 20 µPa)		2×10^2 N/m^2 (or 2×10^8 µPa)		10^7:1
					10^7:1
		2×10^{-4} dynes/cm^2		2×10^3 dynes/cm^2	10^7:1

Note. N = Newtons; *m* = Meters; *cm* = Centimeters; *Pa* = Pascals; *µ* = Micro.

Table 6–2B. MKS and CGS Average Threshold, Upper Limit Values Tolerated Without Pain and Dynamic Ranges for Intensity and Pressure

	MKS Average Threshold	CGS Average Threshold	MKS Upper Limit	CGS Upper Limit	Dynamic Range
Intensity	10^{-12} watts/m^2		1 watt/m^2		10^{12}:1
		10^{-16} watts/cm^2		10^{-4} watts/cm^2	10^{12}:1
Pressure	2×10^{-5} N/m^2 (or 20 µPa)		2×10 N/m^2 (or 2×10^7 µPa)		10^6:1
					10^6:1
		2×10^{-4} dynes/cm^2		2×10^2 dynes/cm^2	10^6:1

Note. N = Newtons; *m* = Meters; *cm* = Centimeters; *Pa* = Pascals; *µ* = Micro.

the absence of pain. Furthermore, the dynamic range of human hearing also represents a ratio of 10 million to 1 (10^7:1) for sound pressure that extends to a level that is tolerated with pain, or 1 million to 1 (10^6:1) for an upper limit that is tolerated in the absence of pain. Furthermore, the use of the term *level* (as in IL) should be taken to mean the same as a ratio and not as an absolute amount of intensity. The same understanding of a ratio interpretation should apply to the term *sound pressure level* (SPL).

Historical Overview: The Bel

In an attempt to develop a more condensed and pragmatic measurement scale that would accurately reflect the dynamic range (or ratio) of sensitivity over which human hearing occurs, the bel was introduced from the telephone engineering trade. The name *bel* originated from and was created in honor of Alexander Graham Bell (Box 6–1 and Portrait 6–1). The bel was introduced not as a linear unit of measure, but as a

Box 6–1. Alexander Graham Bell (1847–1922)

Alexander Graham Bell (1847–1922) was an American scientist and educator who, in 1875, invented the telephone. Bell's invention provided a device that could convert the small mechanical energies of sound into electrical energies, and vice versa (Hirsh, 1952). Bell was born in Edinburgh, Scotland, but moved to Boston in 1871. In 1872 he opened a school for "teachers of the deaf" and in 1873 became a professor at Boston University. In 1876, together with Thomas A. Watson, Bell received a patent for his telephone. The Bell Telephone Company was then established in 1877 and in 1882 Bell became a U.S. citizen.

Portrait 6–1. Alexander Graham Bell (1847–1922). Printed with permission. Wikimedia Commons, public domain.

base 10 logarithmic (log) measurement scale to designate the log of a ratio of signal intensities, or simply the log of the intensity level. Logarithms were introduced in Chapter 2 and are reviewed in Appendix B. Therefore, the bel as a unit of intensity level may be defined as

$$\text{bel} = \text{log of a ratio} \qquad (6\text{–}7)$$

or

$$\text{bel} = \log\left(\frac{\text{observed value}}{\text{reference value}}\right)$$

As with any fraction, the ratio of signal intensities is composed of a numerator and a denominator, and for our purposes, the denominator will always consist of one of the five threshold values (two references for intensity level; three references for sound pressure level) listed in Tables 6–2A–B. The focus of this section is on bels of intensity level. Equation 6–7 may be rewritten or simplified for bels of acoustic intensity level as

$$\text{bel IL} = \log\left(\frac{I_O}{I_R}\right) \qquad (6\text{–}8A)$$

where I_O is the term used for an observed acoustic intensity, and I_R is the term for the reference intensity.

It is important to consider that any number may be expressed as a ratio (or fraction). This is because any number, such as a whole number, may be rewritten or defined as a numerator that is placed over a denominator of 1. All fractions or ratios are understood to imply *relativity* such that the value in the numerator is meaningless unless the value in the denominator is also known. In all ratios, the denominator always serves as a *reference value*. For instance, suppose one makes the claim (or verbalizes an observation) of owning four homes. Without asking for additional clarification, a bystander might interpret such a statement as meaning "an observation was made of four homes relative to one home," or simply 4/1, which would indeed be an observation of four separate homes. Suppose the bystander instead asks the obvious question "an observation of four homes, but relative to what value," or simply "what is the reference value for your observed value of 4 homes?" How would the meaning of the observed value of 4 be altered if the reference value of 1 were to be changed to a 2, or even to a 4? Obviously, an observation of four homes relative to two homes (4/2) would be equal to only 2 homes, or half as many as the original four, and an observation of four homes relative to four homes (4/4) would be equal to only 1 home, or one fourth as many as the original four. Therefore, it must be emphasized and it will be restated in the sections that follow, that whenever measurements such as the decibel (dB) are used, the dB quantities are meaningless unless the reference values in each computation are also specified.

Bel–Intensity Level (IL)

All scales of measurement need a starting point, and zero is an excellent

place to begin any measurement scale, including that of the bel. A relative rather than an absolute zero is also an appropriate starting place to begin a measurement scale that reflects human auditory sensitivity. The bel scale is an exponential interval scale of measurement based on multiples of 10 and has a starting point that employs a non-absolute zero. Recall from Chapter 2 that "interval" scales of measurement in general, employ a relative rather than an absolute zero starting point. Unlike "ratio" scales of measurement in which the starting value of zero indicates the complete and absolute absence of a measurement attribute, the bel scale employs threshold amounts in acoustic intensity and/or sound pressure as the starting (reference) values. This is, of course, in direct contrast to using the total absence of acoustic intensity (or sound pressure) as a reference. Hence, 0 bels is taken to mean "no change from the reference" and is not understood to mean the total absence of sound. To illustrate this point, each of the equations of the bel stated below will indicate how the intensity threshold values provided in Tables 6–2A and 6–2B are to be properly used as the reference (I_R) value for computations of intensity level. Each I_R is to be placed into the denominator of the ratio and this procedure is followed in all computations of the decibel (a derivative of the bel) as indicated later in this chapter. In each of the limited number of examples illustrated below, the observed values (I_O) are placed into the numerator of the ratio, and each I_O could have taken on virtually any intensity value within the dynamic range of hearing sensitivity. In the examples provided, each observed intensity just happens to be equal to the respective, metric-system-appropriate reference values in order to make a point. For our purposes, such as in computations of the bel (and the decibel), the observed (I_O) values (in the numerator) will never be less than the respective, metric-system-appropriate reference (I_R) values (i.e., never less than the threshold in the denominator) or greater than the respective, and metric-system-appropriate upper limit values that are also provided in Tables 6–2A and 6–2B for a given type of energy source (intensity in this case). Thus, for illustrative purposes, in each of the equations shown below for intensity level in bels (Equations 6–8B and 6–8C), the observed values of acoustic intensity have been assigned a value that is equal to the appropriate reference values. Similar equations for bels of sound pressure will be provided in the sections that follow. Therefore, for an observation that is equal to threshold (also the reference), the ratio inside the parentheses will of course always be equal to 1, and the log of 1 is always zero. Consequently, in each instance where I_O is equal to I_R, there is "no change from the reference," which, as stated above, should be taken to be the definition, of "0 bels IL." Hence, Equation 6–7 from the section above that defined the bel as

$$\text{bel} = \log \left(\frac{\text{observed value}}{\text{reference value}} \right) \quad (6\text{–}7)$$

which was also rewritten above for simplicity as bels of acoustic intensity level as Equation 6–8A:

$$\text{bel IL} = \log \left(\frac{I_O}{I_R} \right) \quad (6\text{–}8\text{A})$$

is now applied below in the following two equations to illustrate instances where the I_O is equal to the I_R. To begin with, in terms of intensity level when watts of power are concerned, Equation 6–8B can be used to define the MKS intensity level for 0 bels as

$$\text{bel IL} = \log \left(\frac{10^{-12} \text{ watts/cm}^2}{10^{-12} \text{ watts/cm}^2} \right) = 0$$
$$(6\text{–}8\text{B})$$

Equation 6–8C defines the CGS intensity level for 0 bels as

$$\text{bel IL} = \log \left(\frac{10^{-16} \text{ watts/cm}^2}{10^{-16} \text{ watts/cm}^2} \right) = 0$$
$$(6\text{–}8\text{C})$$

It also follows that if the lower limit (or threshold) of hearing is 0 bels IL, the upper limits of hearing may be defined or expressed in bels employing the upper limit of intensity level that can be painfully tolerated (Equations 6–8D and 6–8E), or the upper limit that may be tolerated without pain (Equations 6–8F and 6–8G). Hence, for intensity level when watts of power are concerned, Equation 6–8D defines the MKS upper limit of intensity level with pain, expressed in bels, as:

$$\text{bel IL} = \log \left(\frac{10^{2} \text{ watts/m}^2}{10^{-12} \text{ watts/m}^2} \right) = 14$$
$$(6\text{–}8\text{D})$$

Equation 6–8E defines the CGS upper limit of intensity level with pain, expressed in bels, as

$$\text{bel IL} = \log \left(\frac{10^{-2} \text{ watts/cm}^2}{10^{-16} \text{ watts/cm}^2} \right) = 14$$
$$(6\text{–}8\text{E})$$

Equation 6–8F defines the MKS upper limit of intensity level without pain, expressed in bels, as

$$\text{bel IL} = \log\left(\frac{1\ \text{watt/m}^2}{10^{-12}\ \text{watts/m}^2}\right) = 12$$

$$(6\text{–}8F)$$

Equation 6–8G defines the CGS upper limit of intensity level without pain, expressed in bels, as

$$\text{bel IL} = \log\left(\frac{10^{-4}\ \text{watts/cm}^2}{10^{-16}\ \text{watts/cm}^2}\right) = 12$$

$$(6\text{–}8G)$$

To summarize, the dynamic range of intensity over which human hearing spans, defined above as a linear ratio, may be defined in terms of an exponential/logarithmic scale. This scale has a range of 0 to 14 bels of intensity level (IL) that represents an upper limit of intensity that is tolerated with pain, or 0 to 12 bels IL that extends to an intensity level that is tolerated without pain. The dynamic range of human hearing based on linear ratios, their exponential equivalents, and their bels of IL equivalents, is presented in Table 6–3.

Table 6–3. Linear Base-10 Ratios for Intensity Level (IL), Their Exponential Equivalents, and Their Equivalent Values in Bels IL

Linear Ratio Intensity Level (IL)	Exponential Equivalent	Bel(s) IL log (ratio)	
1:1	10^0	0	
10:1	10^1	1	
100:1	10^2	2	
1,000:1	10^3	3	
10,000:1	10^4	4	
100,000:1	10^5	5	
1,000,000:1	10^6	6	
10,000,000:1	10^7	7	
100,000,000:1	10^8	8	
1,000,000,000:1	10^9	9	
10,000,000,000:1	10^{10}	10	
100,000,000,000:1	10^{11}	11	
1,000,000,000,000:1	10^{12}	12	
10,000,000,000,000:1	10^{13}	13	With Pain
100,000,000,000,000:1	10^{14}	14	

Note that 0 to 14 bels IL represents the range for human hearing using an upper limit that extends to a level that is tolerated with pain. Zero to 12 bels IL represents the range for human hearing using an upper limit that extends to a level that is tolerated without pain.

Evaluation of the Bel

In terms of its practicality as a scale for descriptions of human hearing, and when used as a measure of relative intensity (intensity level), the bel was found to be less cumbersome to use than the linear ratios shown in Table 6–3. This is because the wide range of linear ratios could now be easily compressed into and described as a simple logarithmic scale from 0 to 14 or 0 to 12 bels. The application of the bel, however, compressed the dynamic range of hearing by too excessive of an amount. While the units of the bel (0 to 12 or 0 to 14) were smaller, they were now too small and once again, impractical to work with. At the same time, each bel represented an impractically large progression from unit to unit (Hirsh, 1952). As indicated in Table 6–3, each increase of 1 bel represents a very large linear increment (by 10-fold) of power, such that a 1-bel increment from 2 bels to 3 bels represents a power ratio leap from 100 to 1,000. Likewise, a 1-bel increment from 6 bels to 7 bels represents a power leap from 1 million to 10 million. Hence, when using the bel, fractional values would be required to achieve greater accuracy of measurement between whole bels, in much the same way as fractions of whole meters might be used in place of centimeters or millimeters, if centimeters or millimeters were unavailable for use (Speaks, 1999). Fortunately, in much the same way that meters may be partitioned into these smaller equally spaced units for greater accuracy, the bel may also be partitioned into smaller, equally spaced units for improved accuracy. Therefore, in order to avoid the unnecessary use of partitioning the bel into decimal parts, it became more convenient to use a scale of measurement that specified smaller ratios of the bel (Hirsh, 1952), and hence, the decibel was introduced.

The Decibel (dB)

Just as there are 100 centimeters in one meter, or 1000 milliseconds in 1 second, there are also 10 decibels in 1 bel, and therefore the decibel is one tenth (1/10) of a bel. As indicated in Appendix C, the prefix for 0.1 (1/10) is deci; each bel is equal to 10 decibels (dB). Therefore, the general solution for bels of intensity level, as given by

$$\text{bel IL} = \log\left(\frac{I_O}{I_R}\right) \qquad (6\text{–}8A)$$

may be restated as the computational equation for decibels (dB) of intensity level (IL) as

$$\text{dB IL} = 10 \times \log\left(\frac{I_O}{I_R}\right) \qquad (6\text{–}9)$$

Table 6–3 numerically illustrates the dynamic range of human hearing based on linear intensity ratios, their exponential equivalents, and their bel IL equivalents. These values are again presented together with their decibel equivalents for intensity level (dB IL) in Table 6–4A. It should be clear from the intensity level ratios provided in Table 6–4A that each dB IL value is simply 10 times the bel, and 0 dB IL, like 0 bels, means "no change from the reference."

Table 6–4A. Linear Base-10 Ratios for Intensity Level (IL), Their Exponential Equivalents, Their Equivalent Values in Bels IL, and Their Equivalent Values in Decibels (dB) IL (dB IL)

Linear Ratio Intensity Level	Exponential Equivalent	Bel(s) IL log (ratio)	Decibels (dB IL) 10 × log (ratio)
1:1	10^0	0	0
10:1	10^1	1	10
100:1	10^2	2	20
1,000:1	10^3	3	30
10,000:1	10^4	4	40
100,000:1	10^5	5	50
1,000,000:1	10^6	6	60
10,000,000:1	10^7	7	70
100,000,000:1	10^8	8	80
1,000,000,000:1	10^9	9	90
10,000,000,000:1	10^{10}	10	100
100,000,000,000:1	10^{11}	11	110
1,000,000,000,000:1	10^{12}	12	120
10,000,000,000,000:1	10^{13}	13	130 ⬇ With Pain
100,000,000,000,000:1	10^{14}	14	140

Note that 0 to 140 dB IL represents the range for human hearing using an upper limit that extends to a level that is tolerated with pain. Zero to 120 dB IL represents the range for human hearing using an upper limit that extends to a level that is tolerated without pain.

Decibels of Intensity Level (dB IL)

We are now ready to compute the MKS and CGS decibels of intensity level (dB IL) using the computational Equation 6–9 provided in the section above and the reference (or threshold) values (I_{R_s}) provided in Tables 6–2A and 6–2B. The MKS/CGS references (I_{R_s}) and upper limit values (I_{O_s}) used in computations of dB IL will be identical of course to those used in the reference (Equations 6–8B and 6–8C) and upper limit computational examples of the bel IL that were provided in the above section of

this chapter (Equations 6–8D through 6–8G). Once again, using the computational equation for dB IL

$$\text{dB IL} = 10 \times \log \left(\frac{I_O}{I_R} \right) \qquad (6\text{–}9)$$

The appropriate MKS reference (I_R) and the corresponding MKS observed intensities (I_{O_s}) expressed in watts of power/area for computations of 0 to 140 dB IL are provided in Table 6–4B. Note that the logs of each of the intensity ratios [log (I_O/I_R)] are computed by dividing each of the observed inten-

Table 6–4B. MKS Decibels of Intensity Level (dB IL) for 0 to 140 dB IL, With the MKS Reference Intensity (I_R) and Observed Intensities (I_O)

MKS Reference Intensity (I_R) watts/m²	MKS Observed Intensity (I_O) watts/m²	Decibel Intensity Level dB IL = 10 × log (I_O/I_R) dB IL =
10^{-12} watts/m²	10^{-12} watts/m²	0
	10^{-11} watts/m²	10
	10^{-10} watts/m²	20
	10^{-9} watts/m²	30
	10^{-8} watts/m²	40
	10^{-7} watts/m²	50
	10^{-6} watts/m²	60
	10^{-5} watts/m²	70
	10^{-4} watts/m²	80
	10^{-3} watts/m²	90
	10^{-2} watts/m²	100
	10^{-1} watts/m²	110
	10^{0} watts/m²	120
	10^{1} watts/m²	130 With Pain
	10^{2} watts/m²	140

Note that 0 to 140 dB IL represents the range for human hearing using an upper limit that extends to a level that is tolerated with pain. Zero to 120 dB IL represents the range for human hearing using an upper limit that extends to a level that is tolerated without pain.

sity values in the second column by the reference intensity in the first column. These ratios would be identical to the intensity level ratios computed for bels of IL listed in Table 6–3. The appropriate CGS reference intensity and the corresponding CGS observed intensities also expressed in watts of power/ area for computations of 0 to 140 dB IL are also provided in Table 6–4C. It is again important to note that 0 dB IL expressed in MKS or CGS metric units of intensity level is always interpreted as "no change from the reference."

Bel–Sound Pressure Level (SPL)

In spite of the impracticality of employing the bel scale for descriptions of human hearing, it is worth noting that measures of the bel can also employ sound pressure thresholds as the starting or reference values (P_{R_S}) as well as observations (P_{O_S}) expressed in units of sound pressure. To illustrate this point, each of the equations for the bel shown below indicates how each of the thresholds for sound pressure from Tables 6–2A and 6–2B are to be

Table 6–4C. CGS Decibels of Intensity Level (dB IL) for 0 to 140 dB IL, With the CGS Reference Intensity Intensity (I_R) and Observed Intensities (I_O)

CGS Reference Intensity (I_R) watts/cm^2	CGS Observed Intensity (I_O) watts/cm^2	Decibel Intensity Level dB IL = 10 × log (I_O/I_R) dB IL =
10^{-16} watts/cm^2	10^{-16} watts/cm^2	0
	10^{-15} watts/cm^2	10
	10^{-14} watts/cm^2	20
	10^{-13} watts/cm^2	30
	10^{-12} watts/cm^2	40
	10^{-11} watts/cm^2	50
	10^{-10} watts/cm^2	60
	10^{-9} watts/cm^2	70
	10^{-8} watts/cm^2	80
	10^{-7} watts/cm^2	90
	10^{-6} watts/cm^2	100
	10^{-5} watts/cm^2	110
	10^{-4} watts/cm^2	120
	10^{-3} watts/cm^2	130 With Pain
	10^{-2} watts/cm^2	140

Note that 0 to 140 dB IL represents the range for human hearing using an upper limit that extends to a level that is tolerated with pain. Zero to 120 dB IL represents the range for human hearing using an upper limit that extends to a level that is tolerated without pain.

properly used as the reference values (P_{R_S}) and placed into the denominator of the metric-system-appropriate ratio for computing bels of SPL. The same references will be employed in computations of dB SPL, as indicated in the sections of this chapter that follow. In each example for bels of SPL, the observed pressures (P_{O_S}) are again placed into the numerator of the ratio, and, as with bels IL described above, the observed pressures may assume virtually any value within the dynamic range of hearing sensitivity. For purposes of illustration, the observed pressures employed in the equations presented below just happen to be equal to the respective metric-system-appropriate reference values. As before, for bels of IL, the computations provided of the bel SPL and for the decibel (dB SPL) utilize observed pressures (P_O) that will never be less than the respective metric-system-appropriate reference (P_R) pressures. The observed (P_O) pressures provided in our examples will also never be greater than the respective, metric- system-appropriate upper limits for pressure that were provided in Tables 6–2A and 6–2B. Hence, in each of the equations shown below for bels of sound pressure level (Equations 6–10B, 6–10C, and 6–10D) the observed pressure (P_O) has been assigned a value equal to the appropriate reference values. Recall that an observation that is equal to the threshold value (or the reference) results in a ratio inside the parenthesis [log (P_O/P_R)] that is always equal to 1, and the log of 1 is always zero. Therefore, in each instance where P_O is equal to P_R, there is once again "no change from the reference," which is understood to be the precise definition, of "0 bels SPL." Equation 6–8A, presented previously for bels of IL, may also be rewritten for bels of SPL as

$$\text{bel SPL} = \log\left(\frac{P_O}{P_R}\right) \quad (6\text{–}10\text{A})$$

where P_O is the term used for an observed sound pressure, and P_R is the term for the reference pressure. Hence, for sound pressure level where newtons (N), dynes, and pascals (Pa) are concerned, it follows that Equation 6–10B defines the MKS sound pressure level for 0 bels as

$$\text{bel SPL} = \log\left(\frac{2 \times 10^{-5}\ \text{N/m}^2}{2 \times 10^{-5}\ \text{N/m}^2}\right) = 0$$
$$(6\text{–}10\text{B})$$

Equation 6–10C defines the MKS sound pressure level for 0 bels in µPa as

$$\text{bel SPL} = \log\left(\frac{20\ \mu\text{Pa}}{20\ \mu\text{Pa}}\right) = 0$$
$$(6\text{–}10\text{C})$$

Equation 6–10D defines the CGS sound pressure level for 0 bels as

$$\text{bel SPL} = \log\left(\frac{2 \times 10^{-4}\ \text{dynes/cm}^2}{2 \times 10^{-4}\ \text{dynes/cm}^2}\right) = 0$$
$$(6\text{–}10\text{D})$$

It also follows that if the lower limit (or threshold) of hearing is 0 bels SPL, the upper limits of hearing may be defined or expressed in bels employing the upper limit of sound pressure level that can be painfully tolerated (Equations 6–10E, 6–10F, and 6–10G), or the upper limit that may be tolerated without pain (Equations 6–10H, 6–10I, and 6–10J). Hence, for sound pressure level, where newtons (N), dynes, and pascals (Pa) are concerned, Equation 6–10E defines the MKS upper limit of sound pressure with pain, expressed in bels, as

$$\text{bel SPL} = \log\left(\frac{2 \times 10^2\ \text{N/m}^2}{2 \times 10^{-5}\ \text{N/m}^2}\right) = 7$$
$$(6\text{–}10\text{E})$$

Equation 6–10F defines the MKS upper limit of sound pressure level in µPa with pain, expressed in bels, as

$$\text{bel SPL} = \log\left(\frac{2 \times 10^8\ \mu\text{Pa}}{20\ \mu\text{Pa}}\right) = 7$$
$$(6\text{–}10\text{F})$$

Equation 6–10G defines the CGS upper limit of sound pressure level with pain, expressed in bels, as

$$\text{bel SPL} = \log\left(\frac{2 \times 10^3\ \text{dynes/cm}^2}{2 \times 10^{-4}\ \text{dynes/cm}^2}\right) = 7$$
$$(6\text{–}10\text{G})$$

Equation 6–10H defines the MKS upper limit of sound pressure level without pain, expressed in bels, as

$$\text{bel SPL} = \log\left(\frac{2 \times 10\ \text{N/m}^2}{2 \times 10^{-5}\ \text{N/m}^2}\right) = 6$$
$$(6\text{–}10\text{H})$$

Equation 6–10I defines the MKS upper limit of sound pressure level in µPa without pain, expressed in bels, as

$$\text{bel SPL} = \log\left(\frac{2 \times 10^7 \ \mu Pa}{20 \ \mu Pa}\right) = 6$$

$$(6\text{--}10I)$$

Equation 6–10J defines the CGS upper limit of sound pressure level without pain, expressed in bels, as

$$\text{bel SPL} = \log\left(\frac{2 \times 10^2 \ \text{dynes/cm}^2}{2 \times 10^{-4} \ \text{dynes/cm}^2}\right) = 6$$

$$(6\text{--}10J)$$

It should be apparent from comparisons of the upper ranges of bels SPL computed in Equations 6–10E through 6–10J, with those of bels IL computed in Equations 6–8D through 6–8G, that the dynamic range of sound pressure over which human hearing spans appears to encompass a more restricted range of values compared to the range of values expressed as acoustic intensity. A range of only 0 to 7 bels SPL may be contrasted with a range of 0 to 14 bels IL for an upper limit of sound with pain, and 0 to 6 bels SPL may be contrasted with a range of 0 to 12 bels IL for an upper limit of sound in the absence of pain. Are these dynamic ranges between SPL and IL really different? What again was the relationship between intensity and pressure discussed earlier in this chapter?

Relationship Between Intensity (*I*) and Pressure (*P*) Revisited

Equation 6–6 may now be recalled from a previous section in this chapter, demonstrating that acoustic intensity (*I*) is proportional, or roughly equivalent to pressure squared (*P²*) and that pressure (*P*) is proportional, or roughly equivalent to the square root of acoustic intensity (√*I*), or

$$I = P^2 \qquad\qquad (6\text{--}6)$$

$$P = \sqrt{I}$$

Hence,

$$\text{bel} = \log\left(\frac{I_O}{I_R}\right) = \left(\frac{P_O}{P_R}\right)^2$$

In Appendix B, Rule VI, or the rule of exponentiation, indicates that the log of a ratio raised to an exponential value is equal to the exponent multiplied by the log of the same ratio or, as indicated in the appendix:

If: $\log (10)^x$;

Then: $\log (10)^x = x \log (10)$

Therefore, Equation 6–10E that defined the MKS upper limit of sound pressure level that can be tolerated with pain, and expressed in bels, can now be changed to

$$\text{bel SPL} = 2 \times \log\left(\frac{2 \times 10^2 \ \text{N/m}^2}{2 \times 10^{-5} \ \text{N/m}^2}\right) = 14$$

The same rule applies to Equation 6–10F that defined the MKS upper limit of sound pressure level in μPa that can be tolerated with pain expressed in bels, which is now changed to

$$\text{bel SPL} = 2 \times \log\left(\frac{2 \times 10^8 \ \mu Pa}{20 \ \mu Pa}\right) = 14$$

Finally, Equation 6–10G that defined the CGS upper limit of sound pressure level that can be tolerated with pain and expressed in bels, may also be changed to

$$\text{bel SPL} =$$
$$2 \times \log\left(\frac{2 \times 10^3 \ \text{dynes/cm}^2}{2 \times 10^{-4} \ \text{dynes/cm}^2}\right) = 14$$

Furthermore, Equation 6–10H that defined the MKS upper limit of sound pressure level tolerated without pain and expressed in bels, is now changed to

$$\text{bel SPL} = 2 \times \log\left(\frac{2 \times 10 \text{ N/m}^2}{2 \times 10^{-5} \text{ N/m}^2}\right) = 12$$

Equation 6–10I that defined the MKS upper limit of sound pressure level in µPa tolerated without pain and expressed in bels, is now changed to

$$\text{bel SPL} = 2 \times \log\left(\frac{2 \times 10^7 \text{ µPa}}{20 \text{ µPa}}\right) = 12$$

Finally, Equation 6–10J that defined the CGS upper limit of sound pressure level tolerated without pain and expressed in bels, is now changed to

$$\text{bel SPL} =$$
$$2 \times \log\left(\frac{2 \times 10^2 \text{ dynes/cm}^2}{2 \times 10^{-4} \text{ dynes/cm}^2}\right) = 12$$

In summary, the dynamic range of sound pressure over which human hearing spans may be expressed either as a linear ratio, or in terms of an exponential/logarithmic scale. This scale has a range of 0 to 14 bels of sound pressure level (SPL), which was also the range indicated for bels of intensity level (IL) and represents an upper sound limit that extends to a value that may be tolerated with pain. Recall from Tables 6–4B and 6–4C that 140 dB IL also represents the approximate upper limit of sound intensity that may be tolerated with pain. The bel scale also has a range of 0 to 12 bels of SPL or IL representing an upper limit of sound extending to a value that may be tolerated without pain. Tables 6–4B

and 6–4C also illustrated that 120 dB IL is the approximate upper limit of sound intensity tolerated without pain. The dynamic range of human hearing based on linear ratios, their exponential equivalents, and their equivalent bels of IL were presented in Tables 6–3 and 6–4A (which also included decibels). The dynamic range of human hearing based on linear ratios, their exponential equivalents, and their equivalent bels (and decibels) of SPL are presented in Table 6–5A.

Decibels of Sound Pressure Level (dB SPL)

We may now compute the MKS and CGS decibels of sound pressure level (dB SPL) using a modification of the dB IL computational Equation 6–9 from the section above and the reference (or threshold) values for sound pressure (P_R) provided in Tables 6–2A and 6–2B. The MKS/CGS references (P_{R_s}) and upper limit sound pressure values (P_{O_s}) used in computations of dB SPL are therefore identical to those used in the computational examples of bels of SPL provided in Equations 6–10B through 6–10D (for reference threshold), and Equations 6–10E through 6–10J (upper limit values). Taking the computational equation for dB IL:

$$\text{dB IL} = 10 \times \log\left(\frac{I_O}{I_R}\right) \quad (6\text{–}9)$$

Recall that the relationship between intensity and pressure was defined as

$$I = P^2 \quad (6\text{–}6)$$

$$P = \sqrt{I}$$

Table 6–5A. Linear Base-10 Ratios for Sound Pressure Level (SPL), Their Exponential Equivalents, Their Equivalent Values in Bels SPL (Where $I = P^2$), and Their Equivalent Values in Decibels (dB) of SPL (dB SPL)

Linear Ratio Sound Pressure Level	Exponential Equivalent	Bel(s) SPL 2 × log (ratio)	Decibels (dB SPL) 20 × log (ratio)
1:1	10^0	0	0
	$10^{0.5}$	1	10
10:1	10^1	2	20
	$10^{1.5}$	3	30
100:1	10^2	4	40
	$10^{2.5}$	5	50
1000:1	10^3	6	60
	$10^{3.5}$	7	70
10,000:1	10^4	8	80
	$10^{4.5}$	9	90
100,000:1	10^5	10	100
	$10^{5.5}$	11	110
1,000,000:1	10^6	12	120
	$10^{6.5}$	13	130 — With Pain
10,000,000:1	10^7	14	140

Note that zero to 140 dB SPL represents the range for human hearing using an upper limit that extends to a level that is tolerated with pain. Zero to 120 dB SPL represents the range for human hearing using an upper limit that extends to a level that is tolerated without pain.

And therefore,

$$\text{dB IL} = 10 \log \left(\frac{I_O}{I_R}\right)^2 = 10 \log \left(\frac{P_O}{P_R}\right)$$

And if, according to Rule VI, or the rule of exponentiation found in Appendix B,

If: $\text{Log } (10)^x$;

Then: $\text{Log } (10)^x = x \text{ Log } (10)$;

or

$$\text{dB SPL} = 2 \times 10 \times \log \left(\frac{P_O}{P_R}\right)$$

We arrive at the computational solution for decibels of sound pressure level (dB SPL) which is,

$$\text{dB SPL} = 20 \times \log \left(\frac{P_O}{P_R}\right) \qquad (6\text{--}11)$$

Decibels of sound pressure are presented using Equation 6–11, employing the sound pressure reference (or threshold) values (P_{R_s}) provided in Tables 6–2A and 6–2B. The appropriate MKS reference sound pressure (P_R) and corresponding MKS observed sound pressures (Po_s) expressed in newtons (N) of force/area for computations of 0 to 140 dB SPL are provided in Table 6–5B. Note that the logs of each of the sound pressure ratios [log (Po/Pr)] are first computed by dividing each of the observed sound pressure values in the second column by the reference sound pressure in the first column. These ratios are of course identical to the sound pressure level ratios obtained for bels (and decibels) of SPL illustrated in Table 6–5A. The appropriate MKS ref-

erence sound pressure (Pr) and the corresponding MKS observed sound pressures (Po_s) expressed in micro pascals (µPa) of pressure for computations of 0 to 140 dB SPL are also provided in Table 6–5C. Note again that the logs of each of the sound pressure ratios [log (Po/Pr)] expressed in µPa are first computed by dividing each of the observed sound pressure values in the second col- umn by the reference sound pressure in the first column. The ratios once again for dB SPL are identical to the sound

Table 6–5B. MKS Decibels of Sound Pressure Level (dB SPL) for 0 to 140 dB SPL, With MKS Reference (Pr) and Observed Pressures (Po) Expressed in Newtons of Force/Area

MKS Reference Pressure (Pr) Newtons (N)/m²	MKS Observed Pressure (Po) Newtons (N)/m²	Decibels Sound Pressure Level dB SPL = 20 × log (Po/Pr) dB SPL =
2×10^{-5} N/m²	2×10^{-5} N/m²	0
	$2 \times 10^{-4.5}$ N/m²	10
	2×10^{-4} N/m²	20
	$2 \times 10^{-3.5}$ N/m²	30
	2×10^{-3} N/m²	40
	$2 \times 10^{-2.5}$ N/m²	50
	2×10^{-2} N/m²	60
	$2 \times 10^{-1.5}$ N/m²	70
	2×10^{-1} N/m²	80
	$2 \times 10^{-0.5}$ N/m²	90
	2×10^{0} N/m²	100
	$2 \times 10^{0.5}$ N/m²	110
	2×10^{1} N/m²	120
	$2 \times 10^{1.5}$ N/m²	130 With Pain
	2×10^{2} N/m²	140

Note that zero to 140 dB SPL represents the range for human hearing using an upper limit that extends to a level that is tolerated with pain. Zero to 120 dB SPL represents the range for human hearing using an upper limit that extends to a level that is tolerated without pain.

Table 6–5C. MKS Reference and Possible Observed Pressures in Micro (μ) Pascals (Pa), and Calculated MKS Decibel Sound Pressure Level (dB SPL)

MKS Reference Pressure (P_R) Micro (μ) Pascals (Pa)	MKS Observed Pressure (P_O) Micro (μ) Pascals (Pa)	Decibels Sound Pressure Level dB SPL = 20 × log (P_O/P_R) dB SPL =
2 × 10 μPa	2 × 10 μPa	0
	2 × 10$^{1.5}$ μPa	10
	2 × 10^2 μPa	20
	2 × 10$^{2.5}$ μPa	30
	2 × 10^3 μPa	40
	2 × 10$^{3.5}$ μPa	50
	2 × 10^4 μPa	60
	2 × 10$^{4.5}$ μPa	70
	2 × 10^5 μPa	80
	2 × 10$^{5.5}$ μPa	90
	2 × 10^6 μPa	100
	2 × 10$^{6.5}$ μPa	110
	2 × 10^7 μPa	120
	2 × 10$^{7.5}$ μPa	130 With Pain
	2 × 10^8 μPa	140

Note that values of 0 to 140 dB SPL represent the range for human hearing using an upper limit that extends to a level that is tolerated with pain. Zero to 120 dB SPL represents the range for human hearing using an upper limit that extends to a level that is tolerated without pain.

pressure level ratios presented for bels and decibels of SPL and are illustrated in Table 6–5A, and in Table 6–5B. Finally, the appropriate CGS sound pressure reference and the corresponding CGS observed sound pressures expressed in dynes (dyn) of force/area for computations of 0 to 140 dB SPL are provided in Table 6–5D. The logs of each of the sound pressure ratios [log (P_O/P_R)] are again first computed by dividing each of the observed sound pressure values in the second column by the reference sound pressure in the first column. The

ratios obtained are once again identical to the sound pressure level ratios presented for bels and decibels of SPL illustrated in Tables 6–5A, 6–5B, and 6–5C. Once again it is important to stress that 0 dB SPL expressed in MKS or CGS metric units of sound pressure is always interpreted as "no change from the reference." This point will again be emphasized in the following section.

In summary, the dynamic range of sound pressure level or intensity level over which human hearing spans is typically expressed as 0 to 140 dB SPL

Table 6–5D. CGS Reference and Possible Observed Pressures in Dynes (dyn) of Force/Area, and Calculated CGS Decibel Sound Pressure Level (dB SPL)

CGS Reference Pressure (P_R) Dynes (dyn)/cm²	MKS Observed Pressure (P_O) Dynes (dyn)/cm²	Decibels Sound Pressure Level dB SPL = 20 × log (P_O/P_R) dB SPL =
2×10^{-4} dyn/cm²	2×10^{-4} dyn/cm²	0
	$2 \times 10^{-3.5}$ dyn/cm²	10
	2×10^{-3} dyn/cm²	20
	$2 \times 10^{-2.5}$ dyn/cm²	30
	2×10^{-2} dyn/cm²	40
	$2 \times 10^{-1.5}$ dyn/cm²	50
	2×10^{-1} dyn/cm²	60
	$2 \times 10^{-0.5}$ dyn/cm²	70
	2×10^{0} dyn/cm²	80
	$2 \times 10^{0.5}$ dyn/cm²	90
	2×10^{1} dyn/cm²	100
	$2 \times 10^{1.5}$ dyn/cm²	110
	2×10^{2} dyn/cm²	120
	$2 \times 10^{2.5}$ dyn/cm²	130 With Pain
	2×10^{3} dyn/cm²	140

Note that values of 0 to 140 dB SPL represents the range for human hearing using an upper limit that extends to a level that is tolerated with pain. Zero to 120 dB SPL represents the range for human hearing using an upper limit that extends to a level that is tolerated without pain.

(Tables 6–5B, 6–5C, and 6–5D) or 0 to 140 dB IL (see Tables 6–4B and 6–4C) representing upper limits of sound pressure or sound intensity that extends to values that are tolerated with pain. The same tables also illustrate that the dynamic range of sound pressure level or intensity level over which human hearing spans is also and is often expressed as 0 to 120 dB SPL or 0 to 120 dB IL, representing upper limits of sound pressure or sound intensity that extend to values that are tolerated in the absence of pain. It should be noted that dB SPL is reliably computed employing the customary MKS and CGS reference (threshold) values provided in Tables 6–2A and 6–2B and in Tables 6–5B, 6–5C, and 6–5D under the assumption that standard atmospheric conditions are met. These standard conditions were specified in Chapter 4 and include a barometric pressure of 760 mm of mercury (Hg), defined also as 1 atmosphere of pressure, which is the equivalent of approximately 1 bar, 101.325 kPa or 14.7 to 15 PSI of pressure, at a temperature of 20° centigrade, or an equivalent 68° Fahrenheit. Table 6–6 also lists some typical environmental sounds and their approximate decibel intensities.

The Concept of Zero Decibels (0 dB)

As indicated in earlier sections of this chapter, the threshold quantities for acoustic intensity and pressure pre-sented in Tables 6–2A and 6–2B provide the starting or reference values that help to define the range of human hearing. The threshold quantities also determine the reference values for computations of the bel and the decibel (dB). Hence, as indicated above, 0 bels or 0 dB is taken to mean "no change from the reference (or referent)," or no change from the starting point for measures of the decibel. The expressions 0 bels or

Table 6–6. Approximate Decibel Values for Some Common Environmental Sounds

Decibels SPL[1] or IL[2]	Type of Sound
0	Reference level: Human threshold of audibility of a 3000 Hz pure tone in a sound-field
10	Falling pin; normal breathing
15	Soft rustling of leaves
20	Whisper from 3 to 4 ft
30	Empty auditorium
40	Soft radio; quiet library
50	Quiet interior of an automobile; department store
50–60	Average conversational speech at 5 ft from speaker
65	Typical newborn intensive care unit
70	Average busy city traffic
80	Shouting at 5 ft from speaker; heavy traffic
90	Train moving past a subway station platform
100	Riveter at 35 ft; machine shop; siren at 30 m
110	Loud thunder
115	Front row of an indoor "rock" concert
120	Boiler factory; nearby air-raid siren; pain threshold
130	Machine gun fire at close range; painful
140	Jet engine at 100 ft (30 m); painful
150	Jet engine at 50 ft (15 m); painful
180	Nearby space shuttle launch

[1]20 µPa; 2×10^{-5} N/m^2; 2×10^{-4} dynes/cm^2
[2]10^{-12} watts/m^2

Source: Giancoli, 2004; Hall and Mueller, 1997; Hewitt, 2010.

0 decibels are not to be interpreted as indicating the total absence of sound. Recall again the computational solution for dB IL as given below:

$$dB\ IL = 10 \times \log\left(\frac{I_O}{I_R}\right) \quad (6\text{--}9)$$

Zero dB IL was defined using the MKS metric reference for power (in watts), as

$$0\ dB\ IL = 10 \times \log\left(\frac{10^{-12}\ watts/m^2}{10^{-12}\ watts/m^2}\right) \quad (6\text{--}12A)$$

Also for intensity level, 0 dB IL was also defined using the CGS metric reference for power, as

$$0\ dB\ IL = 10 \times \log\left(\frac{10^{-16}\ watts/cm^2}{10^{-16}\ watts/cm^2}\right) \quad (6\text{--}12B)$$

Recall that the computational solution for dB SPL was given as

$$dB\ SPL = 20 \times \log\left(\frac{P_O}{P_R}\right) \quad (6\text{--}11)$$

In terms of sound pressure level, 0 dB SPL was defined using the MKS metric pressure reference, expressed in terms of force in newtons (N)/area, as

$$0\ dB\ SPL = 20 \times \log\left(\frac{2 \times 10^{-5}\ N/m^2}{2 \times 10^{-5}\ N/m^2}\right) \quad (6\text{--}12C)$$

Zero dB SPL was also defined using the MKS metric pressure reference, stated in micro pascals (µPa) of pressure, as

$$0\ dB\ SPL = 20 \times \log\left(\frac{20\ µPa}{20\ µPa}\right) \quad (6\text{--}12D)$$

Finally, 0 dB SPL was also defined using the CGS metric pressure reference stated in terms of force in dynes/area, as

$$0\ dB\ SPL =$$
$$20 \times \log\left(\frac{2 \times 10^{-4}\ dynes/cm^2}{2 \times 10^{-4}\ dynes/cm^2}\right) \quad (6\text{--}12E)$$

The Doubling or Halving of Signal Power or Pressure

Intensity Level

What is the effect on the number of decibels when the intensity level (power) is exactly doubled or exactly halved for a given pure tone or other sound? What is the effect on the number of decibels of exactly doubling or exactly halving the sound pressure level (or power) of any pure tone or of other sound? Let us begin first with dB IL and the computational solution for dB IL, as given by

$$dB\ IL = 10 \times \log\left(\frac{I_O}{I_R}\right) \quad (6\text{--}9)$$

The total number of decibels of intensity level may be determined following the combining of two identical-frequency pure tones having the same number of decibels. As an example, we will use two identical pure tones, each delivered at 60 dB IL. In such an example, how many total decibels result from 60 dB IL + 60 dB IL? It should be obvious that the problem is equivalent to that of determining the dB IL of an intensity ratio of 2:1. In this example 60 dB IL + 60 dB IL is equivalent to determining

$$dB\ IL = 10 \times \log\left(\frac{2}{1}\right)$$

According to Table B3–2 found in Appendix B, the log of 2 = 0.301. Therefore,

$$dB \ IL = 10 \times 0.301$$

or $\qquad$ dB IL = 3.0

Hence, how many decibels are 60 dB IL + 60 dB IL? It may be tempting to speculate that the answer is 120 dB IL. The answer, however, is 63 dB IL. Thus, there is a gain of only 3 dB when the intensity level of a signal (in this case, a pure tone) is exactly doubled. An answer of 63 dB IL would also be the result of combining two pure tones, each 60 dB IL, having different frequencies.

The number of decibels of intensity level that are lost following a halving of the intensity level (or power) of a pure tone, or of any other signal, may also be determined. As an example, let us again take a pure tone delivered at 60 dB IL. What then is the consequence in decibels resulting from cutting the power of a 60 dB IL pure tone by one half? The problem is once again equivalent to that of determining the dB IL of an intensity ratio of one half or of 0.5. In this example, halving the intensity level of a 60 dB IL pure tone is equivalent to determining

$$dB \ IL = 10 \times \log \left(\frac{1}{2} \right)$$

According to Table B3–6 found in Appendix B, the log 0.5 = −0.301. Therefore,

$$dB \ IL = 10 \times -0.301$$

or $\qquad$ dB IL = −3.0

Therefore, how many decibels are lost when the power of a 60 dB IL pure tone is cut in half? The answer is −3.0 dB IL, or there is a loss of 3.0 dB IL from the original 60 dB IL signal (in this case, a pure tone) if the intensity level is cut exactly in half.

Sound Pressure Level

In a similar fashion, what is the effect on dB SPL of exactly doubling or exactly halving the sound pressure level of a pure tone, or of any other sound? To answer these questions, we will need to use the computational solution for dB SPL, as given by

$$dB \ SPL = 20 \times \log \left(\frac{P_O}{P_R} \right) \qquad (6\text{–}11)$$

As before, the total number of decibels of sound pressure level may be determined following the combining of two identical-frequency pure tones having the same dB SPL. As an example, we will again use two identical pure tones, each delivered at 60 dB SPL. In such an example, how many total decibels result from 60 dB SPL + 60 dB SPL? Again it is obvious that the problem is equivalent to that of determining the dB SPL of an intensity ratio of 2:1. Therefore, in this example 60 dB SPL + 60 dB SPL is equivalent to determining

$$dB \ SPL = 20 \times \log \left(\frac{2}{1} \right)$$

At this point it should be recalled that the computational solution for dB SPL (Equation 6–10) was derived from the original power ratio that defined dB IL (Equation 6–9) and that intensity and sound pressure are related in the manner described previously

$$I = P^2 \qquad (6\text{–}6)$$

$$P = \sqrt{I}$$

Hence, any intensity ratio $\left(\dfrac{I_O}{I_R}\right)$ is equal to $\left(\dfrac{P_O}{P_R}\right)^{\frac{1}{2}}$

For this reason, the problem as stated above for determining the dB SPL of a pressure ratio of 2:1, or, in this example 60 dB SPL+ 60 dB SPL, is now expressed as

$$dB\ SPL = 20 \times \log\left(\frac{2}{1}\right)^{\frac{1}{2}}$$

The square root ($\sqrt{\ }$) of 2 is 1.414, and according to Table B3–2 in Appendix B, the log 1.414 = 0.15. Therefore, the dB SPL of a 2:1 ratio is expressed as

$$dB\ SPL = 20 \times 0.15$$

or $dB\ SPL = 3.0$

Consequently, to answer the question, how many decibels are 60 dB SPL + 60 dB SPL, it may again be tempting to speculate a solution of 120 dB SPL, or perhaps 66 dB SPL. The answer however is 63 dB SPL. Thus, there is a gain of only 3 dB when either the intensity level (power) or in this case, the sound pressure level of a signal is exactly doubled. An answer of 63 dB SPL would also be the result of combining two pure tones, each 60 dB SPL, having different frequencies.

The number of decibels in sound pressure level that are lost following a halving of the signal pressure of a pure tone, or of any other signal, may also be determined. As an example, let us again take a pure tone delivered at 60 dB SPL. What then is the consequence in decibels that would result from cutting the power or pressure of a 60 dB SPL pure tone by one half? The problem is again one of determining the dB SPL

of a pressure ratio of one half or of 0.5 and halving pressure is equivalent to

$$dB\ SPL = 20 \times \log\left(\frac{1}{2}\right)$$

Remembering that intensity and sound pressure are related in the manner described by

$$I = P^2 \qquad (6\text{–}6)$$
$$P = \sqrt{I}$$

The problem as stated above for determining the dB SPL of a pressure ratio of 1:2, is now expressed as

$$dB\ SPL = 20 \times \log\left(\frac{1}{2}\right)^{\frac{1}{2}}$$

The square root ($\sqrt{\ }$) of 0.5 is 0.707, and according to Table B3–6 in Appendix B, the log 0.707 = −0.15. Therefore,

$$dB\ SPL = 20 \times -0.15$$

or $dB\ SPL = -3.0$

How many decibels are lost when the signal pressure of a 60 dB SPL pure tone is cut in half? The answer is −3.0 dB SPL, or, there is a loss of 3.0 dB SPL from the original 60 dB SPL of any signal, in this case a pure tone, if the signal power or pressure is cut by exactly one half.

Decibel Problems

1. If $10^{0.3} = 2$, then 40 µPa = _____ dB _____.

   It should be apparent in this problem that using the appropriate reference value of 20 µPa leads to a ratio of 2/1, the log of 2 = 0.3, and 20 × 0.3 = 6 dB SPL.

2. If $10^{0.5}$ = 3, then 60 µPa = _____ dB _____.

It should be apparent in this problem that using the appropriate reference value of 20 µPa leads to a ratio of 3/1, the log of 3 = 0.5, and 20 × 0.5 = 10 dB SPL.

3. If $10^{0.6}$ = 4, then 80 µPa = _____ dB _____.

It should be apparent in this problem that using the appropriate reference value of 20 µPa leads to a ratio of 4/1, the log of 4 = 0.6, and 20 × 0.6 = 12 dB SPL.

4. 10^{-12} watts/cm^2 is equal to _____ dB _____.

It should be apparent in this problem that using the appropriate reference value of 10^{-16} watts/m^2 leads to a ratio of $10^4/1$, the log of 10^4 = 4, and 10 × 4 = 40 dB IL.

5. 2×10^3 µPa is _____ dB _____.

It should be apparent in this problem that using the appropriate reference value of 20 µPa that may and should be converted to scientific notation as 2×10 µPa leads to a ratio of $10^2/1$, the log of 10^2 = 2, and 20 × 2 = 40 dB SPL.

6. 2×10^{-5} Pa is _____ dB _____.

It should be apparent in this problem that 2×10^{-5} Pa = 20 µPa, and using the appropriate reference value of 20 µPa leads to a ratio of 1/1, the log of 1 = 0, and 20 × 0 = 0 dB SPL.

7. An observation of 0.0002 newtons/m^2 is equal to _____ dB _____.

It should be apparent in this problem that 0.0002 newtons/m^2 may and should be converted to scientific notation as 2×10^{-4} newtons/m^2, and applying the appropriate reference value of 2×10^{-5} newtons/m^2 leads to a ratio of 10/1, the log of 10 = 1, and 20 × 1 = 20 dB SPL.

8. An observation of 2 newtons/m^2 = _____ dB _____; but an observation of 2 dynes/cm^2 = _____ dB _____.

It should be apparent in this problem that 2 newtons/m^2 may and should be converted to scientific notation as 2×10^0 newtons/m^2, and an application of the appropriate reference value of 2×10^{-5} newtons/m^2 leads to a ratio of $10^5/1$, the log of 10^5 = 5, and 20 × 5 = 100 dB SPL. It should also be apparent in the second part of this problem that 2 dynes/cm^2 may and should be converted to scientific notation as 2×10^0 dynes/cm^2, and the application of the appropriate reference value of 2×10^{-4} dynes/cm^2, leads to a ratio of $10^4/1$, the log of 10^4 = 4, and 20 × 4 = 80 dB SPL.

9. What must the ratio in the parentheses be in order to yield values of 70 dB IL and 40 dB IL?

a. _____ (10,000,000/10) and (10,000/10), respectively

b. _____ ($10^{-9}/10^{-16}$) and ($10^8/10^{-12}$), respectively

c. _____ ($10^{-4}/10^{-11}$) and
($10^{-9}/10^{-13}$), respectively

d. _____ ($10^{-5}/10^{12}$) and
($10^{-9}/10^{16}$), respectively

e. _____ ($10^{-9}/10^{-12}$) and
($10^{-8}/10^{-16}$), respectively

It should be apparent in this problem that the required ratios are $10^{7}/1$ for 70 dB IL, and $10^{4}/1$ for 40 dB IL. Therefore, item C is correct.

10. What must the ratio in the parentheses be in order to yield values of 100 dB IL and 120 dB SPL?

a. _____ (10,000,000/1,000) and (1,000,000/1), respectively

b. _____ ($10^{-6}/10^{-16}$) and
($10^{-2}/10^{-12}$), respectively

c. _____ ($10^{-2}/10^{-16}$) and
($10/10^{-12}$), respectively

d. _____ ($10^{-2}/10^{-12}$) and
($10^{-10}/10^{-16}$), respectively

e. _____ ($10^{6}/10^{-16}$) and
($10^{6}/10^{-12}$), respectively

It should be apparent in this problem that the required ratios are $10^{10}/1$ for 100 dB IL, and $10^{6}/1$ for 120 dB SPL. Therefore, item D is correct.

11. What must the ratio in the parentheses be in order to yield values of 80 dB SPL and 100 dB SPL?

a. _____ (1,000,000/100) and (100,000/10^{5}), respectively

b. _____ ($10^{0}/10^{-4}$) and
($10^{2}/10^{-7}$), respectively

c. _____ ($10^{5}/10$) and ($10^{6}/10$), respectively

d. _____ ($10^{6}/10^{-2}$) and
($10^{7}/10^{-2}$), respectively

e. _____ ($10^{-9}/10^{-4}$) and
($10^{-8}/10^{-2}$), respectively

It should be apparent in this problem that the required ratios are $10^{4}/1$ for 80 dB SPL and $10^{5}/1$ for 100 dB SPL. Therefore, item C is correct.

12. What must the ratio in the parentheses be in order to yield values of 20 dB IL and 20 dB SPL?

a. _____ ($100/10^{0}$) and (10/1), respectively

b. _____ ($10^{-6}/10^{-8}$) and
($10^{-2}/10^{-3}$), respectively

c. _____ ($10^{-2}/10^{-4}$) and
($10^{-11}/10^{-12}$), respectively

d. _____ ($10^{-12}/10^{-14}$) and
($10^{-10}/10^{-11}$), respectively

e. _____ all of the above would work

It should be apparent in this problem that the required ratios are $10^{2}/1$ for 20 dB IL and 10/1 for 20 dB SPL. Because all of the items satisfy this requirement, item E is correct.

13. What must the ratio in the parentheses be in order to yield values of 0 dB IL and 0 dB SPL?

a. _____ ($10^{0}/10^{0}$) and (20 µPa/20 µPa), respectively

b. _____ ($10^{-6}/10^{-6}$) and
($10^{-2}/10^{-2}$), respectively

c. _____ ($10^{-2}/10^{-2}$) and
($10^{-11}/10^{-11}$), respectively

d. _____ ($10^{-14}/10^{-14}$) and
($10^{-10}/10^{-10}$), respectively

e. _____ all of the above would work

It should be apparent in this problem that the required ratios are $10^0/1$ (or 1) for 0 dB IL, and $10^0/1$ (or 1) for 0 dB SPL. Because the log of $1 = 0$, and all of the items satisfy this requirement, item E is correct. Note that in each item, there is no change from the reference (or referent) value.

True or False:

1. _____ Acoustic intensity is equal to power/area.

2. _____ A proper reference value for dB IL is 20 μPa.

3. _____ A proper reference value for dB SPL is 10^{-12} watts/cm²

4. _____ Intensity = Pressure²

It should be apparent in this set of statements that only items 1 and 4 are true. Items 2 and 3 are obviously false.

Sound Level Meters (SLMs)

A sound level meter (SLM) is an electronic instrument that is used to measure a root-mean-square (RMS) sound pressure level (SPL) amplitude in accordance with an accepted national or international set of standards (Lucks-Mendel, Danhauer, & Singh, 1999). The SLM uses a high-quality (electret) microphone that converts sound energy into an electrical signal that is then analyzed for its magnitude by an electrical circuit. The magnitude of the signal is then visibly displayed by the SLM in dB SPL. SLMs serve at least three useful purposes. They are often used to mea-

sure the sound pressure level of signals such as pure tones and narrow-bands of noise (see sections below) from audiometers and/or research instruments. Used in this capacity, they provide the means for an accurate calibration of these devices. They may also be used to determine noise levels (unwanted sounds) in a particular room, in order to assess whether the room or setting is sufficiently quiet to perform audiometric hearing tests. Finally, SLMs are often used in industrial settings to identify potentially hazardous locations where prolonged levels of noise exposure from equipment and machinery may be damaging to the inner ear. Systematic measures of sound levels in industrial settings or in other locations where noise levels are likely to be excessive, such as in airports (from jet engine noise), are referred to as "noise surveys" (Gelfand, 2001). These surveys are performed for several reasons. First, they are used to identify locations where individuals such as employees are exposed to noise levels that could exceed a time weighted average of ≥85 dB (A), and to identify which of the employees are likely to be exposed to such levels. The meaning of the "dB (A)" scale is described below. Second, such information enables the industry to implement the precise engineering controls that are best suited to manage the potentially damaging noise arising from specific noise sources. Third, such information helps to determine the degree of sound attenuation that must be provided by hearing (ear) protection devices such as earplugs or earmuffs, devices that are often worn by employees who are likely to be exposed to such high levels of potentially damaging noise (Gelfand, 2001). SLMs are illustrated in Figure 6–2A.

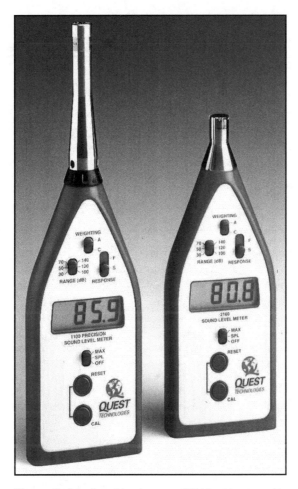

Figure 6–2A. Sound level meters (SLMs) with measuring (electret) microphones (see also Figure 6–2E) attached at the top. Courtesy of Lipin/Dietz Associates, Inc., with permission.

SLM Weighting Networks (Filters)

The SLM has a linear setting that measures the overall SPL for all frequencies that may be detected within the limits of the microphone. SLMs also have weighting networks that are filters that bias or otherwise alter the emphasis (detection sensitivity) placed on certain parts of the frequency spectrum of the sounds detected. Figure 6–2B illustrates the three weighting networks provided by a standard SLM. The horizontal line at 0 dB SPL shown in the figure indicates that the original signal is essentially unchanged, and response properties of the SLM that are defined by this line are linear. The C-network or the dB (C) setting on the SLM represents response properties that are nearly linear. The B- and especially the A-weighting networks on the SLM, also illustrated in Figure 6–2B, represent the degree to which these two filter settings de-emphasize the amplitudes of the lower frequencies, as indicated by the negative decibel values that are shown. The A-weighting network significantly

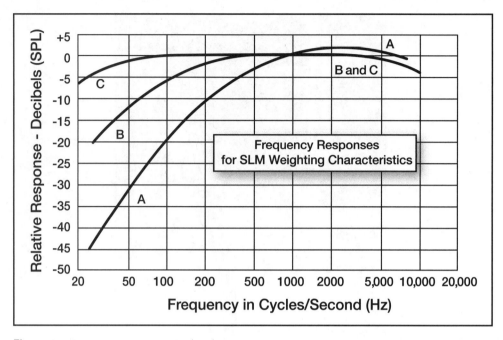

Figure 6–2B. Three sound level meter (SLM) weighting networks. A plot of the degree of signal suppression afforded by the C-, B-, and especially the A-weighting networks, with dB (SPL) shown on the ordinate and frequency (Hz) shown on the abscissa. Note that there is very little signal suppression with the near-linear C-network. Note also the degree of signal suppression provided by the B- and especially the A-weighting networks, as indicated by the negative values expressed in dB (SPL). Courtesy of General Radio Corporation.

de-emphasizes the frequencies that fall below 1000 Hz. The "A" network (curve) indicates that there is signal suppression (decreased detection sensitivity) of about 4 dB at 500 Hz, 11 dB at 200 Hz, 20 dB at 100 Hz, and 30 dB at 50 Hz (Gelfand, 2001). The A-weighting curve also indicates a slight positive biasing (increased detection sensitivity) for some of the mid-frequencies found above 1000 Hz. In terms of assessing the level of noise in a given environment, particularly in an industrial setting, the most commonly used network is the A-weighting that places less emphasis (less weight or less sensitivity) on energy occurring at frequencies below 1000 Hz. In such instances, it is often desirable to exclude the environmental contributions of these lower frequen-

cies. This weighting network attempts to approximate the 40-phon loudness level (or 1-sone loudness-perception) contour from the equal loudness level contours that are based on the minimum audibility curve obtained in the sound-field (Chapter 8). The A-weighting network was originally used for the measurement of sounds existing 40 dB SPL above threshold and takes into account the relatively poorer auditory sensitivity for the relatively weaker-in-intensity and lower-in-frequency sounds in the environmental sounds, based on the human "threshold of audibility" (Chapter 8). Any reference to a measurement that employs the A-weighting or the "dB (A)" scale is made in order to distinguish it from the measurement scale that places equal weight on all spectral components, which would otherwise be known as the linear or the near-linear response of the device (Møller, 2000).

The B-weighting network illustrated in Figure 6–2B also de-emphasizes (decreased detection sensitivity) the lower frequencies, but the amount of signal suppression (insensitivity) is considerably diminished by comparison to the A-network. For instance, there is no suppression at 500 Hz, and only about 4 dB at 200 Hz, 6 dB at 100 Hz, and 14 dB at 50 Hz. The C-weighting network on the SLM affords the least amount of signal suppression and is nearly linear in its response properties. As indicated in the figure, it does afford about 6 to 8 dB of signal suppression at 20 Hz. The C-weighting network is, nevertheless, used in noise level measures and therefore reference to "dB (C)" is commonly made in such instances. However, the B-weighting network is rarely if ever used in noise level measurements, and reference to "dB (B)" is rarely made (Gelfand, 2001).

Octave–Band Analyses

The definition and computations of octave notation were discussed in Chapter 5. The term *bandwidth*, signified by Δf usually refers to the width or the range in whole numbered integers, of separate frequencies (or frequency components) that are either recognized or passed by a filtering device (e.g., a filter). When more detailed and precise spectral information is needed regarding a complex (aperiodic) sound such as a noise, the frequency range of human hearing (from 20 Hz to 20 kHz) can be split into sections or separate frequency bands to enable a more precise "spectral

analysis" (discussed in later sections). This function (octave-band analysis) is performed electronically by the SLM. Hence, SLMs may be used to analyze the amplitudes of narrow-bands (or narrow bandwidths) of noise by employing octave-band (octave-bandwidth) or third-octave-band (third-octave-bandwidth) filters that focus on a specific and restricted range of frequencies in a complex signal (Lucks-Mendel et al., 1999). Such an analysis allows an investigator to identify the portions of a total noise spectrum that contain the greatest amount of energy without a significant degree of spectral contamination arising from unwanted frequencies located below or above the cut-off frequencies of the octave-band filter. The subject of *filters* is discussed in this chapter in subsequent sections that follow. For the present, *octave-band filtering* by a SLM utilizes a series of built-in *band-pass filters*. Because the octave-band (and third-octave-band) filters are essentially band-pass filters, and because in many (but certainly not all) cases, band-pass filters have both an upper and a lower cut-off frequency, octave- (and third-octave) band filters also have upper and lower cut-off frequencies. The cut-off frequency (or frequencies) of any filter is defined as the location(s) in the filter where the power (IL) or pressure (SPL) of the signal is cut (due to filtering) by exactly 50%. The cut-off frequency is also called the half-power point, the −3 dB down point or the half-pressure point, as discussed later in this chapter, in reference to filters.

In terms of octave-band filters, the set of built-in octave-bands within a SLM are designed in such a way so that the upper cut-off frequency is two times (or one octave above) the lower cut-off frequency. In this way, an octave-band analysis can separate an entire frequency spectrum of a complex signal into separate, narrower ranges of frequencies for a more precise spectral (frequency) analysis, with each range (or band) defined as one octave in width (Gelfand, 2001). Each octave-band consists of a center frequency and is traditionally identified in terms of its center frequency. Octave-bands that define the octave-band filters used in SLMs typically begin with center frequencies that start from a low frequency of either 16 or 31.5 Hz, to an upper frequency of at least 16 kHz (Lucks-Mendel et al., 1999). As indicated above, each octave-band has an upper and a lower cut-off frequency, and octave-band cut-off frequencies are easily computed from each center frequency using the solutions (equations) provided in the next section. A series of octave-bands extending up to 64 kHz is illustrated in Figure 6–2C. Each consecutive octave-band overlaps (intersects)

the octave-band before and the octave-band that follows, at their shared cut-off frequencies (not labeled). Each cut-off frequency is located at the intersection of the bottom-most dashed line with the ascending (left) and descending (right) line of each band. In Figure 6–2C, the octave-band for the 1000-Hz center frequency is lightly shaded to better illustrate the locations where the lower-most dashed line intersects the lower cut-off frequency (left) and the upper cut-off frequency (right) for this 1000-Hz octave-band.

An even more precise level of analysis may be achieved with the SLM by selecting and activating the *third-octave-band filtering* system. Third-octave-band filters, like octave-band filters, are also defined by their center frequencies. As their name implies, third-octave-band filters are only one-third of an octave wide. Therefore, the frequency band that is analyzed is much narrower compared to the analysis provided by simple octave-band filtering,

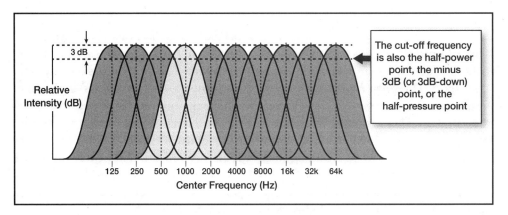

Figure 6–2C. A series of octave-bands with center frequencies ranging from 125 Hz to 64 kHz. The lighter shading of the 1000-Hz octave-band helps to identify the locations where the bottom-most dashed line intersects the lower (*left*) and upper (*right*) cut-off frequencies for this band, as well as for the other octave-bands. Note that the lower cut-off frequency of each octave-band intersects the upper cut-off frequency of the (lower frequency) octave-band located below, and the upper cut-off frequency of each octave-band intersects the lower cut-off frequency of the (higher frequency) octave-band located above.

and the spectral analysis that is performed may be much more specific (Gelfand, 2001).

Determining Cut-Off Frequencies for Octave and Third-Octave-Band Filters

Both an upper and a lower cut-off frequency may be calculated for any given octave or third-octave-band filter of interest. The results of these computations for commonly used octave and third-octave-band filters, defined once again by their center frequencies, are presented in Tables 6–7A and 6–7B.

First, computational equations may be used to calculate both the upper and the lower cut-off frequencies for any octave-band filter with center frequency:

$$C_F$$

The lower cut-off frequency or F_{CL}, and upper cut-off frequency or F_{CU}, are determined using Equation 6–13A, where the lower cut-off frequency is defined as

$$F_{CL} = C_F/2^{1/2} \qquad (6\text{–}13\text{A})$$

and Equation 6–13B, where the upper cut-off frequency is defined as

$$F_{CU} = C_F \times 2^{1/2} \qquad (6\text{–}13\text{B})$$

Table 6–7A. Computed Lower and Upper Cut-Off Frequencies of Several Octave-Band Center Frequencies That Are Typically Used in Acoustical Measurements

Lower Cut-Off Frequency (Hz)	Center Frequency (Hz)	Upper Cut-Off Frequency (Hz)
11	16	23
22	31.5	45
45	63	89
88	125	177
177	250	354
354	500	707
707	1000	1414
1414	2000	2828
2828	4000	5657
5657	8000	11314
11314	16000	22627

Note that the lower cut-off frequency of each octave-band intersects the upper cut-off frequency of the (lower frequency) octave-band located below, and the upper cut-off frequency of each octave-band intersects the lower cut-off frequency of the (higher frequency) octave-band located above.

Table 6–7B. Third (¹/₃)-Octave-Bands

Lower Cut-Off Frequency (Hz)	Center Frequency (Hz)	Upper Cut-Off Frequency (Hz)
14.3	16	17.9
17.8	20	22.4
22.3	25	28.1
28.1	31.5	35.4
35.6	40	44.9
44.5	50	56.1
56.1	63	70.7
71.3	80	89.8
89.1	100	112
111	125	140
143	160	180
178	200	224
223	250	281
281	315	354
356	400	449
445	500	561
561	630	707
713	800	898
891	1000	1122
1114	1250	1403
1425	1600	1796
1782	2000	2245
2227	2500	2806
2806	3150	3536
3564	4000	4490
4454	5000	5612
5613	6300	7072
7127	8000	8980
8909	10000	11225
11136	12500	14031
14254	16000	17959
17818	20000	22449

Note. The computed lower and upper cut-off frequencies of several third-octave-band center frequencies that are typically used in acoustical measurements. Note again that the lower cut-off frequency of each octave-band intersects the upper cut-off frequency of the (lower frequency) octave-band located below, and the upper cut-off frequency of each octave-band intersects the lower cut-off frequency of the (higher frequency) octave-band located above, as also illustrated in Figure 6–2C and in Table 6–7A. Note that if each lower cut-off frequency were to be subtracted from each higher cut-off frequency, the third-octave-filter bandwidths would be much narrower compared to the much wider bandwidths that characterized the octave filters.

In both Equations 6–13A and 6–13B, the value $2^{1/2}$ is equal to 1.4142135623731.

Additional equations may be employed to compute both the upper and the lower cut-off frequencies for any third-octave-band filter with center frequency:

$$C_{F3}$$

The lower cut-off frequency or $F_{CL,}$ and upper cut-off frequency or $F_{CU,}$ are determined using Equation 6–14A, where the lower cut-off frequency is defined as

$$F_{CL} = C_{F3}/(2^{1/2})^{1/3} \qquad (6\text{–}14A)$$

or
$$F_{CL} = C_{F3}/2^{1/6}$$

and Equation 6–14B, where the upper cut-off frequency is defined as

$$F_{CU} = C_{F3} \times (2^{1/2})^{1/3}$$

or
$$F_{CU} = C_{F3} \times 2^{1/6} \qquad (6\text{–}14B)$$

In Equations 6–14A and 6–14B, the value $2^{1/6}$ is equal to 1.1224620482575.

Note also that the octave-band filter cut-off frequency computations provided in Table 6–7A, computed for a relatively limited number of center frequencies, have relatively broad bandwidths. The third-octave-band filter cut-off frequency computations provided in Table 6–7B by contrast, are computed over a relatively larger range of center frequencies. Each of the third-octave-band filter bandwidths would be much narrower if compared to the much wider bandwidths that characterize octave-bands. This would be more apparent if each lower cut-off frequency were to be subtracted from each higher cut-off frequency for each of the corresponding center frequencies.

SLM Calibration

The accuracy of the SLM is maintained by an acoustic calibrator (piston-phone) which is a rugged device that produces a known and quantifiably precise signal that may be directed into the SLM microphone. Piston phones often produce a tone at frequencies of 250 Hz or 1 kHz, at an amplitude of 94 or 114 dB SPL, with a variability in sound pressure that is often less than ±0.12 dB SPL (Gelfand, 2001). A SLM piston-phone calibrator is illustrated in Figure 6–2D.

Types of SLMs

SLMs may be classified by types, based on their degrees of precision and potential

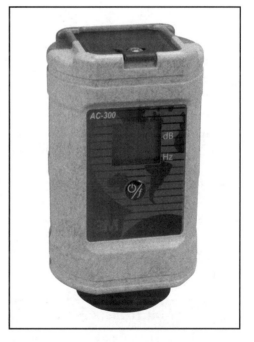

Figure 6–2D. A piston-phone calibration device for the sound level meter (SLM). Courtesy of 3M Technologies with permission: © 2013 3M All Rights Reserved.

application. For instance, there is a Type 0, a Type 1, and a Type 2 SLM. The *Type 0 SLM* is also called the laboratory standard model such that these instruments exhibit the most exacting tolerances. The precision of the Type 0 SLM requires that they be accurate to within ±0.7 dB across a frequency spectrum that ranges from 100 to 4000 Hz. This level of precision, however, is not required for noise-level analyses (Gelfand, 2001). The *Type 1 SLM*, also referred to as a precision SLM, is intended for precise measurements both in the laboratory and in the field, and meets the most rigorous standards and specifications for field testing, especially in sound-field tests that may lead to litigation (Lucks-Mendel et al., 1999). The Type 1 SLM is expected to be accurate to within ±1.0 dB across a frequency spectrum that ranges from 50 to 4000 Hz (Gelfand, 2001). The *Type 2 SLM* or general-purpose SLM, as the name implies, is a general-purpose device that is adequate for most industrial sound measurements (Lucks-Mendel et al., 1999). The Type 2 SLM is a field-measurement instrument with accuracy tolerances as narrow as ±1.5 dB across a frequency spectrum that ranges from 100 to 1250 Hz. The Type 2 SLM is the device required to meet the noise level compliance standards of the Occupational Safety and Health Administration (OSHA), as well as those of other regulatory agencies (Gelfand, 2001).

Microphones

From the preceding section, it should be obvious that the microphone mounted at the top of a SLM enables this device to measure the sound pressure levels of pure tones and narrow-bands of noise from audiometers and/or research instruments, providing the means by which an accurate calibration of such devices may be performed, as described above. The SLM microphone is also an essential component that enables the SLM to determine room (background) noise levels prior to audiometric testing, and in industrial or other public settings, it enables SLMs to perform systematic noise surveys. The measuring electret microphone used by a SLM is shown in Figure 6–2E. Importantly, what is a microphone?

Any device that transforms energy from one form to another is called a transducer (Hirsh, 1952). A microphone is an electronic device that converts or transduces an acoustic signal into an electrical signal. A microphone responds to acoustic sound waves by converting (or transducing) air pressure changes into variations in voltage, and delivers an essentially equivalent electrical wave to additional electronic circuits (Hirsh, 1952). The electrical waveforms are then manipulated by

Figure 6–2E. An electret microphone used with a sound level meter (SLM). The protective grill is removed (shown on the left) to illustrate the diaphragm, shown on the right. From T. A. Hamill and L. L. Price (2014), with permission.

additional electronic circuits. One obvious type of electronic wave manipulation is signal amplification, which may involve several stages. Another type of electronic wave manipulation is signal filtering. Filters will be discussed in the sections that follow.

The most important component located inside of all microphones is the thin, fixed, sheet of resonating material called a diaphragm (Hirsh, 1952; Silman & Emmer, 2012). The diaphragm is made of a material that is either an electrically conductive metal (i.e., titanium, aluminum, aluminum-magnesium alloy, nickel; carbon fiber, beryllium), or some other electrically nonconductive material (i.e., polypropylene, Mylar, silk, fiberglass) that is low enough in density to enable the center of the diaphragm to vibrate in response to the repetitious compressions and rarefactions created by an acoustic stimulus. The inward movement of the diaphragm in response to acoustic compressions, and the corresponding outward movement of the diaphragm in response to acoustic rarefactions represent the (phasic) mechanical displacements that ultimately generate electrical signals. The mechanical displacements of the diaphragm in response to sound are essentially the vibrations that ultimately generate the electrical signals generated by a microphone. It is often the case that the diaphragm is part of an electrical circuit. Therefore, when the diaphragm is caused to vibrate in response to a sound, the vibrations produce changes or variations in the electric current flowing through the circuit (Hirsh, 1952). The displacement of the diaphragm may, for example, cause variations in the resistance of a carbon contact between two plates, variations in electrostatic capacitance between two plates, or variations in the motion of a coil or conductor within (or surrounded by) a fixed magnetic field. The approximate position of the diaphragm is illustrated in Figure 6–3A.

Types of Microphones

Microphones may be divided into two broad categories according to the method (direction) in which the diaphragm responds to sound. These two broad categories are the pressure type and the velocity type of microphones. The pressure type typically contains a thin (often metal) diaphragm that is stretched over a rigid metal frame. In the pressure-type microphones, the sound waves strike the surface of the diaphragm on only one of its sides, the side of the diaphragm that is exposed to the environment. Pressure types include the historically early magnetic

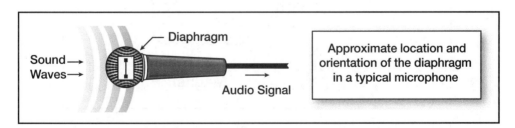

Figure 6–3A. A typical microphone.

microphones. There is also the carbon microphone, the condenser or capacitor microphone, the crystal microphone, and the moving coil or dynamic microphone that uses electromagnetic induction. In the velocity-type microphones, the diaphragm (ribbon) is exposed to sound on both surfaces. Velocity microphones typically employ a light ribbon of aluminum foil suspended in a strong magnetic field. Sound pressure causes the ribbon to vibrate which produces current changes in the ribbon due to the surrounding magnetic field.

Pressure Types of Microphones

The Magnetic and Carbon Microphone

The magnetic microphone (or variable-reluctance microphone) was the first transducer to be patented and used by Alexander Graham Bell in 1876 (see Box 6–1 and Portrait 6–1) in his telephone. Magnetic reluctance is a property that stores magnetic energy within a magnetic circuit. This very early type of microphone consisted of a diaphragm-driven, soft-iron armature encased within the powerful electromagnetic field of a magnet. Because the armature was part of the magnetic circuit, the diaphragm-driven movement of the armature within the electromagnetic field modified the magnetic reluctance of the circuit, and this, in turn, induced a voltage. The early magnetic microphones, however, were of low quality and lacked the stability of the carbon, condenser, dynamic, or ribbon microphones, and were therefore not used extensively. A cross section of a magnetic (variable-reluctance) microphone is provided in Figure 6–3B.

Historically, one of the first successful microphones was the carbon microphone which has largely been

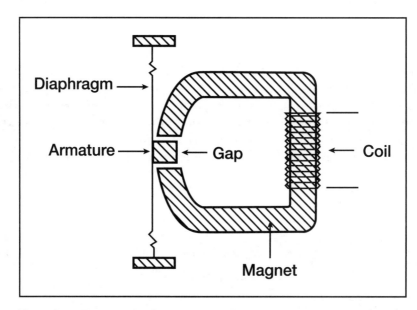

Figure 6–3B. Cross section of a magnetic (variable reluctance) microphone. Note the location of the diaphragm-driven armature surrounded by the electromagnetic field.

associated with telephone transmitters. A cross section of a carbon microphone is provided in Figure 6–3C. The carbon microphone was the replacement for Bell's original magnetic microphone. The carbon microphone is outstanding among the pressure types of microphones. Invented by Thomas A. Edison and Emile Berliner in 1877, the carbon (or carbon button) microphone employs two electrified plates (or electrodes). The outer of the two plates is a very thin diaphragm having an outer surface that always faces toward the sound source. The two plates are separated by tiny granules of carbon that are under constant pressure. A voltage is applied across the two metal plates causing a minute amount of current to flow through the carbon granules. When the thin diaphragm (the outer most plate) is displaced by a sound wave, the change in pressure due to

the compression of the diaphragm deforms the carbon granules and alters the contact area between the two plates. This change in contact area produces a change in the electrical resistance of the carbon granules (Hirsh, 1952). According to Ohm's law,

Current = voltage ÷ resistance

Therefore, a change in resistance (a lowering of resistance) causes a corresponding change in the current flow (an increase in current conductance) through the microphone plates, and produces an electrical signal (Hirsh, 1952). Carbon microphones are very durable and have been used in telephones from 1890 and through to the 1980s. In addition to their durability, their other major advantage is that they can produce high-level audio signals with only a fraction of a volt.

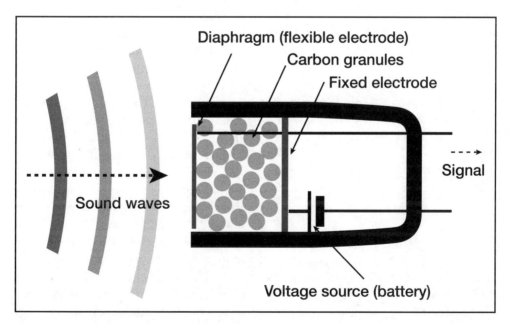

Figure 6–3C. Cross section of a carbon microphone with its two plates (electrodes) separated by tiny carbon granules.

The Condenser (Capacitor) Microphone

Another pressure type of microphone is the condenser or capacitor microphone, invented in 1916 at Bell Laboratories by E. C. Wente. In the condenser microphone, the vibrating diaphragm causes electrical changes in capacitance to occur between the movable, electrically charged diaphragm and a second, permanently fixed electrically charged plate (Silman & Emmer, 2012). First, what is capacitance? Capacitance refers to the property or the ability of a device to store an electrical charge, and any device that can be electrically charged can exhibit the property of capacitance (Giancoli, 2005). A capacitor typically has two parallel plates. An electrical current is applied to both plates in such a way as to create a positive charge on one plate and an equal but opposite negative charge on the other plate (Hewitt, 2010). Hence, the charging of a capacitor by passing a current through the conductor plates creates a stored voltage between the two plates (Hirsh, 1952). Voltage is defined as the electric potential difference between any two points, or in this case, the difference in electric potential energy between the two conductive plates of the capacitor. The capacitor's ability to store an electrical charge (Q) between its plates is proportional to the applied voltage (V) for a capacitor of known capacitance (C), or

$$Q = CV$$

The greater the applied current voltage, the greater will be the charge stored on the plates of the capacitor (Giancoli, 2005). Consequently, when a capacitor is fully charged, a potential difference (voltage) will exist between its parallel conductor plates (Hewitt, 2010). Furthermore, capacitance is directly proportional to the surface area of the parallel conductor plates and is inversely proportional to the separation distance between the two plates (Silman & Emmer, 2012). The larger the surface area of the capacitor's plates and/or the smaller the separation of the two plates, the greater will be the charge that the capacitor can store, and consequently, the greater will be its capacitance (Giancoli, 2005). Finally, capacitance is always positive and is never negative.

The condenser microphone has a thin malleable diaphragm made of a very light conductive material that is separated from the second, fixed parallel plate. The diaphragm acts as one plate of a variable capacitor that is connected in series to a resistor and to a direct current source (Hirsh, 1952). Recall that an electrical current is required to produce the voltage gradient across the two capacitor conductor plates. This current is supplied either by a battery in the microphone or by an external power source (Silman & Emmer, 2012). The distance between the diaphragm and the second plate is about 1/1000th of an inch. As the outer surface of the diaphragm responds to sound waves, the distance between the diaphragm and the second parallel plate also changes, and capacitance is subsequently changed (Hirsh, 1952). When the plates are moved closer together (compression), capacitance increases and a charge current occurs. When the plates are moved apart (rarefaction), capacitance decreases and a discharge current occurs. Movement of the diaphragm in response to sound varies the capacitance and produces a variable electric current (Hirsh, 1952). Condenser microphones exhibit excellent "frequency responses," and their small amount of output is usually boosted by the use of a built-in preamplifier. However, their greater sensitivity renders them more prone to amplitude distortion (Silman & Emmer, 2012), as discussed in the sections below. The components of a condenser microphone are illustrated in Figure 6–3D.

The Electret (Condenser) Microphone

Invented at Bell Laboratories in 1962, the electret microphone is a type of condenser microphone that uses a special type of capacitor. The capacitor is made from ferroelectric material that has been permanently charged and polarized during its manufacture. The microphone is self-biased and can last for up to 100 years (Silman & Emmer, 2012). The material is somewhat similar to a permanent magnet, requiring no external polarizing power for its operation (Giancoli, 2005). Electret condenser microphones usually do include a preamplifier that will still require power. The diaphragm in the electret microphone is made of Teflon material that is about 0.5- to 1-mm thick on one side. The electret microphone is also the smallest and most commonly used microphone in the disciplines of audiology and hearing science. They are found on delicate equipment such as on sound level meters (SLMs) that were discussed above. These microphones have a flat frequency response across a wide range of frequencies, and some present-day electret microphones, such

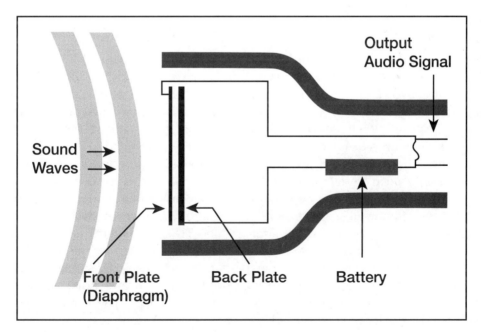

Figure 6–3D. Cross section of a condenser microphone with its two conductive plates. The diaphragm and the back plate taken together form the plates of a variable capacitor.

as the Etymotic Research (ER)-10B and the ER-10C, have a frequency response of up to as high as 20 kHz (Silman & Emmer, 2012). The actual electret microphone that is often used in a SLM was illustrated in Figure 6–2E.

The Crystal and Ceramic Microphone

Still another pressure type of microphone is the crystal microphone, first developed in a useful form in 1931 by C. B. Sawyer. The crystal microphone is based on the principle that some types of crystals have the capability of producing a voltage when they are subjected to mechanical stress and deformation. The pressure-induced current that is generated from these crystals is called piezoelectricity. The piezoelectric effect occurs only in electrically polarized crystals, exhibiting significant amounts of electrical polar symmetry. In the piezoelectric crystal, positive and negative charges are symmetrically distributed. When pressure stress is applied, the electric charge symmetry is disturbed and the crystal generates a voltage. The prefix "piezo" in piezoelectric comes from the Greek verb "to press." Rochelle salt crystals exhibit greater piezoelectric activity than any other known crystals and are commonly used in crystal microphones. Crystal microphones often depend on the pressure-induced generation of a voltage from the deformation of a ferroelectric Rochelle salt crystal (Hirsh, 1952). The piezoelectric crystal transduces the pressure vibrations from the sound into an electrical signal. Greater sensitivity is achieved with a diaphragm-activated type of system in which a moving diaphragm is coupled to the crystal (Figure 6–3E). The amount

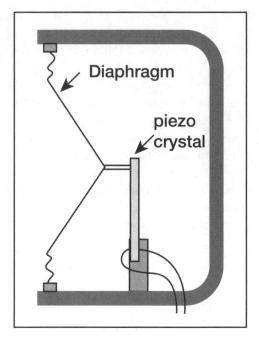

Figure 6–3E. Cross section of a diaphragm-activated crystal microphone that generates a piezoelectric current.

of deformation that occurs to the crystal is very slight, being on the order of nanometers (10^{-9} meters). The vibrating diaphragm twists the piezoelectric crystal and produces an electrical current. Crystal microphones have an advantage such that there is no external voltage or current requirement.

Ceramic microphones are also employed and are constructed of barium titanate, or various other ceramic ferroelectric substances in place of Rochelle salts. The ferroelectric ceramic substance is polarized by the application of a strong direct-current electric field, producing a strong polar symmetry (Giancoli, 2005). The ceramic microphones tend to be less sensitive than the crystal types but have the advantage of exhibiting better tolerances to high temperatures and humidity.

The Dynamic (Moving Coil) Microphone

Finally, another pressure type of microphone is the dynamic or moving-coil microphone, invented nearly simultaneously in 1877 by Charles Cuttris and Jerome Redding in the United States, and E. W. Siemens in Germany. In the dynamic microphone, a small mobile induction coil is attached to the diaphragm. The induction coil is centered within the magnetic field of a permanent magnet (Hirsh, 1952). Neodymium is often used as a replacement for the conventional magnets that have been typically used in dynamic microphones (Silman & Emmer, 2012). When sound waves cause the diaphragm to resonate, the induction coil moves back and forth within the fixed magnetic field of the permanent magnet and produces a variable current in the coil through electromagnetic induction (Figure 6–3F). Dynamic microphones are known for their capacity to suppress noise and other unwanted low-frequency energy and are often used in public address systems and for recording purposes (Silman & Emmer, 2012). Conventional loudspeakers, headphones, and earphones are designed much like the dynamic microphone (with an induction coil and permanent magnet) and work in exactly the reverse functional manner as dynamic microphones (Hewitt, 2010). That is, a loudspeaker transduces electrical signals into the acoustical energy of sound waves (Figure 6–3G). Therefore, the response of a loudspeaker is sound pressure when a voltage is applied, and the response of a microphone is voltage when a sound pressure is applied (Hirsh, 1952).

The Velocity Type of Microphone

The Ribbon Microphone

Invented in 1923 by W. H. Schottky and Erwin Gerlach in Germany, the ribbon microphone is a form of moving-coil

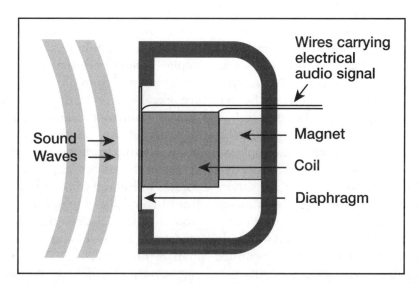

Figure 6–3F. Cross section of a dynamic (moving-coil) microphone that produces a variable current by way of electromagnetic induction.

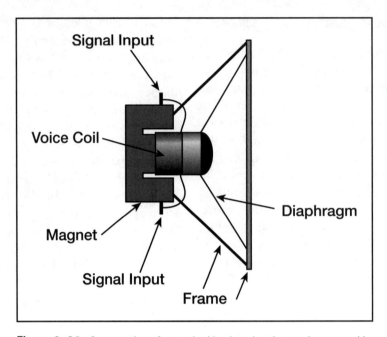

Figure 6–3G. Cross section of a standard loudspeaker that produces sound by way of electromagnetic induction.

(moving-conductor) dynamic microphone that also works by electromagnetic induction. The moving conductor is a thin metallic ribbon, aluminum or microfilm suspended within a magnetic field, normally between the poles of a permanent magnet (Hirsh, 1952; Silman & Emmer, 2012). Sound may be allowed to reach the ribbon on only one of its sides, creating a pressure (ribbon)-type microphone, or the ribbon may be free (free-ribbon type) to be exposed to sound on both of its sides, constituting a velocity (ribbon)-type microphone (Figure 6–3H). The free-ribbon design type with its bidirectional sensitivity responds to pressure gradients rather than just simple sound pressure. Finally, ribbon microphones respond to a wide range of frequencies and produce sounds that have a natural quality (Silman & Emmer, 2012).

Microphone Directionality

Pressure-type microphones are usually designed to detect sounds from any direction. In terms of their response properties, these microphones are often called nondirectional or omnidirectional microphones. As the name implies, omnidirectional microphones detect sounds from all directions and are excellent for communicating in groups (Silman & Emmer, 2012). As indicated above, the free-ribbon type of ribbon microphone exhibits bidirectional sensitivity and responds to sounds presented from in front of and from behind the microphone but not from the sides. Sounds that are generated from the sides are rejected (Silman & Emmer, 2012). These microphones are classified as bidirectional in function. Unidirectional microphones

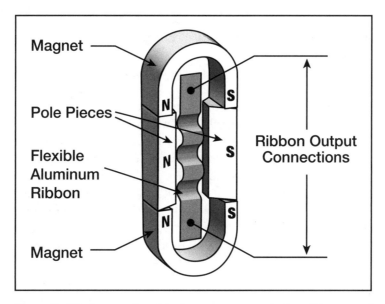

Figure 6–3H. Cross section of the inner components of a free-ribbon-type of velocity microphone in which the flexible aluminum ribbon is exposed to sounds on both of its sides. *N* = north; *S* = south.

are sensitive to sounds that originate from only one direction and are often referred to as cardioid microphones because their receptive field is similar in shape to a valentine heart (Kates, 2008). The characteristic of unidirectionality in microphone performance is often advantageous for minimizing the obstructive and unwanted effects of extraneous sound. For example, unidirectionality in microphone design can help minimize the effects of undesired background noise. Unidirectionality is also helpful for minimizing the kinds of adverse room acoustics that produce unwanted reverberant sounds (echoes), and for reducing unwanted feedback from a nearby loudspeaker when loudspeaker and microphone are in close physical proximity to each other. For such reasons, directional microphones are used in many types of digital hearing aids, the objective being to preserve the desired signal arriving from the front of the listener, while attenuating noise and other interference arriving from beside or from behind the listener (Kates, 2008).

The Sound-Field

By definition, a sound-field is often simply defined as any physical area, space, or environment enclosing a material medium, in which sound waves are present (Lucks-Mendel et al., 1999). By this definition, a sound-field could be any room or environment in which an appropriate elastic or compressible material medium (such as a gas, a liquid, or a solid substance) exists, and within such media, sound waves are being propagated and transmitted. In practice, the act of sound-field testing often refers to procedures in which calibrated auditory signals are delivered through loudspeakers that are strategically placed within a sound-attenuating test chamber. Audiometric sound-field testing is often preferred over the use of headphones when testing children who exhibit a low tolerance for headphones, or simply, when evaluating the performance of hearing aids (Lucks-Mendel et al., 1999).

Types of Sound-Fields

The Free-Field

A free-field (or a free sound-field) refers an idealistic kind of environment that contains no physical objects, and one that is also free from boundaries (Moore, 2012). Where and when boundaries do exist, idealistically they are distant enough as to produce only negligible reflections over the frequency range of audible sound. Therefore, in a free sound-field, sound waves are free to propagate indefinitely because there are no barriers or boundaries that might otherwise "contaminate" the spectral purity and outward progression of the sound waves. Hence, a free sound-field is void of wave reflections, reverberations, diffractions, shadows created by obstructions, sound absorption (damping), and sound wave interference of any kind. As long as there is a free and unobstructed propagation of a spherical wave of sound in this idealized situation, the inverse square law given by Equation 6–4 ($I = P/4\pi r^2$) may be used to predict the sound pressure at any distance from the sound source, based on accurate sound pressure measurements taken from quantified distances

from the sound source (Durrant & Feth, 2013).

The Virtual Free-Field: The Anechoic Chamber

If and when boundaries do exist within an otherwise free sound-field, then a virtual free-field is created. In a virtual free-field, the sound waves will interact with the free-field boundaries and will be absorbed (and not reflected) completely by these boundaries. A virtual free-field is the kind of environment that is approximated by an anechoic chamber because, as the name implies, the anechoic chamber generates no echoes. Hence, the anechoic chamber (a virtual free-field) is the closest approximation to a free sound-field. However, the presence of a listener in the room must also be taken into account because the physical presence of a body could also reflect or absorb waves and/or produce complex wave patterns. Albeit, anechoic chambers are often referred to as *soundproofed* chambers, as they keep sounds from both entering and escaping. In addition to their external steel walls, they contain acoustic material within their inner walls that prevents the propagation of echoes or reverberations from occurring within. Anechoic chambers have highly reflective steel outer walls and very thick, insulated, inner walls. Their reflective outer surfaces will prevent the entry into the chamber of unwanted ambient (external) sounds. In addition, each of the six inner wall surfaces of this virtual free-field is heavily insulated with highly absorptive acoustic material. This material is often composed of many fiberglass wedges (Speaks, 1999) that act like "acoustic sponges" to prevent the exiting of sounds. More importantly, these fiberglass wedges prevent the production of reverberations (reverberant sounds) or echoes (anechoic) from being generated within the chamber (Figure 6–4A). Absorption is the acoustical equivalent of damping (friction) that was encountered in descriptions of mechanical systems discussed in Chapter 5. Therefore, the absorption of sound energy leads to its ultimate transformation into heat. Recall from Chapter 5 that the term *free vibration* is often used to refer to a damped sinusoidal vibration. Hence, free vibrations generated in the air medium of an anechoic chamber will ultimately be damped by the thick internal room acoustics. Anechoic chambers are often used by industry or for research purposes to accurately evaluate the unique electroacoustic properties of loudspeakers. As such, anechoic chambers

are very expensive to build and are not necessary for clinical audiometric testing. Audiometric hearing testing is often performed in relatively less expensive, external steel-walled surfaced, sound-treated (or sound-isolated), sound-attenuating chambers (Speaks, 1999) as illustrated in Figures 6–4B and 6–4C. These sound-attenuating chambers have perforated internal steel wall surfaces that suppress reverberations, and the area between the outer and inner steel surfaces is often very thick and heavily insulated. Absorption is also associated with the term *baffle*.

The Diffuse (Reverberant) Sound-Field

The diffuse or reverberant field is a sound-field having many reflective surfaces and very little sound absorption. A diffuse sound-field environment is therefore the exact opposite of the

Figure 6–4A. The inside of an anechoic chamber. Note that the sound-absorbing wedges covering all of the inner surfaces render the chamber both anechoic and soundproof. Reprinted with permission from Creative Commons; Attribution-Share Alike 3.0 unported.

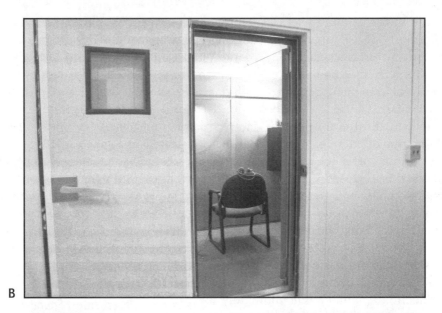

B

C

Figure 6–4B–C. Sound-attenuating test chambers (Cleveland State University Hearing Clinic). Note the external steel-walled surfaces for sound attenuation, the thick walls, and the perforated internal steel wall surfaces that suppress reverberations in both chambers.

type of environment created by an anechoic chamber. The reflected sound in a reverberant field produces echoes. When sound waves are reflected, reverberations (or echoes) occur when the incident (or original) waveform strikes the boundary surface, resulting in a reflected waveform that is perceived by the listener with only a very short time delay between the perception of the incident and the reflected wave. According to the law of reflection (Halliday et al., 2011), sound will reflect from a smooth dense surface in much the same way as light is reflected from a smooth shiny surface (such as a mirror). In either case, the angle of incidence is equal to the angle of reflection to the perpendicular path, as illustrated in Figure 6–5. The law also applies to sounds presented along the perpendicular path where the angle of incidence is 0°; hence, the angle of reflection is also 0°. A diffuse sound-field can usually be found in athletic gymnasia, enclosed Olympic-sized swimming pools, as well as interior spaces having marble, concrete, or glass walls. In the design of an auditorium or a concert hall, both of which are further examples of diffuse sound-fields, a balance needs to be established between reverberation and absorption. If the reflective surfaces are too absorbent, the overall sound levels would tend to fall, resulting in a dull and lifeless acoustic environment. An anechoic chamber is the most extreme

example of an acoustically lifeless or an acoustically dead sound environment. On the other hand, reflections generated in a diffuse sound-field add a nearly uniform fullness and liveliness to the sound-field, similar to what one experiences when singing in the shower or when vocalizing in an empty room having a hard and flat wall, ceiling, and floor surface. If, however, the boundary surfaces in a diffuse sound-field are too reflective, the resulting net sound may grow in intensity and becomes garbled and difficult to understand, as is often the case in a highly reverberant field, defined as a field that exhibits multiple reflections or reverberations.

The Speed of Sound

As indicated in Chapter 5, the fundamental physical properties of a particular medium will determine the speed at which sound will propagate in that medium (Durrant & Feth, 2013). The

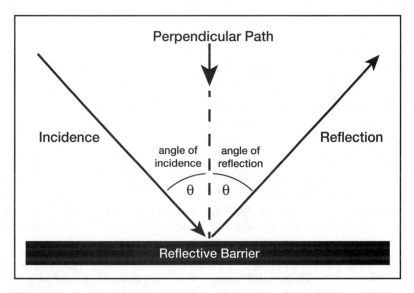

Figure 6–5. The law of reflection, such that the angle of reflection is equal to the angle of incidence to the perpendicular path.

speed of any mechanical wave through a medium depends on both an inertial property of the medium (to store kinetic energy) and an elastic property of the medium (to store potential energy). The relationship of the two may be given (Halliday et al., 2011) by the following Equation (6–15) in which speed through a material medium is defined as the square root of the ratio of the elastic and inertial properties, or

$$\text{Speed} = \left(\frac{\text{elastic property}}{\text{inertial property}}\right)^{\frac{1}{2}}$$

$$(6–15)$$

Recall from earlier in this chapter that the bulk modulus is a measure of an opposition to compression (pressure) and therefore an opposition to the changes that occur in the volume of the compressed medium (Halliday et al., 2011). Bulk modulus was the property that determines the extent to which an element of a medium changes in volume when the pressure on the medium changes. Values of the bulk modulus for various materials were also provided in Table 6–1. For the present, recall that the bulk (or elastic) modulus was a measure of the bulk elastic properties of a material medium. Equation 6–15, which defined the way in which the speed of sound through a material medium may be determined, may also be rewritten (Halliday et al., 2011) by placing the volume density (mass per unit volume) in the denominator for the inertial property, and by placing the bulk modulus into the numerator for the elastic property. Hence, speed through a material medium, which was used in Chapter 5 to define the characteristic impedances (rayls) of various material media (see Table 5–4), is again

presented as the square root of the ratio of the bulk (elastic) modulus and the volume density, or simply,

$$\text{Speed} = \left(\frac{\text{bulk modulus}}{\text{volume density}}\right)^{\frac{1}{2}}$$

$$(6–16)$$

The speeds of sound (c) in various materials that were provided in Table 5–4 along with their characteristic impedance values are once again provided in Table 6–8. In the external environment, the actual speed of sound will depend on wind conditions, temperature, and humidity. Overall, however, the speed of sound does not depend upon the loudness and frequency of the incident waveform. That is, with all environmental factors being equal, all sounds will travel at the same speed (Hewitt, 2010). Therefore, the speed of sound is independent of the frequency of the vibration of the source, since only the characteristics of the medium are important (Speaks, 1999). The speed of sound in air will increase as temperature increases, but at room temperature, which is about 20°C, it travels at about 344 m/s (MKS), or 34,400 cm/s (CGS) as indicated in Table 6–8. The speed of sound in air is also about 1,125 ft/s or about 760 mi/hr.

It is of interest to note that the density of water is almost 1,000 times greater than the density of air. If density were the only relevant factor in determining the speed of sound in material media, we would expect that the speed of sound in water would be considerably less than the speed of sound in air, simply by looking at Equation 6–8. However, the reverse is true as indicated in Table 6–8 because the bulk modulus of water is more than 1,000 times greater

Table 6–8. Speed of Sound (c) in Various Material Media[a]

Medium	Speed (m/s[†]) (cm/s[‡])
Gases	
Air (0°C; 32°F)	331[†]
	33,100[‡]
Air (20°C; 68°F)	343–344[†]
	34,300–34,400[‡]
Helium	965[†]
	96,500[‡]
Hydrogen	1,284[†]
	128,400[‡]
Liquids	
Fresh water (0°C; 32°F)	1,402[†]
	140,200[‡]
Fresh water (20°C; 68°F)	1,482[†]
	148,200[‡]
Seawater[b] (20°C; 68°F)	1,522[†]
	152,200[‡]
Solids	
Aluminum	6,420[†]
Iron and steel	5,941[†]
Granite	6000[†]
Glass	≈ 4500[†]
Hardwood	≈ 4000[†]

[a]At 0°C and 1 atm of pressure, except where noted.
[b]At 3.5% salinity.
Source: Giancoli, 2004; Halliday et al., 2011.

than that of air, as previously shown in Table 6–1 (Halliday et al., 2011). The much greater incompressibility of water, which is another way of expressing the bulk (elastic) modulus, is much greater compared to the much lesser bulk modulus of air. Looking again at Equation 6–16, the density of helium is much less than that of air (Table 6–1), yet the bulk (elastic) moduli of helium and air are not greatly different (Giancoli, 2005). Because of the much lower density of helium relative to air, the speed of sound through helium is almost three times as great compared to the speed of sound through air (Table 6–8). In addition, and as indicated above, the speed of sound in air will progressively increase as environmental temperature increases. Progressive increases in temperature translate to progressive decreases in atmospheric density. For each added degree in environmental temperature above 0°C, the speed of sound in air increases by 0.60 m/s (Hewitt, 2010). This is also to be expected due to the generally greater amount of kinetic energy found in molecules of warmer air. Finally, water vapor in the air, which translates to an increase in humidity and an increase in the elastic modulus, will also slightly increase the speed of sound in air. It should also be obvious from Table 6–8 that compared to solids and liquids, sound does not travel as well in open air, and as indicated above, will never travel in a vacuum.

How does the speed of sound compare to the speed of other waveforms, such as light? Thunder is the sound created by a rapid expansion of the air within and surrounding a bolt of lightning, and represents a sonic shock wave similar to a sonic boom (shock waves and sonic booms are addressed in Chapter 7). However, thunder is heard long after the flash of lightning is actually seen. From a distance, the smoke from a starting pistol that is fired during a track meet can be seen long before the pistol shot is actually heard. These common experiences demonstrate that sound relative to light requires a significant and recognizable amount of time to travel from one location to the next. As indicated in Table 6–8, sound generally travels in 20°C air at a speed of 344 m/s. By comparison, light travels in a vacuum and in air at 299,792,458 m/s. To further illustrate these vast differences in speed, consider that sound travels at 0.344 km/s, whereas light travels at a speed of 300,000 km/s, or at about 186,300 (186,282) mi/s. Finally, and as indicated above, sound travels at about 760 mi/hr compared to light that travels at a speed of 670,616,629 mi/hr (Halliday et al., 2011). In comparison to light, sound travels very slowly. As a general rule of thumb, the distance that an individual is situated from a lightning strike during a storm is understood to be 1 mi for every 5 s of elapsed time between the lightning flash and the audible onset of the thunder (Giancoli, 2005).

Types of Sounds I: Periodic Waveforms

The back-and-forth oscillation or vibratory motion that occurs repeatedly over time and over the same path for any object/mass around a point of equilibrium in response to a displacing force, was described in Chapters 3 and 5 as periodic motion. Recall from Chapter 5 that periodic motion, as applied to the pendulum and spring mass system, is also harmonic motion, and harmonic motion was also described as sinusoidal motion. Sound was described in this chapter as a propagated disturbance in the density of an elastic material medium (Durrant & Feth, 2013; Hirsh,

1952), producing longitudinal wave fronts of compression in all directions (Halliday et al., 2011). Because sound is also defined as a disturbance in particle or in pressure displacement, the notion of periodic, harmonic, and sinusoidal motion may also be applied to different types of sounds, as well as to the two-dimensional waveform descriptions (illustrations) of those sounds.

Simple Periodic Sinusoidal Waveforms: Pure Tones

Recall from Chapter 5 that the pure tone, which is composed of a single frequency of vibration (or a single component), is by definition the simplest (purist) of all types of auditory signals. The pure tone also represents the best example of a periodic sinusoidal waveform. The vast majority of sounds in the natural environment, however, do not consist of single pure tone frequencies. Pure tones are rarely encountered in the environment and are almost exclusively associated with tuning forks and/or audiometric testing equipment such as audiometers. *Sinusoidal* refers to the pure, symmetrical shape of a sine wave, which is most definitely regular and repetitious. *Periodic* also means regular and repetitious and refers to waveform patterns that repeat over time, but when used alone does not mean sinusoidal. Finally, the word *periodicity* refers to the periodic quality of many types of waveform.

Periodic, sinusoidal waveforms depicting five different pure tone frequencies are illustrated in Figure 6–6. Note that the five waveforms also differ in their starting phases but have approximately equal peak-to-peak amplitudes. Note also that these simple, periodic

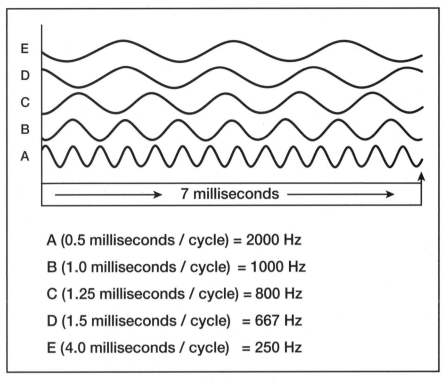

A (0.5 milliseconds / cycle) = 2000 Hz

B (1.0 milliseconds / cycle) = 1000 Hz

C (1.25 milliseconds / cycle) = 800 Hz

D (1.5 milliseconds / cycle) = 667 Hz

E (4.0 milliseconds / cycle) = 250 Hz

Figure 6–6. Periodic sinusoidal waveforms illustrating five pure tone frequencies (A to E) propagated across an overall 7-ms epoch of time. Based on the overall time scale, the period (*T*) and frequency (*f*) for each waveform are provided where 1000 ÷ *T* (in msec.) = *f*. Note that the waveforms have the same or similar peak-to-peak amplitudes and differ only in their frequency and in their starting phases.

and sinusoidal waveforms are presented as though they are propagated across an overall 7-ms epoch of time. In the figure, each of the separate periods (milliseconds/cycle) for each waveform is provided. Recall from Chapter 5 that when the period (*T*) is known and frequency (*f*) is unknown, then Equation 5–1 is used, as illustrated in Figure 6–6.

$$1000 \div T \text{ (in msec.)} = f \quad (5\text{–}1)$$

Combining Pure Tones That Have the Same Frequency

When two or more pure tones having identical frequencies are combined, the result is *not* a complex signal. A com-

plex signal by definition requires the combination of at least two separate frequency components. The combining together of two or more pure tones that have identical frequencies often but not always (see below) results in a composite, sinusoidal periodic waveform that is defined by the same pure tone frequency. The peak amplitude of the composite sinusoidal waveform will directly depend on the individual starting phases and peak amplitudes of the pure tone components that were combined. Recall from Chapters 4 and 5 that simple sinusoidal waveforms are composed of alternating and successive changes in particle and/or pressure density on either side of a point of equilibrium, and that these changes represent variations in energy. Also recall that these alternating, successive variations in energy are called areas of compression and rarefaction. The observed peak amplitude fluctuations in composite waveforms created by combining same-frequency sinusoids are the direct result of the interactions (constructive or destructive) that occur at areas of compression and areas of rarefaction across each individual sinusoidal component (frequency), as these areas systematically overlap at precise moments in time as the sounds are propagated. Peak amplitudes in the composite waveform will be greater or will increase at precise locations where individual sinusoidal areas of compression (+) overlap in time with other areas of compression [(+) + (+) + (+)...], and at precise locations where individual sinusoidal areas of rarefaction (–) overlap in time with other areas of rarefaction [(–) + (–) + (–)...]. Peak amplitudes in the composite waveform will be less or will decline at precise locations where individual sinusoidal areas of compression overlap in time with individual sinusoidal areas of rarefaction [(–) + (+) + (–) + (+)...].

Combining Same-Frequency Pure Tones: Same Amplitudes and Same Starting Phases

Figure 6–7 illustrates the result of adding together two individual pure tones (A) and (B) having identical frequencies, peak amplitudes, and starting phases (270°). Waveforms (A) and (B) in Figure 6–7 could have started at any phase, ranging from 0° to 360°. What is important in the present context is that both waves are equal in their starting phase (i.e., they both begin at the same phase). Because sinusoidal waveforms (A) and (B) have the same frequency and the same starting phase, their common areas of compression (+) and common areas of rarefaction (–) overlap at the same precise moments in time during each cycle of propagation. This results in the regular and repetitious summation of peak amplitudes during each cycle of propagation and produces maximum peak amplitudes in both the compression and rarefaction regions of the composite waveform (C). The amplitude summation of waveforms (A) and (B) in Figure 6–7 illustrates an ideal example of constructive waveform interactions. Because the peak amplitudes in (A) and (B) are equal, the peak amplitude in composite waveform (C) in Figure 6–7 is equal to two times the peak amplitude of (A), or two times the peak amplitude of (B), or simply the sum of the peak amplitudes of (A) and (B).

Combining Same-Frequency Pure Tones: Same Amplitudes/ Different Starting Phases I

As indicated above, combining two or more pure tones having identical frequencies will often but not always result in a composite, sinusoidal periodic waveform defined by the same pure tone frequency. What exactly is meant by not always? Recall that the amplitude of the resulting composite sinusoidal waveform will directly depend on the individual starting phases and amplitudes of the pure tone components that are combined. When two sinusoidal pure tone waveforms both identical in frequency and amplitude are combined, the result will be a total (composite) waveform cancellation if either wave-

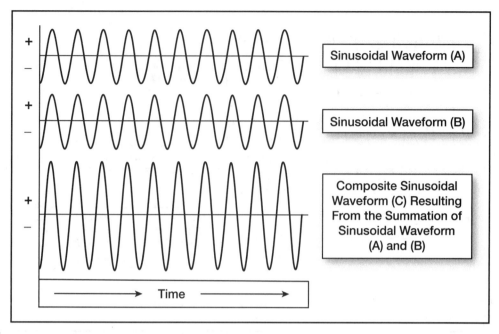

Figure 6–7. Result of combining the two periodic sinusoidal (pure tone) waveforms (A) and (B) having identical frequencies, peak amplitudes, and starting phases (270°) to produce composite waveform (C). Common areas of compression (+) and rarefaction (–) between the two waveforms overlap at the same precise moments in time during each cycle of propagation. Therefore, common areas of compression and common areas of rarefaction completely summate during each propagation cycle, illustrating an ideal example of constructive waveform interactions. As a result, the peak amplitude in composite waveform (C) is simply equal to the sum of the peak amplitudes of both (A) and (B).

form leads or lags the other in phase by 180°. In such instances, the two waveforms are said to be 180° out of phase. Figure 6–8 illustrates the result of adding together two individual pure tones (A) and (B) having identical frequencies and peak amplitudes. However, the starting phase of sinusoidal waveform (A) lags behind sinusoidal waveform (B) by 180°. Conversely, the starting phase of sinusoidal waveform (B) leads sinusoidal waveform (A) by 180°. The two waveforms (A) and (B) are out of phase with each other by exactly 180°. It is important to note that waveforms (A) and (B) in Figure 6–8 could have started at any phase, ranging from 0° to 360°. What is important in the present context

is that both waveforms are 180° out of phase with each other since the mathematical difference in their individual starting phases amounts to exactly 180°. Because sinusoidal waveforms (A) and (B) have the same frequency and have starting phases that differ by exactly 180°, when the two waveforms are combined, areas of compression (+) in waveform (A) will completely overlap with areas of rarefaction (–) in waveform (B), whereas areas of compression (+) in waveform (B) will completely overlap with areas of rarefaction (–) in waveform (A), all at the same precise moments in time during each cycle of propagation. Because the peak amplitudes in both waveforms are equal, the

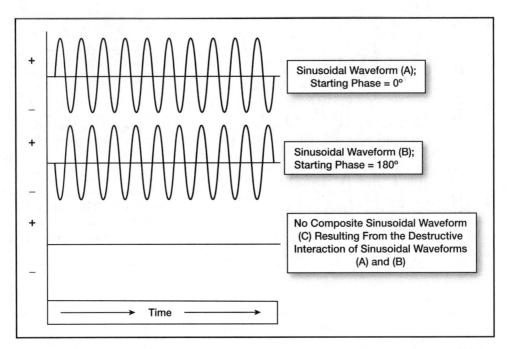

Figure 6–8. Result of combining the two periodic sinusoidal (pure tone) waveforms (A) and (B) having identical frequencies and peak amplitudes but differences in starting phase of 180°. Areas of compression (+) in one wave will overlap with areas of rarefaction (–) in the other wave (and vice versa) at the same precise moments in time during each cycle of propagation. Therefore, the adding together of areas of compression with areas of rarefaction between waveforms (A) and (B) produces total waveform cancellation during each propagation cycle, and subsequently, a waveform (C) is absent. An ideal example of destructive waveform interactions.

overall combining of areas of compression with areas of rarefaction will result in the regular, repetitious, and total (summative) cancellation of amplitudes during each cycle of propagation, and in the complete elimination or absence of a composite waveform (C). The total absence of a composite sinusoidal waveform (C) following a combination of the two, 180° out-of-phase sinusoidal waveforms (A) and (B) in Figure 6–8 illustrates an ideal example of destructive waveform interactions.

Brief Summary

Figures 6–7 and 6–8 illustrated the two extreme examples of phase-dependent changes in waveform amplitudes, using sinusoidal waves with identical frequencies. At the one extreme, no differences in starting phase existed between the two pure tone sinusoids (A) and (B), and as Figure 6–7 illustrated, when two, same-frequency sinusoidal waveforms begin at an identical starting phase, a regular and repetitious summation of amplitudes during each cycle of propagation will occur. As illustrated in Figure 6–7, this constructive waveform interaction will produce maximum peak amplitudes in both the compression and rarefaction regions of a composite waveform. Remember that waveforms (A) and (B) in Figure 6–7 could have started at any phase, ranging from 0°

to 360°. What is important for maximum amplitude summation, however, is that both waves are equal in their starting phase.

At the other extreme, starting phases between the two pure tone sinusoids (A and B) may be in complete (180°) phasic opposition. To be sure, Figure 6–8 illustrated that when two, same-frequency sinusoidal waveforms begin at a different starting phase, such that each wave leads and/or lags behind the other by exactly 180°, a regular and repetitious cancellation of amplitudes will occur during each cycle of propagation. As illustrated in Figure 6–8, this destructive waveform interaction, resulting from combining two, 180° out-of-phase waveforms, will produce no peak amplitudes and no composite waveform.

Combining Same–Frequency Pure Tones: Same Amplitudes/ Different Starting Phases II

Using waveforms (A) and (B), and composite waveform (C) from Figure 6–7, we may now describe the incremental phase-dependent amplitude changes that would be observed in composite waveform (C) if the differences in starting phase between waveforms (A) and (B) were to be progressively manipulated. The starting phase of one of the two waves could be changed so that the phase differences between the two waves fluctuate from the one extreme (both in phase), to the other (both 180° out of phase), and then back again, to where both waves are in phase. In the example that follows, assume that the 270° starting phase of waveform (A) illustrated in Figure 6–7 will remain fixed and unchanged. For simplicity,

imagine that the starting phase of waveform (B) will be singularly manipulated (from 270°, to 315°, 360°, or 0°, 45°, 90°, 135°, 180°, 225°, and back to 270°) before the two waveforms (A and B) are combined to form composite wave (C). Additionally, in describing the phase changes in waveform (B), we will use phase increments of 45°. Once again for simplicity, assume that the peak amplitude of each of the two sinusoidal waveforms (A and B) shown in Figure 6–7 is equal to 1.00. Because waveforms (A) and (B) in Figure 6–7 are initially equal in starting phase, the peak amplitude of the composite waveform (C), as illustrated, would therefore be equal to 1.00 + 1.00 or simply 2.00.

If the starting phase of waveform (B) in Figure 6–7 were to be changed from 270° to 315°, and then to 360° (or 0°), the phase-difference between waveforms (A) and (B) would also change from zero (no difference) to 45° and then to 90°, and there would be a phase-dependent peak amplitude reduction in composite waveform (C). As the phase differences between waveforms (A) and (B) are progressively changed from zero, to 45° and then to 90°, the peak amplitude of composite waveform (C) would also progressively change from the original value of 2.00, to 1.50, and then to 1.00, respectively. How might this phase-dependent peak amplitude reduction in composite waveform (C) be explained?

As the phase difference between waveforms (A) and (B) is progressively increased from zero, to 45° and then to 90°, there is also a progressive reduction in the amount of cycle-by-cycle overlap (from 100%) between common areas of compression and rarefaction within waveforms (A) and

(B). The percentage of overlap in areas of compression and rarefaction with a zero amount of phase-difference is of course 100%, corresponding in this example, to the original peak amplitude of 2.00 in composite waveform (C). With the initial starting phase increment of 45°, or at the starting phase of 315° in waveform (B), the peak amplitude of waveform (C) would change from 2.00 to 1.50 resulting from a 75% overlap between the two waveforms. When the starting phase in waveform (B) is changed again to 360° (or 0°), the peak amplitude of waveform (C) would again be reduced from 1.50 to 1.00, resulting from another reduction to 50% in the overlap between waveforms (A) and (B) and an increased phase difference from 45° to 90° between the two waveforms.

In keeping with starting phase increments of 45°, if the starting phase in waveform (B) is changed from 0° to 45°, the phase difference between waveforms (A) and (B) is progressively increased from 90° to 135°, and the peak amplitude of waveform (C) would again be reduced to 0.50 resulting from the 25% overlap between the two waveforms. When the starting phase in waveform (B) is changed to 90°, the phase difference between waveforms (A) and (B) now becomes 180° (from 135°) and the peak amplitude of waveform (C) is further reduced to the expected 0.00, due to the 0% overlap between successive areas of compression and rarefaction within waveforms (A) and (B), as illustrated in Figure 6–8. Continuing with starting phase increments of 45°, when the starting phase in waveform (B) is changed to 135°, the peak amplitude of waveform (C) would increase from 0.00 to 0.50, resulting again from the 25% waveform overlap and the reduc-

tion from 180° to 135° in the starting phase differences between waveforms (A) and (B).

When the starting phase in waveform (B) is again increased to 180°, the peak amplitude of waveform (C) would increase from 0.50 to 1.00 as a result of the 50% overlap between the two waveforms, as the phase difference between the two waveforms is again reduced from 135° to 90°. A starting phase in waveform (B) of 225° again results in a peak amplitude increase of 1.00 which in waveform (C) would increase from 1.00 to 1.50 resulting from the 75% overlap between the two waveforms, and the decrease in phase difference from 90° to 45°. Finally, and abiding by the 45° increments in starting phase, the return of the starting phase in waveform (B) to 270° results in the original peak amplitude of 2.00 in waveform (C) resulting from the 100% overlap between successive areas of compression and rarefaction in waveforms (A) and (B), as the phase difference between the two waveforms returns again to zero.

Combining Same–Frequency Pure Tones: Different Amplitudes and Starting Phases

Figure 6–9 once again illustrates the result of adding together two individual pure tones (A) and (B), each with identical frequencies. However, the peak amplitude of waveform (A) is exactly twice (2×) that of waveform (B). Furthermore, the starting phase of sinusoidal waveform (A) lags behind sinusoidal waveform (B) by 180°. Conversely, the starting phase of sinusoidal waveform (B) leads sinusoidal waveform (A) by 180°. Hence, the two waveforms (A) and

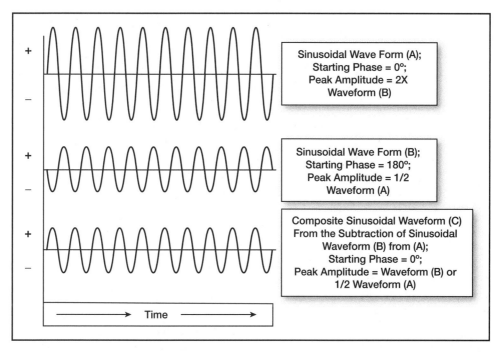

Figure 6–9. Result of combining the two periodic sinusoidal (pure tone) waveforms (A) and (B) having identical frequencies. However, the peak amplitude of waveform (A) is exactly twice (2×) that of waveform (B) and both waves differ in their starting phases by exactly 180°. Areas of compression (+) in one wave will overlap with areas of rarefaction (–) in the other wave (and vice versa) at the same precise moments in time during each cycle of propagation. Therefore, the adding together of areas of compression with areas of rarefaction between waveforms (A) and (B) is tantamount to subtracting each smaller peak amplitude in waveform (B) from each of the larger peak amplitudes in waveform (A) during each cycle of propagation. The peak amplitude of composite waveform (C) will be identical to the peak amplitude of waveform (B) or exactly one half (½) the peak amplitude value of waveform (A), with a starting phase, in this example, of 0°. Another example of destructive waveform interactions.

(B) are out of phase with each other by exactly 180°. It is again important to note that waveforms (A) and (B) in Figure 6–9 could have started at any phase, ranging from 0° to 360°. What is important in the present context is that both waveforms are 180° out of phase (with each other) since the mathematical difference in their individual starting phase amounts to exactly 180°. Because sinusoidal waveforms (A) and (B) in Figure 6–9 have the same frequency and have starting phases that differ by exactly 180°, when the two waveforms are combined, areas of compression (+)

in waveform (A) will completely overlap with areas of rarefaction (–) in waveform (B), whereas areas of compression (+) in waveform (B) will completely overlap with areas of rarefaction (–) in waveform (A), all at the same precise moments in time during each cycle of propagation. Because the peak amplitude in waveform (A) is greater than the peak amplitude of waveform (B), the overall combining of areas of compression with areas of rarefaction will result in the regular and repetitious subtraction of each smaller peak amplitude in waveform (B), from each of the larger peak amplitudes in waveform (A) during each cycle of propagation. What remains from each peak amplitude difference will define the peak amplitude of the composite waveform (C) which will also assume the starting phase of the waveform with the greater amplitude (waveform A). Because the peak amplitude of waveform (A) is exactly twice (2×) that of waveform (B), the composite waveform (C) will have a peak amplitude that is identical to the peak amplitude of waveform (B), or exactly one half (½) the peak amplitude value of waveform (A), but with a starting phase, in this example, of 0°. The synthesis of waveform (C) in Figure 6–9, from the combining of two, same-frequency, 180° out-of-phase sinusoidal signals that differ in peak amplitudes, illustrates yet another example of destructive waveform interactions.

Complex Waveforms

Recall from Chapter 5 that a complex waveform is initially created by two or more simple (different) waveform signals (pure tones) that happen to occupy the same space at the same time. Complex sounds are initially composed of two or more constituent (elemental) sinusoidal pure tones, differing in frequency that are added together in space and time. Complex waveforms are often described in terms of the amplitudes, the frequencies, and the starting phases that characterize the individual sinusoids, which when combined generate the complex sound. Descriptions of complex waveforms that usually include an account of these three properties are said to be descriptions that are made in the frequency domain. An almost endless number of

possible variations in the waveform shape (morphology) of complex signals can be generated when simpler sinusoidal waveforms, distinguished by different frequencies, amplitudes, and starting phases, are combined in the same space and at the same time. Such variation in the waveform morphology observed in composite complex waveforms, in actuality, refers to the often regular, repetitious, periodic (or nonperiodic) patterns of peak amplitude variability that occurs across time. Similar to what was described above for combining same-frequency pure tones, the observed amplitude fluctuations in complex waveforms are the direct result of the interactions (constructive or destructive) that occur at consecutive areas of compression and areas of rarefaction across the individual sinusoidal components (frequencies), as these areas systematically overlap at precise moments in time as the sounds are propagated. Peak amplitudes in the composite waveform will be greater or will increase at precise locations where individual sinusoidal areas of compression (+) overlap in time with other areas of compression [(+) + (+) + (+)…], and at precise locations where individual sinusoidal areas of rarefaction (–) overlap in time with other areas of rarefaction [(–) + (–) + (–)…]. Peak amplitudes in the composite waveform will be less or will decline at precise locations where individual sinusoidal areas of compression overlap in time with individual sinusoidal areas of rarefaction [(–) + (+) + (–) + (+)…].

Complex Periodic Waveforms

The simplest type of complex waveform is a complex periodic waveform. The simplest type of complex periodic waveform is a waveform composed of only two pure tones that differ in frequency, that are combined or added together in the same space and at the same time. What exactly is meant by "adding sinusoidal waves together"? Once again, the process of adding sinusoids together, or adding together any types of waveforms simply involves adding together the respective and overlapping areas of compression and rarefaction of each waveform, cycle by cycle at precise locations and moments in time, and then re-plotting the composite waveform. The process of synthesizing a complex periodic waveform from, or decomposing a complex waveform into individual sinusoids requires an understanding of harmonics. Harmonics, partials, and overtones were discussed in Chapter 5. Synthesizing or constituting a complex periodic waveform from individual sinusoids is called a *Fourier synthesis*, and decomposing or dismantling a complex waveform into its individual constituent sinusoids, is called a *Fourier analysis* in honor of Jean Baptiste Joseph Fourier (1768–1830), illustrated in Portrait 6–2.

Jean Baptiste Joseph Fourier

Fourier was a French mathematician and physicist known best for his work in defining mathematical functions by using sets of trigonometric values. According to Fourier, almost any function of a real variable can be represented by a mathematical series involving sines and cosines of the integral multiples of the variable. A *Fourier series* in mathematics stands for a class of sequencing (a series) that is used to approximate mathematical functions. Any form of synthesis or analysis of a complex periodic wave involving the

Portrait 6–2. Jean Baptiste Joseph Fourier (1768–1830). Printed with permission. Wikimedia Commons, public domain.

sequencing of related terms such as *harmonics* is referred to as a series. Hence, any computation of the component parts of a complex periodic waveform involves the calculation of a Fourier series (Rosen & Howell, 2013).

Examples of Complex Periodic Waveforms

Most environmental sounds are complex and are composed of a combination of not only two, but in most instances numerous separate frequency components. Many of these complex environmental sounds are periodic. This is especially true of the vowel sounds that are found in speech. Recall the complex periodic waveform morphology that was illustrated in Chapter 5 (Figure 5–10C) for the vowel "ahhhh" /ɑ/. Recall as well that pure tones are encountered rarely and are often only associated with tuning forks and/or audiometric testing equipment such as audiometers. Notwithstanding, and in terms of complex sounds, each separate frequency within a complex signal will often exhibit an autonomous frequency, starting phase, and peak amplitude of vibration. Hence, the adding together of simple sinusoidal periodic waveforms often produces a composite complex waveform with a unique waveform morphology. For these reasons, complex periodic sound waves can never be sinusoidal in their composite morphology. For instance, Figure 6–10 illustrates how a complex periodic waveform may be created by the combination of two simple, periodic sinusoidal waveforms composed of different frequencies, but

with identical peak amplitudes and starting phases (0°). In the figure, the simple sinusoidal waveforms represent the pure tone frequencies of 100 and 500 Hz. All of the waves shown in the figure are propagated across an overall 60-ms epoch of time. It should be obvious that the frequency of the 500-Hz waveform corresponds to the fifth harmonic of the 100-Hz waveform. Hence, the frequencies of the two waveforms are harmonically related. According to Fourier's theorem, in order for a complex waveform to be periodic, or to possess a periodic morphology, all of the individual sinusoids that comprise the composite waveform must be composed of frequencies that are integer whole number multiples of the lowest

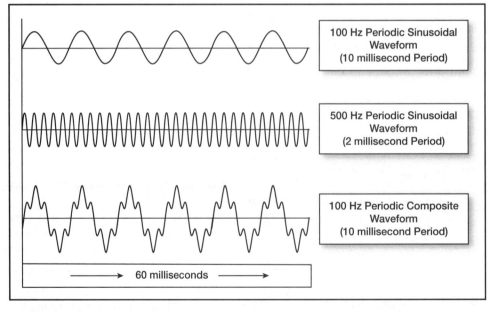

Figure 6–10. A complex periodic waveform may be created by the combination of two periodic sinusoidal waveforms having different frequencies but identical amplitudes and starting phases (0°). In this example, the waveforms represent the pure tone frequencies of 100 and 500 Hz. All waves are propagated across an overall 60-ms epoch of time. Note that the frequency of the 500-Hz waveform corresponds to the fifth harmonic of the 100-Hz waveform. Hence, the frequencies of the two waveforms are harmonically related. The fundamental frequency or repetition rate of the composite waveform is equal to 100 Hz, with a 10-ms period. Note also that the composite waveform is periodic but not sinusoidal.

frequency component (the fundamental frequency) that exists in the composite series of frequencies (Speaks, 1999). Harmonic relations between frequencies were defined and addressed in Chapter 5. The fundamental frequency or repetition rate of the composite waveform illustrated in Figure 6–10 must be equal to 100 Hz, with a 10-ms period. Note also that the composite waveform exhibits periodicity (is periodic), but it is by no means sinusoidal in its morphology.

As another example, Figure 6–11 illustrates how a complex periodic waveform may be created by the combination of two simple, periodic sinusoidal waveforms composed not only of different frequencies but also of different peak amplitudes and starting phases. In the figure, the two simple sinusoidal waveforms represent the pure tone frequencies of 1000 and 2000 Hz. The 1000-Hz sinusoidal wave illustrated has a starting phase of 0°, whereas the 2000-Hz sinusoidal wave begins at a phase of 90°, and therefore leads the 1000-Hz component in phase by 90°. All waves shown in the figure are propagated across an overall 8-ms epoch of time. Because the frequency of the 2000-Hz waveform corresponds to the second harmonic of the 1000-Hz waveform, the two waveforms are harmonically related. The fundamental frequency or repetition rate of the composite waveform must again be equal to 1000 Hz, with a 1-ms period. Note again that

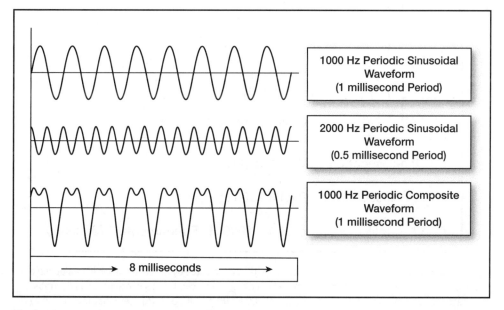

Figure 6–11. A complex periodic waveform may be created by the combination of two periodic sinusoidal waveforms having different frequencies, amplitudes, and starting phases. In this example, the two waveforms represent the pure tone frequencies of 1000 and 2000 Hz. All waves are propagated across an overall 8-ms epoch of time. Note that the frequency of the 2000-Hz waveform, with its starting phase of 90° corresponds to the second harmonic of the 1000-Hz waveform, with its starting phase of 0°. The frequencies of the two waveforms are therefore harmonically related, and the 2000-Hz component leads the 1000-Hz component by 90°. The fundamental frequency or repetition rate of the composite waveform is therefore equal to 1000 Hz, with a 1-ms period. Note again that the composite waveform is periodic but not sinusoidal.

while the composite waveform exhibits periodicity, it is by no means sinusoidal in its morphology.

Figure 6–12 once again illustrates a composite, complex periodic waveform (B + A) that is created by the combination of the two periodic sinusoidal waveforms (B) and (A), propagated across an overall 8-ms epoch of time. Note that in this particular instance,

the two periodic sinusoidal waveforms differ only in their frequency and in their peak amplitude, but not in their starting phases of 0°. The frequencies (1000 and 2000 Hz) of the two sinusoidal waveforms (B) and (A) are again harmonically related. Because 2000 Hz is the second harmonic of the lowest frequency component (which is 1000 Hz) in the series, the composite, com-

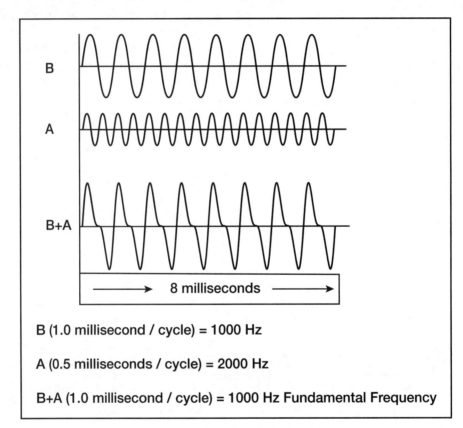

B (1.0 millisecond / cycle) = 1000 Hz

A (0.5 milliseconds / cycle) = 2000 Hz

B+A (1.0 millisecond / cycle) = 1000 Hz Fundamental Frequency

Figure 6–12. A complex periodic waveform (B + A) is created by the combination of two periodic sinusoidal waveforms. All waves are propagated across an overall 8-ms epoch of time. Illustrated are the harmonically related frequencies of 2000 Hz (B) and 1000 Hz (A). Note that the frequency of waveform (A) represents the second harmonic of waveform (B). Period (*T*) and frequency (*f*) for each waveform are provided where 1000 ÷ T (in ms) = f. Note that waveforms (B) and (A) also differ in peak amplitude but have identical starting phases. Because the frequencies of the two waveforms (B) and (A) are harmonically related, the fundamental frequency or repetition rate of (B + A) is equal to 1000 Hz, with a 1-ms period. Note again that the composite waveform is periodic but not sinusoidal. In addition, the morphology of complex waveform (B + A) should be compared to the composite complex periodic waveform illustrated in Figure 6–13.

plex waveform (B + A) illustrated in Figure 6–12 will have a fundamental frequency, or repetition rate, of 1000 Hz with, of course, a 1-ms period.

It is of particular interest at this juncture to compare the morphology of the composite complex periodic waveform (B + A) in Figure 6–12, with the composite complex periodic waveform illustrated in Figure 6–11. Both of these complex waveforms are composed of the same harmonically related sinusoidal frequencies of 1000 and 2000 Hz, and in both figures, the peak amplitude of the second harmonic (2000 Hz) is approximately half the peak amplitude of the waveform with the lower (first harmonic or fundamental) 1000-Hz frequency. In spite of these similarities, the morphology of the two composite, complex periodic waveforms is drastically different. What would account for such morphological differences? The observed differences in waveform morphology can be directly attributed to the differences in the starting phases of each the two separate, 2000-Hz (second harmonic) waveform components. In Figure 6–11, the starting phase of the 2000-Hz component is 90°, or it may be said that this component leads the 1000-Hz component in phase by 90°. In Figure 6–12, the starting phase of the 2000-Hz component is the same as the 0° starting phase of the waveform with the lower (first harmonic or fundamental) 1000-Hz frequency.

What type of waveform morphology might we observe if additional in-phase harmonically related periodic sinusoidal pure tones were to be added to the composite, complex periodic waveform (B + A) that is illustrated in Figure 6–12? The question may be generally restated as, what type of sound is created when a series of discreet, harmonically related, in-phase, periodic sinusoidal waveforms (pure tones) are added together? In Figure 6–13, the composite, complex periodic waveform (B + A) from Figure 6–12 is combined with an additional, higher frequency (pure tone) periodic sinusoidal waveform (C). The frequency (3000 Hz) of the pure tone illustrated by waveform (C) represents the third harmonic in the frequency series, since the series really began with the 1000-Hz pure tone waveform (B) illustrated in Figure 6–12. The 3000-Hz pure tone also represents the third harmonic of the fundamental frequency of the composite, complex periodic waveform (B + A), illustrated in Figure 6–12, as well as of the (same) waveform (B + A) shown in Figure 6–13. Hence, waveform (C) in Figure 6–13 is harmonically related to waveforms (B), (A), and (B + A). It is also noteworthy that waveforms (B + A) and (C) illustrated in Figure 6–13 again differ in their respective peak amplitudes. Moreover, a closer examination reveals that waveforms (B) and (A) from Figure 6–12, and waveform (C) from Figure 6–13 not only differ, but differ systematically in their respective peak amplitudes. The amplitude of waveform (C) shown in Figure 6–13 is about one third the peak amplitude of waveform (B) and is about one sixth the peak amplitude of waveform (A), from Figure 6–12. Furthermore, in Figure 6–12, the peak amplitude of waveform (A) is about one half the peak amplitude of waveform (B). It is also noteworthy that in spite of the obvious, mathematically progressive reductions in peak amplitude that have been imposed with the addition of each new harmonic (see

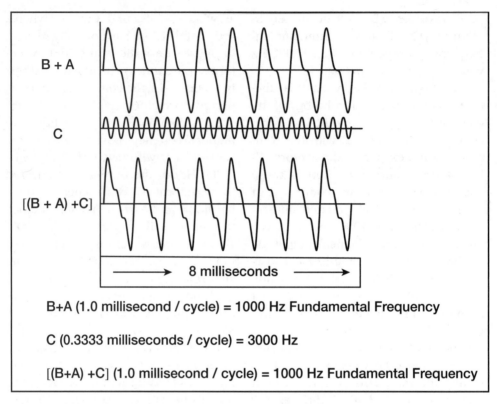

B+A (1.0 millisecond / cycle) = 1000 Hz Fundamental Frequency

C (0.3333 milliseconds / cycle) = 3000 Hz

[(B+A) +C] (1.0 millisecond / cycle) = 1000 Hz Fundamental Frequency

Figure 6–13. A complex periodic waveform [(B + A) + C] is created by the combination of the complex periodic waveform (B + A) borrowed from Figure 6–12, and a harmonically related, periodic sinusoidal waveform (C). As in Figure 6–12, all waves are propagated across an overall 8-ms epoch of time. The frequency of waveform (C) is 3000 Hz and represents the third harmonic of the fundamental frequency (1000 Hz) of waveform (B + A). Period (T) and frequency (f) for each waveform are provided where $1000 \div T$ (in ms) = f. Note that waveforms (B + A) and (C) also differ in amplitude but have identical starting phases of 0°. Because the frequencies of the two waveforms (B + A) and (C) are harmonically related, the fundamental frequency or repetition rate of [(B + A) + C] also equals 1000 Hz (1-ms period). Also note that because the harmonically related waveform (C) is "in phase" with waveform (B + A), the composite [(B + A) + C] begins to approximate the morphology of a periodic (nonsinusoidal) sawtooth waveform.

below), each of the waveforms in Figures 6–12 and 6–13 also happen to have identical starting phases (of 0°).

Sawtooth Waves

When a series of pure tones consisting of a single (fundamental) frequency (f_0) and each of the integer whole number multiples of the fundamental (known as harmonics or partials) are combined such that all frequency components in the series begin at the same starting phase (i.e., all waves are in phase) the composite complex periodic waveform will begin to approximate the morphology of a sawtooth wave, as was illustrated in Figures 6–12 and 6–13. It should be emphasized that while the starting phase of any and of all frequency components may range from 0° to 360°, as a general rule, restriction, or requirement, the starting phases of all the waveform components must be identical in order for a sawtooth wave to be synthesized. Recall from Chapter 5 that a harmonic series is composed of the fundamental frequency (f_0), also defined as the first harmonic ($1 \times f_0$), and each of the higher even- and odd-numbered harmonic frequencies in the series, such as $2 \times f_0$, $3 \times f_0$, $4 \times f_0$, $5 \times f_0 \ldots N \times f_0$, and so forth.

As shown in Figures 6–12 and 6–13, another requirement for the synthesis of sawtooth waveforms is that with each successively higher harmonic added to the frequency series, a systematically progressive amplitude reduction must be imposed on each. The rate of reduction in the peak amplitude of each added higher harmonic (relative to the peak amplitude of the fundamental) is defined by a ratio of $1/N$, where N is equal to the number (1, 2, 3, 4, 5, etc.) of the harmonic (Speaks, 1999). The rate of decline in the peak amplitude of each added harmonic in the series is proportional to the inverse of the harmonic number. Finally, because the inherent frequencies of the two waveforms (B + A) and (C) illustrated in Figure 6–13 are harmonically related, the fundamental (or repetition) frequency of [(B + A) + C] will also be equal to 1000 Hz, with a 1-ms period. Because the harmonically related waveform (C) is in-phase with waveforms (B), (A), as well as with the composite complex wave (B + A) from Figure 6–12, the composite periodic (nonsinusoidal) waveform [(B + A) + C] illustrated in Figure 6–13 just begins to approximate the morphology of a sawtooth wave.

How many discreet, harmonically related, in-phase, periodic sinusoidal (pure tones) must be added together, or stated differently, how long must the harmonic series be in order to achieve

the precise morphology of a sawtooth wave? The answer is that an infinite number of harmonics would be needed. However, a fairly good approximation to a sawtooth wave can be attained using a far fewer number of harmonics. Figure 6–14 illustrates that for any given fundamental frequency of interest (f_0), five harmonically related, in-phase, sinusoidal waveforms may be combined to closely approximate a sawtooth wave. By adding together waveforms that represent integer whole number multiple frequencies of the f_0 (i.e., $1 \times f_0 + 2 \times f_0 + 3 \times f_0 + 4 \times f_0 + 5 \times f_0$), a harmonic frequency series may be generated. All waveforms shown in Figure 6–14 have identical starting phases (of 0°) and each successively higher harmonic added to the series is progressively reduced in amplitude (relative to the peak amplitude of the fundamental) by a ratio of $1/N$. N, of course, is equal to a particular harmonic number (1, 2, 3, 4, 5), and as indicated above, the rate of decline in the amplitude of each added harmonic in the series is proportional to the inverse of the harmonic number. As expected, the composite periodic waveform synthesized will have a repetition rate and period that are identical to the original sinusoidal fundamental frequency. In this instance, the composite wave shown in Figure 6–14 is a closer approximation to the ideal sawtooth waveform morphology, when compared to the composite waveforms illustrated in Figures 6–12 and 6–13. It should also be noted that the peak amplitude of the original (sinusoidal) fundamental frequency will be slightly less than the peak amplitude of the composite, sawtooth wave. This difference in peak amplitude is due, in part, to the fact that the height of the

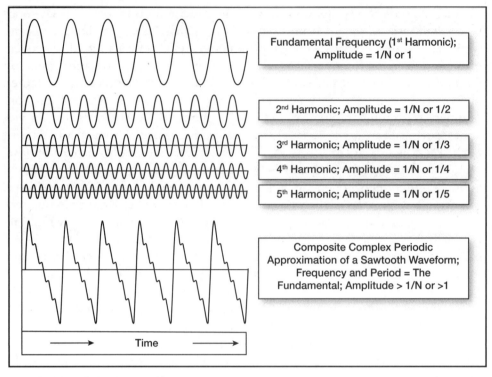

Figure 6–14. The sawtooth wave: By combining five harmonically related, in-phase, sinusoidal frequencies, a complex periodic waveform may be synthesized. For any given fundamental frequency (f_0), a composite waveform may be created by adding together sinusoidal waveforms representing integer whole number multiples of f_0 (i.e., $1 \times f_0$, $2 \times f_0$, $3 \times f_0$, $4 \times f_0$, $5 \times f_0$), to generate a harmonic frequency series. The composite periodic wave that is synthesized has a repetition rate and period identical to the original fundamental frequency, and in this instance, the composite wave closely approximates the sawtooth waveform morphology. Note that each of the waveforms in the series has an identical starting phase (of 0°), and each successively higher harmonic added to the series is progressively reduced in peak amplitude (relative to the peak amplitude of the fundamental) by a ratio of $1/N$, where N is equal to the number (1, 2, 3, 4, 5) of the harmonic. Finally, the peak amplitude of the original (sinusoidal) fundamental frequency will be slightly less than the peak amplitude of the composite periodic sawtooth waveform.

peak of the sawtooth wave represents a sum that is determined not only by the fundamental frequency, but also by the amplitudes of the higher harmonics (Rosen & Howell, 2013). However, to more fully understand why the composite peak amplitude is slightly greater than the peak amplitude of the original fundamental frequency sinusoid would require evoking the higher mathematics of the Fourier theorem, which is beyond the scope and intent of the present chapter.

Figure 6–15 panel A illustrates the effect on wave morphology of adding 10 additional discrete, harmonically related, in-phase, periodic sinusoidal (pure tones) to the original five harmonics in the same series that produced the composite periodic sawtooth-like waveform illustrated in Figure 6–14. By comparing the composite waveform

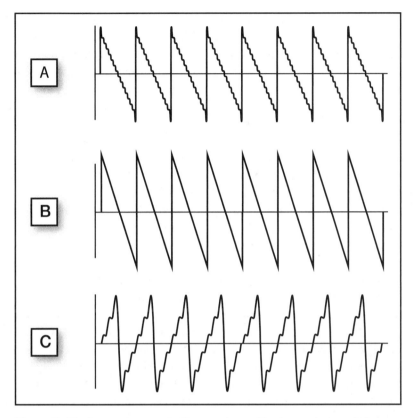

Figure 6–15. Sawtooth waves. **A.** Changes observed in the morphology of the composite waveform previously illustrated in Figure 6–14, resulting from the inclusion of 10 additional harmonic components to the existing series of five. The sharp, saw-like corners resembling teeth on the lagging edge of the waveform are caused by the 10 additional, rapidly cycling higher harmonic frequencies. **B.** An idealized sawtooth waveform hypothetically composed of nearly an infinite number of harmonic components. **C.** The "backward sawtooth" waveform morphology resulting from selectively changing the original starting phases of the (even-numbered) second and fourth harmonics shown in Figure 6–14, from 0° to 180°, and then recombining all five harmonic waveforms.

shown in Figure 6–14 with the composite waveform shown in Figure 6–15 panel A, it is obvious that the addition of more harmonic components changes the composite periodic waveform morphology to a shape that is less smooth. The sharp saw-like corners on the lagging edge of the waveform shown in Figure 6–15 panel A closely resemble teeth. The sharp corners on the teeth are caused by the 10 additional, rap-

idly cycling higher harmonic frequencies. Also, the composite periodic waveform shown in Figure 6–15 panel A, composed of a total of 15 harmonics, even more closely approximates the morphology of an idealized sawtooth wave shown in Figure 6–15 panel B, when compared to the composite waveform shown in Figure 6–14. The idealized sawtooth waveform illustrated in panel B of Figure 6–15 is hypothetically composed of nearly an infinite number of harmonic components. Note that the transition from the leading to the lagging edge in each wave of the complex periodic waveform shown in Figure 6–15 panel B is sharp and abrupt. In addition, the lagging edges of the idealized sawtooth waveform are smooth and straight. The sound of a sawtooth waveform has a harsh buzzing quality like the sound of a security buzzer that when activated by a tenant, unlocks the main entrance to an apartment complex. Finally, Figure 6–15 panel C illustrates the effect of selectively altering the starting phase of just two of the five harmonic components presented in Figure 6–14. The *backward sawtooth* morphology shown in Figure 6–15 panel C results from changing the starting phases of the (even-numbered) second and fourth harmonics in Figure 6–14 from the original 0°, to 180°, and then recombining all five harmonics.

In conclusion, it should be noted that the morphology of a sawtooth waveform can be dramatically altered if the phase or amplitude of any one of the separate component waveforms in the series is modified. Alterations in the composite sawtooth waveform would be apparent if, for instance, the phase of the fundamental frequency in Figure 6–14 were to be changed from 0° to 90°, or if just one successively higher harmonic added to the series were not progressively reduced in peak amplitude by a ratio of $1/N$. However, in either instance, the periodicity of the complex composite waveform would still match that of the fundamental frequency. Even if the waveform representing the fundamental frequency in Figure 6–14 were to be omitted from the series, such that only the waveforms that represent har-

monics 2 through 5 were again combined, the resulting complex composite periodic waveform would still have the same repetition rate (frequency and period) as the *missing fundamental*. If a composite complex periodic signal were composed of only 1000, 1200, and 1400 Hz, a psychological perception of pitch would be perceived by a listener which would correspond to a frequency of 200 Hz. Clearly, 200 Hz is not contained within the composite spectrum of these three frequencies, it is in fact missing. However, all three frequencies are harmonics of 200 Hz and in this particular example they represent the fifth, sixth, and the seventh harmonic of 200 Hz. The perception of the missing fundamental frequency is a complex phenomenon that has been called by many names, such as *residue, periodicity pitch,* and *virtual pitch* (Moore, 2012). Pitch is discussed in greater detail in Chapter 8.

Square Waves

The square wave is another example of a nonsinusoidal complex periodic waveform. When a series of pure tones consisting of a single (fundamental) frequency (f_0) and each of the odd integer whole number multiples of the fundamental (known as odd-numbered harmonics) are combined such that all frequency components in the series begin at the same starting phase (i.e., all are in phase) as illustrated in Figure 6–16, the composite complex periodic waveform will begin to approximate the morphology of a square wave. In the morphology of a square wave, the amplitude alternates at a steady frequency between a fixed minimum and a fixed maximum value. The duration of the minimum and maximum values is also

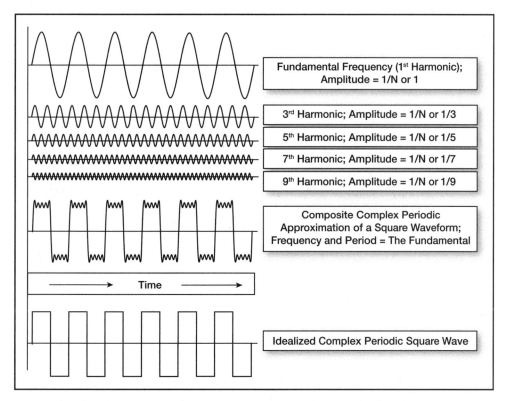

Figure 6–16. The square wave: By combining five odd harmonically related, in-phase, sinusoidal frequencies, a complex periodic waveform may be synthesized. For any given fundamental frequency (f_0), a composite waveform may be created by adding together sinusoidal waveforms representing integer odd-numbered multiples of f_0 (i.e., $1 \times f_0$, $3 \times f_0$, $5 \times f_0$, $7 \times f_0$, $9 \times f_0$) to generate a harmonic frequency series. The composite periodic wave that is synthesized has a repetition rate and period identical to the original fundamental frequency, and in this instance, the composite waveform closely approximates the idealized periodic and non-sinusoidal square waveform morphology, shown also at the bottom of the figure. Note that each of the five waveforms in the series has an identical starting phase (of 0°) and each successively higher harmonic added to the series is progressively reduced in peak amplitude (relative to the peak amplitude of the fundamental) by a ratio of $1/N$, where N is equal to the number (1, 3, 5, 7, 9) of each of the odd harmonics.

fixed, while the transition between minimum to maximum is instantaneous for the ideal square wave (Speaks, 1999). As with the sawtooth wave described above, the synthesis of a square wave also requires that the starting phases of all the waveform components be identical, independent of which starting phase is initially chosen. How many discrete, odd harmonically related, in-phase, periodic sinusoidal (pure tones) must be added together in order to achieve the precise morphology of a square wave? Again, the answer is close to an infinite number. However, a fairly good approximation to a square wave can be attained using a far fewer number of harmonics. Figure 6–16 illustrates that for any given hypothetical fundamental frequency of interest (f_0), five odd harmonically related, in-phase, sinusoidal waveforms may be combined to closely approximate a square wave. By adding together waveforms that represent odd integer whole numbered multiple frequencies of the f_0 (i.e., $1 \times f_0 + 3 \times f_0 + 5 \times f_0 + 7 \times f_0 + 9 \times f_0$), a harmonic frequency series may again be generated. All the waveforms shown in the figure have identical starting phases (of $0°$) and each successively higher harmonic added to the series is progressively reduced in peak amplitude (relative to the amplitude of the fundamental) by a ratio of $1/N$. The N in this case is equal to a particular odd harmonic number (1, 3, 5, 7, 9); therefore, the rate of decline in the peak amplitude of each added harmonic in the series is proportional to the inverse of each odd-numbered harmonic. As anticipated, the composite periodic waveform synthesized will have a repetition rate and period identical to the original fundamental frequency. In this instance, the composite wave shown in Figure 6–16 closely approximates the ideal square waveform morphology. An ideal square wave is also presented below the composite waveform of Figure 6–16. Square waves have a hollow, buzzing quality like the distortion created by an electric guitar amplifier, similar in some respects to the sound of a sawtooth wave, but higher in pitch due to the inclusion of even higher (though odd-numbered) harmonic frequencies.

Triangular Waves

Still another example of a nonsinusoidal complex periodic waveform is the triangular wave. As with the square wave described above, the triangular wave is composed of odd-numbered harmonic frequencies. A series of pure tones consisting of a single (fundamental) frequency (f_0) and each of the odd integer whole number multiples of the fundamental (odd-numbered harmonics) may again be combined such that all frequency components in the series are in phase. However, the composite complex periodic waveform will, very rapidly, approximate the waveform morphology of a triangular wave provided that each successively higher harmonic added to the series is progressively reduced in amplitude (relative to the peak amplitude of the fundamental) by a ratio of $1/N^2$, as illustrated in Figure 6–17. The N^2 is equal (in number) to the particular odd harmonic that is squared (1^2, 3^2, 5^2, 7^2, 9^2), and therefore, the rate of decline in the amplitude of each added harmonic in the series is proportional to the squared inverse of each odd-numbered harmonic. It should be obvious that even though both the square and triangular waves are composed of the same odd-numbered harmonic frequencies, the amplitudes of the odd harmonic frequencies that generate the triangular wave progressively decrease at a much higher rate, compared to those that make up the square wave. As in the synthesis of the sawtooth and the square waves described above, the synthesis of a triangular wave also requires that the starting phases of all the waveform components be identical, independent of which starting phase is initially chosen. A good approximation to an ideal triangular wave is attained using as few as five odd-numbered harmonics. As illustrated in Figure 6–17, for any given fundamental frequency of interest (f_0), harmonically related, in-phase, sinusoidal waveforms may be combined to synthesize a triangular wave. By adding together waveforms that represent integer odd-numbered multiple frequencies of the f_0 (i.e., $1 \times f_0 + 3 \times f_0 + 5 \times f_0 + 7 \times$

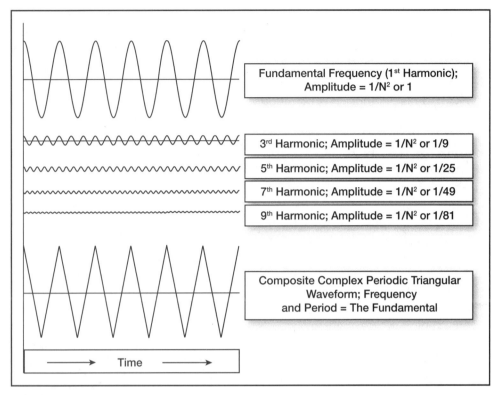

Figure 6–17. The triangular wave: By combining five odd harmonically related, in-phase, sinusoidal frequencies, a complex periodic waveform may be synthesized. For any given fundamental frequency (f_0), a composite waveform may be created by adding together sinusoidal waveforms representing integer odd numbered multiples of f_0 (i.e., $1 \times f_0$, $3 \times f_0$, $5 \times f_0$, $7 \times f_0$, $9 \times f_0$), to generate a harmonic frequency series. The composite periodic wave that is synthesized has a repetition rate and period identical to the original fundamental frequency. Note that each the five waveforms in the series has an identical starting phase (of 90°). Each successively higher harmonic added to the series is progressively and dramatically reduced in amplitude (relative to the peak amplitude of the fundamental) by a ratio of $1/N^2$, where N^2 is equal to the number (1^2, 3^2, 5^2, 7^2, 9^2) of each odd harmonic squared. Because of the dramatic decline in the peak amplitude of each added odd harmonic, the composite waveform composed of only five harmonics will very closely resemble the idealized periodic (nonsinusoidal) triangular waveform morphology.

$f_0 + 9 \times f_0$), a harmonic frequency series is again generated. As illustrated, all the waveforms in this example have identical starting phases (of 90°). As anticipated, the composite periodic triangular waveform that is synthesized will have a repetition rate and period identical to the original fundamental frequency. Triangular waves can be described as producing a somewhat distorted complex, but almost tonal sound.

Types of Sounds II: (Complex) Aperiodic Waveforms

Complex waveforms may also be aperiodic (not periodic). An aperiodic waveform is one whose waveform morphology shows no indication of periodicity over time. That is, complex aperiodic waveforms are without repeating waveform cycles across measurably regular intervals of time, since they lack a well-defined fundamental frequency and/or fundamental period. Instead, complex aperiodic waveforms often exhibit random and unpredictable (versus regular) variations in their instantaneous amplitudes or transient but predictable variations in their overall waveform morphology. Recall that most environmental sounds are complex, often composed of combinations of numerous, separate frequency components. Many of these complex environmental sounds are also aperiodic. Complex aperiodic waveforms may be generated by combinations of other aperiodic signals, or by random combinations of signals, each differing in frequency, amplitude, and phase. They may also be generated in less obvious ways. Complex aperiodic signals will generally fall into two categories. These categories are *transient signals* and *continuous signals*. It is again important to note that an instantaneous amplitude (or magnitude) usually refers to signal amplitude measured as a function of time (Speaks, 1999).

(Complex) Aperiodic Transient Signals

As the name implies, transient aperiodic signals are short, brief, and limited in their duration across regular intervals of time. Their amplitude spectra, however, are continuous, such that they contain many frequencies that occur along a continuum of frequencies and within certain specified limits. Because the amplitude spectra of transients resembles the continuous amplitude spectra that define complex random aperiodic signals having much longer (continuous) durations, transients, too, are clas-

sified as complex signals. Because transient signals have finite durations, they are also classified as predictable (versus random). The sound of a single hand clap is one example of a transient aperiodic signal. Transient bursts of sound are also commonly used for purposes of communication. This is especially true for the voiceless consonant speech sounds /p/, /t/, and /k/. The waveforms that define these bursts of sound last for only a brief period of time and are nonrepeating. However, voiceless consonant bursts like /s/ and /ʃ/ are transient signals as long as their durations are short. If these unvoiced sibilant fricatives are sustained over a significant duration of time, these utterances would correspond to a continuous aperiodic type of signal, or simply, to what would be defined as a noise. Recall the waveform morphology of the complex aperiodic signal illustrated in Chapter 5 for the unvoiced (sibilant fricative) consonant "shhhh" /ʃ/ in Figure 5–10D.

Broadband Acoustic Clicks

Broadband acoustic clicks are a good example of complex transient aperiodic signals. Broadband acoustic clicks are produced by driving a microphone or headphone transducer with a direct current (dc) pulse (rectangular pulse) that is rapidly and abruptly switched on, and then rapidly and abruptly switched off, as illustrated in Figure 6–18 panel A and Figure 6–19 panel A. When a waveform is presented in terms of its instantaneous amplitude (or amplitude variation) as a function of time, it is said to be described in the *time domain* and the description is often called a *time analysis*. The waveforms presented in Figure 6–18 panel A and Figure 6–19 panel A

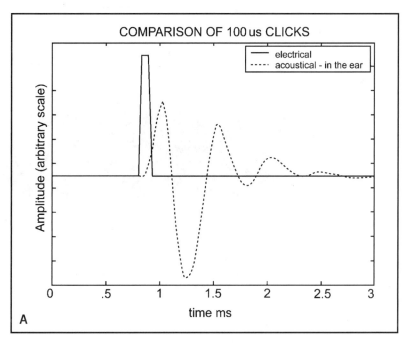

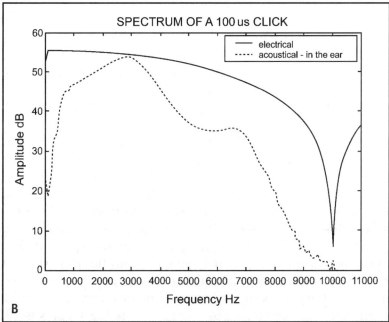

Figure 6–18. Production of an acoustic broadband (compression) click by driving a headphone transducer using a positive polarity, rectangular direct current (dc) pulse that is 100 μs in duration. **A.** Time analysis of both the dc driving pulse (*solid line*) and the acoustic (impulse) response (click) of the transducer (*dashed line*). Note also the "ringing." **B.** Energy spectra (using a linear scale) of the dc pulse (*solid line*) and the acoustic response of the transducer (*dashed line*) to the dc pulse (the acoustic click). From S. Silman and M. B. Emmer (2012), with permission.

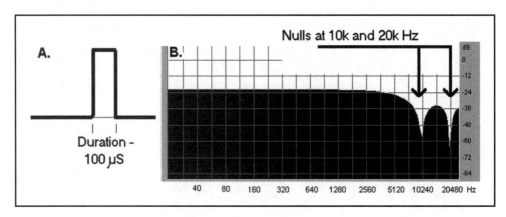

Figure 6–19. A positive polarity, rectangular direct current (dc) pulse that is 100 μs in duration, and used for the production of an acoustic broadband (compression) click. **A.** Time analysis of the 100 μsecond rectangular dc driving pulse. **B.** Energy spectrum of the dc pulse illustrating a continuous (flat) spectrum out to 10 kHz (using a log scale), with spectral nulls at 10 kHz and 20kHz. From T. A. Hamill and L. L. Price (2014), with permission.

are examples of waveforms presented in the time domain. The acoustic click that is generated is referred to as an *impulse response* of the transducer (Hamill & Price, 2014). Therefore, the rectangular dc pulse is a type of impulse signal and the process of abruptly switching the dc pulse on and off is called *gating*. Each rectangular dc pulse has an instantaneous onset and an instantaneous offset, and an overall of duration of only 100 μs. In addition, the polarity (positive or negative) of the dc pulse will directly affect the starting phase of the broadband acoustic click. A starting phase of 0° is associated with a compression click, and a starting phase of 180° is associated with a rarefaction click. In general, a positive polarity dc pulse generates a compression click (Figures 6–18 panel A, 6–19 panel A, and 6–20 panel A), and a negative polarity dc pulse generates a rarefaction click (not shown). The spectrum of the rectangular dc pulse is not, however, affected by polarity (Durrant & Feth, 2013).

The electrical spectra for two 100-μs rectangular dc pulses are illustrated in Figures 6–18 panel B and 6–19 panel B. As shown in the figures, both dc pulses exhibit broad frequency (i.e., broadband) spectra that are continuous and relatively flat. As indicated above, the spectrum of the dc pulse appears to resemble the continuous spectra that define random (aperiodic and continuous) signals that are classified as noise (Durrant & Feth, 2013). However, the amplitude spectra for the 100-μs rectangular dc pulses shown in Figures 6–18 panel B and 6–19 panel B, are only continuous and flat from 0 to 10,000 Hz. At approximately 10,000 Hz there is an obvious loss in spectral energy, as illustrated in Figures 6–18 panel B and 6–19 panel B. The frequency locations where energy drops off in what would otherwise appear to be continuous and flat spectrum are seen as a series of divots that are referred to as *spectral nulls* (Figure 6–19 panel B). Recall from the sections above that the term *bandwidth*, signified by Δ*f* usu-

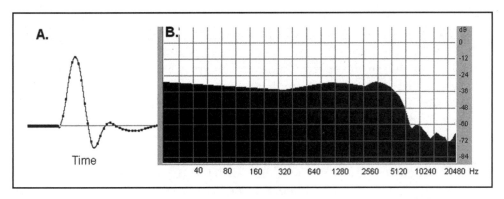

Figure 6–20. An acoustic broadband (compression) click produced by driving a headphone transducer with a positive polarity, rectangular direct current (dc) pulse that is 100 μs in duration. **A.** Time analysis of the acoustic (impulse) response (acoustic click) of the transducer. **B.** Energy spectrum of the transducer's response to the acoustic click (using a log scale) shown in A. Note the "ringing." From T. A. Hamill and L. L. Price (2014), with permission.

ally refers to the width or the range, in whole numbered integers, of separate frequencies (or frequency components) that are either recognized, or passed by a filtering device (e.g., a filter). The initial band of frequencies (from 0 to 10,000 Hz) or the frequency region that begins with the onset of the rectangular dc pulse and ends at the first spectral null will contain most (about 90%) of the total energy in the signal (Rosen & Howell, 2013). This initial bandwidth of frequencies (Δf), or the distance from 0 Hz to the first spectral null is determined by, and is therefore equal to, the reciprocal of the duration (1/duration or $1/D$) of the dc pulse.

Recall that the duration of the rectangular dc pulse is 100 μs. The pulse duration represents time and time corresponds to period. While many sources use 1/D to signify the reciprocal of the duration, and $1/T$ is often used in reference to period, for simplicity, in the present context, $1/T$ should be taken to mean the same as $1/D$, or the reciprocal of the duration of the signal. Hence, the first spectral null should occur at a

frequency that corresponds to 1/duration or to a period of $1/T$, which will also define the bandwidth (Δf) of the initial band of frequencies, or the "main (central) lobe" (Durrant & Feth, 2013), such that $\Delta f = 1000 \div T$ (in ms). A period of 100 μs is equivalent to a period of 0.1 ms. Recall from Chapter 5 that if the period (T) is known, and frequency (f) is unknown, then

$$1000 \div T \text{ (in ms)} = f \qquad (5\text{-}1)$$

Therefore, using a dc pulse duration of 100 μs, $1000 \div 0.1 = 10,000$ Hz. Indeed, 10,000 Hz is where the first spectral null occurs, as illustrated in Figures 6–18B and 6–19B.

Additional higher frequency spectral nulls will arise at integer multiples of the reciprocal of the duration of the dc pulse, or essentially at harmonic frequencies of the first spectral null. The second spectral null (or second harmonic of the first null) can be seen at 20,000 Hz in the dc pulse spectrum illustrated in Figure 6–19B. The region between each spectral null is called a *side lobe* or a *side band*, and each side lobe (band) has spectral energy. The side lobes are the bumps or hills that are located between the spectral nulls (Durrant & Feth, 2013). Note here that each of the side lobes (and the subsequent spectral nulls) fall to the right (only) of the main lobe. Furthermore, note that the reciprocal of the duration of the rectangular dc pulse (1/duration or $1/T$) defines not only the frequency location for each spectral null, but also defines the bandwidth (Δf) of the main lobe and the bandwidths (Δfs) of each of the subsequent side lobes. Therefore, the bandwidth (Δf) of each subsequent side lobe that follows the initial spectral null will also be equal in spectral content (the number of frequencies) to 1/duration or $1/T$ such that $\Delta f = 1000 \div T$ (in ms).

Because most of the energy in the rectangular dc pulse signal is concentrated within the initial band of frequencies (from 0 to 10,000 Hz) that defines the main lobe, the amplitudes of subsequent side lobes to the right of the main lobe will progressively diminish over time as the energy within these lobes also diminishes. Theoretically, an *ideal impulse* is one in which the bandwidth (Δf) of the main spectral lobe is infinite, and therefore, one in which no side lobes exist (Durrant & Feth, 2013). In general, since the duration of the dc pulse and the bandwidth of the main spectral lobe are inversely related, shortening the duration of the dc pulse will increase the bandwidth of the main spectral lobe. For instance, shortening the duration of the dc pulse from 100 to 50 μs would cause the first spectral null and all subsequent nulls to appear at higher frequencies. This would serve to increase the bandwidth of the main

lobe and the bandwidths of each subsequent spectral lobe as the spectral energy spreads to higher frequencies. As before, for a dc pulse of 50 μs, the first spectral null will occur at a frequency that corresponds the reciprocal of the pulse duration (1/duration) or to a period of $1/T$, which will also define the bandwidth (Δf) of the main lobe, such that $\Delta f = 1000 \div T$ (in ms). A period of 50 μs is equivalent to a period of 0.05 ms; therefore, again using Equation 5–1,

$$1000 \div T \text{ (in ms)} = f; \text{ and}$$
$$1000 \div 0.05 = 20000 \text{ Hz} \qquad (5\text{–}1)$$

For a dc pulse that is 50 μs in duration, the first spectral null would appear at 20000 Hz, and the bandwidth (Δf) of the main lobe would of course also extend to about 20000 Hz. Theoretically then, if the duration of the dc pulse were infinitely short, the bandwidth of the main lobe would be infinite, the spectrum would be continuous and perfectly flat, and the result would be the production of an ideal impulse (Durrant & Feth, 2013). However, since the magnitude of the rectangular dc pulse (or any signal) is proportional to its duration, the main lobe would be composed of very little, if any, energy.

Transducer Limitations

Finally, the accurate delivery of acoustic clicks is limited by the less than ideal mechanical properties of most earphone or headphone transducers. As indicated in the sections above, any device that transforms or converts energy from one form to another is called a transducer (Hirsh, 1952) and earphones as well as headphones are electronic devices that transduce electrical signals into the acoustical energy of sound waves. Conventional headphones and earphones are designed much like dynamic microphones, with an induction coil and permanent magnet, but they work in exactly the reverse functional manner. Like a microphone, the most important component found within an earphone or headphone is the thin, fixed sheet of resonating material called the diaphragm, and the diaphragm mechanism or assembly. The electromagnetic mechanism (coil and magnetic armature) in the earphone or headphone will respond to a rapidly gated, impulsive positive electrical dc pulse by abruptly and impulsively pushing the diaphragm assembly in an outward direction. This outward mechanical movement of the diaphragm assembly creates a disturbance in particle or pressure displacement and produces a longitudinal wave front of compression.

The diaphragm (and other mechanical parts of the transduction assembly), of course, has a small degree of mass. Because the diaphragm assembly has mass, it will also have a certain though very small degree of inertia that must be overcome before it can be set into motion, according to Newton's first law of motion (see Chapter 4). Once the inertial force has been overcome by an electrical force, the diaphragm assembly begins to move. Recall as well from Chapter 4 that momentum means inertia in motion and that an object that is set into motion not only has kinetic energy, it also has the force of momentum. It was also stated that kinetic energy is stored in the motion of an object, due to its mass. Inertia will therefore cause the diaphragm assembly to continue to move following the abrupt cessation of the dc pulse,

causing the diaphragm to overshoot its intended degree of outward displacement (Hamill & Price, 2014). Recall as well from Chapter 4 that elasticity is a property of matter that allows an object (mass) to alter its shape and to store potential energy when an external force has been applied. The diaphragm assembly also has a degree of elasticity, and the mechanical force that is applied originates from the electrical energy of the dc pulse. Because the diaphragm assembly has been displaced or even slightly deformed, it will also possess a certain degree of potential energy (as a result of its elasticity), stored in the form of a restorative force. According to Hooke's law (see Chapter 3) and Newton's third law of motion (see Chapter 4), the restorative force of elasticity also resists displacement. When the diaphragm assembly stops moving, inertia must again be overcome before the restorative force of elasticity (elastic recoil) can again draw the diaphragm inward for the rarefaction phase of the cycle. Once (inward) motion is restored, inertia will again cause the diaphragm to overshoot its resting state of equilibrium. Therefore, overshoots occur in both directions as a result of rapidly gating the dc pulse signal. Overshoots are commonly referred to as headphone or earphone "ringing" (Hamill & Price, 2014) and can continue for a few cycles following the termination of the click stimulus (see Figures 6–18A and 6–20B). The presentation of broadband clicks is also limited by the inefficient band-pass filtering characteristics of earphone or headphone transducers that are used for their delivery (Durrant & Feth, 2013). This can be seen in Figure 6–18B comparing the energy spectra of the dc pulse (solid line) with the acoustic response (acoustic click) power spectra of the transducer (dashed line) using a linear measurement scale. Filters and filtering characteristics are discussed in the sections that follow. Such filtering also represents a form of linear distortion discussed much later in this chapter.

Narrow-Band Acoustic Tone Bursts

Other examples of complex transient aperiodic signals are those consisting of a narrow rather than a broad frequency spectrum. When a continuous sinusoidal signal (a pure tone) is gated, the result is a tone burst. The tone burst is one of the most frequently employed types of stimuli in hearing science and is generally used with the intent of concentrating the energy of a signal at a specific frequency, and at a discrete moment in time (Durrant & Feth, 2013). The tone burst is an attempt at a compromise between a signal with an infinitely short duration (a dc impulse), having an infinitely wide spectrum, and a signal with an infinitely long duration having an infinitely narrow frequency spectrum, such as a sinusoid (pure tone). The electrical spectrum of a 2000-Hz pure tone is presented in Figure 6–21. In the design and implementation of electrophysiological tests of hearing that help to neurologically evaluate the human auditory system in terms of its function, the seemingly impossible aim has been to design a frequency-specific signal having an infinitely short duration and an infinitely narrow frequency spectrum that is pure, discrete, and free of unwanted distortion. The objective has been to implement the use of an impulsive (instantaneous onset and offset) auditory stimulus, like a click,

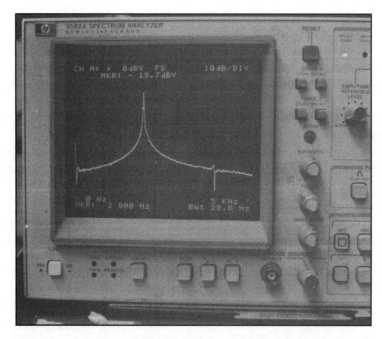

Figure 6–21. Electrical spectrum for a 2000-Hz pure tone visualized on a real-time spectrum analyzer. From S. Silman and M. B. Emmer (2012), with permission.

but unlike the broadband characteristics of a click, one that is also pure and frequency specific. When sinusoids are gated, the sinusoidal frequency of interest is often referred to as the center frequency (CF), or even the carrier frequency (Durrant & Feth, 2013).

The abrupt gating of a particular sinusoidal frequency to 100 ms in duration, for example, results in a frequency spectrum that is still fairly narrow (Figure 6–22). Most of the energy is concentrated within the main lobe, but the main lobe is now symmetrically shaped with the CF that forms its peak (see Figure 6–22). Unlike the flat spectrum of the main lobe described above for the rectangular (100 μs) dc pulse, where the maximum of energy began at 0 Hz and extended (rightward) to the first spectral null at period $1/T$ (10000 Hz), the maximum energy in the amplitude of a gated sinusoid will be concentrated within a symmetrically shaped main lobe, defined at its peak by the CF, and bounded above (to the right) by a higher-in-frequency, first spectral null, and below (to the left) by a lower-in-frequency, first spectral null. The higher and lower first spectral nulls occur on either side of the CF. Beyond each of these first spectral nulls that laterally define the main lobe, additional spectral nulls continue to occur above and below (on either side of) the main lobe. These additional spectral nulls define

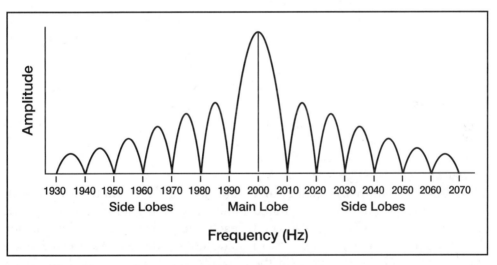

Figure 6–22. An energy spectrum for a gated 2000-Hz sinusoid with a duration of 100 ms. The main (central) lobe is defined by a 2000-Hz peak, center frequency (CF) that is bounded by a higher and by a lower-in-frequency, first spectral null. The bandwidth from the CF to either one of the first spectral nulls is defined by the inverse of the signal duration ($1/T$) or 10 Hz. Therefore, the main lobe, with its 2000-Hz (CF) peak is bounded by a higher-in-frequency first spectral null $CF + f$ (2010 Hz), and by a lower-in-frequency first spectral null $CF - f$ (1990 Hz). Hence, the main lobe has a total spectral bandwidth (Δf) of (2010 to 1990 Hz) or 20 Hz. The bandwidth (Δf) of each individual side lobe (side band) is also equal to 10 Hz. Spectral nulls located to the right of the main lobe occur at higher frequencies, at evenly spaced increments of 10 Hz, or at $[CF + f] + \Delta f + \Delta f + \Delta f \ldots$, and so forth. Spectral nulls located to the left of the main lobe occur at lower frequencies, at evenly spaced decrements of 10 Hz, or at $[CF - f] - \Delta f - \Delta f - \Delta f \ldots$, and so forth. The side bands represent unintended spectral energy, often referred to as "spectral splatter." Spectral splatter represents unwanted distortion and compromises the spectral purity of the desired CF signal.

the boundaries and bandwidths (Δfs) of the (left and right) side lobes. The remaining spectral energy not found in the main lobe will spread into the side lobes, downward in frequency (to the left of the main lobe), to 0 Hz, and infinitely upward in frequency (to the right of the main lobe), as illustrated in Figure 6–22. The amplitudes of the subsequent lower-in-frequency and higher-in-frequency side lobes progressively diminish over time as the energy within these lobes also diminishes. In sum, the net effect of abruptly gating a sinusoid is the creation of a high-energy main lobe, having a peak amplitude at the CF, and flanked on both of its sides by a series of diminishing (in energy) side lobes (Durrant & Feth, 2013). The downward (in frequency) and upward (in frequency) spread of unintended spectral energy within the side lobes, resulting from the abrupt gating of a sinusoid, is often referred to as *spectral splatter*. Spectral splatter represents unwanted distortion and compromises the spectral purity of the desired CF signal.

The bandwidth (Δf) of the main lobe as well as the bandwidths (Δfs) of each of the successive upper frequency and lower frequency side lobes illustrated in Figure 6–22 are once again related to the frequency that corresponds to the reciprocal of the duration (in the present example, 100 ms) of the gated sinusoid (1/duration or 1/T). With a (duration) period of 100 ms, again recall Equation 5–1 from Chapter 5:

If the period (T) is known, and frequency (f) is unknown, then

$$1000 \div T \text{ (in msec.)} = f \quad (5\text{–}1)$$

$$1000 \div 100 = 10 \text{ Hz}$$

Since the main lobe is bounded by both a higher-in-frequency first spectral null and a lower-in-frequency first spectral null, the bandwidth from the center frequency to either of these two, first spectral nulls will again be defined by 1/T or 10 Hz where $\Delta f = 1000 \div T$ (in ms). For any gated sinusoid used as a CF, the higher-in-frequency first spectral null is defined as

$$CF + 1000 \div T \text{ (in ms)} = CF + f$$
$$(6\text{–}17\text{A})$$

whereas the lower-in-frequency first spectral null is defined as

$$CF - 1000 \div T \text{ (in ms)} = CF - f$$
$$(6\text{–}17\text{B})$$

and the total spectral bandwidth (Δf) of the main (central) lobe will be determined by

$$\Delta f = [CF + 1000 \div T \text{ (in ms)}] -$$
$$[CF - 1000 \div T \text{ (in ms)}]$$
$$(6\text{–}17\text{C})$$

or $\quad \Delta f = [CF + f] - [CF - f]$

Furthermore, the bandwidths of each successively higher-in-frequency and each successively lower-in-frequency side lobes (side bands) are also defined by 1/T, where each bandwidth (Δf) = $1000 \div T$ (in ms). For a gated sinusoid that is 100 ms in duration, the bandwidth (Δf) between spectral nulls is equal to 10 Hz. Hence, starting from the higher-in-frequency first spectral null, or at $CF + f$, additional spectral nulls and additional side lobe bands (located to the right of the main lobe) occur at higher frequencies, at evenly spaced increments of 10 Hz, or at [$CF + f$] + Δf + Δf + Δf . . . , and so forth.

Similarly, starting from the lower-in-frequency first spectral null, or at $CF - f$, additional spectral nulls and additional side lobe bands (located to the left of the main lobe) occur at lower frequencies, at evenly spaced decrements of 10 Hz, or at $[CF - f] - \Delta f - \Delta f - \Delta f \ldots$, and so forth.

As an example, let us take a continuous 2000-Hz signal such as the one shown in Figure 6–21 and shorten its duration to 100 ms. As illustrated in Figure 6–22, most of the spectral energy is concentrated within the main lobe with its center frequency (CF) of 2000 Hz. The bandwidth (Δf) of the main lobe as well as the bandwidths (Δfs) of each of the successive upper frequency and lower frequency side lobes are, as indicated above, related to the frequency that corresponds to the reciprocal of the duration of the gated sinusoid (1/duration or $1/T$). Recalling Equation 5–1 once again from Chapter 5,

$$1000 \div T \,(\text{in ms}) = f = 10 \text{ Hz}$$
$$(5\text{–}1)$$

The main lobe is bounded by both a higher-in-frequency first spectral null and a lower-in-frequency first spectral null, and the bandwidth from the CF to either of these two, first spectral nulls is defined by $1/T$, or 10 Hz where $\Delta f = 1000 \div T \,(\text{in ms})$. Using Equation 6–17A, it becomes clear that the higher-in-frequency first spectral null, defined as

$$CF + f, \text{ is equal to}$$
$$2000 \text{ Hz} + 10 \text{ Hz},$$
which is equal to 2010 Hz.

Using Equation 6–17B, it also becomes clear that the lower-in-frequency first spectral null, defined as

$$CF - f, \text{ is equal to}$$
$$2000 \text{ Hz} - 10 \text{ Hz},$$
which is equal to 1990 Hz.

Therefore, using Equation 6–17C, the total spectral bandwidth (Δf) of the main lobe, defined as

$$\Delta f = [CF + f] - [CF - f], \text{ is equal to}$$
$$2010 \text{ Hz} - 1990 \text{ Hz},$$
which is equal to 20 Hz.

Finally, beginning with $[CF + f]$ or (2010 Hz), the bandwidth (Δf) between additional spectral nulls (or the Δf for each side lobe) located to the right of the main lobe, occur at evenly spaced increments of 10 Hz where [2010 Hz + ($\Delta f + \Delta f + \Delta f \ldots$ etc.)] is equal to 2020, 2030, 2040 Hz . . . , and so forth. Likewise, starting from the lower-in-frequency first spectral null $[CF - f]$ or (1990 Hz), the bandwidth (Δf) between additional spectral nulls (or the Δf for each side lobe) located to the left of the main lobe, occur at evenly spaced decrements of 10 Hz where [1990 Hz – ($\Delta f - \Delta f - \Delta f \ldots$ etc.)] is equal to 1980, 1970, 1960 . . . , and so forth, as illustrated in Figure 6–22.

It should be apparent that the side lobes and spectral nulls produced by a gated sinusoid follow a pattern that is similar but not identical to the spectral pattern observed from a single rectangular dc pulse. As previously indicated, rapidly and abruptly switching on, and then rapidly and abruptly switching off an acoustic (CF) signal is called gating, and abruptly gating a sinusoid to produce a tone burst causes energy to be spread into the side lobe frequencies, located above and below the CF. This abrupt initiating and terminating of a signal (instantaneous onset followed by an instantaneous offset) in the course of generating a transient signal produces *transient distortion* (Speaks, 1999). Transient distortion takes the form of spectral splatter, and this unintended spectral energy is, once again, carried in the side band frequencies. Bear in mind that spectral splatter not only represents unwanted distortion, but also compromises the spectral purity of the desired *CF* signal. Consider as well that the bandwidths (Δfs) of the main spectral lobe and each of the side lobes of the tone burst are inversely related to the duration of the gated sinusoid. Shortening the signal duration of the gated sinusoid in an attempt to achieve a more temporally discrete frequency spectrum will only serve to increase the bandwidth of the main spectral lobe, as well as the bandwidths of each of the side lobes (Durrant & Feth, 2013). For instance, shortening the duration of the gated sinusoid to 50 ms results in a main lobe spectral bandwidth of 40 Hz, and side bands, each with bandwidths of 20 Hz. Shortening to 25 ms results in a main lobe spectral bandwidth of 80 Hz, and side bands, each with bandwidths of 40 Hz. Shortening to 5 ms results in a main lobe spectral bandwidth of 400 Hz and side bands, each with bandwidths of 200 Hz, and shortening the duration of the gated sinusoid to 2 ms results in a main lobe spectral bandwidth of 1000 Hz, and side bands, each with bandwidths of 500 Hz. Unfortunately, then, a shortening of the signal duration only results in the occurrence of an even broader degree of spectral splatter (transient distortion) that is generated in the frequency domain (Durrant & Feth, 2013).

From the preceding section, it would seem that spectral splatter might be sig-nificantly reduced by simply increasing the duration of the gated sinusoid. Narrowing the bandwidths of the side lobes can reduce spectral splatter and may even serve to concentrate more spectral energy within the main lobe. However, the overall tonal quality of the tone burst will still be compromised due to the transient distortion produced by the abrupt gating of the signal (Speaks, 1999). Fortunately, the amount of transient distortion in the delivery of an acoustic signal, such as a gated sinusoid, is not completely dependent on the overall signal duration. Transient distortion will also vary as a function of the time required for the signal to rise from zero amplitude to maximum amplitude and/or to decay from maximum amplitude to zero amplitude. By switching (gating) the tone on and off gradually, rather than abruptly, a considerable degree of spectral splatter (transient distortion) can be eliminated such that the overall frequency specific-ity and tonal quality of the tone burst is improved. For this reason, continuous audiometric pure tone signals used in pure tone audiometry are ramped such that the tones are gradually rather than abruptly switched (gated) on and off. Hence, a ramped signal is a gated sig-nal in which the onset duration or *rise-time*, and the offset duration or *fall-time* (also *decay-time*) portions of the signal (usually a tone) have been shaped and modified in the time domain. In general practice, standard rise/fall times (durations) for pure tone signals used in audiometric testing are never less than 20 ms (Speaks, 1999).

Figure 6–23 is presented in order to demonstrate what is meant by the ramping (gradual gating) of a sinusoidal signal. Ramping or tapering the

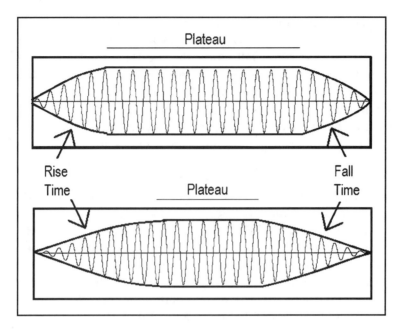

Figure 6–23. Two gated (ramped) sinusoidal amplitude envelopes for the same sinusoidal frequency are illustrated, with propagation cycles illustrated in the rise-time, fall-time, and plateau duration regions of each envelope. The ramping or tapering of a signal is also called windowing. The ramped signal depicted in the upper amplitude envelope has shorter rise/fall times when compared to the rise/fall times of the ramped signal depicted in the lower envelope and would, therefore, generate more spectral splatter. From T. A. Hamill and L. L. Price (2014), with permission.

onset and offset of a signal is also called *windowing*. The amplitude peaks of a ramped sinusoidal wave provide the outline structure for an amplitude *envelope*. Two such *amplitude envelopes* for the same pure tone frequency are illustrated in Figure 6–23. Each amplitude envelope includes a rise-time, a fall-time, and a *plateau duration* (Durrant & Feth, 2013). The plateau duration is the steady-state region of the envelope where the amplitude of the signal is maximum (Hamill & Price, 2014). When the rise/fall times are instantaneous (rise/fall times are zero) as in a rapidly gated (unramped) sinusoid, the overall signal duration is equal to the plateau duration. When measureable rise/fall times exist due to ramping, their shape as well as their durations will affect the spectral purity of the tone burst signal. In general, gradual and longer rise/fall time durations (ramping) will reduce or slow down the amount of spectral splatter found in the side lobes of the tone burst. Note in Figure 6–23 that the gated (ramped) signal depicted in the upper amplitude envelope has shorter rise/fall times when compared to the rise/fall times for the ramped signal depicted in the lower envelope. Therefore, the longer rise/fall times for the ramped signal represented by the lower amplitude envelope would generate less spectral splatter.

Variations in the amplitude envelope for a gated sinusoid are often described in the time domain, wherein rise/fall times and plateau durations are specified in milliseconds. However, it may be desirable to use variable rise/fall time and plateau durations that change as a function of changes in the sinusoidal frequency. In such cases, these signal parameters may be specified in advance in terms of cycles of propagation. As an example, tone burst parameters may be chosen that specify two cycle rise-times, two cycle fall-times, and plateau durations of one cycle (Hamill & Price, 2014). Therefore, a gated 500-Hz tone burst, which has a 2-ms/cycle period, would have rise/fall durations of 4 ms, and a plateau duration of 2 ms. A gated 1000-Hz tone burst, which has 1 ms/cycle period, would have rise/fall durations of 2 ms, and a plateau duration of 1 ms. Finally, a gated 2000-Hz tone burst, which has 0.5 ms/cycle period, would have rise/fall durations of 1 ms,

and a plateau duration of 0.5 ms. Figure 6–23 illustrates cycles of propagation in the rise/fall and plateau regions of the two amplitude envelopes illustrated for the same gated pure tone frequency. In Figure 6–24, a 2000-Hz tone burst with four cycle rise-times, four cycle fall-times, and a plateau duration of two cycles is shown. Therefore, the tone burst shown in Figure 6–24 has rise/fall durations of 2 ms and a plateau duration of 1 ms.

With sufficiently long rise/fall and plateau durations, the spectral characteristics of a tone burst may begin to quite closely resemble those of a continuous sinusoidal tone (Durrant & Feth, 2013). However, just lengthening the onset and the offset of the gated (ramped) sinusoid alone cannot completely eliminate transient distortion. Recall that when measureable rise/fall

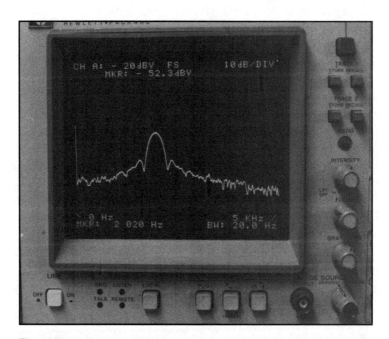

Figure 6–24. An electrical spectrum for a 2000-Hz tone burst with four-cycle rise and fall times (2 ms), and a two-cycle plateau (1 ms) duration. From S. Silman and M. B. Emmer (2012), with permission.

times exist due to ramping, their shape will also affect the spectral purity of the tone burst signal (Hamill & Price, 2014). The amount of spectral splatter occurring in the side lobes (side bands) can be appreciably reduced even further by manipulating the shape of the gating (ramping) function. As indicated above, ramping or tapering a signal to create various onset and offset durations is also called *windowing*, and amplitude envelopes for ramped sinusoids are often described as *windowing functions*. Figure 6–25 illustrates three ramped windowing functions that can be differentiated on the basis of the shapes of their amplitude envelopes. Shown also are the effects of each windowing function on the amplitude spectra of three tone burst signals. In general, linear windowing functions are the least preferred, as they result in the greatest degree of side band spectral splatter. The (linear) rectangular (boxcar window) windowing function provides essentially no ramping and results in the greatest degree of spectral splatter (not shown). However, some spectral splatter in the side bands can be reduced by the (linear) triangular windowing function, which is illustrated in Figure 6–25. Nonetheless, spectral purity is appreciably enhanced and side band spectral splatter is significantly reduced when the windowing functions are nonlinear (Hamill & Price, 2014). Curvilinear windowing functions include but are not limited to the Welch, the Parzen, the Hanning, the Hamming, and the Blackman. The Blackman windowing also has two hybrid functions: the Blackman-Harris and the Blackman-Nuttall. The envelope of the Welch windowing function is identical in many respects to the sine envelope (also called the cosine envelope) windowing

function. The sine envelope windowing function is also illustrated in Figure 6–25. As indicated, more of the spectral energy appears to be concentrated within the *CF* of the main lobe, whereas some of the side band spectral splatter closest to the main lobe also appears to have been reduced. Other curvilinear windowing functions like the Parzen, Hanning (or cosine squared), Hamming, and Blackman each have amplitude envelopes that are similar in shape, and each will reduce spectral splatter even more significantly than the Welsh (and sine wave) windowing functions. A considerable degree of spectral purity is achieved using a Blackman windowing function, as indicated in Figure 6–25. Furthermore, side band splatter is reduced appreciably, and spectral purity is enhanced significantly, though at the cost of a somewhat broader main (central) lobe (Durrant & Feth, 2013).

(Complex) Aperiodic Continuous Signals

Recall that complex aperiodic sounds often exhibit random, unpredictable, repeating variations in their instantaneous amplitudes. Most notably, they lack waveform cycles that repeat across measurably regular intervals of time because they lack a well-defined fundamental frequency and/or fundamental period. Continuous complex aperiodic sounds are often composed of a mix of many frequencies that bear no harmonic relationship with each another. Perceptually, the quality or subjective pleasantness of any complex sound will depend upon a number of properties, including the way in which sounds of differing frequencies fit together. That is,

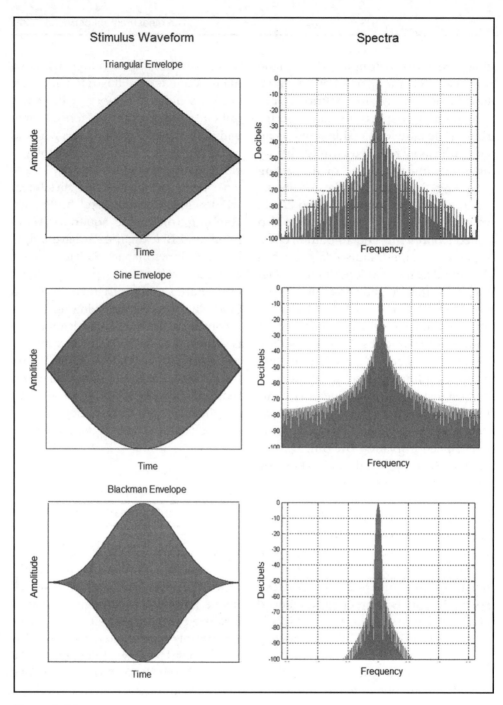

Figure 6–25. Three ramped windowing functions with different amplitude envelopes (*shown on the left*) and the effects of each windowing function on the amplitude spectra of three tone burst signals (*shown on the right*). The (linear) triangular (or Bartlett) windowing function (*shown at the top*) reduces some of the side band spectral splatter. The (curvilinear) sine envelope windowing function (*shown in the middle*) concentrates energy within the CF of the main lobe and reduces side band spectral splatter located close to the main lobe, which is an improvement in spectral purity relative to the linear function (*shown at the top*). The (curvilinear) Blackman windowing function (*shown at the bottom*) appreciably reduces side band spectral splatter with a considerable degree of improvement in spectral purity, relative to the linear and the sine envelope windowing functions. From T. A. Hamill and L. L. Price (2014), with permission.

we prefer listening to complex signals that contain frequency components, such as overtones, that are harmonically related in time (Moore, 2012). The simpler component tones within complex signals will blend together harmoniously, but only when they share a common fundamental frequency. When complex signals are composed of component tones that are simple integer ratios of each other, the term *consonance* is often used to describe the pleasant sound quality that results. When departures from simple integer ratio relations occur within the components of a complex signal, the result is a less pleasant and even harsh, discordant perception of the sound, a term often referred to as *dissonance*. Because complex aperiodic sounds lack harmonic structure, they also lack the pleasant tonal sound quality associated with the harmonic orderliness of complex periodic sounds. Complex periodic sounds include the resonances (or periodic vibration patterns) produced by string and wind musical instruments, as well as the human vocal tract resonances commonly known as the vowels of speech. The pleasant experience (consonance) of listening to the singing performance of a professional vocal artist is attributed to the skillful production by the vocalist of a variety of sustained vowels. One could hardly imagine the degree of dissonance generated, should the *vocal performance* be composed of the skillful production of a variety of sustained (complex aperiodic) consonants, such as sibilant fricatives, for instance. The discordant auditory experience resulting from the production of any sustained (continuous) complex aperiodic sound is often classified perceptually as noise.

Noise

Noise is often broadly defined as any unwanted or undesired sound stimulus. This broad psychological definition merely allows us to differentiate noise from a *signal*, whereby a signal typically has a higher probability of corresponding to a biologically important or biologically relevant stimulus. However, with such a broad definition, even a complex periodic sound that the listener deems annoying or irrelevant would be classified as noise. When complex waveforms lack regular, repeating cycles over regular intervals of time, the result is a noise. Therefore, noise may be defined simply as a complex aperiodic signal or sound, having instantaneous amplitudes that randomly vary over time (Yost, 2007).

White Noise

Perceptually, white noise has been described as a complex sound that has no distinctive pitch (Moore, 2012). Subjective dissonance, a term discussed in the above section, also results when a clear perception of pitch is not present. The perceptual phenomenon of the missing fundamental frequency, residue, periodicity pitch, or virtual pitch discussed earlier in this chapter illustrates that pitch processing often depends on the presence of harmonic ratios (Moore, 2012). White noise has also been likened to the hissing sound created by escaping steam (Hirsh, 1952), or the sound of an FM receiver that is not tuned to any station (Durrant & Feth, 2013).

White noise is the quintessential example of a random signal. It is usually composed of spectral energy that spans the entire audible frequency range, which in humans, extends from a lower frequency limit of 20 Hz to an upper frequency limit of 20 kHz. The name *white noise* is analogous to the white light that results when all the pure hues in the visible spectrum are combined, or added together. Just as white light results from a mixture of all of the visible frequencies (wavelengths) of light, white noise results from a mixture of all of the pure tone frequencies within the human audible spectrum (Hirsh, 1952). All of the possible starting phases for each of the separate frequency components are also randomly present in white noise. Consequently, because white noise contains the entire auditory spectrum of frequencies, white noise is also referred to as wide-band noise or, when passed through a headphone transducer, as broadband noise. The instantaneous amplitudes (and phases) of white noise vary randomly over time (they are randomly distributed), with a chance probability of occurrence that is normally distributed according to the "standard normal" (statistically

bell-shaped) Gaussian distribution. For this reason, white noise is additionally referred to as Gaussian noise. Statistically, the standard normal distribution is a theoretical distribution with a mean of zero. Accordingly, the mean instantaneous amplitude at any moment in time for white noise is also zero. As a result, Gaussian noise is predictable only in terms of its average (RMS) amplitude (Durant and Feth, 2013). Variations in the instantaneous amplitudes of white noise, shown as a function of time (time analysis) are presented in Figure 6–26. As illustrated, the instantaneous amplitudes of white noise fluctuate from moment to moment, in a completely random and unpredictable (aperiodic) manner.

White noise is random, continuous, and is therefore considered to have an infinitely long duration. While variations in the instantaneous amplitude of white noise are unpredictable at any given moment in time, the average RMS (amplitude) spectrum of a white noise waveform is highly predictable

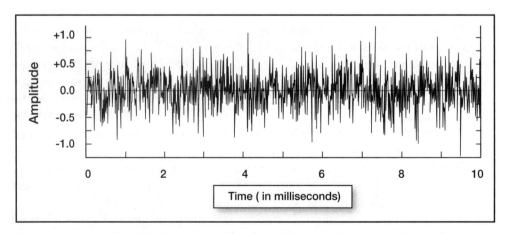

Figure 6–26. Time analysis (instantaneous amplitudes as a function of time) of white noise. White noise is also called Gaussian noise or wide-band noise.

over time. White noise exhibits equal amounts of energy (or equal amplitudes) at each frequency within its entire spectral bandwidth, or at each frequency within any specified bandwidth within the total range of frequencies that define its spectrum. Recall from the previous discussion of sound level meters (SLMs), that detailed and precise (amplitude by frequency) information may be obtained regarding the spectra of complex aperiodic signals, when employing an octave-band or a third-octave-band analysis. An octave or third-octave-band analysis of the total white noise spectrum would reveal equal amounts of energy per frequency, within each octave-band, or within each third-octave-band of frequencies.

The intensity of white noise is frequently described in terms of its "average noise energy (or power) per unit bandwidth," which is also more commonly referred to as the "spectrum level," "pressure (dB SPL) spectrum level" (Speaks, 1999), "power (dB IL) spectrum level," or as the "level-per-cycle (LPC)" of the noise (Yost, 2007). More precisely, the LPC actually refers to "level-per-cycle-per second," or simply the "level-per-frequency" of the noise (Durrant & Feth, 2013). The spectrum level (LPC) is a frequency by frequency type of analysis that is defined as the average energy level (in pressure or power) in a frequency band defined as a "unit bandwidth" of 1 Hz, and centered at some particular frequency. The LPC is often expressed (see below) in decibels (SPL or IL) and refers to the energy level (or average noise power) in any 1 Hz-wide frequency band, regardless of the frequency upon which the band is centered (Speaks, 1999). The names "spec-

tral density" (Rosen & Howell, 2013) or "energy density" (Moore, 2012) are yet additional terms that refer to the energy contained within the 1 Hz wide-band at a given frequency. Hence, any noise may be characterized by its "spectrum level as a function of frequency," but white noise has a spectrum level that does not vary with frequency (Moore, 2012). That is, all frequencies within the specified bandwidth are not only present, but they are present at the same average intensity. Hence, white noise has equal amounts of energy per cycle, which means the same as having equal amounts of energy per frequency.

The instantaneous amplitude of white noise is again presented as a function of time (time analysis) in the upper left panel A of Figure 6–27. Figure 6–27B (upper right panel) illustrates a pressure (or power) spectrum level (in decibels) for white noise. The spectrum level for the white noise illustrated in Figure 6–27B (upper right panel) is continuous and flat, and is similar to the spectrum illustrated for the dc pulse (transient) in Figure 6–19B. Because the spectrum level for the white noise is flat, the spectrum has a slope of zero. In general, the continuous and flat spectrum level of white noise becomes flat only when the signal is averaged over a long duration of time. Finally, like the transducer limitations previously discussed in the delivery of transient signals, an accurate delivery of the broad spectral bandwidth characteristics of white noise will also be limited by the less than ideal mechanical properties of most earphone, headphone or loudspeaker transducers. When this occurs, often the result is the production of a broadband noise.

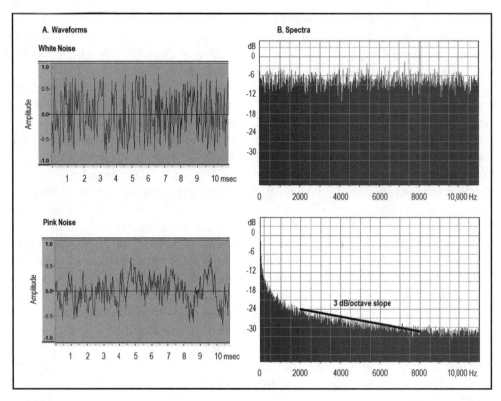

Figure 6–27. A. (*upper left*): Time analysis (instantaneous amplitudes as a function of time) of white noise. **B.** (*upper right*): Pressure (or power) spectrum level (in decibels) for white noise. The spectrum level is continuous and essentially flat. **A.** (*lower left*): Time analysis (instantaneous amplitudes as a function of time) of pink noise. **B.** (*lower right*): Pressure (or power) spectrum level (in decibels) for pink noise. The spectrum level is continuous but has a slope of –3 dB/octave. From T. A. Hamill and L. L. Price (2014), with permission.

Broadband Noise

Broadband noise is white noise that has been routed through a transducer, such as an earphone, headphone, or loudspeaker (Silman & Emmer, 2012). As a result, the wide expanse of spectral energy that characterizes white noise is reduced in size and is, in effect, shaped or essentially filtered due to the limited resonating properties (frequency response) of the transducer. The transducer fundamentally acts like a bandpass filter (discussed in the sections below) and reduces the overall bandwidth of the original signal (Silman &

Emmer, 2012). Illustrated in Figure 6–28 is the electroacoustic spectrum of a broadband noise with a spectrum level that is essentially uniform and flat. Note, however, that the spectrum level energy falls off at frequencies upward of 6000 Hz, due of course to the limited frequency response properties of the headphone transducer.

Spectrum Level or Level-per-Cycle

Recall that the spectrum level or level-per-cycle (LPC) was defined above as the average intensity or average noise power in a band of noise (called the

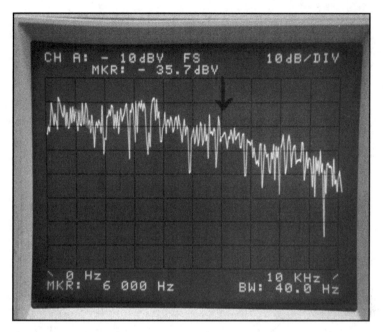

Figure 6–28. Electroacoustic spectrum for a broadband noise visualized on a real-time spectrum analyzer. From S. Silman and M. B. Emmer (2012), with permission.

unit bandwidth) that is 1-Hz wide (Yost, 2007). The overall level or total power (*TP*) is taken as the overall signal intensity of the noise, expressed in pressure (dB SPL) or in power (dB IL). The overall bandwidth (ΔF) is the overall range or total bandwidth of frequencies contained within the noise. The LPC in decibels (SPL or IL) is computed by taking the TP in decibels (SPL or IL) and subtracting from it, the value that is equal to 10 × log of ΔF. For example, the white noise illustrated in Figure 6–27B (upper right panel) has a ΔF of 10000 Hz. It should be remembered that within that 10000 Hz ΔF, are 10000 separate unit bandwidths, each 1 Hz in width (Durrant & Feth, 2013). All the same, the formula for computing the spectrum level or LPC may be written as

$$LPC = TP - 10 \times \log \Delta F \qquad (6\text{–}18)$$

Taking the example provided in Figure 6–27A and 6–27B (upper left and upper right panels), what would the spectrum level (*LPC*) be for white noise, having an overall bandwidth (ΔF) of 10000 Hz, when presented at an overall level (*TP*) of signal intensity (pressure) of 120 dB SPL? Using equation 6–18,

$$LPC = [120 \text{ dB SPL} - 10 \text{ (4)}] =$$
$$[120 \text{ dB SPL} - 40] = 80 \text{ dB SPL}$$

The spectrum level of 80 dB SPL in this example could be envisioned as if 10,000 individual frequencies (pure tones), each 80 dB SPL, having random phases and random instantaneous amplitudes, were added together to generate the 120 dB SPL white noise (Durrant & Feth, 2013).

What would be the spectrum level for the broadband noise illustrated in

Figure 6–28 if the overall bandwidth (ΔF) were 6 000 Hz, and if the noise were to be presented at an overall level (*TP*) of 120 dB SPL? Once again, using Equation 6–18,

$$LPC = [120 \text{ dB SPL} - 10 \times \log (6000)]$$

Recall that the number 6,000 may be rewritten in scientific notation as 6×10^3. Referring to Appendix B (Table B3–2), the log of (6×10^3) is equal to the log of (10^3), plus the log of (6) which is therefore equal to 3 + 0.78 or simply 3.78. Hence,

$$LPC = [120 \text{ dB SPL} - 10 \times (3.78)] =$$
$$[120 \text{ dB SPL} - 37.8] = 82.2 \text{ dB SPL}$$

As a result, the spectrum level for the broadband noise presented in this example would be 82.2 dB SPL.

Pink Noise

Another complex aperiodic signal (sound) is pink noise. Because pink noise contains relatively more energy in the lower frequency spectrum, the name *pink* is used in an analogous manner to refer to the longer wavelengths (see Chapter 7) in the visible spectrum that correspond to the lower (or the infrared) frequencies of light. Pink noise has relatively less high frequency energy because its spectrum level decreases by 3 dB for each doubling of frequency, across the overall range or across the total bandwidth of frequencies contained within the noise. The spectrum level of pink noise exhibits a halving of amplitude (or power) at each octave frequency. Recall from previous sections in this chapter in reference to

the decibel that cutting the power or the pressure by one half results in a loss of exactly 3 dB. The spectrum level of pink noise exhibits a –3 dB/octave slope. It can also be said that pink noise has a *roll-off rate* of 3 dB/octave. The instantaneous amplitude of pink noise is presented as a function of time (time analysis) in the lower left panel of Figure 6–27A. Figure 6–27B (lower right panel) illustrates a pressure (or power) spectrum level (in decibels) for pink noise. As indicated, the spectrum level for pink noise is continuous but not flat like white noise, because pink noise has a –3 dB/octave slope. Hence, pink noise has a spectrum level that varies with frequency.

Pink noise is additionally defined by the fact that the total power within each *octave-band* of pink noise remains constant, provided that the actual bandwidths of each of the octave-bands are proportional to their center frequencies (Yost, 2007). For instance, a band of pink noise centered at 1000 Hz, having a bandwidth of 500 Hz (or 250 Hz on either side of the center frequency) is equal in total power to a band of pink noise centered at 2000 Hz, having a bandwidth of 1000 Hz (or 500 Hz on either side of the center frequency). Both of these bands of pink noise would also be equal in power to a band of pink noise centered one octave higher, at 4000 Hz with a bandwidth of 2000 Hz (or 1000 Hz on either side of the center frequency). At each successively higher octave, the associated bandwidth must also increase proportionally to encompass, or to take in, an even greater range of frequencies. As each successive bandwidth increases, the number of separate unit bandwidths within each of those bands of pink noise also increases. Because the power spectrum level for pink noise is cut in half at each octave frequency, and the total power within each band is the summed intensity of all of the sinusoids within the band, the total power will remain constant within any (proportionally wider) octave-band of pink noise (Yost, 2007).

Narrow–Band Noise

As the name implies, narrow-band noise (NBN) contains limited numbers of frequency components. NBN is also referred to as *frequency-limited noise* or as *band-limited noise* to indicate that the signal has been restricted to a limited range (bandwidth) of frequencies (Speaks, 1999). Narrow-band noises are regularly used in pure tone audiometric testing, when it becomes necessary to mask (prevent) unwanted pure tones from being heard (from bone transmission) in the nontest (inner) ear. When used in this way, the center frequency of each NBN is also the actual frequency of the pure tone that is to be masked. NBN is created by passing a wide-band stimulus (white noise) through a band-pass filter (discussed later). The bandwidth of a NBN is therefore defined by the bandwidth of the band-pass filter that is used to create the NBN. The bandwidth of any band-pass filter is defined by the difference (in Hz) between the upper and the lower cut-off frequencies. The cut-off frequencies for band-pass filters are the two, half-power (pressure) points that define the *pass band* of any band-pass filter. Recall from the above, discussion of octave-band analyses early in this chapter, that the cut-off

frequency of any filter is defined as the location in the filter where the power (IL) or pressure (SPL) of the signal is cut (due to filtering) by exactly 50%, as previously shown in Figure 6–2C. The cut-off frequency is also called the half-power point, the half-pressure point, or the −3 dB down point (also discussed later). Bandwidths for NBN can vary between one-half to one-third octave (Hamill & Price, 2014), though many other bandwidths are possible (Durrant & Feth, 2013). Many commercially available audiometers employ third-octave-bandwidths for NBN signals (Silman & Emmer, 2012). Recall that octave-band filter computations for the lower (Equation 6–13A) and upper (Equation 6–13B) cut-off frequencies were provided in Table 6–7A for a relatively limited number of center frequencies. Third-octave-band filter computations for the lower (Equation 6–14A) and upper (Equation 6–14B) cut-off frequencies were also provided in Table 6–7B for a relatively larger range of center frequencies. Table 6–9 again provides third-octave-band filter computations for the lower (F_{CL}) and upper (F_{CU}) cut-off frequencies, as well as the NBN and band-pass filter bandwidths (Δf) computed by subtracting each (lower) F_{CL} from each (higher) F_{CU} for each of the corresponding, octave and interoctave (between octave) audiometric (center) frequencies that are commonly used in pure tone hearing tests. Additional equations could be employed to compute both the upper and the lower cut-off frequencies for any half-octave-band filter, with a center frequency of (C_F). The lower cut-off frequency or F_{CL}, and upper cut-off frequency or F_{CU} for a half-octave-band filter are determined using Equa-

Table 6–9. Third-Octave-Band Lower (F_{CL}) and Upper (F_{CU}) Cut-Off Frequency (Limits) and Computed NBN and Filter Bandwidths (Δf) for Octave and Interoctave (Between Octave) Audiometric (Center) Frequencies Commonly Used in Pure Tone Hearing Tests

Frequency (cycles/second)	Filter Limits		Bandwidth
	F_{CL}	F_{CU}	Δf
250 Hz	223	281	58
500 Hz	445	561	116
750 Hz	668	842	174
1000 Hz	891	1123	232
1500 Hz	1336	1684	348
2000 Hz	1782	2245	463
3000 Hz	2673	3367	694
4000 Hz	3564	4490	926
6000 Hz	5345	6735	1390
8000 Hz	7127	8980	1853

tion 6–19A, where the lower cut-off frequency is defined as

$$F_{CL} = C_F/2^{\frac{1}{4}} \quad \text{(6–19A)}$$

and

where the upper cut-off frequency is defined as

$$F_{CU} = C_F \times 2^{\frac{1}{4}} \quad \text{(6–19B)}$$

In both equations (6–19A and 6–19B), the value $2^{\frac{1}{4}}$ is equal to 1.189207115.

NBN will also vary in terms of the degree of slope (dB/octave) in the rejection or roll-off rates (discussed below) provided by the filter. The rejection rates (or slopes) on either side of the pass-band of a band-pass filter will determine how much relative suppression of the unwanted, useless, or harmful frequencies is provided by the filter. Conversely, the rejection rates on either side of the pass band will also determine how much of the unwanted part of the original signal is relatively permitted to pass through the filter with the NBN. Rejection rates (discussed later) can vary, up to as high as 60 to 90 dB/octave (Silman & Emmer, 2012). The electroacoustic spectrum of a narrowband noise is illustrated in Figure 6–29.

Speech Noise

Broadband noise that is band-pass filtered from 250 to 4000 Hz, having a center frequency at 1000 Hz, is also regularly used during speech audiometry to mask (prevent) unwanted speech signals from being heard (from bone transmission) in the nontest (inner) ear. Speech noise is high-pass filtered (on the left) from 250 to 1000 Hz, at a slope of 3 dB/octave. The filter also rejects frequencies above 1000 Hz, or is low-

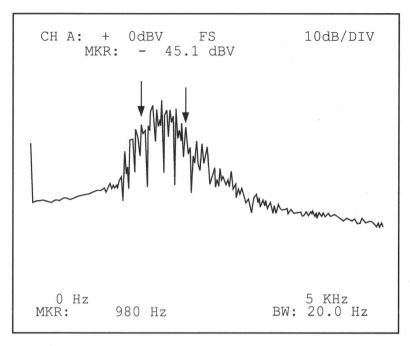

```
CH A:   +   0dBV      FS              10dB/DIV
   MKR:   -   45.1 dBV




      0 Hz                            5 KHz
   MKR:          980 Hz           BW: 20.0 Hz
```

Figure 6–29. Electroacoustic spectrum for a narrow-band noise visualized on a real-time spectrum analyzer. From S. Silman and M. B. Emmer (2012), with permission.

pass filtered (on the right), from 1000 to 4000 Hz, at a –12 dB/octave roll-off rate. Consequently, with the much steeper filter slope of –12 dB/octave for frequencies above 1000 Hz, speech noise follows the acoustic spectrum for a speech signal by providing more masking energy in the lower frequency regions (Silman & Emmer, 2012).

Modulated Signals

Recall from previous sections that sinusoidal waveforms are often combined with other sinusoidal waveforms to create complex periodic waveforms. Looking again at the illustrations provided in Figures 6–10 through 6–13, it might be said that the larger amplitude of the fundamental frequency (sinusoid 1), combined with the smaller amplitude of sinusoid 2, resulted in a modification, or in essence a modulation in the amplitude of sinusoid 2, as evidenced by the amplitude in the composite, complex periodic waveform. Recall as well, the synthesis of the sawtooth wave (see Figure 6–14), of the square wave (see Figure 6–16), and of the triangular wave (see Figure 6–17). In each instance, the (sinusoidal) fundamental frequency at the top of each illustration has the greatest amplitude. It might also be said the fundamental frequency, combined with the complex periodic waveform that would have been created by the remaining (even and/or odd) harmonics, resulted in a modulation of the potential amplitude and the potential frequency of the resulting complex waveform. This point is again suggested by each of the composite complex periodic waveforms shown at the bottom of each figure. In each case, the frequency of the composite waveform is always equal to the original fundamental frequency. In sum, it should be clear that sinusoids have the capability of modulating not only complex periodic waveforms, but other sinusoids as well. A more straightforward example of amplitude and frequency modulation, however, is provided by the radio (and television) communication trade. In this particular case, a complex and mostly periodic signal is used in order to modulate a sinusoidal waveform.

Radio and television devices do not receive sound waves, they receive electromagnetic waves that are essentially low frequency light waves (Hewitt, 2010). These waves are, nevertheless, still extremely high in frequency and are beyond the range of human hearing. Recall from Chapter 3 that electromagnetic waves such as light and radio waves travel at 186,000 mi/sec and require no transmitting medium. Recall as well from Chapter 5 that it was Heinrich Rudolph Hertz (1857–1894) who devoted considerable effort and attention to the theoretical study of electromagnetic waves, as he demonstrated beyond doubt that light waves and electromagnetic waves are identical. Furthermore, it was the work of Hertz that led others to develop what we recognize presently as the radio, television, and even radar.

The much lower-in-frequency sound signal that is to be communicated is first changed into an electrical signal, called an *audio-frequency signal*. The audio-frequency signal is complex, and mostly periodic. The audio-frequency signal, composed of frequencies that fall within the human audibility range (20 Hz to 20 kHz), is then electronically amplified and fed into a mixer (Giancoli, 2005). At this juncture, the audio-frequency signal is mixed with (or superimposed upon) a much higher-in-frequency, electromagnetic radio-frequency signal, or what is commonly referred to as a *carrier wave*. The carrier wave is sinusoidal. The carrier wave is generated by a radio-frequency oscillator and is the waveform that is transmitted at the particular frequency (carrier frequency) that is assigned individually to each broadcaster (Giancoli, 2005). This is the same frequency that is indicated on the radio or television channel selector that allows the listener to tune into each carrier wave separately.

The mixing of the audio-frequency signal with the carrier frequency is accomplished by two primary methods. In the first method, the amplitude of the higher-in-frequency carrier wave is made to vary proportionaletly, so that it follows the amplitude variations of the lower-in-frequency, audio-frequency signal (Giancoli, 2005). The audio-frequency signal represents the modulator (modulation) frequency (or the modulation rate), which is the frequency (or rate) of the change in the amplitude of the carrier wave. Because the amplitude in the carrier wave is made to vary in proportion to the changing amplitudes in the audio-frequency signal, the modification of the carrier wave is called *amplitude modulation*, and the resulting radio signal is called an *amplitude modulated signal*, or simply AM. This method of modulation is illustrated in Figure 6–30 where signal A is the complex and mostly periodic, audio-frequency signal (modulator); and signal B is the carrier wave that has been amplitude modulated by signal A. AM

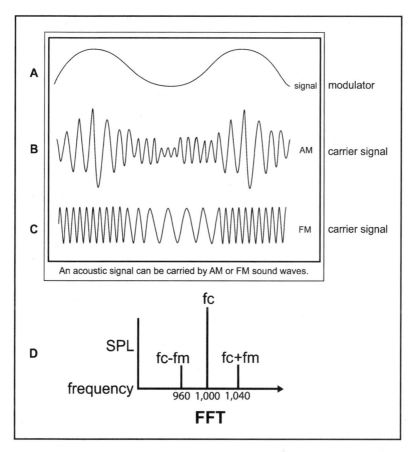

Figure 6–30. Amplitude and frequency modulation. Signal **A** is the complex, relatively low-in-frequency, mostly periodic, audio-frequency signal (modulator). Signal **B** is the carrier wave that has been amplitude modulated (AM) by signal A. Signal **C** is the carrier wave that has been frequency modulated (FM) by signal A. Signal **D** represents the spectral analysis (line spectrum) of the AM carrier wave where "fc" is the carrier frequency and "fm" is the modulator frequency (modulation rate) or the frequency (or rate) of the change in the amplitude of the carrier, which is 40 Hz in this example. The line spectrum (discussed later) that is presented consists of a center frequency (fc), and two side band frequencies of fc – fm, and fc + fm. Not shown are the unmodulated (original) carrier waves. From S. Silman and M. B. Emmer (2012), with permission.

carrier frequencies typically range from 530 to 1605 kHz. In the second method of modulation, the frequency of the carrier wave is made to vary proportionalelty, so that it follows the amplitude variations of the audio-frequency signal (Giancoli, 2005). Again, the audio-frequency signal represents the modulator (modulation) frequency (or the modulation rate), which is frequency (or rate) of the change in the frequency of the carrier wave. Because the frequency in the carrier wave is made to vary (within a specified frequency bandwidth) in proportion to the changing amplitudes in the audio-frequency signal, the modification of the carrier wave by this method is called *frequency modulation*, and the resulting radio signal is called a *frequency modulated signal*, or simply FM. This second method of modulation is illustrated in Figure 6–30 where sgnal A is the complex and mostly periodic, audio-frequency signal (modulator) and signal C is the carrier wave that has been frequency modulated by signal A. The much higher FM carrier frequencies typically range from 88 MHz Hz to 108 MHz. Shown as signal D in Figure 6–30 is a spectral analysis (line spectrum) of the AM carrier wave, where fc is the carrier (or center) frequency, and fm is the modulator (modulation) frequency. Because fm represents the frequency of the change in the amplitude of the carrier wave (or the modulation rate), the *line spectrum* (discussed later) of the AM modulated carrier frequency shown in Figure 6–30 consists of the center frequency (fc), and the two side band frequencies of $fc - fm$, and $fc + fm$ (Yost, 2007). In the illustration, the modulation frequency (fm) is 40 Hz. The differences in the amplitude between the center frequency and each of the side band frequencies represents the *modulation depth*, or the magnitude of the amplitude modulation (Yost, 2007). Not shown in Figure 6–30 are the unmodulated (original) carrier waves. AM has been said to be analogous to rapidly changing the brightness (intensity) of a constant-color light bulb, whereas FM is analogous to rapidly changing the color of a constant-brightness (intensity) light bulb (Hewitt, 2010).

Warble Tones

Warble tones represent an example of frequency modulated signals. Warble tones are used clinically during sound-field testing in order to prevent the occurrence of standing waves (see Chapter 7). A warble tone is a frequency modulated pure tone with a ±5% change in frequency/second. For instance, a 500-Hz warble tone will (modulate) fluctuate between 475 and 525 Hz (a 25-Hz warble) per second, a 1000-Hz warble tone will fluctuate between 950 and 1050 Hz (a 50-Hz warble) per second, and a 2000-Hz warble tone will fluctuate between 1900 and 2100 Hz (a 100-Hz warble) per second (Silman & Emmer, 2012).

The Spectral Analysis and the Amplitude Spectrum

Recall that decomposing or dismantling a complex waveform into its individual constituent sinusoids is called a Fourier analysis. A Fourier analysis is a *spectral analysis* of the frequency by frequency content of a waveform presented as a function of amplitude. Such an analysis not only provides information regarding which frequencies are contained within a signal, but it also reveals how each of the frequency components contributes to the total energy of the waveform. Such information may not be apparent from an inspection of the signal's instantaneous amplitude over time (Durrant & Feth, 2013) and is rarely available (except for Gaussian noise) from the spectrum level of a complex waveform. A convenient way of graphically conveying the amplitude by frequency function for a waveform is by the use of a spectrum, *amplitude spectrum*, or *amplitude by frequency spectrum*. These terms are all equivalent and refer to a graphic method that is used to depict the range of absolute or relative amplitudes expressed in the frequency domain (Speaks, 1999). Therefore, an amplitude spectrum is a method of illustrating the amplitude by frequency content of a waveform, the substance of which is based on the spectral information gleaned from a Fourier (spectral) analysis. The amplitude spectrum, therefore, provides a graphic alternative to a presentation of the actual waveform (Rosen & Howell, 2013).

The Line Spectrum

As indicated above, the spectral analysis of a waveform is often graphically depicted by an amplitude spectrum. The amplitude spectrum (spectra) for simple and/or complex periodic waveforms will take the form of a *discrete spectrum*, a *line amplitude spectrum*, or simply a *line spectrum* (Speaks, 1999). The line spectrum of either a simple or a complex periodic waveform will consist of either one or a series of vertical lines. Each vertical line depicts a discrete sinusoidal component, and the length of each vertical line is directly proportional to the amplitude or magnitude of the frequency component that the line represents. Each vertical line begins at single point located at an appropriate height relative to the amplitude scale designated along the ordinate (vertical axis), and is drawn (downward) from that point to another point located along the frequency scale of the abscissa (horizontal axis) that represents the frequency of the component. A spectral analysis of a (sinusoidal) pure tone gives way to the simplest type of waveform that can be graphically depicted. As illustrated

in Figure 6–31, the analysis of a pure tone (panel 1A) yields a line spectrum (panel 1B) with a single line located at the appropriate single frequency (not scaled) along the abscissa, with amplitude expressed either relatively (as shown), as an RMS amplitude, or in terms of dB SPL or dB IL (Durrant & Feth, 2013). In Figure 6–31, the analysis of a higher-in-frequency and lower-in-amplitude pure tone (panel 2A) yields a line spectrum (panel 2B) with a single and shorter line, located at a different (not scaled) higher-in-frequency location along the abscissa. It should be clear from the (discrete) line spectra illustrated in panel 1B and panel 2B of Figure 6–31 that the location of a particular line in the frequency domain (abscissa) identifies the frequency of the component, and the height of the line that falls along the amplitude (ordinate) identifies the amount of energy (amplitude) contained within the frequency component (Speaks, 1999).

A complex periodic waveform such as the one shown in panel 3A of Figure 6–31 may be created from the combination of the two sinusoidal waveforms shown in panel 1A and panel 2A of Figure 6–31. The complex periodic waveform illustrated in panel 3A of Figure 6–31 is obviously composed of two sinusoids that differ in both frequency and amplitude, and is similar in morphology to the composite waveform illustrated previously in Figure 6–16. A spectral analysis of a complex periodic waveform such as the one illustrated in panel 3A of Figure 6–31 yields the line spectrum shown in panel 3B that depicts one line for each of the two frequency components. Additional line spectra may be generated for other complex periodic waveforms such as the

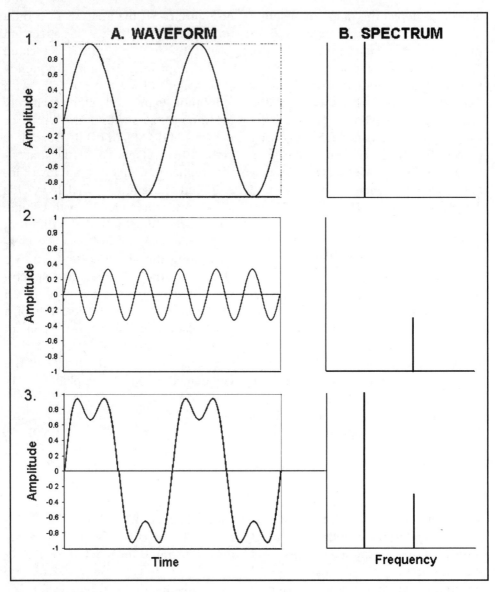

Figure 6–31. 1A. Time analysis for a sinusoidal waveform. **1B.** The discrete line spectrum for the sinusoid shown in panel 1A. **2A.** Time analysis for a higher-in-frequency, lower-in-amplitude (relative to 1A) sinusoidal waveform. **2B.** The discrete line spectrum for the sinusoid shown in panel 2A. **3A.** A complex periodic waveform created from the combination of the two sinusoidal waveforms shown in panels 1A and 2A. **3B.** The discrete line spectrum for the complex periodic waveform shown in panel 3A. From T. A. Hamill and L. L. Price (2014), with permission.

triangular wave (see Figure 6–17), the square wave (see Figure 6–16), and the sawtooth waves (see Figure 6–14) presented earlier in this chapter. Recall from Figure 6–17 that the triangular wave is composed of odd-numbered harmonic frequencies, consisting of a fundamental (f_0) and each of the odd-integer whole-number multiples of the fundamental, all of which are in phase.

Recall as well that each successively higher harmonic added to the harmonic series is progressively reduced in peak amplitude by a ratio of $1/N^2$ such that N^2 is equal (in number) to the square of each consecutive odd harmonic (1^2, 3^2, 5^2, 7^2, 9^2). Hence, the rate of decline in the peak amplitude of each added harmonic is proportional to the squared inverse of each odd-numbered harmonic.

A spectral analysis of a triangular waveform, such as the one illustrated in the top left panel A of Figure 6–32 with the 2-ms period, yields the line spectrum shown in the top right panel B

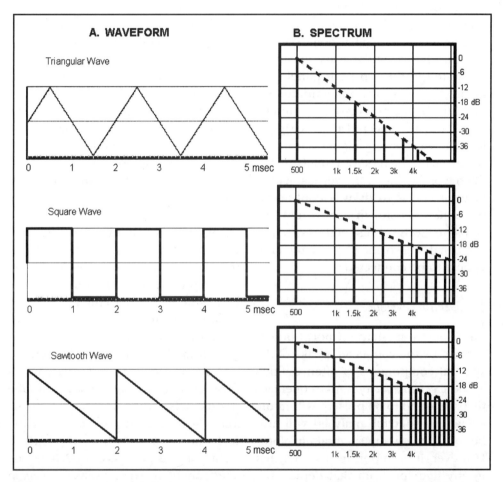

Figure 6–32. A. (*top left*): Amplitude variation of a triangular waveform (2-ms period) illustrated in the time domain. (*middle left*): Amplitude variation of a square waveform (2-ms period) illustrated in the time domain. (*lower left*): Amplitude variation of a sawtooth waveform (2-ms period) illustrated in the time domain. **B.** (*top right*): (Relative) amplitude by frequency (*line*) spectrum for the same triangular wave having a fundamental frequency of 500 Hz and a spectral envelope (*dashed line*) with a slope of –12 dB/octave. (*middle right*): (Relative) amplitude by frequency (*line*) spectrum for the same square wave having a fundamental frequency of 500 Hz and a spectral envelope (*dashed line*) with a slope of –6 dB/octave. (*lower right*): (Relative) amplitude by frequency (*line*) spectrum for the same sawtooth wave having a fundamental frequency of 500 Hz and a spectral envelope (*dashed line*) with a slope of –6 dB/octave. From T. A. Hamill and L. L. Price (2014), with permission.

of Figure 6–32. The line spectrum of the triangular waveform (2-ms period) depicts one spectral line for each of several odd-numbered harmonic components, beginning with a fundamental frequency (f_0) of 500 Hz in this example. Starting with the third (1500 Hz), and continuing to the fifth (2500 Hz), to the sevenenth (3500 Hz), and then to the ninth (4500 Hz) harmonic, there is an obvious and systematic decline in the amplitude of each harmonic component, in the triangular wave spectrum illustrated in the top right panel A of Figure 6–32. This drop in amplitude is indicated by the progressive shortening of each of the spectral lines assigned to each successively higher harmonic. A convenient method of visualizing the degree of decline in the vertical length of each line is to draw a continuous or dashed (as shown) horizontal line across the tops (peaks) of the (spectral) lines. In doing so, the peaks of the lines appear to be connected.

The Spectral Envelope

The spectrum shape (morphology) defined by the connected peaks of the spectral components is often defined as the *spectral envelope*. All frequencies that are found to be present within the signal (by spectral analysis) will also be found below the spectral envelope. However, it is important to note that in any line spectrum that depicts the spectral contents of a complex periodic waveform, energy will be present only at the frequencies represented by the vertical lines. That is, even though the spectral envelope connects the tops (peaks) of the spectral lines, there is no assumption of energy being present between the spectral lines (Speaks, 1999). Any amplitude spectrum that indicates the presence energy between the spectral lines (or at all frequencies located below the spectral envelope) is an amplitude spectrum that describes a type of noise (see below). Finally, note that the line spectrum for the triangular waveform illustrated in the top right panel B of Figure 6–32 indicates that no spectral energy exists at the even-numbered harmonics. Nevertheless, the slope of the spectral envelope indicates a consistent and systematic reduction in signal amplitude for every doubling of frequency. That is, at each octave frequency (i.e., from 500 Hz to 1000 Hz; 1000 Hz to 2000 Hz; 2000 Hz to 4000 Hz) the rate of decline in the slope of the spectral envelope for the triangular wave is –12 dB/octave. In conclusion, the roll-off rate of 12 dB/octave in the slope of the spectral envelope of the triangular wave shown in the top right panel B of Figure 6–32 is consistent with the fact that the rate of the decline in the amplitude of each (odd) harmonic that is added to a triangular wave is proportional to the squared inverse of each added odd-numbered harmonic, as indicated earlier in this chapter.

A spectral analysis of a square waveform, such as the one illustrated in the middle left panel A of Figure 6–32, again with a 2-ms period, yields the line spectrum shown in the middle right panel B of Figure 6–32. The line spectrum of the square waveform again depicts one spectral line for each of several odd-numbered harmonic components, beginning once again with a fundamental frequency (f_0) of 500 Hz in this example. Recall from Figure 6–16 that, like the triangular wave, the square wave is also composed of odd-numbered harmonic frequencies, consisting of a fundamental (f_0) and each odd integer whole number multiple of the fundamental, all of which are in phase. It should also be recalled that each successively higher harmonic added to the harmonic series is progressively reduced in peak amplitude by a ratio of $1/N$ such that N is equal (in number) to each consecutive odd-numbered harmonic (1, 3, 5, 7, 9). Therefore, the rate of decline in the peak amplitude of each added harmonic is proportional to the inverse of each odd-numbered harmonic. Once again, starting with the third (1500 Hz), and continuing to the 5th (2500 Hz), to the 7th (3500 Hz) and then to the 9th (4500 Hz) harmonic and beyond, there is an obvious and systematic decline in the amplitude of each harmonic component, in the square wave spectrum illustrated in the middle right panel B of Figure 6–32. This drop in amplitude is indicated by the progressive shortening of each of the spectral lines assigned to each successively higher harmonic. Once again, note that the line spectrum for the square waveform illustrated in the middle right panel B of Figure 6–32, indicates that no spectral energy exists at the even-numbered harmonics. Nevertheless, the slope of the spectral envelope indicates a consistent and systematic reduction in signal amplitude for every doubling of frequency. That is, at each octave frequency (i.e. from 500 Hz to 1000 Hz; 1000 Hz to 2000 Hz; 2000 Hz to 4000 Hz) the rate of decline in the slope of the spectral envelope for the square wave is 6 dB/octave. In conclusion, the roll-off rate of –6 dB/octave in the slope of the spectral envelope of the square wave shown in the middle right panel B of Figure 6–32 is consistent with the fact that the rate of the decline in the

amplitude of each (odd) harmonic that is added to a square wave is proportional to the inverse of each added odd numbered harmonic, as also indicated earlier in this chapter.

Finally, a spectral analysis of a sawtooth waveform, such as the one illustrated in the lower left panel A of Figure 6–32, also with a 2 millisecond period, yields the line spectrum shown in the lower left panel B of Figure 6–32. The line spectrum of the sawtooth waveform depicts one spectral line for each of several (even and odd) harmonic components, beginning (again) with a fundamental frequency (f_0) of 500 Hz, in this example. Recall from Figure 6–14 that, unlike the triangular and square waves, the sawtooth wave is composed of both even and odd numbered harmonic frequencies, consisting of a fundamental (f_0) and each of the integer whole number multiples of the fundamental, all of which are in phase. Recall as well that each successively higher harmonic added to the harmonic series is progressively reduced in peak amplitude by a ratio of $1/N$ such that "N" is equal (in number) to each consecutive harmonic (1, 2, 3, 4, 5, 6, 7, 8, 9). Hence, the rate of decline in the peak amplitude of each added harmonic is proportional to the inverse of each harmonic frequency. In this instance, starting with the second (1000 Hz), and continuing to the third (1500 Hz), to the fourth (2000 Hz), and then to the fifth (2500 Hz), and even to the sixth (3000 Hz), the seventh (3500 Hz), and to the eights (4000 Hz) harmonic, and beyond, there is an obvious and systematic decline in the amplitude of each harmonic component in the sawtooth wave spectrum illustrated in the lower right panel B of Figure 6–32. As expected, this drop in amplitude is indicated by the progressive shortening of each of the spectral lines assigned to each successively higher harmonic. Once again, note that the line spectrum for the sawtooth waveform illustrated in the lower right panel B of Figure 6–32 indicates that spectral energy exists at all (and only) the harmonic frequencies. The slope of the spectral envelope once again indicates a consistent and systematic reduction in signal amplitude for every doubling of frequency. That is, at each octave frequency (i.e., from 500 to 1000 Hz; 1000 to 2000 Hz; 2000 to 4000 Hz), the rate of decline in the slope of the spectral envelope for the sawtooth wave is 6 dB/octave. In conclusion, the roll-off rate of –6 dB/octave in the slope of the spectral envelope of the sawtooth wave shown in the lower right panel B of Figure 6–32 is consistent with the fact that the rate of the decline in the amplitude of each harmonic frequency that is added to a sawtooth wave is proportional to the inverse of each added harmonic frequency, as also indicated earlier in this chapter. By now it should obvious that discrete line spectra, gleaned from a spectral analysis of the frequency by frequency energy content of a complex periodic waveform, provide information that is not immediately available from an inspection of a signal's instantaneous amplitude over time.

The Continuous Spectrum

As indicated in the above sections, spectral information gleaned from a Fourier (spectral) analysis is graphically presented by the amplitude by frequency spectrum, and for simple and/or complex periodic waveforms, amplitude spectra take the form of discrete, line spectra. An amplitude spectrum is also a useful method for illustrating the spectral content of a complex aperiodic waveform following a spectral analysis. However, bear in mind that complex aperiodic sounds exhibit random, unpredictable variations in their instantaneous amplitudes. They also lack regular, repeating waveform cycles because they are composed of many harmonically unrelated frequencies, and therefore lack a well-defined fundamental frequency and/or fundamental period. Also recall that when complex waveforms lack repeating cycles over regular intervals of time, the result is the production of a noise, defined previously as a complex aperiodic signal (sound) having instantaneous amplitudes that randomly vary over time (Yost, 2007).

Because periodic waveforms are created by the summation of harmonics, periodic waveforms are, as indicated above, best represented by line spectra. Noises, on the other hand, and especially white noise, are best described by continuous spectra (Durant & Feth, 2013). Recall the long-term averaged spectrum for white noise that was illustrated in the upper right panel B of Figure 6–27. White noise has a spectrum level that does not vary with frequency, and therefore, has equal amounts of energy per cycle, or, equal amounts of energy per frequency. Because white noise includes the entire audible spectrum of frequencies, a line spectrum, if drawn, would contain an infinite number of vertical spectral lines within the designated bandwidth of the white noise signal. Furthermore, energy would be present between the spectral lines, or at all frequencies located below the spectral envelope. In general, a continuous amplitude spectrum is also one in which energy is present at all frequencies positioned between the lower and the upper frequency limits of the waveform (Speaks, 1999). Hence, the long-term average spectrum of white noise illustrates the simplest and best example of a continuous spectrum (Durrant & Feth 2013).

As illustrated in the upper right panel B of Figure 6–27, the long-term average pressure (or power) spectrum level for white noise is continuous and essentially flat (zero slope). For this reason, spectral lines, which would be infinite in number if they were shown, would all have the same length. Because the spectral lines represent an infinite number of spectral components, the spectral envelope created by connecting the peaks of all the lines results in a smooth, straight, horizontal line across the top of the amplitude by frequency spectrum, as illustrated in panel A of Figure 6–33. The zero slope of the spectral envelope in the amplitude spectrum for white noise indicates that the energy in this signal exists equally at, and across, all frequencies.

A continuous amplitude spectrum is also a useful method for illustrating the spectral content of other complex aperiodic waveforms, such as pink noise. Recall the long-term averaged spectrum for pink noise that was illustrated in the lower right panel B of Figure 6–27. Like white noise, pink noise contains the entire audible spectrum of frequencies, and, like white noise, if a line spectrum would to be drawn, it would contain an infinite number of vertical spectral lines within the designated bandwidth of the pink noise signal. Also like white noise, the energy of pink noise would be present between the spectral lines, or at all frequencies located below the spectral envelope. However, unlike white noise, pink noise has a spectrum level that varies with frequency, and therefore, pink noise does not have equal amounts of energy per cycle as does white noise. As illustrated in the lower right panel B of Figure 6–27, the long-term pressure (or power) spectrum level for pink noise is continuous but has a slope of –3 dB/octave. Consequently, the spectral envelope created by connecting the peaks of an infinite number of spectral lines (if they were shown) results in a continuous, curved line with a negative slope of 3 dB/octave, beginning at 0 Hz as illustrated in panel B of Figure 6–33. Therefore, the spectral envelope, like the spectrum level for pink noise, has a roll-off rate of 3 dB/octave.

The Phase Spectrum

When providing an overall description of a particular waveform, it is customary to treat information related to phase separately from information that is related to amplitude. However, like information related to spectral content, information regarding the starting phases of each sinusoidal frequency component in a complex periodic signal is not available from an inspection of the signal's instantaneous amplitude over time, and is rarely available (except for noise) from the spectrum level of a complex waveform. A convenient way of graphically conveying the starting phase of each component (as a function of frequency) is by the use of a phase spectrum in the frequency domain, or simply, by a *phase spectrum* (Speaks, 1999). Like the (line) amplitude

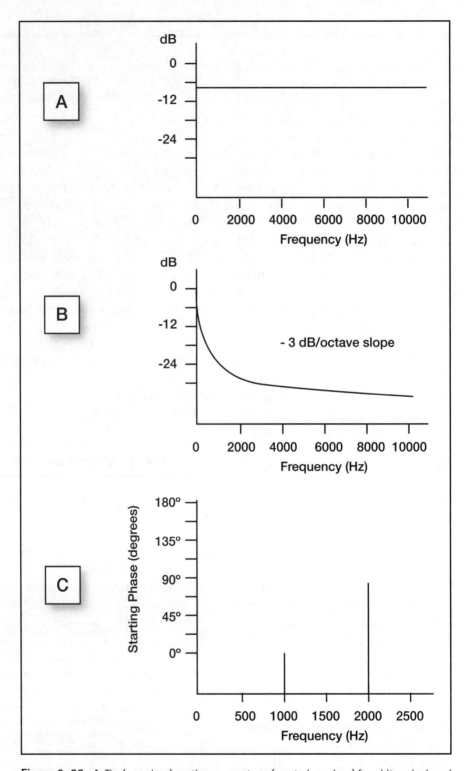

Figure 6–33. A. The (zero slope) continuous spectrum (spectral envelope) for white noise based on the long-term averaged spectrum level for white noise presented in the upper right panel B of Figure 6–27. **B.** The (–3 dB/octave slope) continuous spectrum (spectral envelope) for pink noise based on the long-term averaged spectrum level for pink noise presented in the lower right panel B of Figure 6–27. **C.** The phase spectrum for the complex periodic waveform presented in Figure 6–11.

spectrum, the phase spectrum for either a simple or a complex periodic waveform will consist of either one or a series of points or of vertical lines. If vertical lines are used, each line begins at a single point located at an appropriate location (height) relative to the phase scale (in degrees) that is designated along the ordinate (vertical axis). The line is drawn (downward) from that point to another point located along the frequency scale of the abscissa (horizontal axis) that represents the frequency of the component.

The phase spectrum of a (sinusoidal) pure tone is the simplest type of phase spectrum that can be presented graphically. Almost as simple is the phase spectrum illustrated in panel C of Figure 6–33 for the complex periodic waveform shown previously in Figure 6–11. As illustrated in panel C of Figure 6–33, each vertical line (two in number) depicts a discrete sinusoidal component (abscissa), and each line begins at a single point located at an appropriate location (height) relative to the phase scale (in degrees), designated along the ordinate. A phase spectrum for the composite sawtooth waveform illustrated in Figure 6–14 would be depicted by five lines, one for each discrete sinusoidal component, from the fundamental frequency to the fifth harmonic. Each line would be drawn from the appropriate location along the abscissa to a height, for all the components, that is consistent with a starting phase of 0° relative to the ordinate. A phase spectrum for the composite square waveform illustrated in Figure 6–16 would be depicted again by five lines, one for each discrete sinusoidal component, consisting of the fundamental frequency and each odd harmonic, from the third to the ninth.

Each line would be drawn from the appropriate location along the abscissa to a height, for all the components, that is again consistent with a starting phase of 0° relative to the ordinate. Finally, a phase spectrum for the composite triangular waveform illustrated in Figure 6–17 would be depicted once again by five lines, one for each discrete sinusoidal component, consisting of the fundamental frequency and each odd harmonic, from the third to the ninth. Each line would be drawn from the appropriate location along the abscissa to a height, for all the components, that is consistent with a starting phase of 90° relative to the ordinate. Therefore, a phase spectrum defines the starting phase of each sinusoidal frequency component within a complex waveform. A combination of both the amplitude spectrum and the phase spectrum will, in the frequency domain, completely define any waveform (Yost, 2007).

Spectral Shaping: Filters

The spectrum of any signal can be shaped. The concept of spectral shaping and filtering was touched upon previously in reference to the design limitations and, therefore, the limited frequency response (or transfer functions) characteristics of transducers. Recall that the presentation of both transient signals and white noise is somewhat hampered by the unintentional spectral shaping and filtering of these signals, resulting from the limited and inefficient resonating properties of the earphone/headphone transducers used for their delivery. Transducers fundamentally act like unintentional band-pass-filters during the delivery of these kinds of signals (Silman & Emmer, 2012). Even the telephone band-pass filters speech sounds, selectively passing only the frequencies found within a limited bandwidth ranging from 300 to 3000 Hz, a limitation that is based on economic constraints (Durrant & Feth, 2013). For the present, however, filters will be addressed and treated as devices that intentionally shape, or otherwise selectively alter the amplitudes of signals, as a function of frequency. The intentional filtering of signals was addressed earlier in this chapter in reference to the octave and third-octave-band filtering properties employed by sound level meters (SLMs) in the analysis of environmental sounds. Also discussed earlier in this chapter were the octave and third-octave-band filtering properties employed by audiometers in the generation of narrow-bands of noise. Moreover, the computed upper and lower cut-off frequencies for both octave and third-octave-band filters were also provided in this chapter, in Tables 6–7A, 6–7B, and 6–9. The preceding sections in this chapter described the use of filters in the analysis of stimuli. However, as indicated in the sections that follow, filters are also used for manipulating and shaping stimuli.

In general, when a signal is delivered into the input side of a system that employs filters, the filtering properties (or filter devices) of the system alter (shape) the spectral properties of that signal. The shaped or otherwise altered signal that is delivered from the output side of the system no longer bears an exact resemblance in its spectral content to that of the original signal. Hence, filters are devices that shape signals by selectively passing some frequencies and by selectively blocking (attenuating) others. Filters do not amplify signals—that role is reserved for amplifiers. Filters do, however, exert relative control over which of the frequencies originating on the input side of a system, will be expressed or passed through to the output side of the system.

Types of Filters I: Ideal Filters

It is useful to compare and contrast the four types of ideal filters with the four types of real filters. The four types of filters, whether ideal or real, are the low-pass filter, *high-pass filter*, *band-pass filter* which was discussed earlier in this chapter, and *band-reject* (band-stop) *filter*. Each of these four filter types specifies a different spectral shaping strategy or method. Idealized filters help to elucidate the "ideal" intent of each of the four filtering methods. A description of the four ideal filter types also serves to highlight the limitations that exist, and hence, the filter specifications that are required in each of the four, real-world filter counterparts. Unlike real filters, ideal filters exert absolute (as opposed to relative) control over which frequencies will be permitted to pass through to the output side of a system. Ideal filters either absolutely pass or absolutely do not pass (attenuate) certain frequencies. Therefore, ideal filters have discrete *cut-off frequencies* that yield perfectly rectangular filtering spectra (Durrant & Feth, 2013). As illustrated in Figure 6–34 panels A–D, spectral energy that falls on either side of a specified cut-off frequency or f_c is either absolutely passed, as indicated

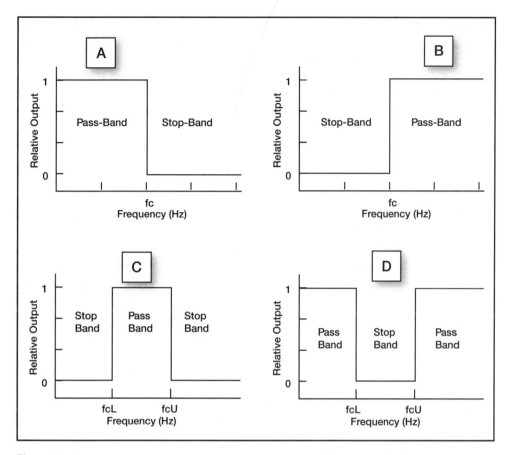

Figure 6–34. Ideal filters. **A.** An ideal low-pass filter illustrating the pass-band, stop-band, and cut-off frequency (f_c). **B.** An ideal high-pass filter illustrating the pass-band, stop-band, and cut-off frequency (f_c). **C.** An ideal band-pass filter illustrating the pass-band, two stop-bands, as well as lower (f_cL) and upper (f_cU) cut-off frequencies. **D.** An ideal band-reject (stop) filter illustrating the two pass-bands, stop-band, as well as lower (f_cL) and upper (f_cU) cut-off frequencies. Spectral energy that falls on either side of the specified cut-off frequencies is either absolutely passed, as indicted by the relative output of 1, or is absolutely attenuated as indicated by the relative output of 0.

by the relative output of 1, or is absolutely attenuated as indicated by the relative output of 0.

The ideal low-pass filter (see Figure 6–34 panel A) selectively passes only frequencies that fall below a specified cut-off frequency (f_c), while absolutely rejecting the energy contained within the frequencies that fall above the f_c. As illustrated in Figure 6–34 panel A, the area of the filter spectrum in which

frequencies are passed (to the left of the f_c) is called the *pass-band* of the low-pass filter. The area outside of the filter spectrum where no frequencies are passed (to the right of the f_c), is called the *stop-band* of the low-pass filter. The ideal high-pass filter (see Figure 6–34 panel B) selectively passes only frequencies that fall above a specified f_c while absolutely rejecting the energy contained within the frequencies that fall below the f_c. As illustrated in Figure 6–34 panel B, the area of the filter spectrum in which frequencies are passed (to the right of the f_c) is the pass-band of the high-pass filter. The area outside of the filter spectrum where no frequencies are passed (to the left of the f_c), is the stop-band of the high-pass filter. A band-pass filter only passes or permits a particular band of frequencies to appear at the output of a system. The ideal band-pass filter, as illustrated in Figure 6–34 panel C, only passes frequencies that fall within a specified range or band of frequencies (i.e., within the pass-band), while absolutely rejecting those that fall to the left or to the right of a specified f_c. Because band-pass filters often (but not always) have lower (f_{cL}) and upper (f_{cU}) cut-off frequencies, an ideal band-pass filter absolutely rejects energy in any frequency that falls to the left of the f_{cL} and/or to the right of the f_{cU}. As illustrated in Figure 6–34 panel C, these two areas outside of the filter spectrum, where no frequencies are passed (i.e., to the left of the f_{cL} and/or to the right of the f_{cU}) are the stop-bands of the ideal band-pass filter. The frequency band that is passed falls between the two cut-off frequencies, restricting the bandwidth of an ideal band-pass filter to the frequency range that is located between the f_{cL} and the f_{cU}. This area of the filter spectrum in which frequencies are passed is, as indicated above, the pass-band of the band-pass filter. Finally, a band-stop or band-reject filter blocks or stops a band of frequencies from appearing at the output of a system. The ideal band-stop filter (see Figure 6–34 panel D) only rejects frequencies that fall within a specified range or band of frequencies, while absolutely passing those that fall to the left or to the right of a specified f_c. Like band-pass filters, band-stop filters often have lower (f_{cL}) and upper (f_{cU}) cut-off frequencies. An ideal band-stop filter absolutely passes energy for any frequency that falls to the left of the f_{cL} and/or to the right of the f_{cU}. As illustrated in Figure 6–34 panel D, these two areas outside of the filtering spectrum, where frequencies are passed (i.e., to the left of the f_{cL} and/or to the right of the f_{cU}) are the pass-bands of the band-stop filter. The frequency band that is rejected falls between the two cut-off frequencies, restricting the rejected bandwidth of an ideal band-stop filter to the frequency range that is located between the f_{cL} and the f_{cU}. This area of the filtering spectrum in which frequencies are rejected is the stop-band of the band-stop filter. In sum, because ideal filters have discrete cut-off frequencies that yield perfectly rectangular filtering spectra, the pass-bands of ideal filters contain 100% of the spectral energy, while the stop-bands of ideal filters contain 0% of the spectral energy. With ideal filters, the transition between pass-band and stop-band is absolute and occurs instantaneously at the cut-off frequency. Pragmatically, however, it is not possible to implement filters that have instantaneous (discrete) cut-off frequencies and perfectly rectangular filtering spectra.

Types of Filters II: Real Filters

Real filters exert relative (as opposed to absolute) control over which frequencies will be permitted to pass through to the output side of a system. Unlike idealized filters, the cut-off frequency of a real filter is characterized and measured by the *3-dB down point* of its response function, which is also referred to as the *(minus) −3 dB down point*. The 3-dB down point is also called the *half-power* (half-pressure) *point*, and represents a point of gradual rather than an absolute transition between the pass-band and the stop-band. Recall that ideal filters, with their perfectly rectangular filtering spectra, specify no loss in power or in pressure at the cut-off frequency (f_c), but do specify the absolute loss in power or pressure on the opposite side of the f_c. Finally, the 3-dB down points for some octave-band frequencies were illustrated earlier in this chapter, in Figure 6–2C.

The Cut-Off Frequency

How does a loss of 3 dB at the f_c of a real filter correspond to a halving of power or a halving of pressure? As indicated in previous sections of this chapter, the number of decibels in intensity level that are lost following a halving of the intensity level (or power) of a signal is easily computed. The dB IL of an intensity ratio of one half or of 0.5, or a halving of the intensity level of a signal is equal to

$$dB\ IL = 10 \times \log\left(\frac{1}{2}\right)$$

According to Table B3-6 found in Appendix B, the log 0.5 = −0.301. Therefore,

$$dB\ IL = 10 \times -0.301$$

or $\quad\quad dB\ IL = -3.0$

Therefore, the number of decibels lost when power is cut in half amounts to a loss of 3.0 dB IL. Likewise, the number of decibels in sound pressure level

that are lost following a halving of the pressure level of a signal is also easily computed. The dB SPL of a pressure ratio of one half or of 0.5, or a halving of the pressure level is equal to

$$dB\ SPL = 20 \times \log\left(\frac{1}{2}\right)$$

Remembering again that intensity and sound pressure are related in the manner described by Equation 6–6.

$$I = P^2 \quad\quad (6\text{–}6)$$

$$P = \sqrt{I}$$

The pressure ratio of 1:2, is now expressed as

$$dB\ SPL = 20 \times \log\left(\frac{1}{2}\right)^{\frac{1}{2}}$$

The square root ($\sqrt{}$) of 0.5 is equal to 0.707, and according to Table B3–6 in Appendix B, the log 0.707 = −0.15. Therefore,

$$dB\ SPL = 20 \times -0.15$$

or $\quad\quad dB\ SPL = -3.0$

Therefore, the number of decibels lost when pressure level is cut in half once again amounts to a loss of 3.0 dB SPL.

The Roll-Off Rate

The concept of a *roll-off rate* (rejection rate or attenuation rate) was addressed above in sections of this chapter illustrating both the spectrum level (see Figure 6–27 panel B lower right) and the spectral envelope (see Figure 6–33 panel B) for pink noise. The band-pass filtering characteristics of speech noise were also discussed. Spectral envelope roll-off rates for the triangular, square, and sawtooth waveforms were additionally illustrated in the upper, middle, and lower B panels (respectively) of Figure 6–32. Real filters are also characterized by their rejection slopes, rejection rates, or roll-off rates that are measured by so many dB/octave of signal suppression or signal attenuation. Also recollect from a previous discussion in this chapter of narrow-band noise (NBN), that the band-pass filter rejection rate on either side of the pass-band for a NBN not only determines how much relative (not absolute) suppression of the unwanted frequencies is provided by the filter, but also how much of the unwanted part of the original signal is relatively (not absolutely) permitted to pass through the filter with the NBN.

Ideal filters, with their perfectly rectangular filtering spectra, specify no rejection (roll-off) rates, since the slopes of their (rectangular) attenuation functions are absolute. By contrast, real filters not only specify a 3-dB down point, they also specify a roll-off rate. The roll-off rate (dB/octave) is a rate of signal attenuation that occurs beyond the -dB down point, or simply, beyond the initial loss of 3 dB that is specified at the f_c. Nevertheless, the octave notation (i.e., per octave) upon which the rate of the roll-off is based begins at the frequency that is specified as the f_c and requires using the f_c as if it were the fundamental or starting frequency for the octave scaling. Subsequently, the amount of signal attenuation as specified by the roll-off rate, progressively accumulates at each octave frequency beyond the f_c. As an example, suppose a low-pass filter has a cut-off frequency

at 500 Hz and a rejection rate specified by a 12 dB/octave slope. At the first octave frequency of 1000 Hz (i.e., 1000 is the first octave of 500) the roll-off rate that is observed is, of course, –12 dB. However, more needs to be said in terms of the actual basis for the initial attenuation of 12 dB at this particular octave (the first octave), the subject of which is addressed below. At the second octave (2000 Hz), the roll-off rate of 12 dB is again expressed and is added to the amount of signal attenuation previously observed (at the first octave of 1000 Hz), resulting in a composite signal attenuation value at the second octave, of –24 dB. At the third octave (4000 Hz), the roll-off rate of 12 dB is again expressed, and is again added to the amount of signal attenuation previously observed at the first (1000 Hz) and second (2000 Hz) octaves, resulting in a composite signal attenuation value at the third octave, of –36 dB, and so forth. Hence (and in terms of low-pass filter functions), at each successively higher octave (away from initial cut-off frequency), the amount of signal attenuation, as specified by the roll-off rate is repetitively added and continues to accumulate as the distance increases between the f_c and each successively higher octave. For high-pass filters, the amount of signal attenuation, as specified by the roll-off rate would be repetitively added but at each successively lower octave (away from initial cut-off frequency) and would continue to accumulate as the distance increased between the f_c and each successively lower octave. Note here that low-pass filters or low-pass filter functions for band-pass or band-reject filters are often the most useful and easiest to conceptualize when it comes to explanations of filter functions that involve octave notation.

The roll-off rate of a filter slope is, to be sure, a specified amount of signal attenuation that is observed at the first octave above the f_c and is cumulatively added at each subsequent octave frequency thereafter. However, the point needs to be made that the degree of attenuation (as specified by the roll-off rate) that is observed at the first octave (only), will include or will take into account, the initial 3 dB of signal attenuation that occurs at the cut-off frequency. Traditionally, the actual roll-off rate of a filter is calculated by computing the difference in signal attenuation between two consecutive octave frequencies located at a region in the filter slope where the gradient is both maximum and linear (Rosen & Howell, 2013). This maximum degree of slope linearity is usually observed beyond the first octave, at a location between the first and second octaves, and then thereafter. Take again the example provided above that described a low-pass filter with cut-off frequency at 500 Hz and a rejection rate specified by a 12 dB/octave slope. At the third octave (4000 Hz), the composite attenuation value was 36 dB. At the second octave (2000 Hz), the composite attenuation value was 24 dB. Therefore, this filter has a roll-off of 36 − 24 = 12 dB/octave. Likewise, at the second octave of 2000 Hz, the composite attenuation value was 24 dB, and it was 12 dB at the first octave frequency of 1000 Hz. Therefore, this filter once again has a roll-off of 24 − 12 = 12 dB/octave. If, however, the roll-off rate were to be calculated in the same manner, but from the first octave (1000 Hz) to the f_c (before the filtering response has reached its maximum slope), the signal attenuation would only amount to 9 dB, or simply 12 dB minus 3 dB (Rosen & Howell, 2013). This difference should be intuitively obvious since the filtered signal has already been attenuated by 3 dB at the f_c.

Finally, it is important to note that unlike the initial loss of 3 dB at the f_c, the roll-off rate is a characteristic of real filters that is independently specified. That is, for real filters, a loss of 3 dB always occurs at the f_c, whereas roll-off rates will vary from filter to filter depending upon the requirements of the systems in which they are found. Filter roll-off rates may be specified across a wide range of possible slopes. Filter slopes that range from −3 dB/octave to values that are just under −18 dB/octave are considered to be very shallow to fairly shallow. Filter slopes that range from −18 dB/octave, up to −48 dB/octave are regarded as moderately steep. Finally, filter slopes of −90 dB/octave are generally viewed as very steep. As the roll-off rate becomes increasingly steeper, the amplitude response (and slope) of the filter will more closely approximate the characteristics of an ideal filter (Rosen & Howell, 2013).

The Low-Pass Filter

A real low-pass filter (see Figure 6–35 panel A) as opposed to an ideal low-pass filter will faithfully pass most (but not all) frequencies that fall within the pass-band which is located below (in frequency) or to the left of the specified cut-off frequency (f_c). In the pass-band,

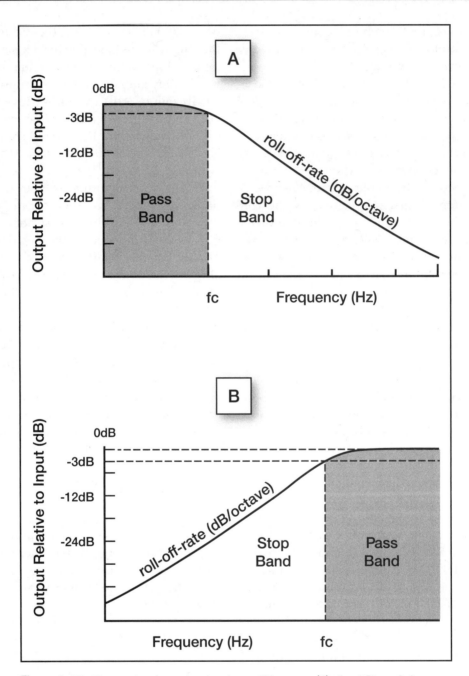

Figure 6–35. The pass-band, stop-band, and cut-off frequency (f_c) of real filters. **A.** Low-pass filter. **B.** High-pass filter.

the frequencies that are very close to, but just slightly lower in Hz relative to the f_c are attenuated minimally (by less than 3 dB), while the expected –3 dB of signal attenuation occurs at the f_c. A real low-pass filter will attenuate most (but not all) of the spectral energy contained within the stop-band, which is composed mostly of relatively higher frequency energy located to the right of the f_c (see Figure 6–35 panel A). In the stop-band, the frequencies that are very close to, but just slightly higher in frequency relative to the f_c are attenuated the least. The amount of signal attenuation for the increasingly higher frequencies in the stop-band progressively increases to a level that is specified by the roll-off rate of the particular filter. Hence, in a real low-pass filter, a small amount of the intended lower frequency energy located within the pass-band will be attenuated, while some of the unintended higher frequency energy located within the stop-band will be passed.

The High-Pass Filter

A real high-pass filter (see Figure 6–35 panel B) as compared to an ideal high-pass filter will faithfully pass most (but not all) frequencies that fall within the pass-band which is located above (in frequency) or to the right of the specified cut-off frequency (f_c). In the pass-band, the frequencies that are very close to, but just slightly higher in Hz relative to the f_c are attenuated minimally (by less than 3 dB), while the expected –3 dB of signal attenuation occurs at the f_c. A real high-pass filter will attenuate most (but not all) of the spectral energy contained within the stop-band, which is composed mostly of relatively lower frequency energy located to the left of the f_c (see Figure 6–35 panel B). In the stop-band, the frequencies very close to but just slightly lower in Hz relative to the f_c are attenuated the least. The amount of signal attenuation for the increasingly lower frequencies in the stop-band progressively increases

to a level that is specified by the roll-off rate of the particular filter. Hence, in a real high-pass filter, a small amount of the intended higher frequency energy located within the pass-band will be attenuated, while some of the unintended lower frequency energy located within the stop-band will be passed.

The Band-Pass Filter

Recall that a band-pass filter only passes or permits a particular band of frequencies to appear at the output of a system. A band-pass filter is often created by cascading, or connecting a high-pass filter with a low-pass filter (Durrant & Feth, 2013). An illustration of a real band-pass filter is provided in panel A of Figure 6–36. It should be obvious from the figure that the high-pass filtering properties of a band-pass filter are found to the left of the pass-band, while the low-pass filtering properties are found to the right of the pass-band. Recall that band-pass filters often have lower (f_{cL}) and upper (f_{cU}) cut-off frequencies, as illustrated in Figure 6–36 panel A. Hence, in a band-pass filter, the f_{cU} of the pass-band corresponds to the f_c of the low-pass filter component, whereas the f_{cL} of the pass-band corresponds to the f_c of the high-pass filter component. A real, as opposed to an ideal band-pass filter will faithfully pass most (but not all) frequencies that fall within the pass-band. The frequencies in the pass-band that are located very close to, but just slightly higher in Hz relative to the f_{cL} are attenuated minimally (by less than 3 dB). Likewise, those frequencies in the pass-band that are located very close to but just slightly lower in Hz relative to the f_{cU} are also attenuated minimally, while the

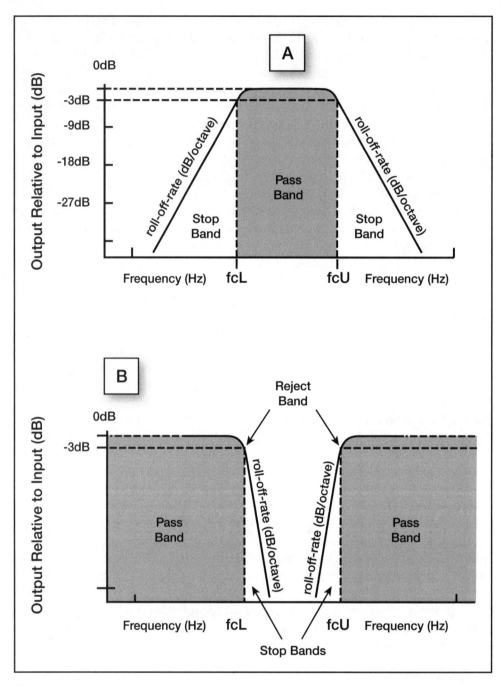

Figure 6–36. Lower (f_cL) and upper (f_cU) cut-off frequencies of two real filters. **A.** The pass-band and the two stop-bands of a band-pass filter. **B.** The two pass-bands, two stop-bands, and reject-band of a band-reject (band-stop) filter.

expected –3 dB of signal attenuation occurs at both the f_{cL} and the f_{cU} as illustrated in panel A of Figure 6–36. The pass-band of a band-pass filter is also the filter's bandwidth (Δf), where $\Delta f = f_{cU} – f_{cL}$, and this particular bandwidth is defined as the width of the band of frequencies that are passed by the band-pass filter (Speaks, 1999). Because the bandwidth of a real band-pass filter is equal to the frequency range that exists between the lower and upper cut-off frequencies, which in essence are the two 3-dB down points, the pass-band of a real band-pass filter is also referred to as the *half-power bandwidth* or the *nominal bandwidth* (Durrant & Feth, 2013).

A real band-pass filter will also attenuate most (but not all) of the spectral energy contained within each of the two stop-bands. The stop-bands are composed of frequencies that are lower in Hz relative to the f_{cL} and those that are higher in Hz relative to the f_{cU} as illustrated in Figure 6–36 panel A. The frequencies in the stop-bands that are very close to but are either slightly lower in Hz relative to the f_{cL} or slightly

higher in Hz relative to the f_{cU} are attenuated the least. Beyond these frequencies, the amount of signal attenuation of the increasingly lower and increasingly higher frequency energy in the stop-bands will progressively increase to levels specified by the low-pass and high-pass roll-off rate functions (respectively) of the particular band-pass filter, as illustrated in panel A of Figure 6–36. Hence, in a real band-pass filter, a small amount of the intended lower and higher frequency energy located within the pass-band will be attenuated, while some of the unintended lower and higher frequency energy located within each of the two the stop-bands, will be passed.

Also recall that a band-pass filter can often be created by the cascading or connecting of a high-pass filter with a low-pass filter. Figure 6–37 presents the output frequency spectrum of low-pass

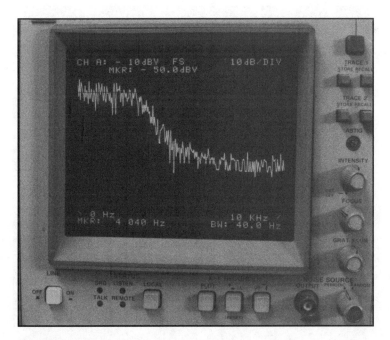

Figure 6–37. The output frequency spectrum of low-pass filtered white noise, viewed on the monitor of a real-time analyzer. From S. Silman and M. B. Emmer (2012), with permission.

filtered white noise, viewed on the monitor of a real-time analyzer. As shown, the lower frequencies in the signal's spectrum (to the left) are passed, while the higher frequencies in the signal's spectrum (to the right) are attenuated above a particular cut-off frequency (Silman & Emmer, 2012). Figure 6–38 presents the output frequency spectrum of high-pass filtered white noise, viewed on the monitor of a real-time analyzer. As shown, the higher frequencies in the signal's spectrum (to the right) are passed, while the lower frequencies in the signal's spectrum (to the left) are attenuated below a particular cut-off frequency (Silman & Emmer, 2012).

The Band-Reject (Band-Stop) Filter

Finally, recall that a band-reject or band-stop filter blocks or stops a band of frequencies from appearing at the output of a system. That is, a band-reject filter rejects rather than passes energy for a specified set of frequencies located between an upper and lower cut-off frequency. As illustrated by the real band-reject filter provided in panel B of Figure 6–36, such filters tend to be relatively narrow. Like a band-pass filter, a band-reject filter is often created by cascading, or connecting a high-pass filter with a low-pass filter. Recall that band-reject filters also have lower and upper cut-off frequencies. The frequency region in which a band-reject filter provides attenuation is often called the *reject-band* of the band-stop filter (Yost, 2007). As illustrated in Figure 6–36 panel B, the reject-band is located between the lower (f_{cL}) and the upper (f_{cU}) cut-off frequencies, and includes the two stop-bands that

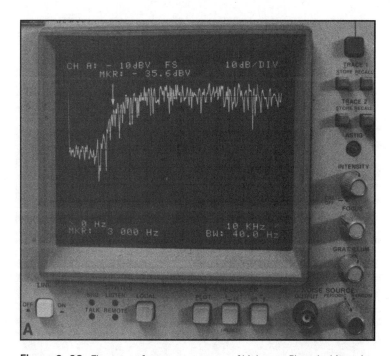

Figure 6–38. The output frequency spectrum of high–pass filtered white noise, viewed on the monitor of a real-time analyzer. From S. Silman and M. B. Emmer (2012), with permission.

are also shown in the figure. It should be clear from panel B of Figure 6–36 that the high-pass filtering properties of a band-reject filter can be found to the right of the reject-band, while the low-pass filtering properties can be found to the left of the reject-band. Hence, in a band-reject filter, the f_{cU} of the reject-band corresponds to the f_c of the high-pass filter component, whereas the f_{cL} of the reject-band corresponds to the f_c of the low-pass filter component. A real, as opposed to an ideal band-reject filter will faithfully block most (but not all) frequencies that fall within the reject-band. In the ideal band-reject filter discussed above, the stop-band was equivalent to the reject band. In a real band-reject filter, the frequencies in the reject-band that are located very close to but just slightly higher in Hz relative to the f_{cL} are attenuated the least. Likewise, the frequencies in the reject-band that are located very close to, but just slightly lower in Hz relative to the f_{cU} are also attenuated the least. Frequency energy in the reject-band that is increasingly higher in Hz relative to the f_{cL} or increasingly lower in Hz relative to the f_{cU} will be progressively attenuated or blocked at the rate specified by the low-pass and high-pass roll-off rate functions (respectively) of the particular band-reject filter, as illustrated in Figure 6–36 panel B.

A real band-reject filter will also faithfully pass most (but not all) of the spectral energy contained within each of the two pass-bands. The pass-bands are composed of frequencies that are lower in Hz relative to the f_{cL} and those that are higher in Hz relative to the f_{cU} as illustrated in panel B of Figure 6–36. In the pass-bands, frequencies that are very close in Hz but are either slightly lower relative to the f_{cL} or slightly higher relative to the f_{cU} are attenuated the least (by less than 3 dB), while the expected –3 dB of signal attenuation occurs at both the f_{cL} and the f_{cU} as illustrated in panel B of Figure 6–36. Hence, in a real band-reject filter, some amount of the unintended lower and higher spectral energy within the reject-band will be passed, while a small amount of the intended lower and higher frequency energy located within each of the two pass-bands, will be attenuated.

The 60–Hz Notch–Filter

A special type of band-reject filter is designed with a very narrow reject-band that is often used to filter, prevent, or block the electromagnetic noise that is often picked up by the electrical circuits of audio devices, from reaching the output side of these systems. The source of the noise is the electromagnetic field created by the alternating current-type of electrical energy that is commonly generated by power plants located in North American countries. The alternating current generates a *line frequency* that originates from an electric power grid and is transmitted from a power plant. The line frequency is eventually transmitted through to the wires found in dwellings where it is ultimately delivered to the user. The alternating current that generates the line frequency is created by alternating the polarity of the voltage at the power source. This action results in a sinusoidal movement of electrons, and causes the electrons to oscillate (in their motion) around relatively fixed positions, first in one direction and then in the opposite direction. The line frequency is the frequency of these alternating current oscillations, which amounts to 60 cycles per second. Therefore, the result of the alternating current is the generation of a 60-Hz electromagnetic field that is carried within the line. The 60-Hz band-reject filter that is also called the *60-Hz notch-filter* is designed to reject energy that exists at one specific frequency. Hence, the 60-Hz notch-filter is often employed to reduce or to eliminate the 60-Hz humming that is generated from the output side of audio systems, caused by the electrical line noise resulting from alternating current power sources.

Filters in Personal Amplification

Almost two decades ago, all hearing aids were composed entirely of *analog* components and in fact, were analog-type amplification devices. The first practical *digital* hearing aids were only introduced in 1996, and since that time, the hearing aid industry has rapidly grown from the production of simpler analog-type hearing aids to the implementation of complex digital amplification devices. Currently, the vast majority of hearing aids are digital and incorporate among other features, a wide range of sophisticated *digital signal–processing* (DSP) *algorithms*, directional microphones (discussed earlier in this chapter), and sophisticated filters for spectral shaping and speech enhancement (Kates, 2008).

Analog Signals, Analog Hearing Aids, and Analog Filters

Amplification devices are, for the most part, electronic systems. A *system* may be defined as any device that performs an operation on, or a transformation of, an input signal in order to produce an output signal. Both input and output signals may be electrical, as in an amplifier, or the input signal may be electrical with an acoustic output signal (sound), such as in headphones, or they may be switched such as in microphones, as addressed earlier this chapter (Rosen & Howell, 2013). What is meant by the term, *analog signal?* For the present discussion, an analog signal is an electrical signal that exhibits continuous variations in amplitude over time, and essentially mimics the original waveform that characterizes the original sound stimulus. Hence, an analog signal is a signal that is analogous to the original waveform of the signal. Many such analog waveforms have been illustrated in the preceding sections. In an analog-type hearing aid, a continuous-time input signal is processed to produce a continuous-time output signal (Kates, 2008). The filters in analog hearing aid devices are often composed of a resistor and a capacitor. Resistance refers to an opposition to the current flow and is often associated with impedance (Z) as discussed in Chapter 5. When resistive devices (such as resistors) are placed together in series, or simply placed end to end, they greatly increase resistance and greatly decrease conductance. Capacitors also block or resist the flow of current, but accumulate and store electrical charges, as discussed above in reference to the types of microphones. Capacitors then release the charge and in so doing, add the dimension of a time delay or latency to the electrical events. In analog amplification devices, the circuit that modulates the frequency response (tone control) acts by splitting the electrical signal into two separate frequency regions so that electrical resistance may be added as needed, in order to attenuate energy in either region. For example, if the analog circuit is designed to emphasize lower frequencies (low-pass filter), the higher frequencies will be de-emphasized by the addition of resistance to the higher frequency components (Hamill & Price, 2014). In a low-pass analog filter, the current flows through the resistor and the output voltage is taken across the capacitor, which then delivers the filtered output voltage to the next processing stage (Silman & Emmer, 2012). Recall that the output of a low-pass analog filter was presented in Figure 6–37. If an analog circuit is designed to emphasize higher frequencies (high-pass filter), the lower frequencies will be de-emphasized by the addition of resistance to the lower frequency components (Hamill & Price, 2014). In a high-pass analog filter, the current flows first through the capacitor and the filtered output voltage, consisting of higher frequencies with much of the lower frequency components attenuated, is taken across the resistor. The output of a high-pass analog filter was also presented in Figure 6–38. A band-pass analog filter is also created by the combination of a low-pass and high-pass filter that combines a resistor, a capacitor, and an *inductor*. An inductor is a device that stores energy in the form of a magnetic field when a changing current passes through it, and it is said to produce inductive reactance. In a band-pass analog filter, the filtered output voltage is also taken across the resistor (Silman & Emmer, 2012).

Digital Signals, Digital Hearing Aids, and Digital Filters

Analog signals are often contrasted with digital signals. Digital signals, by comparison are composed of a series of discrete numerical binary values consisting of sets of base-2 combinations of ones and zeros. These binary digital code sets are generated by *digital signal–processing* (DSP) circuits and are implemented for the purpose of providing digital representations (or the digitization) of the original analog signals. As indicated above, digital hearing aids employ DSP circuits. In DSP hearing aids, the DSP not only refers to the digital circuitry that converts continuous analog signals in time, into discrete (binary) data points in time, but also refers to the multiple mathematical algorithms that enable spectral shaping and noise-reduction processing functions on the digital signals (Hamill & Price, 2014). In short, DSP circuits convert analog signals to digital signals by analog-to-digital conversion and then manipulate the digital signals according to a set of mathematical signal-processing algorithms. The DSP circuit then converts the digital signals back into analog signals by digital-to-analog conversion. Therefore by definition, an analog-to-digital (A-to-D) converter is an electronic device that converts a continuously varying electrical (analog) signal into a series of numeric values that are then manipulated or processed by a computer or by a digital hearing aid, according to a set of mathematical signal-processing algorithms. As the name implies, a mathematical signal-processing algorithm is a set of specific mathematical operations or instructions that are systematically performed by computers and digital hearing aids in order to accomplish specific tasks or to perform specific functions. Also by definition, a digital-to-analog (D-to-A) converter is an electronic device that converts a series of electrical, numeric values back into a continuously varying electrical (analog) signal after they have been processed by a computer or by a digital hearing aid, according to the set of specified algorithms (Silman & Emmer, 2012).

Figure 6–39 illustrates the signal-processing stages in a DSP hearing aid. DSP and the conversion of an analog signal to a digital signal will entail the sampling and the binary code digitization of the amplitude and frequency components of the analog signal. Sampling simply means taking measures of the signal's amplitude value at equally spaced moments in time. The sampling and binary code digitization is performed by the A-to-D converter (Rosen & Howell, 2013). In the DSP hearing aid, as well as in other digital systems, analog signal samples are obtained at discrete (equally spaced) time intervals that are defined by specified A-to-D sampling rates. Each signal amplitude sample that is acquired is represented by a numerical code value. The digitization rate of the A-to-D converter is the frequency at which the digital samples are obtained and measured as a waveform is converted from an analog signal into the digital format of binary numbers. However, the sampling rate of the A-to-D converter places an upper limit on the highest signal frequency that can be processed (Silman & Emmer, 2012). This upper signal frequency value is based on the *Nyquist theorem*. The Nyquist theorem states that a continuous-time signal can only be accurately digitized and (subsequently) accurately reproduced in numerical code, if the sampling frequency is equal to or exceeds a value that is twice the highest frequency within the analog signal. That is, in order for an A-to-D converter to obtain an accurate spectral analysis of a signal, at least two samples must be

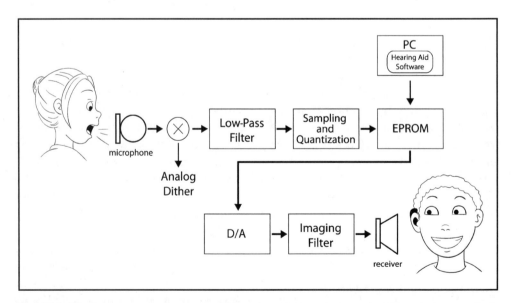

Figure 6–39. Signal processing stages in a DSP hearing aid. Shown is the analog dither, the low-pass anti-aliasing filter. The analog-to-digital (A-to-D) converter is shown as "sampling and quantization." Also shown is the erasable programmable read-only memory (EPROM) and the digital-to-analog (D-to-A) converter with the associated low-pass anti-imaging filter. From S. Silman and M. B. Emmer (2012), with permission.

taken for every cycle of an analog waveform (Hamill & Price, 2014). Because at least two samples must be taken for every waveform cycle, the *Nyquist frequency* is the frequency that is equal to one-half of the sampling rate, and therefore, the Nyquist frequency represents the highest frequency of an analog signal that can be sampled and processed accurately. For instance, many digital hearing aids have A-to-D circuits that use sampling rates of 16 kHz. Hence, the Nyquist frequency in these devices would be no higher than 8 kHz, or simply one-half of 16 kHz (Rosen & Howell, 2013). The sampling of an analog signal having a frequency component that is higher than the imposed Nyquist frequency results in the digitization of an inadequate number of samples (<2) per cycle, for a particular high-frequency component (Rosen & Howell, 2013). The end result is the digital acquisition and reconstruction of an incorrect, lower-in-frequency rendition (or alias) of the original higher-in-frequency analog signal component, a phenomenon known as *aliasing*.

Both analog as well as digital filtering is available in DSP hearing aids. However, analog filters require dedicated filtering circuitry, whereas DSP filtering algorithms are flexible and easily programmable. Electronic filter circuits that do not employ DSP technology tend to be bulky and expensive. Digital circuits provide high-quality filtering with less bulkiness, greater portability, and lower cost. Digital filtering involves the application of DSP algorithms to digitized data, producing filter effects that are similar to those of analog filtering on analog signals. However, DSP filtering is achieved without the use of bulky analog filtering circuits and their component capacitors and resistors. In many respects, digital technology has led to the phasing out of such devices (Silman & Emmer, 2012). Electronic filters that employ DSP technology can closely approximate the ideal filtering characteristics that were addressed earlier in the preceding sections of this chapter.

Again, Figure 6–39 illustrates that before the analog signal is sent to the A-to-D converter for sampling, a small amount of random noise is sometimes added to the analog signal. This random noise helps to reduce distortion and can provide an added safeguard in the prevention of aliasing error that might result from the sampling of higher frequency analog signal components (Silman & Emmer, 2012). This random, low-level noise is called *analog dither*. The analog signal and the analog dither are then sent through a low-pass *anti-aliasing* filter to remove the relatively higher frequencies in the analog signal and dither that exceed the Nyquist frequency (Moore, 2012). DSP hearing aids often employ low-pass anti-aliasing filters with upper limits of 6000 or 8000 Hz that allow speech signals to pass through with high quality (Silman & Emmer, 2012). While anti-aliasing filtering is often built into A-to-D circuits, such filtering will attempt to remove the relatively higher frequencies before the signal reaches the digitization process (Hamill & Price, 2014). However, effective anti-aliasing filters must meet two requirements. First, they must pass as many of the analog signal components as possible that fall below the Nyquist frequency, and second, they must attenuate as many of the analog signal components as possible that fall above the Nyquist frequency. However, no filter is perfect, and on occasion an anti-aliasing filter will permit signal components that fall above the Nyquist frequency to leak through to the A-to-D circuits (Kates, 2008).

After the A-to-D conversion, the digitized signal is sent to an integrated (DSP) circuit that contains the signal-processing algorithms. The algorithms that have been selectively programmed are stored in an erasable programmable read-only memory (EPROM), as illustrated in Figure 6–39. The EPROM represents reprogrammable permanent memory storage (Silman & Emmer, 2012). While the digitization process has many advantages, it creates unwanted noise in the digital samples. The digitization noise can cause some degree of misrepresentation at all frequencies (Hamill & Price, 2014). The digitization noise added to the digital signals is random and has equal amounts of energy per frequency (or per cycle). Recall that this is also the definition of white (Gaussian) noise provided earlier. Therefore, before the digital signal is directed into a fast Fourier transform (FFT) algorithm for spectral analysis, the noise in the raw digital samples is filtered (Hamill & Price, 2014). Digital filtering at this stage consists of digital signal averaging. This noise-reduction filtering involves the application of yet another algorithm, and by signal averaging, much of the white noise in the digitized signal is filtered away.

Following the noise-reduction filtering process, the digital samples are directed into the FFT algorithm where the digitized signal is analyzed for its frequency content. The FFT algorithm attempts to estimate the frequency spectrum of the original analog signal from the samples that were taken during the digitization process, and essentially performs a frequency by amplitude analysis (or spectrum analysis) on the digital samples (Silman & Emmer, 2012). The FFT determines not only the separate phases of each frequency component, but also determines the signal level that is present within the many but very narrow frequency bands. The DSP algorithms then permit the amplification of signals within each separate frequency band, resulting in precise filtering capabilities (Hamill & Price, 2014). Digital amplification may also employ multichannel filter banks composed of parallel low, high, and band-pass filters and linear-phase systems that control the phase of each frequency component, independent of how steep or how shallow the filtering slopes happen to be (Kates, 2008). Finally, when the digital signal is reconverted to an analog signal by D-to-A conversion, high-frequency distortion is often introduced into the signal which must again be filtered, as further illustrated in Figure 6–39. The high-frequency distortion is called *imaging* that produces *imaging distortion* and requires the addition of an *anti-imaging filter*. Anti-imaging filtering is once again accomplished by a low-pass filter that is built into the D-to-A circuits (Silman & Emmer, 2012).

Linear Systems

As indicated in the preceding section, a system may be defined as any device that performs an operation on, or a transformation of, an input signal in order to produce an output signal. The term *transfer function* is often used to describe what happens to signals as they are transferred through a system. Transfer function is also a term that is synonymous with the terms *amplitude response* and *frequency response* (Rosen & Howell, 2013). Recall that frequency response is an expression that has been used often throughout this chapter in reference to microphone systems. To begin with, the concept of a linear transfer function (or linearity) in linear systems means that the output from a system can only occur at the same frequencies that were originally introduced into the system's input. That is, if a linear system is activated at its input by a single sinusoid, the frequency observed at the output of the system can only consist of the same sinusoidal frequency that was originally introduced into the system. Sinusoidal inputs to a linear system will always result in the production of sinusoidal outputs, such that the sinusoidal shape will always be preserved at the output of a linear system, though the amplitude and phase may be slightly altered (Rosen & Howell, 2013). Furthermore, if a sinusoid is introduced into the input side of a linear system, and if that system is known to alter both the phase and the amplitude as defined by its transfer function, then the amplitude and phase of the sinusoid may indeed be altered, but there will be no other frequencies added by the system, to the system's output. To be sure, if the input to a linear system consists of a combination of sinusoids at different frequencies, only those frequencies defined by the complex signal will be present in the system's output, because the output of a linear system will not and should not contain frequencies that were not originally present at the input side of the system (Kates, 2008).

If the input signal to a linear system has been doubled in amplitude, the output signal from the linear system will also be doubled in amplitude. A signal's amplitude measured at the output side of a linear system may equal the signal's amplitude at the input side, but it could also be greater in amplitude (as in amplification) or less in amplitude (as in attenuation). What is important in a linear system is that the relationship between the input amplitude and output amplitude for any given signal is linear and proportional (Rosen & Howell, 2013). That is, changes in the input level of a signal should produce proportional changes in the output level of the signal because the transfer function is linear (Speaks, 1999). In addition, if a sinusoid is introduced into the input side of a linear system, adding a second sinusoidal frequency to the input side will result in the separate outputs of both sinusoids, but the second sinusoid will not affect the amplitude or phase of the first sinusoidal frequency, at the output of the system. Furthermore, if the input to a linear system consists of several separate sinusoidal frequencies, each with their own separate outputs, the output for the complex signal will be the sum of the outputs of each of the separate frequency components (Kates, 2008). Finally, linear systems often exhibit the property of *linear time-invariance*. In a linear time-invariant system, the linearity of the system does not change over time, and therefore the input-output transfer function will not change over time (Moore, 2012). The system will exhibit the same frequency response as reflected in the output, independent of the time at which a particular signal (or signals) is introduced into the input side of the system (Rosen & Howell, 2013).

Linear Distortion

Distortion is said to occur when the waveform of a signal is intentionally or unintentionally altered in some way, after the signal has been transferred from the input side, through to the output side, of a physical system. If a signal is faithfully passed through a system, such that the signal at the output side is identical to the original waveform at the input side (even in terms of amplitude and phase), then the signal can be said to have passed through the system, undistorted. However, recall that even though frequency may be faithfully transferred in linear systems, the amplitudes and phases of each component frequency may still be slightly altered (Rosen & Howell, 2013). In actuality, when any sound or electrical signal is transferred through a physical system, the spectrum of the signal always undergoes some degree of change. The signal at the output side of a system is never an exact representation of the signal that was originally introduced into the input side, but is always changed or distorted to some degree (Durrant & Feth, 2013). Recall that a signal's amplitude, measured at the output side of a linear system may be greater (as in amplification) or less (as in attenuation) relative to the amplitude of the input signal. A waveform signal that is intentionally boosted or intentionally attenuated in amplitude at the output side of a linear system is a waveform that by definition

has been altered. While either instance would hardly be thought of as distortion, and much less, would never be labeled as amplitude distortion (which is in fact a type of nonlinear distortion discussed below), technically speaking, both instances could be classified as types of linear distortion.

Frequency Distortion

Filters have been addressed and treated in previous sections of this chapter as devices (systems) that intentionally shape or otherwise selectively alter the amplitudes of signals as a function of their frequency. When signals are passed through filter systems, the amplitudes of some frequencies are passed faithfully, while the amplitudes of other frequencies are partially attenuated. When any system favors some frequencies and attenuates other frequencies, by definition, the total waveform expressed at the output side of the system has been altered. Therefore, this type of distortion is called *frequency distortion*, and frequency distortion caused by filters represents a type of linear distortion. Not all filtering is intentional. Recall that the telephone band-pass filters speech sounds, and selectively passes only frequencies found within a limited bandwidth ranging from 300 to 3000 Hz. This type of filtering is intentional as these systems are designed for a relatively accurate reproduction of speech signals. Nevertheless, frequency distortion occurs because these filtering systems do not or cannot reproduce with equal amplitudes all of the frequencies that are introduced at the input side of the system. Frequency distortion is linear as long as no additional frequency components are added to the output side of a filter system. It is the amplitude response that indicates the manner in which signals show signs of frequency distortion on the output sides of linear filter systems (Speaks, 1999).

Nonlinear Distortion

Nonlinear distortion usually refers to unintentional alterations in a signal at the output of a system, due to an inaccurate production, transfer, or reproduction of the input signal (Hamill & Price, 2014). In practice, many systems respond linearly, provided that the magnitude of the input signal is not too great. Excessively high signal input intensities may cause a linear system to become nonlinear, even though most of the time the system operates linearly (Speaks, 1999). In actuality every system tends to exhibit small amounts of nonlinear distortion. The nonlinear distortion is typically ignored in computing linear transfer functions, as long as the behavior of the system is predominantly linear (Katz, 2008). In a nonlinear system or in a linear system that has been driven to nonlinearity, the relationship between the input amplitude and output amplitude for any given signal is no longer proportional. That is, changes in the input level of a signal do not produce proportional changes in the output level of the signal, because the input-output transfer function is nonlinear. Furthermore, if a sinusoid or a combination of sinusoids at different frequencies (a complex signal) is introduced to the input side of a nonlinear system, other frequency components are likely to be added to the system's output, because the output of nonlinear systems contains frequencies not originally present at the input side of these systems.

Amplitude Distortion

As indicated above, excessively high signal input intensities may cause a linear system to become nonlinear, even though most of the time the system operates linearly. Overdriving a nonlinear system (or system that has the potential for nonlinear responses) beyond its elastic limits will cause maximum instantaneous amplitudes at the input side of the system to fall at or near the nonlinear part of the system. Overdriving a system beyond its elastic limits means that the amount of mechanical displacement in the system is disproportionate to or exceeds the system's restorative force. When the system's capacity for elastic recoil is compromised, the peak amplitudes representing the natural resonances (or natural vibration patterns) of the system will also be compromised (reduced) and morphologically altered. When the amplitude of the output from a system falls off or saturates in spite of increments in the input amplitude, the system is said to exhibit a saturating nonlinearity, frequently resulting in severe morphological alterations of the amplitude peaks, a phenomenon known as *peak clipping* (Rosen & Howell, 2013). The term *saturation* is often used synonymously with the term *peak clipping* and at those higher input amplitudes, the input-output transfer function of the system is no longer linearly proportional

(Speaks, 1999). In terms of the input-output function for amplitude, overdriving the system leads to a condition of diminishing returns. Peak clipping is therefore indicative of nonlinear *amplitude distortion* because the instantaneous amplitudes of the input signal have exceeded the limits of linearity in the input-output function of the nonlinear system. That is, peak clipping takes place in the nonlinear portion of the input-output transfer function, and hence, amplitude distortion is also synonymous with nonlinear distortion (Speaks, 1999).

Peak clipping may be symmetrical, meaning that both positive and negative peaks may be clipped equally. The amount of symmetrical peak clipping may also be so severe that the clipped waveform begins to approximate the morphology of a square wave, as illustrated in Figure 6–40. Peak clipping may also be asymmetrical where, for instance, only the positive peaks are clipped, leaving the center portions and negative peaks unaffected. Center clipping of the signal can also occur in which only the center portions of the peaks are eliminated and the positive and negative peaks are preserved (Speaks, 1999). Amplitude distortion, with its concomitant peak clipping, is the most common form of nonlinear distortion. Amplitude distortion is often associated with the less than pleasant and even harsh, discordant, and noise-like perception of sound that is generated by a poorly constructed audio sound system, when too much ampli-

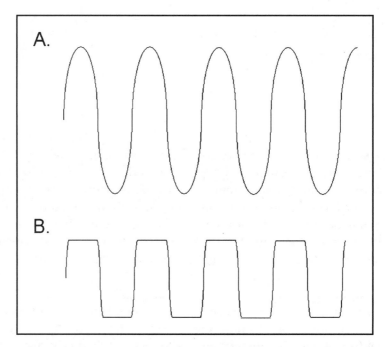

Figure 6–40. Symmetrical peak clipping. **A.** The original sine wave is introduced into the input side of a nonlinear system. **B.** The same sine wave with severe, symmetrical peak clipping resulting from (nonlinear) amplitude distortion. From T. A. Hamill and L. L. Price (2014), with permission.

tude (volume) is applied. Amplitude distortion is also associated with, or follows from, *harmonic distortion*. Amplitude distortion is also synonymous with harmonic distortion.

Harmonic Distortion

As indicated above, amplitude distortion results from overdriving a nonlinear system (or system that has the potential for nonlinear responses) beyond its elastic limits. When a system (or object-load) is overdriven by too much power, force, or pressure at one particular frequency, different regions of the system or object-load begin to vibrate unnaturally at different rates, as opposed to naturally, at one particular fundamental frequency. This asymmetric pattern of vibration creates unwanted harmonic frequencies in the output of a system or in any object-load undergoing forced vibration. Recall from Chapter 5 that when forces are applied in excess, or at frequencies known to be significantly different from the fundamental frequency of the resonating load, there will quite often be the creation of unnatural and/or unwanted resonances (vibration patterns) at other frequencies. Hence, in a system exhibiting nonlinear amplitude distortion, the output side of the system will deliver frequencies that were not originally part of the sinusoidal input signal, and the unwanted energy will be created at harmonic frequencies, and hence the term *harmonic distortion*. Recall that a complex waveform is defined as two or more (different) signals that occupy the same space at the same time. Hence, amplitude (harmonic) distortion changes a simple sinusoidal (pure tone) waveform into a complex sound, composed of the original fundamental frequency, plus one or more of its harmonics.

Recall again that harmonics are defined as integer whole number multiples of a particular fundamental (f_0) frequency. Harmonic distortion is usually expressed as a percentage (%) and reflects the amount of undesired signal energy expressed within a system's output signal, relative to the amount of desired signal energy that is found within the fundamental frequency (f_0) at the input side of the system. The undesired signal energy is the energy within the total number (n) of harmonics (f_2, f_3, f_4, f_5, f_n . . . etc.) of the f_0, and specifically, those frequencies located above the first harmonic (f_1). Because the f_0 is also contained within the output signal, the total energy will be equal to the sum of the desired energy (f_0), and the undesired energy found within the harmonics. The amount of harmonic distortion is therefore expressed as the proportion of the total energy in the output signal that is composed of undesired energy. Signal energy, measured in intensity or pressure, is determined at the f_0, and at each of the separate harmonic frequencies above the first harmonic. Measurements are made with a spectral wave analyzer composed of a volt-meter, combined with a narrowly tuned band-pass filter equipped with an adjustable center frequency (Speaks, 1999). When the total amplitude (energy) of the second harmonic and each higher harmonic are expressed as a percentage of the amplitude of the fundamental frequency, the measure that is taken is called the *total harmonic distortion* or THD (Moore, 2012). The sum of the energy contained within each of the harmonic frequencies is placed into the numerator, and the energy at the fundamental frequency, plus the sum of the energy contained within each of the harmonic frequencies, is placed into the denominator. The energy ratio is then multiplied by 100 to arrive at the percentage of THD (Speaks, 1999), as shown below:

$$\text{THD} =$$
$$[(f_2 + f_3 + f_4 + f_5 + f_n \ldots \text{etc.}) \div f_0 + (f_2 + f_3 + f_4 + f_5 + f_n \ldots \text{etc.})] \times 100$$

The more severe the inherent nonlinearity in a system, and/or the greater the driving force applied to a nonlinear system, the greater will be the amplitude of the harmonic components relative to the fundamental frequency. Furthermore, the more severe the inherent nonlinearity in a system, and/or the greater the driving force applied to a nonlinear system, the greater will be the total number of harmonic components. In either case, the amount of amplitude (harmonic) distortion will be greater.

Nonlinear Transient and Imaging Distortion

Recall that transient distortion is produced by the generation of both broadband acoustic clicks and narrow-band acoustic tone bursts, and was addressed in the sections above. Transient distortion takes the form of spectral splatter, and this unintended spectral energy is carried in the side band frequencies. Transient distortion was defined by the creation of harmonically related side lobes (spectral splatter) on either side of the main lobe in the production of clicks, from rectangular pulses, and in the production of tone bursts, from sinusoids. Recall that spectral splatter

not only represented unwanted distortion, but also compromised the spectral purity of the desired center (fundamental) frequency signal. Hence, transient distortion represents yet another type of nonlinear amplitude (harmonic) distortion. Another type of nonlinear distortion is imaging distortion. Recall that when a digital signal is reconverted to an analog signal by D-to-A conversion, unwanted high-frequency (imaging) distortion is often introduced into the digitized signals, requiring the use of an anti-imaging filter, as illustrated in Figure 6–39.

Intermodulation Distortion: Combination Tones

Amplitude (harmonic) distortion may also be applied to complex signals composed of two or more sinusoidal frequencies. As indicated previously in this chapter, most environmental sounds are complex, composed of a combination of not only two, but in most instances, numerous separate frequency components. Many of these complex environmental sounds are periodic but many are also aperiodic. For simplicity, if the input to a nonlinear system consists of two sinusoids, called the *primary frequencies* or *primaries*, symbolized as $f1$ and $f2$, what might be expected at the output side of the nonlinear system? Bearing in mind that the primaries $f1$ and $f2$ are essentially two separate fundamental frequencies, the output will consist of the two primaries, plus the separate harmonics of the two primaries. However, in addition, the output might also include combinations of frequency components derived from the two primary input frequencies.

The different possible combinations of frequency components that may be derived from the primaries, and quite possibly generated by a nonlinear system, are called *combination tones*. The range of possible combination tones is easily determined mathematically as they are systematically generated from both the sums and the differences of the primary input frequencies. Hence, combination tones are split into two general categories, *summation tones* and *difference tones*. The generation of both categories of combination tone components is the result of *intermodulation distortion* that occurs in nonlinear systems, and collectively, the combination tones are called *intermodulation distortion products*.

In theory, the combination tones comprise all possible sums and differences of the primary frequencies, as well as all possible sums and differences of the all integer multiples of the primaries. In actuality, the energy within many of the higher-in-frequency combination tones will be sufficiently weak, such that their contribution to the total energy of the output signal of the nonlinear system will be negligible (Speaks, 1999). The general equation that defines the primaries ($f1$ and $f2$), the harmonics of the primaries, the summation tones of the primaries and their harmonics, and the difference tones of the primaries and their harmonics, is given by

$$xf1 \pm yf2 \qquad (6\text{--}20)$$

In which

x represents all integer values: 0, 1, 2, 3, 4 . . . n; and

y represents all integer values: 0, 1, 2, 3, 4 . . . n.

Because the fundamental frequency (f_0) is also equal to the first harmonic (f_1), Equation 6–20 may be used to compute the two primary frequencies, which may be represented as $1f1 + 0f2$ and $0f1 + 1f2$. The harmonics of the first primary ($f1$) would also consist of $2f1 + 0f2$, $3f1 + 0f2$, $4f1 + 0f2$, $5f1 + 0f2$, and so forth, and the harmonics of the second primary ($f2$) would then consist of $0f1 + 2f2$, $0f1 + 3f2$, $0f1 + 4f2$, $0f1 + 5f2$, and so forth.

Employing Equation 6–20, the combination tones of the two primaries may also be computed and would consist of the summation tone: $1f1 + 1f2$, and the difference tone: $1f1 - 1f2$. The combination tones of the harmonics of the first primary could similarly be computed and would consist of the summation tones: $2f1 + 1f2$, $3f1 + 1f2$, $4f1 + 1f2$, and so forth, and the difference tones: $2f1 - 1f2$, $3f1 - 1f2$, $4f1 - 1f2$, and so forth. Similarly, the combination tones of the harmonics of the second primary would consist of the summation tones: $1f1 + 2f2$, $1f1 + 2f2$, $1f1 + 4f2$, and so forth, and the difference tones: $1f1 - 2f2$, $1f1 - 3f2$, $1f1 - 4f2$, and so forth.

Finally, employing Equation 6–20, the combination tones of the harmonics of both the first and second primaries could be computed and would consist of the summation tones: $2f1 + 2f2$, $2f1 + 3f2$, $2f1 + 4f2$, and so forth; also $3f1 + 2f2$, $3f1 + 3f2$, $3f1 + 4f2$, and so forth; and $4f1 + 2f2$, $4f1 + 3f2$, $4f1 + 4f2$, and so forth. The difference tones of the harmonics of the first and second primaries would then be $2f1 - 2f2$, $2f1 - 3f2$, $2f1 - 4f2$, and so forth; also $3f1 - 2f2$, $3f1 - 3f2$, $3f1 - 4f2$, and so forth; and $4f1 - 2f2$, $4f1 - 3f2$, $4f1 - 4f2$, and so forth. Note that whereas harmonic frequencies always appear above or at higher frequencies than the fundamental primaries, intermodulation distortion products, resulting from summation and difference tones, appear above and also below the fundamental primary frequencies. Recall from earlier in this chapter that departures from simple integer ratio relations within the components of a complex signal result in a less than pleasant and even harsh, discordant perception of the sound. The term that was used to describe this perception was dissonance. Because intermodulation distortion results in the possible production of complex aperiodic sounds, characterized by a lack of harmonic structure, it is not difficult to understand why intermodulation distortion is considered to be more strident, discordant, and displeasing to the ear than the harsh and unpleasant sound created by harmonic (amplitude) distortion (Durrant & Feth, 2013).

The Cubic Difference Tone

One of the combination tones of the harmonics of the first primary (listed above), consisting of the difference tone $2f1 - 1f2$, is also referred to as the *cubic difference tone*. The cubic difference tone intermodulation distortion product is especially noteworthy. When two primaries ($f1$ and $f2$) are delivered simultaneously into the sealed human external auditory ear canal and ultimately (via the middle ear) into the nonlinear system of the inner ear, at moderate intensity levels, a prominent *distortion product otoacoustic emission* (DPOE) is recorded from the external ear canal. This DPOE is the cubic difference tone, and it is obtained best when the ratio of the higher frequency primary ($f2$) to the lower frequency primary ($f1$) is about

1.22 (Hall, 2014). That is, the primaries need to be relatively close together in frequency. For instance, when $f2$ is 1200 Hz, $f1$ should be about 1000 Hz, as illustrated in Figure 6–41. The cubic difference tone is also an otoacoustic emission, because it represents an extremely faint (output) sound that is generated by the nonlinear properties of the inner ear. It is also a major clinical response parameter because the response is expected to be very large in normal, healthy inner ears. Figure 6–41 conceptually illustrates the relatively greater amplitude of the $2f1 - 1f2$ cubic difference tone intermodulation distortion product (otoacoustic emission), relative to other nonlinear distortion products, for the primaries $f2$ (1200 Hz) and $f1$ (1000 Hz). Note that the ratio of $f2$ to $f1$ in the figure is the accepted 1.2 (Silman & Emmer, 2012). The presence of the cubic difference tone not only reflects the normal, inherent nonlinear properties of the inner ear, but its presence is also indicative of healthy outer hair cells (OHCs) within the organ of Corti. It is, in fact, generated by the micromechanical (motility) properties of the OHCs, and damage to the OHCs from age, noise exposure, or chemicals that are toxic to the inner ear, will bring about a reduction in the amplitude of the cubic difference tone. The relatively close proximity of the two primary frequencies activates a very limited region of OHCs within the (inner ear) organ of Corti. The distortion products, generated by the OHCs, travel from the inner ear, back through the middle ear, and into the external auditory canal where they are detected with a very sensitive probe connected to an otoacoustic emissions device (Hall, 2014).

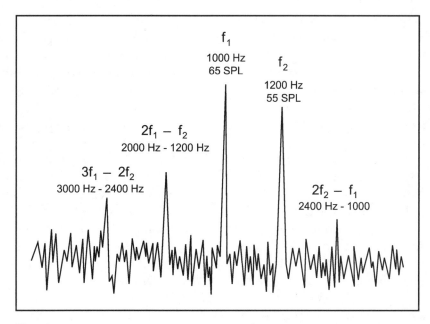

Figure 6–41. Conceptualized examples of distortion product otoacoustic emissions (DPOEs). Note the relatively greater amplitude of the $2f1 - 1f2$ (cubic difference tone) intermodulation distortion product (otoacoustic emission), relative to other nonlinear distortion products, for the primaries $f2$ (1200 Hz), and $f1$ (1000 Hz). Note that the ratio of $f2$ to $f1$ in the figure is the accepted 1:2. From S. Silman and M. B. Emmer (2012), with permission.

Chapter Summary

■ In this chapter, sound was defined as a disturbance in particle or in pressure displacement, producing longitudinal wave fronts of compression in all directions. Sound can only be propagated in an elastic or compressible medium, and isotropic propagation was defined as sound that is transmitted with equal intensity in all directions.

■ In this chapter, the bulk modulus (of elasticity) was defined as the property that determines the extent, or the upper limit, to which a medium can change in volume, when pressure is applied and volume density is the amount of mass per unit volume of a particular medium.

■ In this chapter, acoustic intensity was defined as power divided by area or as the rate at which work is performed as the power (or energy per unit time) is transported across the unit area of the wave front, perpendicular to the direction of the flow of energy.

■ In this chapter, the inverse square law was defined by the observation that the acoustic intensity (I) of a waveform at any observed wave front location (*d*) is inversely proportional to the square of the relative distance of that observed waveform front from the original sound (point) source.

- Auditory threshold was defined as the least amount or level (acoustic intensity or sound pressure) of an environmental stimulus (sound) that can be detectable on the average by individuals, in the absence of any other environmental sounds.

- Absolute threshold was defined as the least amount or level of an environmental stimulus (sound) that can be detectable on the average by an individual, in the absence of any other environmental sounds. The absolute threshold was also defined behaviorally in terms of the listener's ability to confirm either the presence or the absence (in absolute terms) of a sound.

- In this chapter, the dynamic range over which human hearing operates for acoustic intensity and/or for sound pressure was defined as the range that begins from the lowest fractional amount of intensity or sound pressure required to produce a threshold response, to the upper limits of intensity or sound pressure that can be painfully tolerated, or tolerated without pain.

- In this chapter, both MKS and CGS reference values were defined for bels of intensity level (IL) and for bels of sound pressure level (SPL). Both MKS and CGS decibel reference values were defined for intensity level (IL) and for sound pressure level (SPL) for use in computations of dB IL and dB SPL, respectively.

- In this chapter, computations of both the bel and decibel (dB), measured in MKS and in CGS metric quantities were provided for acoustic intensity level (dB IL) and for sound pressure level (dB SPL), and the relationship between intensity and pressure was also defined.

- Computational problem sets were also provided for the decibel.

- In this chapter, the sound level meter (SLM) was defined as an electronic instrument used to measure a root-mean-square (RMS) sound pressure amplitude level (SPL) in accordance with an accepted national or international set of standards.

- Sound level meter (SLM) weighting networks and bandwidth filter settings were also defined.

- In this chapter, a microphone was defined as an electronic device that converts or transduces an acoustic signal into an electrical signal. The working parts of microphones were also discussed.

- Different types of microphones were presented with a discussion of how each functions.

- In this chapter, the sound-field was defined as any physical area, space, or environment enclosing a material medium in which sound waves are present. The different types and varieties of sound-field were also defined.

- In this chapter, the speed of sound was defined and was

provided numerically for various media.

■ In this chapter, types of sounds were defined as simple periodic, complex periodic, and complex aperiodic. Examples were provided for each type.

■ Complex aperiodic transient sounds (signals) such as broadband acoustic clicks and narrow-band acoustic tone bursts were also defined, as well as the transducer limitations that exist in their production. Windowing function options were also presented for the control of side band spectral splatter that occurs in the generation of tone bursts.

■ In this chapter, important phase-dependent relations that exist for sinusoids that are combined to form complex periodic wave-forms were illustrated. Phase was shown to play a major role in determining the waveform morphology of complex periodic signals resulting from the combination of harmonically specific sinusoids.

■ In this chapter, complex aperiodic continuous sounds (signals) such as white noise (or Gaussian noise), broadband noise, pink noise, narrow-band noise, and speech noise were defined and discussed. Spectrum level, or level-per-cycle (LPC), was also defined as the average intensity or average noise power in a band of noise (called the unit bandwidth) that is 1-Hz wide. The formula for computing the spectrum level or LPC was also provided.

■ Amplitude and frequency modulation (AM and FM, respectively) were also defined and discussed, and examples of each type of modulation were provided.

■ In this chapter, a Fourier analysis was defined as a spectral analysis of the frequency by frequency content of a waveform signal that is presented graphically as a function of amplitude. The graphic method used to depict the range of absolute or relative amplitudes expressed in the frequency domain was also defined as a spectrum, amplitude spectrum, or amplitude by frequency spectrum that provides a graphic alternative to a presentation of the actual signal waveform.

■ In this chapter, the amplitude spectrum (spectra) for simple and/or complex periodic wave-forms was defined as a discrete spectrum, a line amplitude spectrum, or simply, a line spectrum. Illustrations of line spectra were provided for sinusoidal as well as complex periodic waveforms.

■ An amplitude spectrum (spectra) illustrating the spectral content of a complex aperiodic waveform was also defined as a continuous (amplitude) spectrum, in which spectral energy is present at all frequencies positioned between the lower and the upper frequency limits of the waveform.

■ In this chapter, a convenient way of graphically conveying the starting phase of each frequency component in a sinusoidal or complex periodic waveform (signal) was also defined as a phase spectrum.

■ In this chapter, filters were defined as a method that is used for spectral shaping. Filters were divided into ideal filters and real filters. Both ideal and real filters were further classified as low-pass filters, high-pass filters, band-pass filters, and band-reject (stop) filters. Properties of each type of filter, such as the pass-band, the stop-band, the cut-off frequency (f_c), and the roll-off rate (or rejection rate) were also defined and illustrated.

■ In this chapter, digital filtering and digital signal–processing (DSP) methods were discussed in relation to personal amplification systems.

■ In this chapter, linearity and the concept of a linear system were defined and discussed. Linear distortion was also defined and discussed in relation to (linear) frequency distortion.

■ Nonlinear distortion was also defined and discussed in relation to (nonlinear) amplitude distortion and peak clipping, harmonic distortion, transient and imaging distortion, and finally, inter-modulation distortion.

Chapter 6 Questions

1. Why is lightening seen before thunder is heard?

2. In the stands of a race track, you notice the smoke from the starter's gun before you hear the gun. Why is this?

3. Provide some examples of complex periodic sounds in the environment. Provide some examples of complex aperiodic sounds in the environment.

4. What is the relationship between acoustic intensity and sound pressure?

5. How is the computation of the root-mean-square (RMS) amplitude in hearing science similar to the computation of the standard deviation in statistics?

6. What are the lowest fractional amounts of intensity and/or sound pressure that are required to produce a threshold response in individuals with "normal" hearing sensitivity?

7. Does a change in frequency cause a change in period? Why or why not? Does a change in frequency cause a change in the speed of the sound through air? Why or why not?

8. Why is phase so important in determining the waveform morphology of complex periodic signals resulting from the combination of harmonically specific sinusoids?

9. Distinguish between amplitude modulation and frequency modulation.

10. Compare and contrast the amplitude spectrum for a simple pure tone, with the amplitude spectrum for a complex aperiodic waveform.

11. Compare and contrast the four types of ideal filter with the four

types of real filters. How are they similar? How are they different?

12. What distinguishes linear distortion from nonlinear distortion?

References

Durrant, J. D., & Feth, L. L. (2013). *Hearing sciences: A foundational approach*. Upper Saddle River, NJ: Pearson Education.

Gelfand, S. A. (2001). *Essentials of audiology* (2nd ed.). New York, NY: Thieme.

Giancoli, D. C. (2005). *Physics: Principles with applications* (6th ed.). Upper Saddle River, NJ: Prentice Hall.

Hall, J. W. (2014). *Introduction to audiology today*. Upper Saddle River, NJ: Pearson Education.

Hall, J. W., & Mueller, H. G. (1997). *Audiologists desk reference* (Vol. I.) San Diego, CA: Singular.

Halliday, D., Resnick, R., & Walker, J. (2011). *Fundamentals of physics* (9th ed.). Hoboken, NJ: Wiley.

Hamill, T. A., & Price, L. L. (2014). *The hearing sciences* (2nd ed.). San Diego, CA: Plural.

Hewitt, P. G. (2010). *Conceptual physics* (11th ed.). Upper Saddle River, NJ: Pearson Education.

Hirsh, I. J. (1952). *The measurement of hearing*. New York, NY: McGraw-Hill.

Kates, J. M. (2008). *Digital hearing aids*. San Diego, CA: Plural.

Lucks-Mendel, L., Danhauer, J. L., & Singh, S. (1999). *Singular's illustrated dictionary of audiology*. San Diego, CA: Singular.

Møller, A. R. (2000) *Hearing: Its physiology and pathophysiology*. San Diego, CA: Academic Press.

Moore, B. C. J. (2012). *An introduction to the psychology of hearing* (6th ed). Leiden, The Netherlands: Brill.

Rosen, S., & Howell, P. (2013). *Signals and systems for speech and hearing* (2nd ed.). Leiden, The Netherlands: Brill.

Silman, S., & Emmer, M. B. (2012). *Instrumentation for audiology and hearing science*. San Diego, CA: Plural.

Speaks, C. E. (1999). *Introduction to sound: Acoustics for the hearing and speech sciences* (3rd ed.). San Diego, CA: Singular.

Yost, W. A. (2007). *Fundamentals of hearing: An introduction* (5th ed.). San Diego, CA: Academic Press.

Chapter 7

Acoustics

Calvary troops marching across a footbridge near Manchester, England in 1831 inadvertently caused the bridge to collapse when they marched in rhythm with the bridge's "natural frequency." Since then, it is customary to order troops to "break-step" when crossing bridges . . .

Hewitt, 2010, p. 389

Alphabetized Listing of Key Terms Discussed in Chapter 7

absorption

absorption coefficient

acoustic compliance

acoustic inertance

antinode

barrier

blue-shift

bulk modulus (of elasticity)

compression

constructive interference

destructive interference

diffraction

displacement antinode

displacement node

Doppler effect

Doppler, Johann Christian

external auditory canal

first harmonic

first resonance

foghorns

formant frequencies

fundamental frequency

half-wave resonance

half-wave resonating system

harmonic frequency

harmonic resonance

harmonics

head diffraction

head-shadow

impedance mismatch

incident wave

interference

lambda (λ)

longitudinal standing waves

longitudinal wave motion

Mach cone

Mach, Ernst (1838–1916)

Mach number

material media

medium

natural frequency

Newton's third law of motion

node

opposition to the flow

pitch

plane wave

pressure antinode

pressure node

principle of resonance

principle of superposition	second harmonic	strings
quarter-wave resonance	second resonance	temperature inversion
	shadow region	third harmonic
quarter-wave resonating system	shock wave	third resonance
	sonic boom	transverse standing wave
rarefaction	sound	
rayls	sound barrier	transverse wave motion
red-shift	sound-field	vocal tract
	sound-field calibration	volume density
reflected wave	sound-shadow	warble tone
reflection	speed of sound in air	water wave
refraction	speed of sound in water	wave front
resonance		wave inversion
resonant frequencies	standing waves	wavelength (λ)

Acoustics Defined

Recall that the definition of acoustics was presented in Chapter 3 as the science of sound. Acoustics may also be defined as the study of the physics of sound. Chapter 6 provided an analysis of the physical attributes and properties of waveforms. The physical attributes and properties described in Chapter 6 occurred at different locations and at different times during the propagation of the waveforms that were illustrated. Hence, the kinds of descriptions presented in Chapter 6 are often found under the general heading of acoustics. Acoustic phenomena may be observed through the measurement of fundamental quantities such as velocity, frequency, sound pressure and/or intensity, and impedance. Recall that amplitude, frequency/period, and phase

are the main parameters of sound that must always be determined in order to completely specify and measure a particular sound stimulus, and the methods used to physically measure the amplitude of sound were extensively provided in Chapter 6. To be sure, both the MKS and the CGS reference values were defined for decibels of acoustic intensity level (dB IL) and for sound pressure level (dB SPL), and their uses in decibel computations were discussed in detail. Tables of MKS and CGS computations for dB IL and dB SPL that employ these reference values were also provided. Waveform amplitude was defined by the inverse square law that states that the acoustic intensity of a waveform, at any observed wave front location, is inversely proportional to the square of the relative distance of the waveform front from the original sound (point) source. In Chapter 6, measures of the decibel were also applied to filter roll-off rates, to signal modulation (AM), and in descriptions of amplitude (harmonic) distortion. Methods used to physically measure the frequency and/or the period of waveforms of sound were also provided in Chapter 6. Measures of the fundamental frequency, the harmonic frequencies, and the octave frequencies were defined, quantified, and applied in numerous examples. These physical measures of frequency were applied to sinusoids as well as to complex periodic and nonperiodic (aperiodic) waveform signals. Measures of frequency were also applied to the frequency response characteristics of a variety of systems, as well as to filter bandwidths, signal bandwidths, and signal modulation (FM). Additional physical measures of frequency were applied to the spectral analysis of signals and to their amplitude spectra. Physical measures of frequency were applied to the spectral shaping of signals as in filter cut-offs and filter roll-off rates, to digital filtering and sampling rates, and finally, to measures of distortion that included harmonic (amplitude) and intermodulation. Phase angle, introduced in Chapter 5 was applied in numerous instances in Chapter 6 to illustrate the important phase-dependent relations that exist within sinusoids, as sinusoids are combined to form complex periodic waveforms. Phase relations were shown to play a major role in determining the waveform morphology of complex periodic signals as each of the harmonically specific sinusoids is combined into a composite waveform. Also falling under the general heading of acoustics are waveform types that are based on the respective shapes of the waveforms.

Waveform shapes that were described in Chapter 6 included sinusoidal waves, periodic nonsinusoidal waves, and aperiodic waves.

Acoustics may also be defined as a study of the waveform properties of sound, which is the focus of Chapter 7. A study of the waveform properties of sound is tantamount to a consideration of the behavior of sound in a soundfield. To this end, amplitude, frequency/period, and phase will again be called upon in descriptions of sound wave phenomenon throughout Chapters 7 and 8. One important added measurement parameter has yet to be discussed which is also central to any discussion of acoustics. This measurement parameter is *wavelength*. Wavelength was only briefly mentioned in Chapter 6 in reference to the analogy between the frequency spectra of visible light and the frequency spectra of white and pink noise.

Wavelength

One of the most basic of the physical concepts related to the study of acoustics is wavelength. Wavelength is measured in centimeters/cycle (CGS) or meters/cycle (MKS) and is the physical distance that the waveform travels over the course of one completed cycle (Figure 7–1). Recall from Chapter 5 that one completed cycle represents 360° of excursion and that the time it takes to complete one cycle is defined as the period of the signal. Recall as well from Chapter 3 that period and frequency are inversely related (see Table 3–1). Relatively higher frequencies have

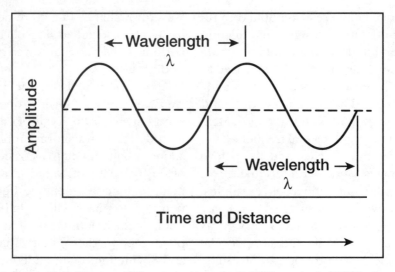

Figure 7–1. Wavelength (λ), measured in cm/cycle (CGS) or m/cycle (MKS) is the physical distance a waveform travels over one completed cycle. In terms of phase, one cycle represents 360° of excursion. In terms of time, period is the time taken to complete one cycle. Hence, wavelength is the waveform distance traveled during 360° (one cycle) of excursion or during one period.

shorter periods, and relatively lower frequencies have longer periods (Tables 7–1 and 7–2). In terms of wavelength, period and wavelength are directly related, whereas frequency and wavelength, like frequency and period, are inversely related. Therefore, relatively higher frequencies have shorter periods and shorter wavelengths. Correspondingly, relatively lower frequencies have longer periods and longer wavelengths (see Tables 7–1 and 7–2). One way to think about wavelength and period is that, given the speed of sound in a particular medium, it would take more time (period) to complete one cycle if the cycle must travel a longer distance (wavelength), and less time if the cycle travels a shorter distance. Bear in mind that frequency is a measure of cycles that occur in one second of time (cycles/second), period is a measure of time (*T*) taken (seconds or milliseconds) to complete one cycle (*T*/cycle),

and wavelength is a measure of distance traveled (meters or centimeters) in one cycle (distance/cycle). This point should be clear from Tables 7–1 and 7–2. It should also be understood that wavelength is the distance traveled by one cycle in one period of time or over 360° of excursion, and period is the time taken to travel a distance of one wavelength, also over 360° of excursion. Simply put, wavelength is equal to the distance between two points on a sinusoidal cycle that are exactly one period apart.

The Greek symbol lambda (λ) is often used to designate wavelength. Calculating wavelength is a relatively straightforward procedure. In order to calculate the wavelength of a signal, only two kinds of information are needed: the frequency of the waveform of interest and the speed of sound (or *c*) in the particular medium of interest. In most cases, the medium will be air, and the

Table 7–1. Select Frequencies (Hz), Their Corresponding Periods, and Their Corresponding MKS or CGS Wavelengths (λ) in Air*

Frequency (cycles/s)	Period (ms/cycle)	Wavelength (λ) MKS m/cycle	Wavelength (λ) CGS cm/cycle
10 Hz	100.00	34.400	3440
50 Hz	20.000	6.8800	688
100 Hz	10.000	3.4400	344
250 Hz	4.0000	1.3760	137.6
500 Hz	2.0000	0.6880	68.80
1000 Hz	1.0000	0.3440	34.40
2000 Hz	0.5000	0.1720	17.20
4000 Hz	0.2500	0.0860	8.600
8000 Hz	0.1250	0.0430	4.300
10,000 Hz	0.1000	0.0344	3.440
20,000 Hz	0.0500	0.0172	1.720

*At a temperature of 20°C or 68°F; 344 m/s (MKS speed); 34,400 cm/s (CGS speed); seconds (s); milliseconds (ms); meter (m); centimeter (cm).

Table 7–2. Select Frequencies (Hz), Their Corresponding Periods, and Their Corresponding MKS or CGS Wavelengths (λ) in Freshwater*

Frequency (cycles/s)	Period (ms/cycle)	Wavelength (λ) MKS m/cycle	Wavelength (λ) CGS cm/cycle
10 Hz	100.00	148.20	14820
50 Hz	20.000	29.640	2964
100 Hz	10.000	14.820	1482
250 Hz	4.0000	5.9280	592.80
500 Hz	2.0000	2.9640	296.40
1000 Hz	1.0000	1.4820	148.20
2000 Hz	0.5000	0.7410	74.10
4000 Hz	0.2500	0.3705	37.05
8000 Hz	0.1250	0.1853	18.525
10,000 Hz	0.1000	0.1482	14.820
20,000 Hz	0.0500	0.0741	7.410

*At a temperature of 20°C or 68°F; 1482 m/s (MKS speed); 148,200 cm/s (CGS speed); seconds (s); milliseconds (ms); meter (m); centimeter (cm).

speed of sound air (20°C; 68°F) is 344 meters/second (m/s; MKS) or 34,400 centimeters/second (cm/s; CGS) as indicated in Chapter 6 (see Table 6–8). The wavelength (λ) of a signal at a given frequency will be defined as the MKS or CGS speed of sound (c) divided by the frequency (f) of interest, or

$$\lambda = c/f \qquad (7\text{–}1)$$

Sound Transmission and Wavelength

As indicated in Chapter 6, opposition to sound transmission will exist at any boundary between different sound transmitting media. Vibratory energy, and the subsequent reduction in amplitude that is lost in the transfer of sound energy between media, was understood to be due to an impedance mismatch, as defined in Chapter 5. In addition, recall that differences in both the density and in the bulk (elastic) modulus of sound-transmitting media are directly responsible for the differences in the speed that sound travels (or c) through various media, as indicated in Chapter 6 (see Table 6–8). From Equation 7–1 it is also clear that for any given frequency of interest, the wavelength (λ) of the signal in a particular medium is directly proportional to the speed (c) that sound travels in that medium. When an incident sound is transmitted from one medium into a second medium, there will be change in the wavelength but not in the frequency of the signal that is transmitted into the second medium. Table 7–1 lists the MKS and CGS wavelengths for a select number of frequencies transmitted in air. The periods of the select frequencies are also provided

for direct comparisons with each of the respective wavelengths. The speed of sound in air is again provided at the bottom of Table 7–1 and borrowed from Table 6–8 in Chapter 6. As an example of the manner in which each value in Table 7–1 was calculated, we take a 1000-Hz pure tone traveling in air at room temperature (20°C). This 1000-Hz pure tone has an MKS speed of 344 m/s. Therefore, using Equation 7–1,

$$\lambda = 344/1000, \text{ and}$$
$$\lambda = 0.344 \text{ meters/cycle}$$

Hence, a 1000-Hz pure tone traveling in air at a room temperature of 20°C has a wavelength of 0.344 m/cycle. What will happen to the wavelength when the 1000-Hz pure tone enters a second medium, such as a medium with greater density like freshwater? Table 7–2 lists the MKS and CGS wavelengths for the same sound frequencies that were provided in Table 7–1, but transmitted in freshwater. The periods of the same frequencies for sound are again provided for direct comparisons with each of the wavelengths. The speed of sound in freshwater is again provided at the bottom of Table 7–2, also borrowed from Table 6–8. Once again, as an example of how each value in Table 7–2 was calculated, a 1000-Hz pure tone traveling in freshwater at room temperature (20°C) has an MKS speed of 1482 m/s. Therefore, using Equation 7–1,

$$\lambda = 1482/1000, \text{ and therefore,}$$
$$\lambda = 1.482 \text{ meters/cycle.}$$

Hence, when an air-borne incident sound enters a second medium such as freshwater, the wavelength changes, and in this particular instance, it gets longer. Water has a greater density compared to air, and the speed of sound is also greater in water compared to the speed of sound in air. The wavelength for each frequency listed in Table 7–2 is longer than each of the wavelengths for the identical frequencies listed in Table 7–1. How might we explain the longer wavelengths observed for the same frequencies when the material medium changes from air to water? The greater speed of sound in water means that each cyclic longitudinally propagated wave front travels a greater distance per second, consequently increasing the physical distance (wavelength) between each subsequent wave crest. In addition to changes in wavelength, when an incident waveform is transmitted from air into a second medium such as water, the waveform, in all likelihood, will also be bent or refracted as discussed in the sections that follow.

Types of Waveform Motion

As indicated in Chapter 6, sound propagation represents the production of predictable rather than random waveform patterns. Recall from Chapter 4 that although waves may travel over large distances, the particles found within any transmitting medium exhibit only a limited amount of motion and distance. The waves themselves are not equal to the particle matter but instead represent oscillations that travel within matter, without carrying the matter with them (Giancoli, 2005). Also recall from the same chapter that it is only the waveform that advances or propagates in a medium in response to a disturbance. It is not the individual particles

of mass that comprise the material medium that advance in response to a disturbance. The waveform and not the particles of mass in the material medium carries the energy through the medium and away from the source of the disturbance. Even so, the rather limited amount of motion of the particles found within any transmitting medium is often described and defined in relation to the waveform that propagates outward in response to, and away from, a wave-generating disturbance. This limited amount of particle motion in the transmitting medium may occur in a vertical direction (up and down) or in a horizontal (lateral) direction (side to side). Hence, waveforms may be classified according to the direction of the vibration and subsequent movement of the medium, relative to the direction of the waveform that carries the energy through the medium from the source of the disturbance (Speaks, 1999). The two classifications of waveform propagation are *transverse wave motion* and *longitudinal wave motion*.

Transverse Wave Motion

Transverse wave motion is motion in which the direction of the particle vibration within a particular medium is at right angles (90°) or is perpendicular to the direction of the waveform that is being propagated through the medium. Hence, in transverse wave motion, the direction of the waveform differs from the direction of the limited amount of particle movement that occurs within the medium. The direction of the waveform typically represents horizontal motion, while the particle direction of the medium usually represents vertical motion. The simplest example of transverse wave motion is demonstrated by a rope that is fastened at one end to a wall. A series of dots is then placed along the length of the rope with an ink marker. The free end of the rope is hand-held so that the rope may be pulled taut (horizontally), under tension and at right angles to the wall. If the free end of the rope is suddenly and rapidly jerked, first in an upward direction from equilibrium, then in a downward direction and back to equilibrium, what happens? Because the rope is taut and is under tension, a pulse wave of compression is generated in the rope. The (incident) pulse wave of compression will travel horizontally from the handheld free end of the rope to the wall. While the pulse wave of compression travels horizontally from left to right, the ink marks will remain in place horizontally but will move upward (vertically) with compression peak. Furthermore, the vertical oscillations of each mark on the rope will occur at the same rate or frequency as the motion of any other ink mark. The relatively limited amount of vertical motion exhibited by the ink marks in this example is symbolic of the limited particle motion within the medium (the rope). When the horizontally traveling pulse wave of compression reaches the wall, it exerts an upward force on the wall. The wall in turn exerts an equal but opposite (downward) force on the rope, according to Newton's third law of motion. The downward force, in turn, generates a reflected but inverted (rarefaction) pulse wave that travels from the wall, back to the handheld free end of the rope (Halliday, Resnick, & Walker, 2011). This last point will again be addressed later in this chapter. For the present, what is important is that the vertical motion of the ink marks (or particle motion within the medium) will always occur at right angles to the horizontal (lateral) motion of the waveform. By definition, in this example the vertical or perpendicular particle motion of the medium is transverse to the horizontally directed motion of the waveform, and therefore, this type of waveform activity is called *transverse wave motion*.

As another example of transverse wave motion, recall the vibration and the subsequent surface waves produced in a fluid medium in response to an applied force, as illustrated in Chapter 3 (see Figure 3–3). When a small stone is thrown into a still, unmoving body of water such as a pond, the disturbance creates successive surface waves of compression and rarefaction that move outward in all directions from the entry point of the stone, or simply, outward from the location wherein the initial displacement of water occurred. The stone initially creates an area of rarefaction by displacing water in all directions. The creation of an initial area of rarefaction is then quickly and rapidly followed by the creation of a second ring of compression. As the water waves move outward, many of the molecules of the water medium move in a vertical (up and down) direction at right angles, or perpendicular to the direction of the movement of the ever-expanding waveform. Placing a cork on the surface of the water not far from the location of the initial disturbance can provide an illustrative example of the transverse wave motion of the molecules within the water medium. Figure 7–2A illustrates the transverse motion of a cork relative to the lateral (from left to right)

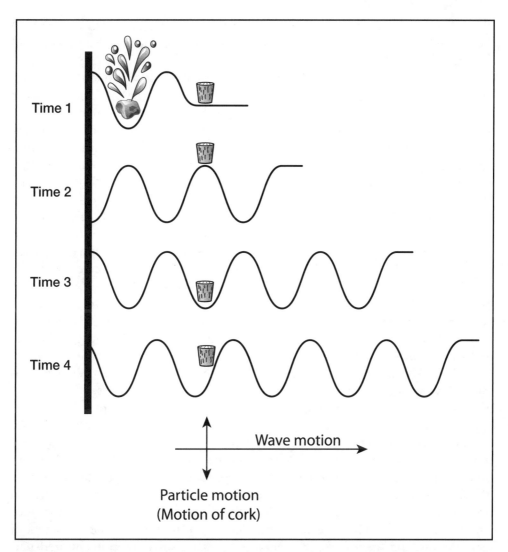

Figure 7–2A. Transverse wave motion. A surface waveform created by a waterborne disturbance begins at time zero and moves from left to right. The motion of the cork represents the motion of molecules within the water medium. When the laterally directed surface wave on the water reaches the cork, the cork will exhibit vertical motion. The cork will bob up and down in a relatively stationary location at approximately right angles, which is perpendicular or transverse to the outward or lateral motion of the water wave.

motion of water waves, in response to a disturbance. As the surface waveform of the water-borne disturbance moves outward in all directions (or from left to right as shown in Figure 7–2A) and reaches the cork, the cork will bob up and down in a relatively stationary location at approximately right angles, or perpendicular to the outward (lateral) direction of the water wave. That is, the cork bobs up and down but horizontally remains in place, relatively speaking, just as many of the molecules of water remain in a relatively fixed position during the propagation of water waves. Because the vertical motion of the cork (or molecule motion within the water medium) is transverse to the horizontally directed (lateral) motion of the water wave, the relationship between the motion of the cork and the waveform may again be taken as an example of transverse wave motion. However, it should be added that the motion of surface waves on water actually represents a combination of both transverse and longitudinal wave propagation (Durrant & Feth, 2013).

Longitudinal Wave Motion

Sound was described in Chapter 6 as a propagated disturbance in a material medium that produces longitudinal wave fronts of compression in all directions (Halliday et al., 2011). Longitudinal wave motion is motion in which the direction of the particle vibration within a particular medium is parallel to the direction of waveform propagation through the medium. Hence, in longitudinal wave motion, the direction of the waveform is the same as that of the limited amount of particle movement that occurs within the medium. Sound represents the transfer of energy through an elastic medium (Speaks, 1999), and the transfer of energy during the propagation of sound follows the same laws of physics previously discussed in detail in Chapters 3 and 4 for the moving pendulum. In longitudinal wave motion, the component particles of the medium are minimally displaced from their points of equilibrium. Like the movements of a pendulum, these component particles of the medium are displaced laterally from side to side. As the component particles of the medium are laterally displaced, they collide with

adjacent particles. Recall (see Chapter 4) that when a disturbance such as sound is propagated in an elastic medium, elastic collisions will often occur with little or no loss (or transfer) of energy away from the medium. That is, momentum and kinetic energy are easily transferred from one elastic mass to another as both momentum and kinetic energy are conserved (Hewitt, 2010), as previously illustrated in Figure 4–3. As each particle collides with adjacent particles, successive areas of compression and rarefaction are created, and these areas of compression and rarefaction define the propagated waveform that is created by the sound source. The areas of compression and rarefaction generated in longitudinally propagated waves will also correspond to the crests and troughs that were created in the generation of transverse waves.

Figure 4–4 from Chapter 4 illustrated a series of longitudinally placed elastic particle collisions depicting the creation of the kinds of waves that might occur over time in the propagation of sound through an elastic medium. Note that in the figure, the source of the disturbance occurs at "time 1." The development of successive areas of concentrated particle density (compression), followed by areas in which particles appear to be widely dispersed (rarefaction), can also be visualized in Figure 4–4. The waveform created by a sound source will therefore consist of compression peaks and rarefaction valleys that move laterally (horizontally) in time, away from the source of the disturbance, while the direction of particle movement, however limited, is parallel rather than perpendicular to the direction of the propagated waveform. Because the horizontal or lateral particle motion of the medium is parallel to the horizontally directed motion of the waveform, this type of waveform activity is called longitudinal wave motion. Sound waves represent longitudinal wave motion such that the particles of the medium vibrate in a direction, albeit limited, that is parallel to the direction of the energy transfer. Sound waves are also called longitudinal waves.

Longitudinal wave motion is additionally demonstrated using a spring-mass system (Slinky) that is fastened at one end to a wall. The physical properties of spring-mass systems set into motion were also discussed in detail in Chapters 3 and 4. The free end of the Slinky is hand-held so that the Slinky can be raised to a horizontal position that is at right angles to the wall. Longitudinal wave motion is then generated by rapidly pushing and pulling the free end of the Slinky from side to side (Figure 7–2B). That is, the free end of the Slinky is first rapidly pushed toward the wall then rapidly pulled away from the wall. This results in a relatively limited amount of lateral (side-to-side) displacement of the component parts within the Slinky that again resemble the motion of a pendulum. The pushing and pulling (or the application of force) cause the laterally displaced component parts of the Slinky to collide with adjacent component parts. The collisions create areas that are compressed (areas of compression) and areas in the Slinky that are expanded or stretched (areas of rarefaction). These successive areas of compression and rarefaction define the waveform that travels horizontally (laterally) along the Slinky toward the wall as illustrated in Figure 7–2B. Because the motion of the laterally displaced component parts of the Slinky is parallel to the horizontally directed motion

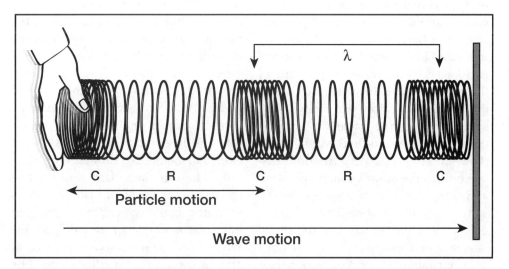

Figure 7–2B. Longitudinal wave motion. The free end of the Slinky is rapidly pushed toward the wall then rapidly pulled away from the wall, resulting in a limited amount of lateral (side-to-side) displacement of the component parts within the Slinky. The laterally displaced component parts of the Slinky collide with adjacent component parts and create successive areas of compression and rarefaction. The successive areas of compression and rarefaction define the longitudinally propagated waveform that travels laterally, in the same direction as the motion of the laterally displaced (side-to-side) component parts of the Slinky.

of the waveform, this waveform activity is again an example of longitudinal wave motion. Many of the illustrations of sound wave phenomena presented in this chapter depict longitudinal waveform propagation.

The Behavior of Sound in a Sound-Field

The concept of a sound-field was defined in Chapter 6 as any physical area, space, room, or environment enclosing an appropriate elastic or compressible material medium (such as a gas, a liquid, or a solid substance) in which sound waves are being propagated and transmitted. The different types and varieties of sound-field were also defined in Chapter 6. What generally happens to sound in a sound-field? At distances that are very near to a sound source, or approximately 1 m or so from the source, and in the absence of physical objects or barriers, the signal intensity in a sound-field would be determined exclusively by the power or pressure of the incident wave. In such cases, when the listener is in close proximity to the sound source, the idealistic properties of a free sound-field would apply (Durrant & Feth, 2013). At some distance from the sound source, presumably more than several meters from the source, and in the absence of physical objects or reflective barriers, the signal intensity in a sound-field would obey the principles of the inverse square law, as presented in Chapter 6 (see Figure 6–1C). In such instances, the idealistic properties of a free sound-field are still likely to apply (Durrant & Feth, 2013).

The proximity and/or the distance from a sound source are obviously an important determining factor in defining the fate of sound in any sound-field. At a relatively greater distance from the sound source, the incident sound waves are more likely to interact with boundaries and with physical objects, at locations where they are found. What overall changes in the energy of the incident waveform can be expected when such interactions occur?

Sound Transmission and/or Reflection

Recall from Chapter 5 that when an attempt is made to transfer the vibratory energy of a sound from one medium (or object) to another medium or object during forced vibration, there is the possibility that vibratory energy will be lost in the transfer. The loss of sound energy transfer is of course due to differences in mass and in the overall elastic properties between the two media in question. The vibratory energy that is lost (reduced waveform amplitude) in the transfer of sound energy between media was said to be lost due to an impedance mismatch. The absolute transfer of sound energy from one medium to another is possible only when the impedances of the two media are the same, or matched. However, how could such a perfect transference of sound energy ever be possible when every conceivable reflective or absorptive physical medium, may it be solid, gaseous, or liquid, will possess its own unique density, elasticity, and characteristic impedance? If the impedance offered by the reflective barrier (or second medium boundary) is infinite, then the amplitude intensity of the reflected wave will equal the amplitude intensity of the incident wave, as would be the case in a the highly reverberant field described above. The inverse square law as defined in Chapter 6 by Equation 6–4 does not apply to sound propagation in a medium with highly reflective surfaces, or, by definition, will not apply in a diffuse, highly reverberant sound-field. In a highly reverberant sound-field all of the energy of the incident waveform will be reflected off of and away from the boundary (or secondary reflective medium). It should also be obvious that absolutely no sound energy will be transmitted into (or absorbed by) the second (reflective) medium. Hence, when sounds are propagated in a medium with highly reflective surfaces, all of the sound energy is retained within the medium. If the impedance offered by the reflective barrier (or second medium boundary) is *not* infinite, then the amplitude intensity of the reflected wave will be less than the amplitude intensity of the incident wave (Speaks, 1999).

Because every conceivable reflective or absorptive physical medium possesses its own unique density, elasticity, and characteristic impedance, it is a common experience that some sound-field boundaries simply impede, more or less, the transmission of sound energy. Opposition to sound transmission will exist at any boundary between different transmitting media, distinguished each by their own separate characteristic impedances (Speaks, 1999). In a room with thick concrete walls, only negligible amounts of airborne sound energy will be transmitted into and

through the concrete boundary and into the next room. But in a room with thin plasterboard walls, significant amounts of airborne sound energy may be transmitted through this second medium (Durrant & Feth, 2013). Therefore, it is quite often the case that some but certainly not all of the energy of incident waveforms found in a sound-field will be effectively transmitted into a second medium from an initial (first) medium. Of particular relevance is the degree to which airborne sound is reflected when attempts are made to transfer sound energy from the air into a fresh (or salt) water boundary. The degree to which airborne sound is reflected from a water boundary may be determined. To begin with, in Chapter 5 the characteristic impedance (Z_c) was defined as the MKS product of the density (kg/m^3) and the (c) speed of sound (meters/second) for a given material media as:

$$Z_c = \text{density} \times c \qquad (5\text{–}6)$$

Looking at the computed rayls of characteristic impedance (for any two substances) such as air and freshwater that were provided in Table 5–4, recall that the proportion of transmitted sound energy (T) between two media such as air (Z_b) and freshwater (Z_a) may also be predicted (Durrant & Feth, 2013) using Equation 5–7 from Chapter 5:

$$T = 4Z_b Z_a \div [Z_b + Z_a]^2 \qquad (5\text{–}7)$$

In the above equation, the characteristic impedances that were provided in scientific notation in Table 5–4 for air (4.16×10^2 or 416 rayls) and water (1.48×10^6 or 1,480,000 rayls) may now be applied, and T is once again the proportion of energy transmitted from the first medium Z_b (air) to the second medium Z_a (water). Therefore,

$$T = 4(4.16 \times 10^2)\,(1.48 \times 10^6) \div$$
$$[(4.16 \times 10^2) + (1.48 \times 10^6)]^2$$

Solving for the numerator,

$$4(4.16 \times 10^2)\,(1.48 \times 10^6) =$$
$$(16.64 \times 10^2)\,(1.48 \times 10^6) =$$
$$(24.6 \times 10^8) = (2.46 \times 10^9)$$

Solving for the denominator,

$$[(4.16 \times 10^2) + (1.48 \times 10^6)]^2 =$$
$$[(416) + (1.48 \times 10^6)]^2 =$$
$$[(416) + (1{,}480{,}000)]^2 =$$
$$[1{,}480{,}416]^2 = (2.19 \times 10^{12})$$

Combining the numerator and the denominator,

$$T = (2.46 \times 10^9) \div (2.19 \times 10^{12}) =$$
$$1.123 \times 10^{-3}$$

$$T = 0.001 \text{ or } 0.1\%$$

Therefore, the amount of sound energy from an air medium that is transmitted into freshwater is only 0.1% of the total. This means that about 0.1% of the incident sound energy penetrates the water boundary surface and travels as a sound wave in the water medium. In addition, in all likelihood, the waveforms that are transmitted into the water will also be bent or refracted (see sections below). This also means that the remaining 99.9% of the total sound energy originating from the air medium is reflected off of the water boundary and is retained in the air medium (Speaks, 1999). In terms of dB IL, how much of the airborne sound is lost from the air, or is actually transmitted from the air medium into the freshwater medium? Using Equation 6–9 from Chapter 6:

$$\text{dB IL} = 10 \times \log\left(\frac{I_O}{I_R}\right) \quad (6\text{–}9)$$

The value for T (0.001) may be placed into the numerator as 10^{-3} and I_R is equal to 1; hence,

$$\text{dB IL} = 10 \times \log\left(\frac{10^{-3}}{1}\right)$$

and $\text{dB IL} = 10 \times -3$ or -30 dB IL

In terms of dB SPL, how much of the airborne sound is lost from the air or transmitted from the air medium to the freshwater medium? In an analogous manner utilized in the computation of dB IL, Equation 6–11 from Chapter 6 may be employed in the following way:

$$\text{dB SPL} = 20 \times \log\left(\frac{P_O}{P_R}\right) \quad (6\text{–}11)$$

and recalling the relationship between intensity and pressure provided in Chapter 6 by Equation 6–6:

$$I = P^2 \quad (6\text{–}6)$$

$$P = \sqrt{I}$$

Equation 6–6 may be rewritten as

$$\text{dB SPL} = 20 \times \log\left(\frac{10^{-3}}{1}\right)^{\frac{1}{2}}$$

which is now equal to

$$\text{dB SPL} = 20 \times \log\left(\frac{10^{-1.5}}{1}\right)$$

and

$$\text{dB SPL} = 10 \times -1.5 \text{ or } -30 \text{ dB SPL}$$

Therefore, approximately 30 dB IL or 30 dB SPL of airborne sound is lost from the air medium and is actually transmitted from the air medium into the freshwater medium. It is also likely that the transmitted waveforms will additionally be bent or refracted as they enter the second (water) medium (see sections below).

Sound Transmission and/or Absorption

Sound wave absorption is inversely proportional to sound wave reflection (Speaks, 1999). If the total energy of the incident sound is reflected by the boundary of a second medium, then no part of the total energy will be absorbed by (or transmitted into) the second medium, as indicated above. Materials that are hard, dense, and smooth, having impedances that are nearly infinite, will provide very poor, if any, absorption (Durrant & Feth, 2013). To be sure, reflection represents an "opposition to the flow" which is the definition of impedance presented in Chapter 5; therefore, it is easy to see why impedance and reflection would be directly related. But even if the impedance offered by the boundary is not infinite, opposition to sound transmission will still exist, because it exists at any boundary between different transmitting media (Speaks, 1999). However, the opposition in such a case may not be characterized in total, by reflection. Part of the opposition may be characterized by absorption. In most instances, absorption, like reflection, impedes sound wave transmission (energy flow) through a second medium. However, the fraction of sound absorbed by a medium is not just determined by the acoustic impedance of the material medium. The fraction of sound absorbed by a material medium is also a function of the frequency of the incident wave, as well as the incident angle of the sound wave (Speaks, 1999).

In a sound-field, that part of the total energy of an incident sound that strikes a physical boundary and is *not* reflected (away) may be transmitted through the second medium. However, even for the part of the total energy that was transmitted, a still smaller part of that transmitted energy will be absorbed by the material of the second medium. If no part of the total incident sound is reflected by the boundary of a second medium, some of the total transmitted energy may be absorbed. Soft materials like cloth (curtains, drapes, rugs, and carpets), those that are porous (like fiberglass insulation), and those having rough surfaces are better absorbers of sound energy (Durrant & Feth, 2013). If the total incident sound energy is neither reflected by a physical boundary nor transmitted through the second medium, then the total energy of the incident sound has been completely absorbed by the second medium. This last scenario (total sound absorption) would best describe the behavior of sound waves in an anechoic chamber.

Absorption is the acoustic equivalent of damping (friction) that was encountered in descriptions of mechanical systems discussed in Chapter 5. Therefore, the absorption of sound energy leads to the ultimate transformation of this energy into heat. As in damping, absorption results in a reduction in the amplitude energy of the waveform, and not a change in signal's frequency or wavelength (see sections below). The magnitude of sound wave absorption may be quantified by the *absorption coefficient*. Recall that the computed value of *T* from Equation 5–7 is a measure of the amount of sound energy transmitted through a second medium. It is computed using the characteristic impedance of the second medium, and it may also be used to indicate the amount of energy that is absorbed (Speaks, 1999) by the second medium or I_a. The equation for the computation of the absorption coefficient (α) is shown as Equation 7–2, which may be defined as

$$\alpha = I_a \div I_i \qquad (7\text{–}2)$$

This represents the ratio of the sound energy absorbed (I_a) to the sound energy contained in the incident wave (I_i), or simply, the sound energy absorbed ÷ total incident sound energy. It should be obvious that the absorption coefficient, which is a ratio, can take on values that range between the extremes of 0 and 1. An absorption coefficient of 0 indicates that no part of the sound energy is absorbed and all of the sound energy is reflected. An absorption coefficient of 1 indicates that all of the sound energy is absorbed, and no part of the sound energy is either reflected or transmitted. Sound-field boundaries constructed of unpainted concrete, marble, or glazed tile have an absorption coefficient of about 0.01. However, those materials absorb about 10 times more sound energy as freshwater which has an absorption coefficient of only about 0.001 (Speaks, 1999). Heavy carpet attached to concrete or marble walls will increase the absorption coefficient up to about 0.37, indicating that approximately one third of the incident sound energy may be absorbed by this

material. Even though the value of the absorption coefficient is not affected by the overall intensity of the incident sound wave, the type of material found in the second medium and the frequency of the incident sound wave can often interact, affecting the absorption coefficient often in a complex manner. For instance, with some material media, the absorption coefficient increases with frequency increments in the incident sound wave (carpeting installed over concrete), and with other material media (plywood) the absorption coefficient decreases with frequency increments in the incident sound wave (Speaks, 1999). It should be clear, however, that the net effect of absorption is to decrease the sound energy in that part of a waveform that is reflected, and to reduce the amount of sound energy in that part of a waveform that is transmitted, through a second medium (Durrant & Feth, 2013). The concept of wavelength (λ) was defined and addressed in the above sections. Wavelength has particular relevance to discussions of diffraction and to sound-shadow effects in the sections that follow.

Sound Transmission and Diffraction

One of the most striking properties of sound is the ability of sound waves to bend around small or finite obstacles and/or to spread or scatter on the other side of a large barrier through a small opening. Diffraction occurs only for the energy carried by the sound waves, and not for the energy carried by the material particles that make up the medium. For such reasons, we are able to hear sounds around the corners of the openings (windows and doors) of large barriers, and we are able to localize low frequency sounds in a sound-field. This second point will be covered in greater detail later in this chapter. This phenomenon of wave bending and/or wave scattering around obstacles is a universal property of all waves, and it is known simply as diffraction. Light exhibits this property, but obviously not as pronounced as the diffraction exhibited by sound, although we can see light that diffracts around the corners of the openings in barriers. When water waves (with long wavelengths) are generated in a lake, they will, from time to time, encounter relatively smaller obstacles such as pier pilings. When this occurs, the water waves will bend around the piling and the motion of the wave will continue as if the barrier did not exist. In general, when a relatively low-frequency sound strikes an obstacle (barrier) of finite size having a width that is less than the wavelength (λ) of the incident wave front, some of the sound energy will be reflected, some of the energy may be absorbed by and/or transmitted through the obstacle, but in general, most of the sound wave energy will make its way around the obstacle, and is therefore said to be diffracted. When sound is diffracted, it is also customary to say that the sound is scattered. The degree of bending/scattering depends on the relationship between the wavelength of the primary or incident wave, and the dimensions (or simply the width) of the finite obstacle, or the width of the opening in the large barrier.

Foghorns

When relatively small environmental obstacles, such as the tiny water droplets created in a foggy atmosphere, lie in the path of diffracted sound waves, the transmitted sound waves will be bent and scattered (diffracted) around the tiny obstacles (water droplets) in all directions. As a practical example, take the maritime foghorns that are often used by ships at sea, by floating buoys, and by coastal installations to warn of navigational hazards. These foghorns emit very low, rather than relatively higher frequency sounds. The reason for the use of lower frequencies is that foggy air contains tiny water droplets with diameters that are much smaller, relative to the much longer wavelengths that are characteristic of lower frequency (foghorn) sounds. The longer wavelengths characteristic of the lower frequency sounds are able to bend around the relatively tiny diameters (widths) of the water droplets, and continue to be transmitted as an effective warning signal. If higher frequency foghorn signals were to be used, the generated sound energy contained within the much shorter wavelengths of the higher frequencies would be absorbed or reflected (see sections below) by the tiny water droplet barriers. This would greatly diminish the effectiveness of the foghorn as a warning signal (Speaks, 1999).

Radio Waves

Radio waves provide good examples of signals that can bend (diffract) around barriers. Recall that amplitude modulated (AM) and frequency modulated (FM) waveform signals were discussed in Chapter 6. The wavelengths of standard AM broadcast signals are very long in comparison to the size of most objects or barriers located in their path.

The wavelengths of AM radio signals can range from 180 to 550 m, permitting AM radio waves to diffract easily around buildings and other large barriers. The wavelengths of standard FM broadcast signals, however, are much shorter. The wavelengths of FM radio signals range from 2.8 to 3.4 m, and therefore, FM signals cannot diffract nearly as well around large buildings or barriers. For these reasons, FM reception is often relatively poor in environmental locations where AM reception is unhindered (Hewitt, 2011).

Figure 7–3 illustrates what can happen when an incident plane (sound) wave, traveling from left to right, encounters a finite barrier (small black rectangle) having a width that is less than the wavelength of the incident wave front. In the physics of wave propagation a "plane wave" is an idealized constant-frequency wave whose wave fronts are infinite and are composed of parallel planes of constant peak-to-peak amplitude and unchanging phase (Speaks, 1999). As indicated above and as illustrated in Figure 7–3, some of the incident sound energy is reflected back from the small barrier, some incident energy may be transmitted through the obstacle (not shown), and some of that

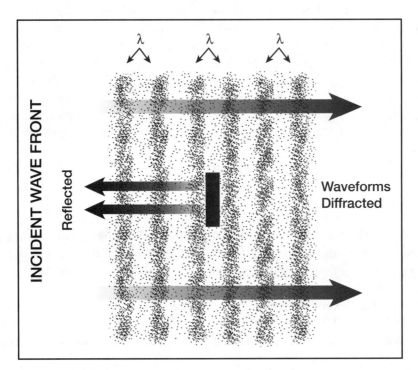

Figure 7–3. An incident plane wave that is longitudinally propagated from left to right encounters a finite barrier (shown by the black rectangle) having a width less than the wavelength (λ) of the incident wave front. Some of the sound energy is reflected from the barrier, some may be absorbed (*not shown*) and some may be transmitted through the obstacle (*not shown*). Most of the sound wave energy, however, is diffracted around the finite obstacle barrier to the side of the barrier facing away from the incident sound source. The finite barrier therefore has almost negligible effects on the frequency and intensity of the diffracted waveforms on the side of the barrier facing away from the sound source, as simplistically illustrated.

energy still may in fact be absorbed (not shown). In general, however, most of the energy of the incident sound wave makes its way (scatters) around to the opposite side of the finite obstacle unaffected and is therefore said to be diffracted.

Head Diffraction

The most obvious and interesting example of sound diffraction is provided by the human head. The manner in which humans are able to localize the source of a sound in a sound-field is conditioned by the fact that the human hearing apparatus is embedded in a more or less solid sphere. The subject of sound localization is discussed in Chapter 8. For the present, recall from the above sections and from Figure 7–3 that when an incident wave encounters a finite barrier having a width that is less than the wavelength of the incident wave front, the sound wave that is transmitted is diffracted or bent around to the opposite side of the finite barrier, in all directions. Because lower frequency sounds have relatively longer wavelengths, they are more likely to bend or diffract around finite barriers, in comparison to higher frequency sounds. If it is assumed that the human head (a finite barrier) is approximately 15 to 17 cm in width, but ear-to-ear is about 23 cm, then we might approximate which frequencies would or would not be expected to diffract. Therefore, for an incident sound approaching the head from either the right or the left side only, we will employ Equation 7–1:

$$\lambda = c/f \qquad (7\text{–}1)$$

Beginning with a sound having a wavelength of about 23 cm/cycle (the approximate width of the barrier in this case), we can solve for frequency (f) using the CGS speed of sound (see Table 6–8), in the following way:

$$23 \text{ cm cycle} = 34{,}400 \text{ cm/second/``}f\text{''}$$

$$f = 1500 \text{ cycles/second}$$

Equation 7–1 may also been rewritten as $f = c/\lambda$. This rewritten form of Equation 7–1 will be useful in fundamental frequency computations for half- and quarter-wave (tube) resonances, as well as for defining and describing the half-wave resonances of vibrating strings. The "principle of resonance" and the concept of resonant frequencies that are generated within certain kinds of tubes were first introduced in Chapter 5 (see Figure 5–15). Resonance is also discussed later in this chapter. On the average, given that all human heads are not exactly 23 cm in width, sound presented in a sound-field to one ear or to the other is likely to result in waveform diffraction when the incident wavelengths are greater than 23 cm, or when the incident waveform contains frequencies that are less than 1500 Hz. Diffraction of the relatively lower frequencies will occur on the side of the head facing away from the source of the incident waveform. This point may be illustrated in Figure 7–4. As before, some fraction of the sound energy may be reflected by the head (not shown), some fraction may actually be transmitted through the head (not shown) if the incident signal is sufficiently intense, and some fraction of that energy still, may in fact be absorbed by the head (not shown). In general, however, most of the relatively lower frequency sound waves make their way (scatter) around to the opposite side of the head (they diffract). The waves that are diffracted,

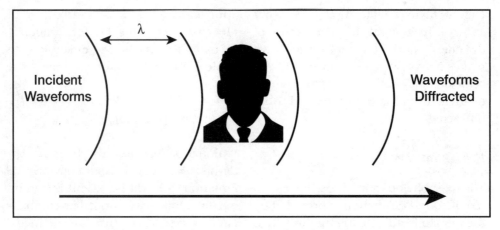

Figure 7–4. Diffraction around the human head by incident low-frequency sounds can be illustrated with longitudinally propagated waves that travel from left to right (*as indicated by the larger arrow*). Some fraction of the sound energy may be reflected (*not shown*), some fraction may be absorbed (*not shown*), and some of the incident wave energy may even be transmitted through the obstacle (*not shown*) if the signal is sufficiently intense. In general, however, signals having wavelengths (λ) greater than 23 cm (approximate width of the human head) will result in waveform diffraction on the side of the head facing away (or opposite) from the source of the incident waveform. Hence, frequencies that fall below approximately 1500 Hz will be diffracted. The barrier (head) has almost negligible effects on the amplitude and frequency of the diffracted waveforms that bend around to the side of the head (specifically the ear) that is opposite from the incident sound source, as simplistically illustrated.

or bent around to the side of the head, and specifically the ear that faces away from the source of the incident waveform, are virtually unaffected with respect to frequency and intensity, as simplistically illustrated in Figure 7–4. The role played by diffraction in the binaural localization of low frequency sounds is addressed in greater detail in Chapter 8.

Diffraction and Scattering

Diffraction is not only the bending of waves around finite obstacles, it is also the spreading or scattering of waves that are made to travel through small openings. A small opening in a large barrier might be analogous to an opened window or opened door in a relatively larger barrier, such as the wall of a house. In Figure 7–5, the incident wave that is traveling from left to right encounters a large barrier having a small opening. In this illustration, the width (and length) of the opening is shorter than the wavelength of the incident wave. The incident wave (or longitudinally propagated waveform) in Figure 7–5 is illustrated by the curved areas of compression to the left of the barrier. Some of the energy of the incident waveform will be reflected back, as indicated by the arrows pointing to the left from the large barrier surface. Some of the sound energy may be absorbed (not shown). However, the part of the wave that strikes the small opening will pass through the opening and will be transmitted. The small opening in the barrier will in fact act like a new sound source. The force of the incident waves upon the very narrow opening will act as a point source of the new waves that will

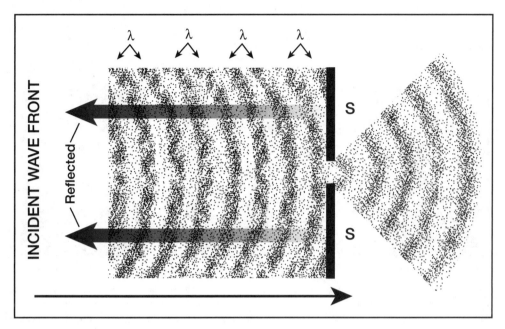

Figure 7–5. Diffraction of waves that are longitudinally propagated from left to right (*as indicated by the large arrow*) through a small opening in a large barrier. The narrow width of the opening is shorter than the wavelength (λ) of the incident plane wave. Some of the sound energy is reflected off the large barrier (*dark black arrows*), and some energy may even be absorbed (not shown) by the barrier. The part of the wave that strikes the small opening in the barrier passes through and is transmitted. The transmitted wave is then reconstituted (diffracted) on the other side of the barrier. The small opening in the barrier acts like a new sound source. Because of the shorter width of the barrier opening relative to the longer wavelength of the incident plane waves, there is a great deal of bending by the waves into the shadow region (s), indicating significant amounts of diffraction.

fan out (diffract) on the other side of the large barrier (Hewitt, 2011). In this way, and on the other side of the large barrier, the waveform will reconstitute (diffract). The degree of the bending/scattering pattern will depend on the relationship between the wavelength of the primary or incident wave, and the dimensions (width) of the obstacle. In Figure 7–5, the obstacle is the narrow width of the opening in the large barrier. If the width of the opening is much narrower than the wavelength of the incident waveform, the degree of bending (diffraction) will be relatively great, as illustrated in Figure 7–5. Note also that at the extreme corners of the

small opening, the waves are bent into a "shadow region" labeled by an *s*.

In Figure 7–6, the plane waves illustrated at the bottom of each panel are incident upon three sizes of openings in a large barrier. In panel A, the opening in the barrier is wide, and is wider than the wavelength of the incident plane wave. The plane wave continues through the large opening virtually unchanged except at the corners of the opening where the waves are slightly bent into the shadow region marked with an *s*. When the width of the opening is narrowed (see Figure 7–6 panel B) to a value that more closely approximates the wavelength of the incident

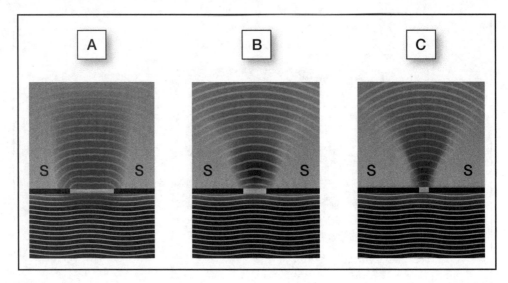

Figure 7–6. A–C. Plane waves passing through large barriers with openings of three sizes. The shorter the width of the barrier opening relative to the wavelength of the incident plane waves, the greater will be the bending of the waves at the edges of the opening, and hence, the greater the degree of diffraction. Because the opening in the large barrier in **C** is smaller (shorter width) than the longer wavelength of the incident plane waves, there is a greater degree of bending of the waves into the shadow region (s), indicating greater diffraction in **C** relative to **A** or **B**.

plane wave, less of the incident wave is transmitted through the opening and the bending (diffraction) of the waves into the shadow region becomes more pronounced. In panel C of Figure 7–6, the width of the opening in the large barrier is reduced even further and even less of the incident wave is transmitted. However, note in panel C the greater degree of diffraction in the transmitted waves relative to the other two panels. This increased degree of diffraction is illustrated by the greater degree of bending of the waves into the shadow region at the edges of the openings.

Diffraction effects involving the scattering of waves through small openings occur in everyday experiences. Take for example an individual sitting in a room listening to rock music at a fairly high volume from a high-quality sound system. Because the individual is situated close to the source of the incident sounds (the speakers), the individual hears the full range of frequencies, from bass (low frequencies) to mid-range, to treble (high frequencies). The individual then decides to leave the dwelling to relocate on an outdoor deck, but leaves a screened window open as the music continues to play. Although the music continues to be heard from the outside deck, it sounds different. From the deck outside, the most prominent sounds are the low-frequency beats from the percussion instruments (drums) and the sounds from the bass guitar. However, much of the mid-range and all of the much higher pitched treble sounds have become inaudible. Why is this? Unlike the higher frequency sounds, the lower frequencies are more easily scattered through the small opening provided by the screened windows and will easily diffract to the outdoor deck. Similarly, what sounds can be heard from the sidewalk as loud rock music is being played from the inside of a passing vehicle? Once again, the most prominent sounds one experiences from a passing vehicle are the low frequencies generated by the base guitar and the percussion instruments.

Sound Transmission and Sound-Shadow Effects

As illustrated in Figures 7–5 and 7–6, waves passing through a small opening in a large barrier can often result in waveform diffraction on the opposite side of the barrier. The degree of diffraction will depend upon the width of the opening relative to the wavelength of the incident waveform. Recall as well that in addition to wave diffraction, a (sound) shadow region is often created on the opposite side of a barrier. The sound-shadow regions were clearly labeled in Figures 7–5 and 7–6. The shadow regions represented areas in which sound waves fail to propagate. The reason that sound wave transmission fails to occur in the shadow regions is attributed in a large part to the reflection of incident waves as they strike the large barrier. There is also the possibility that at least some of the incident waveform energy is absorbed by the large barrier, and therefore may also contribute in some way to the shadow region. In either case, waveform reflection and/or absorption will prevent sounds from being transmitted to the opposite side of a large barrier,

and these waveform properties tend to result in the formation of shadow regions.

For sound wave transmission that occurs across barriers having a finite size, it is clear from the above presentation that diffraction effects are largely dependent upon the wavelength of the incident signal. It should not be too surprising that sound-shadow effects, resulting from sound wave transmission across a barrier with a finite size, are also largely dependent upon the wavelength of the incident signal. When a relatively high-frequency sound strikes an obstacle (barrier) of finite size, and the barrier has a width that is greater than the wavelength (λ) of the incident wave front, some of the sound energy may be absorbed by the barrier. Perhaps some of the sound energy of the incident wave might even be transmitted through the barrier or obstacle. However, most of the incident sound wave energy will be reflected off the surface of the barrier. This is because higher frequency sounds have relatively short wavelengths and higher frequency sounds cannot simply leap over or bend around barriers when the widths of those barriers exceed their wavelengths. In such instances, the higher frequency components within an incident waveform will in fact be blocked from crossing to the opposite sides of such barriers. When the higher frequency components of a signal are blocked by reflection and/or by absorption effects, a sound-shadow is cast on the opposite side of the barrier. A sound-shadow is simply an area in which sound waves fail to propagate.

Figure 7–7 simplistically illustrates what can happen when an incident plane wave, longitudinally propagated from

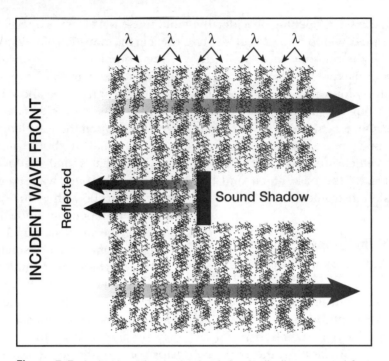

Figure 7–7. An incident plane wave that is longitudinally propagated from left to right encounters a finite barrier (*shown by the black rectangle*) having a width greater than the wavelength (λ) of the incident wave front. Much of the sound energy is reflected from the barrier (*dark black arrows*), and some of the energy may be absorbed (*not shown*) by the barrier. Under idealistic conditions, the combined effects of reflection and absorption will result in a sound-shadow on the opposite side of the finite barrier, as simplistically illustrated.

left to right, encounters a finite barrier (small black rectangle) having a width that is greater than the wavelength of the incident wave front. As illustrated, the reflection and/or absorption of part of the incident the incident wave by the barrier casts a sound-shadow on the opposite side of the barrier. Bear in mind that some of the sound energy, if sufficiently intense, may still be transmitted through the barrier. Therefore, unlike the idealized image depicted in Figure 7–7, in real environmental situations, it should not be expected that all (100%) of the higher frequency sound energy will be blocked (Durrant & Feth, 2013). Nevertheless, when sound-shad-ows are produced, they can result in significant consequences with respect to the intensity of the sound that ultimately reaches the opposite side of the barrier. The generation of a sound-shadow will affect the intensity sound that is perceived on the opposite side of the barrier, or on the side facing away from the sound source. The negative consequence of using high-frequency maritime foghorn signals to protect ships at sea from the navigational hazards created by other ships and/or from coastal installations was previously discussed. Additional perceptual outcomes resulting from sound-shadow effects are addressed later in this chapter.

Head-Shadow Effects

Another interesting phenomenon attributed to the human head is the sound (head)-shadow effect. As with diffraction, the production of a head-shadow is also largely dependent upon the relationship between the width of the human head and the wavelength of the incident waveform. As discussed above and illustrated in Figure 7–7, relatively higher frequency incident sounds (those having short wavelengths) cannot simply leap over or bend around a barrier if the width of the barrier exceeds their wavelengths. The higher frequencies within the incident wave will, in fact, be blocked from crossing to the opposite side of the barrier. As discussed above, higher frequencies will be blocked by reflection and/or by absorption effects. Once again, the human head may also be thought of as a finite barrier. If it is assumed, as before that the human head measures in width between 15 to 17 cm, but ear-to-ear is actually about 23 cm, then we may again determine, more or less, which frequencies would or would not be expected to succumb to head-shadow effects. For an incident sound approaching the head from either the right side or the left side, we may once again employ Equation 7–1 and solve for frequency (f) using the CGS speed for a sound having a wavelength of about 23 cm/cycle. Hence,

$$\lambda = c/f$$

$$23 \text{ cm cycle} = 34,400 \text{ cm/s}/f$$

$$f = 1500 \text{ cycles/s}$$

All human heads are not exactly 23 cm in width. Notwithstanding, on the average, sounds presented in a sound-field to one ear or to the other are likely to result in head-shadow effects on the side of the head facing away from the source of the incident waves, or simply in the opposite ear, when some of the incident sound frequencies have wavelengths that are less than 23 cm. That is, head-shadow effects are likely to occur for the relatively higher frequencies within the incident waveform, such as those signals with frequencies greater than 1500 Hz. The head-shadow effect is simplistically illustrated in Figure 7–8. Once again, it should be noted that if the incident sound wave is sufficiently intense, some of the sound energy may be transmitted through the head. Therefore, unlike the idealized image depicted in Figure 7–8, in real environmental situations, we should not expect that all (100%) of the higher frequency sound energy will be blocked (Durrant & Feth, 2013). Nevertheless, the head-shadow effect of blocking relatively higher frequency sounds can have significant consequences on the intensity of the waveforms that are perceived on the opposite side of the head, or in the ear facing away from the incident sound source. The role played by the head-shadow effect in the binaural localization of higher frequency sounds is addressed in greater detail in Chapter 8.

The Doppler Effect

Another wavelength-related sound-field phenomenon is the Doppler effect, named after the Austrian scientist Johann Christian Doppler (1803–1853). Doppler was able to draw an analogy between changes that occur in a steady-state sound (the sound of trumpets)

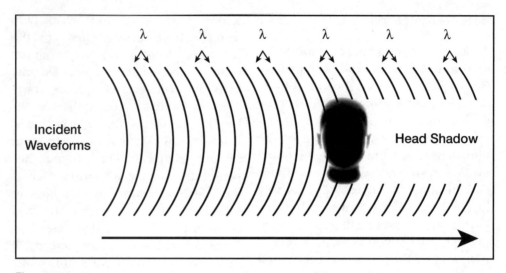

Figure 7–8. The head-shadow effect resulting from the presentation of high-frequency sounds is illustrated using longitudinally propagated incident waveforms that travel from left to right (*as indicated by the large arrow*). Some fraction of the sound energy may be transmitted through the head (*not shown*) if the signal is sufficiently intense. However, most of the relatively high-frequency energy within the incident waveform will be blocked from crossing to the opposite side of the barrier. Signals having wavelengths (λ) less than 23 cm and/or frequencies greater than 1500 Hz will be blocked on the side of the head facing away (or opposite) from the source of the incident waveform by reflection and/or absorption effects.

emitted from a moving source (a locomotive), and the changes that occur in light that is given off from moving objects in the visible universe, such as comets, stars, and galaxies (Halliday et al., 2011). The speed of these light-generating objects in the cosmos, as well as the direction in which they are moving, whether toward or away from the earth, is easily determined by analyzing their (light) frequency spectra. When a particular cosmologic object is at rest relative to the earth's position, the light emitted from the distant object takes on a recognized and appropriate fundamental frequency and wavelength based on known material composition (Halliday et al., 2011). However, if the object is moving directly toward or away from the earth, the expected fundamental frequency and spectral signature (color) of the emitted light will shift,

due to motion-related changes in wavelength. Ultraviolet (UV) light, composed of very high frequencies of approximately 790 tera Hz (tHz) and relatively short wavelengths of 400 nanometers (nm)/cycle is found at one end of the visible light spectrum (Giancoli, 2005). Note that *tera* is the prefix for 10^{12} or, one trillion, and *nano* is the prefix for 10^{-9} or, one billionth (Appendix C). A spectral shift into the UV range or a *blue shift* is the term borrowed from the field of astronomy to describe relatively shorter wavelengths and changes in the frequency spectrum indicating that distant light-emitting objects in the cosmos are traveling directly toward earth. On the other hand, infrared light, composed of relatively lower frequencies of approximately 430 tHz and relatively longer wavelengths that are 700 nm/cycle, is found at the other end of the visible light spectrum (Giancoli, 2005). A spectral shift into the infrared range or a *red shift* is also the term borrowed from astronomy to describe relatively longer wavelengths and changes in the frequency spectrum indicating that distant light-emitting objects in the cosmos are traveling away from the earth. For example, distant galaxies exhibit low-frequency signatures (a red-shift) indicating that they are moving away from our galaxy at great speeds. Also, a rapidly spinning star exhibits a red shift on the side spinning away from our viewing angle, and a blue shift on the side spinning in the direction of our viewing angle, all of which enables a computation of the star's spin rate (Hewitt, 2011).

Sound Transmission and the Doppler Effect

The Doppler effect for sound transmission may be defined as the pitch change that is experienced in a steady-state signal due to the relative motion between an observer and a signal-generating source. The Doppler effect for sound is therefore a motion-related, wavelength-related, and therefore, a frequency- and (perceptual) pitch-related phenomenon (Halliday et al., 2011). Pitch is the subjective psychological perception and correlate of frequency. As frequency increases or decreases, pitch also respectively increases or decreases, though frequency is not equal to pitch. Frequency is measured in cycles/second, whereas pitch is measured in *mels*. The concept of pitch is addressed in detail in Chapter 8. The Doppler effect for sound transmission is evident when one stands on a sidewalk as a car rapidly passes by with its horn

blaring incessantly. The change in the pitch of the horn that is experienced as the car approaches and then speeds off are due to the Doppler effect. As the car approaches, the pitch experienced is higher than it would normally be if the car were not moving. As the car passes, and at a distance thereafter, the pitch drops to a level experienced that is again, lower than at rest. Changes in pitch due to the Doppler effect may be detected for speeds upward from as low as 10 mi/hr.

The Doppler effect (and change in wavelength) for sound transmission is illustrated in Figure 7–9. In panel A, the siren on the unmoving emergency vehicle is emitting a constant and unchanging auditory signal with a known fundamental frequency. The sound is being propagated equally in all directions. Hence, the siren's waves (wavelengths) are being propagated equally into the regions located both in the front of the unmoving vehicle and behind the unmoving vehicle. Note that in both of these locations in panel A of Figure 7–9 there is equal spacing between each longitudinally propagated wave crest. Furthermore, person *x* standing on the sidewalk behind the unmoving vehicle will experience the same pitch of the siren as person *y* who is located on the sidewalk in front of the unmoving vehicle. In panel B, the same emergency vehicle with the same active siren is now racing forward in the direction of person *y*. The sound of the siren is again propagated equally in all directions, since wave velocity depends only on the material medium and not on the velocity of the source, or of the observer (Giancoli, 2005). Nevertheless, the siren's waves (wavelengths) that are being propagated into the area behind

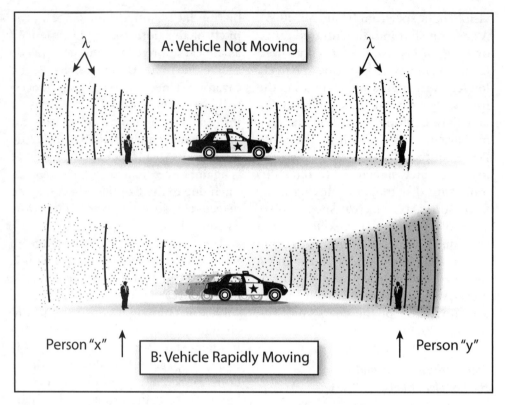

Figure 7–9. The Doppler effect. **A.** The siren on the unmoving emergency vehicle produces a constant and unchanging auditory signal. The sound is propagated equally in all directions. The siren's waves (wavelengths) propagated into the area in the front of the vehicle are the same as those that are propagated into the area behind the vehicle. Person *x* in the area behind the vehicle experiences the same pitch of the siren as person *y* located in the area in front of the vehicle. **B.** The same vehicle (with siren) is racing toward person *y*. The sound is propagated equally in all directions but the siren's waves (wavelengths) in the region behind the vehicle are much longer compared to **A.** Person *x* experiences a drop in the pitch of the siren relative to the pitch experienced in **A** (*red shift*). The siren's waves (wavelengths) in the region ahead of the vehicle are much shorter compared to **A.** Person *y* in **B** experiences an increase in the pitch of the siren relative to the pitch experienced in **A** (*blue shift*).

the fast-moving vehicle are now significantly longer compared to the same area depicted in panel A when the vehicle was not moving. Furthermore, person *x* will experience a drop in the pitch of the siren relative to the pitch that was experienced when the vehicle was at rest, in panel A. Moreover, the siren's waves (wavelengths) that are being propagated into the area ahead of the vehicle are now significantly shorter compared to the same area depicted in

panel A when the vehicle was not moving. Likewise, person *y* will experience an increase in the pitch of the siren relative to the pitch that was experienced when the vehicle was at rest, in panel A.

Given that the actual resting frequency of the siren has not changed from panel A to panel B in Figure 7–9, what would explain the motion-related changes in pitch experienced by persons *x* and *y* in panel B? Let us begin with an explanation of the change in pitch experienced by person y in panel B of Figure 7–9. As the emergency vehicle's active siren races forward, each new wave front that is propagated out ahead of the vehicle toward person y partially closes the distance (wavelength gap) with each wave front propagated just prior to it. That is, each forwardly propagated wave front is unable to advance fast enough or far enough out in front of the vehicle, from each consecutive wave front that follows. Hence, each newly propagated wave front almost "catches up" with each previously generated wave front, so that the forward propagated wave fronts begin to pile up with a greater frequency, in the area just ahead of the racing vehicle. All of this is due of course to the forward motion of the sound source. This also means that successive areas of compression and rarefaction are being squeezed closer together such that the wavelength of the total signal is compressed, or is simply made shorter, as illustrated in panel B of Figure 7–9. Person y is therefore bombarded more frequently by the longitudinally propagated wave crests as the emergency vehicle continues to move rapidly into the path of the incident waves that are being propagated toward person y. The more frequent bombardment of person y with propagated wave crests translates to a higher rate of bombardment, relative to panel A of Figure 7–9. An increased rate of propagated signals with shorter wavelengths into the forward path of the vehicle translates to a motion-induced increase in frequency, all of which translates to the perception of a higher pitch (a blue shift) that is experienced by person y.

How might the change in pitch experienced by person x in panel B be explained? As the emergency vehicle's active siren races forward, new wave fronts are also propagated outward toward the rear (the departing side) of the vehicle, and toward person x. Due of course to the forward motion of the sound source, there is an increase in the distance (wavelength gap) of each new wave front from each wave front propagated just prior to it. This means that successive areas of compression and rarefaction propagated in the direction of person x are being pulled farther apart (stretched) due to the forward motion of the sound source as illustrated in panel B of Figure 7–9. Hence, the wavelength of the total signal is stretched, or is simply made longer. Each new wave front that is propagated from the rapidly departing vehicle is also rapidly departing from each wave front that came before, as each wave front that came before is left behind at a relatively greater distance from each new wave front. Person x is therefore bombarded less frequently by the longitudinally propagated wave crests as the emergency vehicle continues to move rapidly away from the path of the departing incident wave fronts. The less frequent bombardment of person x by propagated wave crests translates to a lower rate of bombardment relative to panel A of Figure 7–9. A decreased rate of propagated signals with longer wavelengths into the trailing path of the vehicle translates to a motion-induced decrease in frequency, all of which translates to the perception of a lower pitch (a red shift) that is experienced by person x. The Doppler effect also occurs when the source is at rest and the observer is in motion and moving toward or away from the source of the sound.

Sound Transmission and Shock Waves

In the description of the Doppler effect (see Figure 7–9 panel B), the emergency vehicle sped forward and each new waveform generated by the forward-moving siren was described as almost "catching up" with previously generated sound waves. The forward propagated waves were said to begin to pile up in the regions located ahead of the vehicle as successive areas of compression and rarefaction in these regions were said to be squeezed closer together (compressed) due to the forward motion of the sound source. Extending the effects that were described above, what happens if the vehicle, or in this case an aircraft, begins to approach, catches up with, and then exceeds the speed of sound for the air medium in which it is moving? If the speed of a sound source in a medium exceeds the speed of sound in the medium, then the Doppler effect no longer applies (Halliday et al., 2011). When approaching the speed of sound (at subsonic speeds) waveforms from the moving object (or sound source) will begin to "outrun" the forward motion of the sound that is being generated (Giancoli, 2005). When the forward speed of the aircraft is as great as the speed of the sound waves that it produces, sound waves can no longer be propagated forward into the region ahead of the aircraft (Figure 7–10). Hence, at the speed of sound, the wave fronts (crests) that have piled up along the sides of the moving aircraft now

Figure 7–10. Aerodynamic shock waves produced by the wings of a Navy FA18F jet traveling at Mach 1. The sudden and dramatic decrease in air pressure just behind the cone of much higher pressure nearer to the apex of the aircraft causes water molecules in the air to condense around the wings, creating a fog. U.S Navy photo, courtesy of PH2 Mark A. Ebert.

overlap and form a single, very large crest, or area of compression. It was once believed that this pileup of wave crests ahead of the aircraft imposed a "sound barrier" that had to be broken. Though the sound barrier is not real, the overlapping wave crests do disrupt and impede the flow of air over the wings of the aircraft, making control of the aircraft more difficult at that instant in time (Hewitt, 2011). With an added thrust of power, the aircraft can pass through this region of turbulence and exceed the speed of sound. When an aircraft travels in excess of the speed of sound, its speed is supersonic. At supersonic speeds, the aircraft flies into smooth undisturbed air since there are no longer any wave fronts propagated in its forward path to impede its forward motion (Giancoli, 2005).

When an aircraft reaches a speed that is at and just beyond (supersonic) the speed of sound, a tremendous disturbance in the air is created by large amounts of high-pressure energy, much the same as the sudden expansion of air that is generated by an explosion (Hewitt, 2011). The disturbance takes the form of three-dimensional shock wave crests that are heard by those on the ground as a "sonic boom." The shock wave crests that are produced are actually composed of two extreme pressure cones. The apex of a high-pressure (compression) cone is located at the bow of the aircraft. Behind this large compression cone is a very large, negative trough that reaches a maximum (apex) of low pressure (rarefaction) near the tail. As illustrated in Figure 7–10, the rapidly expanding rarefied air associated with a sudden and dramatic decrease in air pressure just behind the cone of compression (located near to the apex of the aircraft) causes water molecules in the air to condense around the wings. The sudden overpressure created at the bow followed by the sudden under pressure generated from regions just behind the bow to the tail, actually creates shock waves composed of two (or more) sonic booms (Giancoli, 2005) in which the air pressure first suddenly increases well above and then suddenly decreases well below normal, before returning to equilibrium (Halliday et al., 2011). Therefore, the thunderous sound of sonic booms created by the two or more shock waves forming in the front and rear, as well as at the wings of the aircraft, are heard when the cone-shaped shell of compressed and rarefied air reaches the ground (Hewitt, 2011). This cone of compressed and rarefied air is often referred to as a Mach cone, as illustrated in Figure 7–11 (Halliday et al., 2011). Finally, it was once mistakenly thought that sonic booms were produced only at the precise moment that an aircraft breaks through the sound barrier. On the contrary, the shock waves follow the aircraft for the full duration of time that the craft is traveling at supersonic speeds (Giancoli, 2005). The shock waves formed by the Mach cone together with the ensuing sonic booms are swept continuously behind and below (see Figure 7–11) an aircraft that is traveling faster than the speed of sound in air (Hewitt, 2011).

A convenient method for designating the speed of a subsonic or a supersonic aircraft is to use the Mach number, named after the Austrian physicist Ernst Mach (1838–1916). The Mach number expresses the speed of an aircraft or any moving projectile relative to the speed of sound in the medium in which the

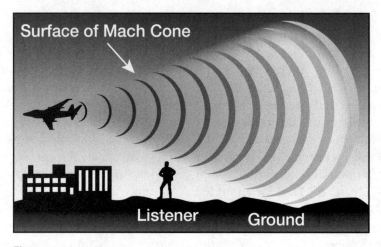

Figure 7–11. The thunderous sound of sonic booms are created by shock waves as the cone-shaped shell of compressed and rarefied air, referred to as a Mach cone, reaches the ground. The shock waves follow the aircraft for the full duration of time that the craft is traveling at supersonic speeds. The shock waves formed by the Mach cone, together with the ensuing sonic booms, are swept continuously behind and below an aircraft that is traveling faster than sound.

object is moving. The Mach number is actually a ratio that employs a reference value (denominator) and an observed value (numerator), which is simply the ratio of the speed of the object to the known speed of sound in the particular material medium (Giancoli, 2005). Hence,

$$\text{Mach number} = s^o/s^r \quad (7\text{–}3)$$

in which s^o is the observed object's speed, and s^r is the known speed of sound in the material medium (or reference speed) that the object is moving. If for example, under ideal conditions of density and temperature, the speed of sound is 760 mi/hr which is the equivalent of 344 m/s as indicated in Table 6–8, then either of these two values could be used in the denominator (s^r) of Equation 7–3. If an aircraft is observed (s^o) to be traveling at 380 mi/hr or 172 m/s, the aircraft is traveling at the subsonic speed of Mach 0.5, or half the speed of sound. If the value for s^o should happen to change to 760 mi/hr or to 344 m/s, the aircraft would be traveling at Mach 1, or at the speed of sound. If again the value for s^o should happen to change to 1520 mi/hr or to 688 m/s, the aircraft is then traveling at the supersonic speed of Mach 2, or twice the speed of sound.

Sound Transmission and Refraction

What else can occur to sound in a sound-field? Refraction is the change in the direction of a wave front that occurs when changes are made in the transmitting medium through which the waveform is propagating. Refraction for sound is most commonly observed when an incident sound wave passes from one medium into a second medium, and the speed of sound within the two media is not equal. As indicated in Chapters 5 and 6, the fundamental physical properties of a particular medium will determine the speed at which sound will propagate in that medium (Durrant & Feth, 2013). In Chapter 6, the speed of a sound wave through any material medium depended on both an inertial property of the medium (to store kinetic energy) and an elastic property of the medium (to store potential energy), and the relationship between the two was provided by

$$\text{Speed} = \left(\frac{\text{elastic property}}{\text{inertial property}}\right)^{\frac{1}{2}}$$
(6–15)

Recall also that the bulk (or elastic) modulus discussed in Chapter 6 was a measure of the bulk elastic properties of a material medium (see Table 6–1) and that the volume density was defined the amount of mass per unit volume in the medium. Equation 6–15 in Chapter 6 was also defined by placing the volume density in the denominator for the inertial property, and by placing the bulk modulus in the numerator for the elastic property (Halliday et al., 2011). In this way, the speed of sound through any material medium was redefined by Equation 6–16 as the square root of the ratio of the bulk (elastic) modulus and the volume density, or simply,

$$\text{Speed} = \left(\frac{\text{bulk modulus}}{\text{volume density}}\right)^{\frac{1}{2}}$$
(6–16)

The speed of sound (c) for various materials was also provided in Tables 5–5 and 6–8.

When an incident sound wave from one medium enters a second (and different) material medium, the incident sound waves will, in all likelihood, bend. The bending occurs as parts of the incident wave front travel through the second medium at a correspondingly different speed. As long as most or part of the incident sound is faithfully transmitted into the second medium, and not completely absorbed or completely reflected, a bending of the incident wave front will be a distinct possibility. The bending of the transmitted wave front is called *refraction* and unless the incident wave front strikes the surface of the second medium at a perpendicular plane (0° of incidence or at 90° relative to the surface), the wave front will bend as it is transmitted into the second medium (Halliday et al., 2011). The second material medium may, of course, include water. The perpendicular path taken by a wave front to a second medium was also illustrated in the previous chapter (see Figure 6–5) in reference to angles of reflection.

Environmental Atmospheric Temperature and Refraction

Atmospheric temperature almost always exhibits a vertical gradient that extends from warm to cool, such that the air is usually warmer closer to the surface of the earth and is progressively cooler at higher elevations. Looking at Table 6–8 in Chapter 6, it is also clear that sound travels faster in warmer air than it travels in colder air. Because negative temperature gradients (warmer temperatures at lower regions of the atmosphere) are the norm, it can be expected that environmental atmospheric sound will rarely travel through the air in straight lines from the source of a sound. Hence, due to environmental atmospheric temperature gradients, sounds propagated in air will be refracted or bent. Because sound normally travels faster closer to the ground where the air is usually warmer, the bottom most parts of an incident wave front will travel faster relative to the slower, uppermost parts of the same incident wave front. Traveling at the higher but cooler atmospheric regions, the upper parts of the wave front are essentially held back by the cooler temperature and will lag behind the faster moving lower parts of the wave front. The faster moving lower most parts of the wave then move out ahead of the upper parts of the total wave front, causing the incident wave front to bend (back) and rise on an upward angle. Under most daytime circumstances, environmental sounds propagated in the atmosphere are bent or are refracted upward, which limits the relative range or distance that these sounds can travel. The upward refraction of sound waves in air is indicative of a negative temperature gradient, as illustrated in panel A of Figure 7–12.

When the upper regions of the atmosphere are relatively warmer than the cooler lower regions, the temperature gradient is said to be positive. This positive temperature gradient (colder temperatures at lower regions of the atmosphere) is referred to as a *temperature inversion*. Temperature inversions are often transitory. That is, they occur only for brief periods of time just before sunrise when the ground is cool, or for short periods of time over a cold lake when the early morning air in the upper regions of the atmosphere is warmer. By late morning, however, these conditions are often changed back to the normal negative temperature gradient, as the air nearer to the ground and in the lower regions of the atmosphere

is warmed. Under some geographical conditions, large parcels of cold air can sink and remain trapped in the lower regions of the atmosphere by warmer air that is also trapped in the upper atmospheric regions by mountains. Long-term temperature inversions produced by unique geographical conditions notoriously trap smog and other thermal pollutants, creating respiratory hazards (Hewitt, 2011). Notwithstanding, the real question is why do sounds appear to travel farther distances on a cold day, at night, or early in the morning when the layer of air nearest to the ground is cold relative to the air at higher elevations? When a positive temperature gradient exists, sound travels slower closer to the ground where the air is cool, as the uppermost parts of the incident wave front travel faster relative to the slower, and lower most parts of the same incident wave front. Traveling slower at the lower but cooler atmospheric regions, the lower parts of the wave front are essentially held back by the cooler temperature and will lag behind the faster moving (warmer) upper parts of the wave front. The faster moving uppermost parts of the wave move out ahead of and essentially overtake the lower parts of the total wave front, causing the incident wave front to bend or refract (forward) and arc on a downward angle. When the layer of air nearest the ground is colder than the air above, environmental sounds are bent or refracted downward. The downward refraction extends the relative range or distance that environmental sounds can travel. The downward refraction of environmental sound waves in air that exhibits a positive temperature gradient (temperature inversion) is illustrated in panel B of Figure 7–12.

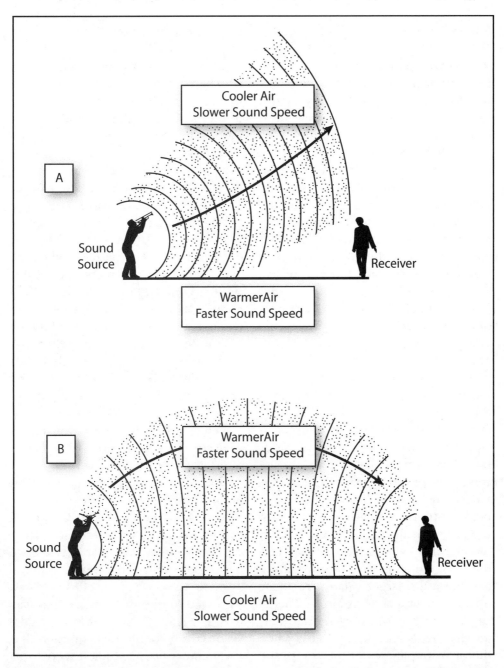

Figure 7–12. A. An upward refraction of environmental sound waves (*shown by the upwardly curved arrow*) is created by an upper and lower atmosphere that exhibits a normal (negative) temperature gradient. The upward refraction of the wave front shortens the distance traveled by the sound and prevents the delivery of the signal to the receiver. **B.** A downward refraction of environmental sound waves (*shown by the downwardly curved arrow*) is created by an upper and lower atmosphere that exhibits a temperature inversion. The positive temperature gradient lengthens the distance traveled by the sound and facilitates the delivery of the signal to the receiver.

Sound Transmission and Interference

When two separate waveforms overlap in the same place and at the same time, the *principle of superposition* states that the shape of the composite (also called the resultant) waveform will be obtained by combining the separate contributions, or algebraic sums of the separate displacements, of the two individual waveforms. Two waveforms that combine according to the principle of superposition are said to interfere with each other, and the phenomenon of combining waveforms often results in what is also referred to as *interference* (Halliday et al., 2011). As with diffraction, interference occurs only for the energy carried by the sound waves, and not for the energy carried by the material particles that make up the medium. Overlapping interfering waves do not alter the motion of each other, and once the waveforms cease to overlap, they return to their original, separate waveform shapes. The composite waveform resulting from the interference may exhibit larger or smaller peak amplitudes relative to either of the two constituent waveforms. Interference that is additive occurs when the peak amplitudes of the composite waveform are larger relative to those of the constituent waveforms. This is called *constructive interference*. Interference that is subtractive occurs when the peak amplitudes of the composite waveform are cancelled or are reduced relative to those of the constituent waveforms. This is called *destructive interference*. Recall that constructive and destructive interactions between propagated waveforms were addressed in some detail in Chapter 6. Summarily, when the areas of compression (crests

or positive peak amplitudes) of one wave overlap in time with the areas of compression of another wave, such as when the waveforms are in phase, there is an additive effect or an increase in the positive peak amplitude at that particular moment in time for the composite waveform. Several illustrative examples of constructive interactions (constructive interference patterns) for propagated periodic waveforms were provided in Figure 6–7 and in Figures 6–10 through 6–14, as well as in Figures 6–16 and 6–17. Alternatively, when the areas of compression (crests or positive peak amplitudes) of one wave overlap in time with the areas of rarefaction (troughs or negative peak amplitudes) of another wave, such as when the waveforms are out of phase, there is a subtractive effect or a decrease in the positive peak amplitude at that particular moment in time for the composite waveform. Two illustrative examples of destructive interactions (destructive interference patterns) for propagated periodic waveforms were provided in Figures 6–8 and 6–9. The examples provided by the figures in Chapter 6 essentially illustrated constructive/destructive interactions or interference patterns for transverse wave motion.

Recall the surface waveform created by a waterborne disturbance that was used in Figure 7–2A to illustrate transverse wave motion. Bear in mind that the motion of surface water waves also represents longitudinal wave propagation. Hence, the longitudinal wave propagation of surface waves on water may also be used to demonstrate constructive/destructive interactions that produce interference patterns for transverse wave motion. When two small stones are simultaneously thrown in relatively close proximity to each other into a still, unmoving body of water such as a pond, the disturbance creates two sets of surface water waveforms. Each waveform is composed of successive areas of compression and rarefaction that move outward in all directions from the entry point of each stone. Because of the relatively close proximity of the two disturbances, the outwardly moving surface waves from each disturbance eventually begin to overlap and interfere with each other, as the waveforms continue to expand outward from their points of disturbance. Figure 7–13 illustrates transverse wave interference patterns for two longitudinally propagated water waves that have started to overlap as both waveforms continue to travel (expand) outward in all directions. As indicated in the figure, in some overlapping areas,

the crests (areas of compression labeled *C*) from each of the two waveforms will repetitively meet and interact. In other overlapping areas, the troughs (areas of rarefaction labeled with *R*) from each of the two waveforms will also repetitively meet and interact. Locations in the composite interactive waveform where crests meets crests and troughs meet troughs, are where constructive interference occurs. Several of the locations where constructive interference would occur are labeled with a plus sign (+) in Figure 7–13. At each of these locations, the composite waveform will oscillate vertically (up and down) with greater amplitude than the amplitude of either wave taken separately. At such locations, the cork shown in Figure 7–2A would also bob up and down at a much greater amplitude, but in a relatively stationary location, at approximately

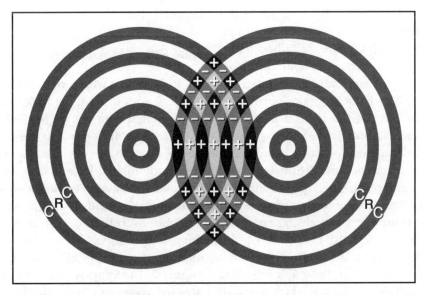

Figure 7–13. Two longitudinally propagated water waves. The water waves have started to overlap, creating interference patterns for transverse wave motion. Labeled are the waveform crests or the areas of compression (*C*), and the troughs or the areas of rarefaction (*R*). Several locations are also labeled where constructive (+) and destructive (–) interference would occur.

right angles to the outward direction of both water waves. Alternatively, in some overlapping areas, the crests from one of the two waveforms will repetitively meet and interact with the troughs from the other, and vice versa. Locations in the composite interactive waveform where crests meet troughs will result in destructive interference. Several of the locations where destructive interference would occur are labeled with a minus sign (–) in Figure 7–13. At each of these locations, the composite waveform will not oscillate, or may oscillate vertically (up and down) with far less amplitude than the amplitude of either wave taken separately. At such locations, the cork shown in Figure 7–2A would also cease to bob up and down or would move only minimally.

Wave Reflection and Wave Inversion

An example of wave reflection was provided earlier in this chapter in the description of transverse wave motion. Recall in the example described that a rope was fastened at one end (only) to a wall and was made taut. We can label this as Time 1 as illustrated in Figure 7–14. The free end of the rope is then suddenly and rapidly jerked upward from equilibrium, then downward (and back) to equilibrium at Time 2. Subsequently, an incident pulse wave of compression is generated in the rope. The incident pulse wave then travels horizontally from the handheld free end of the rope to the wall. When the pulse wave reaches the wall at Time 5, a reflected but "inverted" pulse wave is generated, as per Newton's third law of motion (Time 6). That is, the pulse wave from the rope exerts an upward force on the wall and the wall in turn exerts an equal

but opposite force on the rope. Hence, a reflected and inverted pulse wave (of rarefaction) then travels back to the handheld end of the rope at Time 9. In the present context, there are two important items to consider. The first is that the reflection of the incident wave in this example is restricted to only one boundary or barrier. That is, only one end of the rope is anchored to the wall. The second is that the motion of the free end of the rope in this example is limited to a nonrepetitive, half-cycle of displacement. That is, in the present context, the displacement that occurs at the rope's free end is limited to a single upward (positive) motion from equilibrium, followed by a single downward motion back to equilibrium. For both of these reasons, only one waveform, either the incident (compression) wave or the inverted reflected (rarefaction) wave, is propagated by the rope at any given moment in time, as illustrated in Figure 7–14.

Wave Reflection and Wave Interference

As indicated earlier in this chapter, incident sound waves propagated in a medium that contains highly reflective surfaces will often result in the production of reflected waveforms that exhibit amplitude intensities equal to those of the incident waves. Furthermore, when sounds are propagated in a medium with highly reflective surfaces, all of the sound energy is retained within the medium (Speaks, 1999). Refer again to Figure 7–14. Suppose that the single upward (positive) then single downward motion back to equilibrium of the free end of the rope (half-cycle of motion) as illustrated in Figure 7–14 were to be followed by the addition of

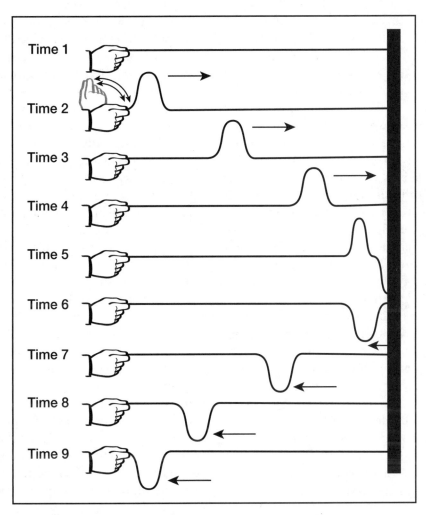

Figure 7–14. Example of wave reflection and wave inversion. At Time 1 a rope is fastened at one end to a wall and is made taut. At Time 2 the free end of the rope is rapidly jerked upward and then downward generating an incident pulse wave of compression. The incident pulse wave travels horizontally to the wall, reaches the wall at Time 5 and is reflected and inverted. At Time 6 the reflected and inverted pulse wave of rarefaction is generated. By Time 9 the inverted pulse wave travels back to the hand-held end of the rope.

a downward (negative), and then an upward motion back to equilibrium, for a total of one full cycle of motion. Furthermore, suppose that this full cycle of motion occurred rapidly and was repeated many times in what could loosely be defined as shaking the free end of the rope. If a periodic (360°) vibratory force were to be applied

repetitively to the free end of the rope, many incident and many reflected waves would be simultaneously generated. Under these conditions, even the hand-held end of the rope would behave like a fixed barrier (Durrant & Feth, 2013). Hence, a repetitive sinusoidal vibratory force applied to the illustration shown in Figure 7–14 would initially generate a sinusoidal wave that would be propagated to the right. When the wave hits the fixed barrier (wall), it is then reflected as an inverted (in-phase) sinusoidal waveform that propagates to the left but overlaps, while moving, with the next wave that is being propagated to the right. When the leftward moving wave reaches the handheld end of the rope, it is again reflected as an inverted waveform that propagates to the right but will overlap with other leftward and additional rightward propagated waves. In a very short span of time, there would be many overlapping waves traveling simultaneously in both directions within the same medium. In general, whenever incident and reflected waves occupy the same space (medium) at the same time, incident and reflected sound waves will produce wave interference patterns. Interference patterns resulting from interactions between incident and reflected waves will first be described for transverse wave motion.

Wave Reflection, Transverse Wave Motion, and Standing Waves

In the present context it will be useful to continue with the example provided above, wherein a repetitive sinusoidal vibratory force (shaking) was applied to the free end of a rope, creating overlapping waves that traveled simultaneously in both directions. As indicated, most of the overlapping incident and reflected waves would interact in a completely random manner resulting in the rapid production of chaotic wave interference patterns. Many of the reflected waves will interfere destructively, and their energy will be dissipated. However, if just the right amount of periodic vibratory force, at an appropriate rate

(frequency), were to be applied to the handheld end of the rope, a distinctive (not random) and persistent transverse wave interference pattern would then appear. What would constitute an appropriate frequency? The *principle of resonance* from Chapter 5 stated that when a periodically vibrating force is applied to an elastic system (the rope), the elastic system will be forced to vibrate, and will initially vibrate under forced vibration at the frequency of the force that is being applied. The nearer the frequency of the applied force is to the natural (fundamental) frequency of the elastic system, the greater will be the resulting amplitude of vibration in the elastic system (Speaks, 1999). If the driving frequency is either less than or greater than the natural (fundamental) frequency of the elastic system, the elastic system will vibrate at an amplitude that is much less than the maximum possible.

If the rate (frequency) of the vibratory force applied to the handheld end of the rope were to be exactly doubled, a second distinctive and persistent transverse wave interference pattern would emerge. As the frequency of the vibratory force applied to the handheld end of the rope continues to increase by integer multiples, a new and distinctive transverse wave interference pattern would appear for each subsequent harmonic frequency. In the rope example provided, the emergence of the frequency-specific sets of distinctive and persistent interference patterns referred to as a consequence of shaking the free end of a rope in the manner described are known as *transverse standing waves*. Reflected sounds often produce standing waves. Standing waves occur when an incident wave and a reflected wave are each generated at precisely the same frequency and amplitude, and travel within the same medium but in opposite directions. Standing waves are generated because all of the sound energy propagated within a medium will be retained within the medium, if the medium contains highly reflective surfaces (Speaks, 1999).

Standing Waves and the Vibration of Strings

A more convenient method of illustrating transverse wave interference and the production of transverse standing waves is provided by the example of a guitar string or thin wire that is fixed

(anchored) at either end and stretched between two stationary supports or barriers, as shown in Figure 7–15. The elastic string is under tension and is fixed at right angles to supports which are essentially boundary surfaces (not shown). As the central area of the string is plucked, a large number of frequencies in the form of pulse waves are generated. Figure 7–15 in the top panel illustrates the string (darker line), as it is displaced from equilibrium or plucked by the two fingers that are shown. The lighter array of solid lines in the top panel (below the plucked string) illustrates a series of displacement patterns occurring over time, after the string has

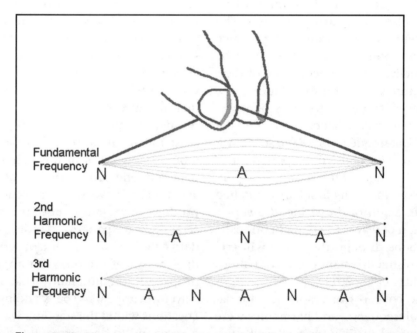

Figure 7–15. Transverse wave interference and the production of transverse standing waves on a string are illustrated. Displacement nodes (*N*) and displacement antinodes (*A*) are illustrated for each harmonically related standing wave pattern. The wavelength of the first resonance or the f_0 of the string is twice as long as the length of the string. The amplitude of the displacement antinode is also the greatest at the first harmonic resonance. The wavelength of the second resonance or second harmonic frequency (f_2) is equal to the length of the string. The wavelength of third resonance or third harmonic frequency (f_3) is equal to two-thirds the length of the string. From T. A. Hamill and L. L. Price (2014), with permission.

been displaced. Both a leftward and a rightward traveling pulse wave are horizontally propagated from the central area of displacement until they reach their respective barriers. Because the string is fixed at both ends, the two pulse waves will exert upward forces on the barriers. The barriers will in turn exert equal but opposite (downward) forces on the string, again according to Newton's third law of motion. The downward forces will generate reflected, inverted pulse waves that will travel back toward the center of the string from both barriers.

If the string is subjected to the right amount of tension and is plucked with just the right amount of force, a variety of frequencies in the form of vibratory pulse waves are generated. The frequencies generated will produce random interference patterns, and by destructive interference, many of their amplitudes will rapidly fade away. However, vibratory patterns of waveform frequencies that correspond to the "resonant frequencies" of the string will be distinctive and will be persistent. If the wavelength of the sound wave generated on the string is suitably matched to the length of the string, the superposition of waves traveling in opposite directions through the string will create a distinctive standing wave pattern (Halliday et al., 2011).

The concepts of resonance, fundamental frequency, and harmonics were introduced in Chapter 5. Recall once more that the harmonic frequencies are resonant frequencies and that the lowest such resonant frequency is, of course, the fundamental frequency. Also bear in mind that the fundamental frequency (f_0), which is also the first harmonic, is also the *first resonance*. Like

all objects and vibratory systems that are set into motion, the string will resonate best or with maximum efficiency at the first resonance or at its f_0. Once again, the terms *best* and *maximum efficiency* should be taken to mean that relatively little effort (minimum force) will be required to initiate and maintain vibratory motion (Durrant & Feth, 2013) and to obtain large resonating amplitudes. The object (string) vibrates with greatest amplitude at its first resonant frequency (f_0). It will also vibrate relatively efficiently at higher frequencies that correspond to its natural or resonant (harmonic) frequencies. However, and as illustrated, with the production of each progressively higher harmonic (beginning with the second resonance), observed amplitudes are progressively decreased. Nevertheless, standing waves are said to be produced at *resonance*, and therefore, standing wave patterns will be generated at the first and at each subsequently higher resonant frequency of the string.

At the f_0, as well as at other harmonic frequencies of the string, incident and reflected waves will interfere, and their transverse interference will produce large-amplitude transverse standing wave patterns. Standing waves derive their name from the observation that the waveform does not appear to propagate longitudinally. That is, the waveform appears to be "standing still." Locations within the standing wave that correspond to destructive interference are the locations on the string that do not vibrate. These areas are called the *displacement nodes*. At the displacement nodes, the string is at rest, there is zero displacement, there is minimal or zero energy, and there is no energy transmitted. Displacement nodes or simply "nodes" are always found at the fixed ends of the string. At these locations, the string is fixed and cannot oscillate. As the transverse standing wave patterns change, additional nodes will appear at locations between the two fixed ends. Locations within the standing wave that correspond to constructive interference are also the locations in the string that vibrate with maximum amplitude and maximum transverse displacement. These areas are called the *displacement antinodes*. At the displacement antinodes, or simply *antinodes* the standing wave oscillates with transverse wave motion in a fixed pattern. The antinodes always occur halfway between a pair of nodes. Therefore, at the resonant frequencies of the string, transverse interference produces transverse standing wave patterns that are characterized by the presence of nodes and relatively large-amplitude antinodes. Locations of the displacement nodes (*N*) and the displacement antinodes (*A*) for three transverse standing wave patterns are illustrated in the three panels of Figure 7–15.

As indicated above, standing waves occur at the resonant frequencies of the string, and each standing wave pattern is unique for each harmonic frequency. That is, a new and distinctive transverse standing wave pattern will appear at each harmonic frequency of vibration and for any given harmonically driven standing wave pattern, the position (locations) of the nodes and antinodes will remain fixed. If the string were to be oscillated at frequencies other than those that correspond to its natural, resonant frequencies, a standing wave pattern will not emerge. The lowest resonant frequency of vibration that is capable of producing a transverse

standing wave pattern in a string is, of course, the first resonance or fundamental frequency (f_0). String vibration that occurs at the first resonance will generate the fixed waveform pattern that is illustrated in the top panel of Figure 7–15. Note that this persistent standing wave pattern is characterized by a single large displacement antinode at the center of the vibrating string, surrounded by the two displacement nodes positioned at the fixed ends of the string. The distinct advantage of generating a standing wave pattern at the f_0 of a string is that the string will then resonate with very large and sustained amplitude and will generate a distinctly audible sound wave at the same frequency as the string is resonating.

Look closely at the fixed standing wave pattern illustrated in the upper panel of Figure 7–15, and note that the upper and lower parts of the displacement antinode envelope stretch end-to-end across the length of the string. The upper (compression) and lower (rarefaction) parts of the envelope each resemble one half-cycle of a sinusoidal (standing) wave. Therefore, the string resonates at its f_0 with one half of a wave of resonance of either compression or rarefaction that spans the length (*L*) of the string. In terms of classifying the string as a vibrating object, the string may be called a *half-wave resonating system* that produces *half-wave resonances*. Furthermore, if the string resonates at its f_0 with one half of a wave of resonance that spans the length (*L*) of the string, then the length of the string is equivalent to only one half of the wavelength of the first resonance of the string. Summarily, the first resonance (or f_0) of a string is a sinusoidal frequency that generates a corresponding sinusoidal standing wave with a wavelength (λ) that is equal to twice the length (L) of the string, or simply $2L$. Hence, in terms of defining the wavelength of the f_0 for any string, $\lambda = 2L$.

It should be apparent that if the length of any string is known, the wavelength of the string's fundamental frequency can always be determined. If the wavelength of the fundamental frequency for any string is known, the actual fundamental frequency for the string can also be determined. Recall the computational equation for wavelength that has been presented repeatedly in this chapter:

$$\lambda = c/f \qquad (7\text{--}1)$$

As indicated in a previous section of this chapter, Equation 7–1 may also be rewritten as

$$f = c/\lambda$$

This equation states that the first resonance or fundamental frequency (f_0) of a string is directly proportional to the speed of sound (c) in the medium and is inversely proportional to the wavelength (λ). Because $\lambda = 2L$ the rewritten form of Equation 7–1 now changes to

$$f_0 = c/2L \qquad (7\text{--}4)$$

Equation 7–4 again states that the first resonance or fundamental frequency (f_0) of a string is directly proportional to the speed of sound (c) in the medium and is inversely proportional to twice the length of the string. The last component needed in the equation is the speed of sound (c) in the medium. The medium in this case is the string. Recall once again from Chapter 6 that the speed of a sound wave (c) through any

material medium depends on an inertial property of the medium (to store kinetic energy) or simply mass, and on an elastic property of the medium (to store potential energy). The relationship between the two was provided by

$$\text{speed } (c) = \left(\frac{\text{elastic property}}{\text{inertial property}} \right)^{\frac{1}{2}}$$
$$(6\text{--}15)$$

Hence, it should come as no surprise that the speed of a sound wave along a string (c) is also defined as the square root of the tension of the string (stiffness) divided by the cross-sectional mass of the string (Speaks, 1999), or simply,

$$\text{speed } (c) = \left(\frac{\text{string tension}}{\text{cross-sectional mass}} \right)^{\frac{1}{2}}$$
$$(7\text{--}5)$$

If Equation 7–4 were to be restated as $[f_0 = (c) \times (1/2L)]$, then Equation 7–5 may also be rewritten as

$$f_0 = \left(\frac{\text{string tension}}{\text{cross-sectional mass}} \right)^{\frac{1}{2}} \times (1/2L)$$
$$(7\text{--}6)$$

Equation 7–6 now states that the first resonance or fundamental frequency (f_0) of a string is directly proportional to the square root of the spring's tension (stiffness), inversely proportional to the square root of the spring's cross-sectional mass, and is inversely proportional to twice the length of the string (Speaks, 1999).

Additional standing waves will emerge at the harmonic resonances of the string. These will arise most often by increasing the tension (stiffness) and less often by increasing the amount of force (pushing or pulling) applied to the string, This is because the first resonance or fundamental frequency (f_0) of a string is directly proportional to the square root of the spring's tension, as indicated above. Once again, these harmonic resonances correspond to integer whole numbered multiples of the fundamental frequency of vibration, and each harmonic frequency will generate a unique standing wave pattern. For a half-wave resonating system such as a string, additional harmonic resonances may be predicted using Equation 7–7. In the equation f refers to frequency, n refers to the nth harmonic (i.e., first, second, third, fourth, etc.), and c once again refers to the speed of a sound wave along the string. Therefore,

$$fn = nc/2L \qquad (7\text{–}7)$$

Therefore, the fundamental frequency or first resonance may be expressed as

$$f_1 = 1c/2L$$

Furthermore, the wavelength for any standing wave that is propagated along a half-wave resonating system such as a string with a length (L), is given by Equation 7–8 where n again refers to the nth harmonic (i.e., first, second, third, fourth, etc.):

$$\lambda = 2L/n \qquad (7\text{–}8)$$

The wavelength of the first resonance, first harmonic, or simply the f_0 for any string has already been defined as

$$\lambda = 2L$$

String vibration that occurs at the second resonance (second harmonic)

will generate the fixed waveform pattern that is illustrated in the middle panel of Figure 7–15. Note that this persistent standing wave pattern is characterized again by two displacement nodes positioned at the fixed ends of the string, and a third node positioned at the center of the string. There are also two relatively large displacement antinodes on either side of the center node of the vibrating string. The amplitudes of the antinodes will progressively decrease with each increase in harmonic resonance. Call to mind from Chapter 5 (see Figure 5–16B) that with the production of each progressively higher harmonic, beginning with the second harmonic resonance, observed amplitudes are progressively decreased due to an increased opposition to vibration, called mass reactance ($2\pi fm$). In any case, for the half-wave resonances of a string, the second harmonic (f_2) may also be predicted, and defined by Equation 7–7 as

$$f_2 = 2c/2L$$

Furthermore, the wavelength for a standing wave that is propagated at the second resonance along a string is also given by Equation 7–8, as

$$\lambda = 2L/2 \text{ or simply } \lambda = L$$

Therefore, the wavelength of second resonance or second harmonic frequency (f_2) is equal to the length of the string, as illustrated in Figure 7–15.

Finally, string vibration that occurs at the third resonance (third harmonic) will generate the fixed waveform pattern that is illustrated in the lower panel of Figure 7–15. Note that this persistent standing wave pattern is characterized again by two displacement nodes positioned at the fixed ends of the string, and three displacement antinodes, each bound by additional nodes. For the half-wave resonances of a string, the third harmonic (f_3) is also be predicted, and defined by Equation 7–7, as

$$f_3 = 3c/2L$$

The wavelength for a standing wave that is propagated at the third resonance along a string is again given by Equation 7–8 as

$$\lambda = 2L/3 \text{ or simply } \lambda = 2/3 \ L$$

Therefore, the wavelength of third resonance or third harmonic frequency (f_3) is equal to two-thirds the length of the string, as illustrated in Figure 7–15. If the harmonic progression for the string resonances were to be continued beyond the third resonance, increasingly more complex standing wave patterns would emerge. With each additional harmonic resonance, the standing wave pattern on the string would include one additional displacement node and one additional displacement antinode than the preceding harmonic. Furthermore, with each additional harmonic resonance, an additional half wavelength ($\lambda/2$) of a standing wave would be squeezed onto the length of the string.

Wave Reflection, Longitudinal Wave Motion, and Standing Waves

Standing wave interference resulting from interactions between incident and reflected waves may also be described for longitudinal wave motion in a sound-field. Sound produces longitudinal wave fronts consisting of successive areas of compression and rarefaction that define the propagated waveform. Incident sound waves propagated in a sound-field medium containing highly reflective surfaces will often result in the production of reflected waveforms. Because reflected waves often exhibit amplitude intensities that are equal to those of incident waves, reflected sounds in a sound-field are likely produce standing waves. The production of standing waves is likely to result when longitudinally propagated incident and reflected sound waves are generated at precisely the same frequency and amplitude, then travel in opposite directions at the same location within the sound-field, and with a phase difference of 180°. Figure 7–16 panel A illustrates destructive interference and waveform cancellation in a sound-field for an incident and reflected waveforms that are 180° out of phase. Destructive interference for longitudinal wave motion occurs when areas of compression and areas of rarefaction overlap at precise moments in time as the two sounds are simultaneously propagated in the same medium. The destructive interference and waveform cancellation for longitudinal wave motion illustrated is analogous to the lack of vibratory energy that occurs at the nodes, described above for transverse wave interference. Alternatively, maximum constructive interference is likely to result when longitudinally propagated incident and reflected sound waves are generated at precisely the same frequency and amplitude, then travel in opposite directions and in phase, at the same location within the sound-field. Figure 7–16 panel B illustrates maximum constructive interference (reinforcement) and waveform enhancement

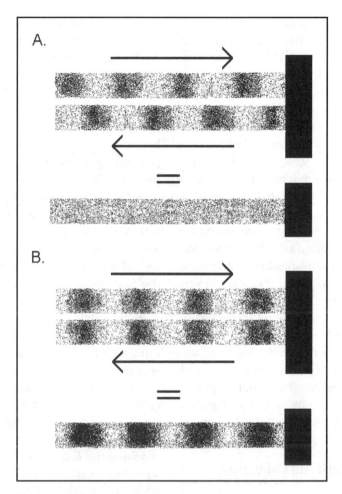

Figure 7–16. Two examples of longitudinal wave interference. **A.** Destructive interference and waveform cancellation in a sound-field for an incident and a reflected waveform that are both 180° out of phase. **B.** Constructive interference and waveform enhancement in a sound-field, for an incident and a reflected waveform that are both in phase. From T. A. Hamill and L. L. Price (2014), with permission.

in a sound-field for an incident and a reflected waveform that are in phase. Maximum constructive interference for longitudinal wave motion occurs when areas of compression overlap and areas of rarefaction also overlap, at precise moments in time as the two sounds are simultaneously propagated in the same medium. The maximum constructive interference and waveform enhancement for longitudinal wave motion illustrated is analogous to the maximum amplitude and vibratory energy that occurs at the antinodes, described above for transverse wave interference. Finally, partial constructive interference (reinforcement) is also likely to result for the same longitudinally propagated incident and reflected sound waves travelling in opposite directions that are partially in phase and/or partially out of phase with each other at the same location within the sound-field. Complete destructive and/or maximum constructive interference of longitudinally propagated sound waves in a room designed for audiometric sound-field testing can create areas in the sound-field where energy is enhanced, in combination with other areas in which sound energy is greatly diminished. It is for this reason that the ensuing variability in wave propagation resulting from reflection and the creation of standing waves in a reverberant sound-field is problematic. As indicated in Chapter 6, the prevention of standing waves in a sound-field is greatly aided by the implementation of sound-field testing in sound attenuating test chambers (see Figures 6–4B and 6–4C). Recall that this type of sound-field has perforated internal steel wall surfaces that are designed to suppress reflective, reverberant sounds.

Sound-Field Calibration

Sound-field testing that is conducted in sound attenuating test chambers (see Figures 6–4B and 6–4C) is often performed out of necessity, under a variety of conditions. Sound-field testing procedures are often useful in hearing tests conducted in pediatric and in other difficult-to-test populations. Testing that is performed in a sound-field is also useful in the evaluation of hearing-aid (amplification) devices. Sound-field testing requires the routing of auditory signals through a (loud) speaker or through a set of speakers, rather than through headphones or any other small transducer device. That is, the incident sound waves used

for sound-field testing are propagated directly into the sound-field medium. As indicated above, the prevention of standing waves in a sound-field is greatly aided by sound-field testing that is conducted in sound attenuating test chambers. However, additional precautionary measures may also be taken to prevent their occurrence. As an added measure in their prevention, warble tones are often used (in place of pure tones) as a stimulus during sound-field tests of hearing conducted in sound attenuating test chambers. That is, the use of warble tones greatly assists in the prevention of standing waves during sound-field testing. Warble tones were introduced in Chapter 6 and were defined as a frequency modulated pure tone with a ±5% change in frequency/second (Silman & Emmer, 2012).

One important goal of sound-field calibration is to ensure that the warble tones and/or narrrow bands of noise (also used in sound-field testing) are reaching the test subject at an accurate signal intensity. Table 7–3 specifies the ANSI/ASA S3.6-2010 reference equivalent sound pressure level (SPL) thresholds for either a virtual free (sound) field, or a diffuse (sound) field. Recall from Chapter 6 that a virtual free-field refers to the acoustic conditions that exist within an anechoic chamber. The use of the term *diffuse field* in the present context refers to the acoustic conditions that exist within a sound attenuating test chamber (Silman & Emmer, 2012). As indicated in Table 7–3, the ANSI/ASA S3.6-2010 standard also provides different reference levels for sound-field testing that is performed under monaural (predominantly one ear) or binaural listening conditions. That is, different reference levels are

Table 7–3. Reference Equivalent Threshold Sound Pressure Levels (RETSPLs) (dB re: 20 μPa) for Sound-Field Testing

Frequency (Hz)	Binaural Listening in Free-Field			Diffuse-Field Listening[a]		
	0-Degree Incidence	45-Degree Incidence	90-Degree Incidence	0-Degree Incidence	45-Degree Incidence	90-Degree Incidence
125	22.1	21.6	21.1	22.1	21.6	21.1
160	17.9	16.9	16.4	17.9	16.9	16.4
200	14.4	13.4	12.9	14.4	13.3	12.9
250	11.4	10.4	9.4	11.4	10.4	9.4
315	8.6	7.1	6.1	8.4	6.9	5.9
400	6.2	3.7	2.7	5.8	3.3	2.3
500	4.4	1.4	−0.1	3.8	0.8	0.8
630	3	−0.5	−2	2.1	−1.4	−2.9
750	2.4	−1.1	−2.6	1.2	−2.3	−3.8
800	2.2	−1.3	−2.8	1	−2.5	−4
1000	2.4	−1.6	−3.1	0.8	−3.2	−3.2
1250	3.5	−0.5	−2.5	1.9	−2.1	−4.1
1500	2.4	1.1	−2.6	1	−2.5	−4
1600	1.7	−1.8	−2.8	0.5	−3	−4
2000	−1.3	−4.3	−3.3	−1.5	−4.5	−3.5
2500	−4.2	−7.7	−6.2	−3.1	−6.6	−5.1
3000	−5.8	−10.5	−8.3	−4	−9	−6.5
3150	−6	−11	−8	−4	−9	−6
4000	−5.4	−9.4	−4.9	−3.8	−7.8	−3.3
5000	−1.5	−7.5	−5.5	−1.8	−7.8	−5.8
6000	4.3	−3.2	−5.2	1.4	−6.1	−8.1
6300	6	−1.5	−4	2.5	−5	−7.5
8000	12.6	−7.1	4.1	6.8	1.3	−1.7
9000	13.8	8.8	6.8	8.4	3.4	1.4
10000	13.9	9.4	7.9	9.8	5.3	3.8
11200	13	9	6	11.5	7.5	4.5
12500	12.3	10.8	4.3	14.4	12.9	6.4
14000	18.4			23.2		
16000	40.2			43.7		
18000	73.2					
Speech	14.5	12.5	11			

[a]ISO 389-7 Acoustics-Reference zero for the calibration of audiometric equipment, Part 7: Reference threshold of hearing under free-field and diffuse field listening conditions. From S. Silman and M. B. Emmer (2012), with permission of the Acoustical Society of America.

used depending upon the location of the speaker relative to the subject's head. Monaural listening conditions exist when the speaker is located at either a 45° incidence, or a 90° incidence, relative to the (stationary) head of the test subject. A binaural listening condition exists when the speaker is located at a 0° incidence (directly in front) relative to the (stationary) head of the test subject. Step-by-step procedures for calibrating warble tones and narrow-bands of noise in a sound-field are provided elsewhere (see Silman & Emmer, 2012).

Resonators

Almost any object can be made to resonate, and therefore most objects could be classified as resonators. Objects such as the vibrating strings that were discussed above, glass bottles (or tubes), and steel tuning forks all provide examples of simple resonators, once they are set into resonance. Because such objects are simple in their material composition, they have one (simple) major fundamental (first) mode of resonance which is also the frequency with the largest response amplitude (Halliday et al., 2011). As indicated in Chapter 5, only a modest amount of force is required to set a handheld tuning fork into vibration at the particular fundamental frequency for which it was designed to resonate. That is, the tuning fork resonates with maximum efficiency at its fundamental frequency. When more than adequate amounts of force are applied to the tines, a handheld tuning fork will be forced to resonate, not only at its fundamental frequency, but

also at the combined higher harmonic frequencies of its fundamental or first harmonic resonance.

Elasticity and mass are both important and general characteristics of all matter and were discussed in detail in Chapters 3 and 4 in reference to the displacement properties of simple spring-mass systems. Recall that elasticity is composed of the properties of stiffness and compliance, and both are inversely related to each other. Because the fundamental frequency of any vibrating object is strictly determined by the particular and relative amounts of elasticity and mass inherent within the object, larger, more massive objects resonate at lower fundamental frequencies than smaller, less massive objects. This occurs because the first resonant or fundamental frequency for any object set into motion, will be inversely proportional to the square root of its mass. The greater the object's mass, the lower will be the object's fundamental frequency. It follows then, that larger, more massive tines on tuning forks (Figure 7–17 panel A) will resonate at lower fundamental frequencies than smaller, less massive tuning fork tines (see Figure 7–17 panel B). Because the tines of each tuning fork are constructed from the same type of material, the aspect of elasticity (stiffness and compliance) is less relevant. Recall as well (Chapter 5) that the lowest frequency of resonance in any vibrating object (the fundamental) determines the perceptual experience of frequency, known as *pitch*. Therefore, larger, more massive tuning forks, resonating at their natural lower fundamental frequencies, will generate low pitches. Likewise, smaller, less massive tuning forks, resonating at their natural higher fundamental frequencies, will generate high pitches.

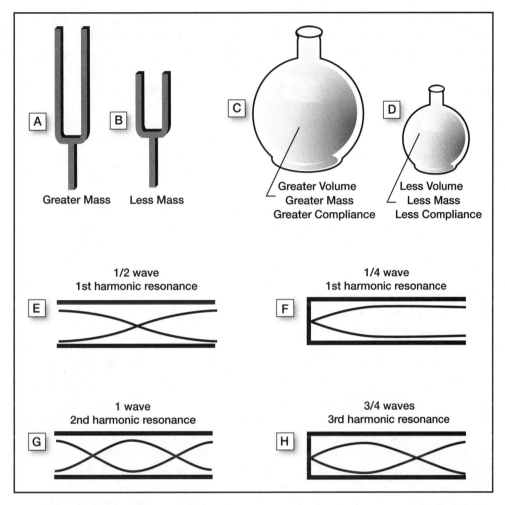

Figure 7–17. Examples of resonating objects that differ in terms of their mass, their volume density (mass), and their tube dimensions. **A–B.** Two tuning forks. **C–D.** Two glass bottle resonators. **E–G.** Two half-wave resonating tubes. **F–H.** Two quarter-wave resonating tubes.

As indicated in Chapter 6, air is also an elastic and compressible medium that can be made to resonate. The column of air within a glass bottle can be set into vibration by blowing air (a force) across the open end of the bottle. Because the enclosed volume of air within the bottle will vibrate as a cohesive unit of mass, the enclosed volume of air within the bottle constitutes an *acoustic inertance* (Durrant & Feth, 2013). The term *inert* signifies that the property of mass, by definition, does not represent an active (elastic) process. The property of compliance, on the other hand, does represent an active elastic process. The volume of air within the bottle is, of course, elastic and compressible, and the extent to which a medium such as air can change in volume (compliance) when pressure is applied was defined in Chapter 6 as the bulk (or elastic) modulus. Recall that the bulk modulus of elasticity (B) was defined as a measure of the bulk elastic properties of a material medium (see Table 6–1) and was presented as the ratio of the change in pressure to the fractional amount (or degree) of volume compression in the compressible material medium, by Equation 6–1B:

$$B = \frac{\Delta P}{\Delta V / V_o}$$

where ΔP is a measure of the change in the pressure of a substance when a force is applied, that then leads to the change in volume; and ΔV is the change in volume that is proportional to the original volume V_o, and to the increase or change in pressure, ΔP. Bulk modulus was also a measure of an opposition to compression and therefore an opposition (as in elastic compliance) to the changes that occur in the volume of the compressed medium (Halliday et al., 2011). The greater the (original) volume within the bottle, the less will be the opposition to compression, and therefore, the greater will be the compressibility of the volume. The greater the compressibility of the enclosed volume of air within the bottle, the greater will be the *acoustic compliance* of the enclosed air medium (Durrant & Feth, 2013). Finally, recall again from Chapters 2 and 6 that density is an indication of how much mass occupies a given space (Halliday et al., 2011). Density is often referred to as the mass per unit volume or as the volume density of a particular medium. Volume density was defined previously as,

$$\text{Mass} = \text{density} \times \text{volume}$$

$$(6\text{–}1A)$$

Returning now to the resonances of enclosed volumes of air within bottles,

the fundamental frequency of a vibrating air medium is also determined by the relative amounts of elasticity and mass inherent within the air medium. Large glass resonating bottles (see Figure 7–17 panel C) with large volumes of air (more mass) will resonate at lower fundamental frequencies than small bottles (see Figure 7–17 panel D) with small volumes of air (less mass). Once again, this is because the first resonant or fundamental frequency for an enclosed medium of air that is set into motion will be inversely proportional to the square root of the enclosed volume density (mass). The greater the enclosed volume density, the lower will be the bottle's fundamental frequency. Furthermore, and as indicated above, the greater the volume density within the bottle, the greater is the acoustic compliance of the enclosed air medium. Because fundamental frequency is directly proportional to the square root of stiffness, and stiffness is inversely proportional to compliance, the fundamental frequency of the bottle will also be inversely proportional to the square root of its acoustic compliance. Therefore, large bottles with greater amounts of volume density (mass) and compliance, will resonate at lower natural fundamental frequencies, and will produce lower pitches. Small bottles with lesser amounts of volume density (mass) and compliance, will resonate at higher natural fundamental frequencies, and will produce higher pitches.

Resonances of Air-Filled Tubes

The concept of resonant frequencies generated within certain kinds of air-filled tubes was first introduced in Chapter 5 (see Figure 5–15). Standing

waves are created in air-filled tube resonators in much the same way as they
are created in vibrating strings. Many
aspects of standing wave patterns in
string waves are similar to the patterns
observed in air-filled tubes. Sound waves
propagated in air-filled tubes will be
reflected from the surface of the closed
end of the tube and/or from the inside
surfaces of the tube. Standing waves
occur in tubes when the incident and
reflected sound waves, delivered at
the resonant frequencies of the tube,
occupy the same space at the same time
and produce wave interference patterns. If the wavelength of the sound
wave that causes the tube to resonate
is suitably matched to the length of the
tube, the superposition of waves traveling in opposite directions through the
tube will create standing wave patterns
(Halliday et al., 2011). The wavelength
that is required for the production of
a standing wave will be a wavelength
that corresponds to the fundamental
or the first resonant frequency (f_0) of
the tube. Additional harmonics of the
fundamental frequency of the air-filled
tube will also emerge in the form of
(additional) unique standing wave patterns. Once more, bear in mind from
Chapter 5 (see Figure 5–16B) that with
the production of each progressively
higher harmonic, beginning with the
second (or in some cases the third) harmonic resonance, observed amplitudes
will be progressively decreased due to
the increased opposition to vibration.
Notwithstanding, the distinct advantage
of generating a standing wave pattern
at the f_0 of a tube resonator is that the
tube will then resonate with large and
sustained amplitude. As a result, a distinctly audible sound wave will be generated through one of the open ends
of the tube at the same frequency that

the tube is resonating. The volume of
air within resonating tubes will vibrate
in the form of longitudinal standing
waves. However, a convenient method
of representing the longitudinal standing wave patterns created in tubes will
be to depict them as transverse standing wave (string wave) patterns. Accordingly, in the illustrations presented in
Figures 5–15 and 7–17, the half- and
quarter-wave resonance standing wave
patterns are intended to represent the
upward and downward air particle displacement through the length of each
tube, over time. Illustrated, however,
are only the standing wave envelopes
depicting maximum and minimum wave
displacement.

Half-Wave Resonating Tubes

Half-wave resonances are generated in
air-filled tubes that are open at both
ends (see Figure 5–15 column B). From
an acoustical point of view, the standing
wave patterns that were observed in
the vibrating string with fixed ends (see
Figure 7–15) are directly analogous to
the standing wave patterns generated in
air-filled tubes having both ends open
(Durrant & Feth, 2013). The simplest
standing wave pattern that can be generated in an open-ended tube will be
created when the tube is vibrated at
the fundamental or the first (harmonic)
resonant frequency (f_0) of the tube. This
half-wave resonance pattern is illustrated in the first panel (of column B)
of Figure 5–15, and again in Figure
7–17 panel E. Once more, remember
that the standing waves illustrated are
depicted as transverse standing wave
(string wave) patterns. The half-wave
resonance pattern generated at the
f_0 of the tube is characterized by displacement antinodes at each open end,

referred to as "half loops" (Speaks, 1999). When displacement antinodes occur at both open ends of the tube, there must also be at least one displacement node within the tube if a standing wave is to be generated (Giancoli, 2005). The half-wave resonance pattern generated at the f_0 of the tube is also characterized by one displacement node that is located within the center of the tube, as illustrated in the first panel of Figure 5–15 (column B), and in Figure 7–17 panel E. Because the distance between the two successive displacement antinodes is only one-half the wavelength (λ) of the standing wave (for the f_0 of the tube), only one half of the wavelength of the standing wave (or the f_0) is able to fit within the length of the tube at any given moment. Therefore, since the tube length (L) = ½ λ of the standing wave, the wavelength (λ) of the first resonant frequency that generates a half-wave resonance pattern must have a wavelength that is $2L$. Summarily, the first resonance (or f_0) of a half-wave resonating tube is a sinusoidal frequency that generates a corresponding sinusoidal standing wave with a wavelength (λ) that is equal to twice the length (L) of the tube, or simply $2L$. Hence, in terms of defining the wavelength of the f_0 for any half-wave resonating tube (a tube open at both ends), $\lambda = 2L$.

As with the resonances of strings that were discussed above, if the length of any half-wave resonating tube is known, the wavelength of the tube's fundamental frequency can always be determined. If the wavelength of the fundamental frequency for any half-wave resonating tube is known, the actual fundamental frequency for the tube can also be determined. Because the wavelength of

the f_0 for any half-wave resonating tube is defined as $\lambda = 2L$, Equation 7–4 may again be applied:

$$f_0 = c/2L \qquad (7\text{–}4)$$

The speed of sound (c) in the medium is also needed, and in this case, the medium is air. Both the MKS (344 m/s) and the CGS (34,400 cm/s) values for the speed of sound in air were provided in Chapter 6 (see Table 6–8).

As in descriptions of the resonances of strings, additional half-wave resonant standing wave patterns will emerge at the harmonic resonances of the tube. These will most often emerge by increasing the amount of air pressure applied to the inside of the tube. As with resonating strings, these harmonic resonances correspond to integer whole number multiples of the fundamental frequency of vibration, and each harmonic frequency will generate a unique standing wave pattern. For half-wave resonating tubes, additional harmonic resonances may again be predicted using Equation 7–7. In the equation f refers to frequency, n refers to the nth harmonic (i.e., first, second, third, fourth, etc.), and c once again refers to the speed of sound in air.

$$fn = nc/2L \qquad (7\text{–}7)$$

Therefore, the fundamental frequency or first resonance is, as in the string, expressed as

$$f_1 = 1c/2L$$

As before, the wavelength for any standing wave that is propagated in a half-wave resonating tube with a length (L), is given again by Equation 7–8 where

n refers to the nth harmonic (i.e., first, second, third, fourth, etc.):

$$\lambda = 2L/n \qquad (7\text{--}8)$$

The wavelength of the first resonance in a half-wave resonating tube was already defined as

$$\lambda = 2L$$

Half-wave resonance that occurs at the second harmonic will generate the fixed waveform pattern illustrated in the second panel down in Figure 5–15 (column B), and in Figure 7–17 panel G. The half-wave resonance pattern generated at the second resonance or second harmonic (f_2) of the tube is again characterized by displacement antinodes (two half loops) at each open end, and one displacement antinode within the tube. The half-wave resonance pattern generated at the f_2 of the tube is also characterized by two displacement nodes located within the tube, as illustrated in the second panel down in Figure 5–15 (B), and in Figure 7–17 panel G. Because the distance between the two successive displacement antinodes is one full wavelength (λ) of the standing wave generated by the second harmonic, one full wavelength of the standing wave is able to fit within the length of the tube at any given moment. Therefore, since the tube length (L) = 1λ of the standing wave, the wavelength (λ) of the second resonant frequency that generates a half-wave resonance pattern must have a wavelength that is equal to L. Summarily, the second resonance (or f_2) of a half-wave resonating tube is a sinusoidal frequency that generates a corresponding sinusoidal standing wave with a wavelength (λ)

that is equal to the length (L) of the tube, or simply L. Hence, in terms of defining the wavelength of the f_2 for any half-wave resonating tube, $\lambda = L$.

Applying Equations 7–7 and 7–8, for a half-wave resonating tube, the second harmonic (f_2) is also predicted and defined by Equation 7–7 as

$$f_2 = 2c/2L$$

Furthermore, the wavelength for a standing wave that is propagated at the second resonance in a half-wave resonating tube is also given by Equation 7–8 as

$$\lambda = 2L/2 \text{ or simply } \lambda = L$$

The wavelength of the second resonance or second harmonic frequency (f_2) in a half-wave resonating tube is equal to the full length (L) of the tube, as illustrated in the second panel down in Figure 5–15 (B), and in Figure 7–17 panel G.

Finally, half-wave resonance that occurs at the third harmonic will generate the fixed waveform pattern illustrated in the third panel down in Figure 5–15 (B). The half-wave resonance pattern generated at the third resonance or third harmonic (f_3) of the tube is once again characterized by displacement antinodes (half loops) at each open end and two displacement antinodes within the tube. The half-wave resonance pattern generated at the f_3 of the tube is also characterized by three displacement nodes located within the tube, as illustrated in the third panel down in Figure 5–15 (B). Because the distance between the two successive displacement antinodes is one-and-one-half, or 3/2 wavelengths (λ) of the standing wave generated by the third harmonic, 3/2 wavelengths are able to fit within the length of the tube at any given moment. Therefore, since the tube length (L) = $3/2\lambda$ of the standing wave, the wavelength (λ) of the third resonant frequency that generates a half-wave resonance pattern must have a wavelength that is equal to $2/3L$. Summarily, the third resonance (or f_3) of a half-wave resonating tube is a sinusoidal frequency that generates a corresponding sinusoidal standing wave with a wavelength (λ) that is equal to $2/3$ the length (L) of the tube, or simply $2/3L$. In terms of defining the wavelength of the f_3 for any half-wave resonating tube, $\lambda = 2/3L$.

Applying Equations 7–7 and 7–8, for a half-wave resonating tube, the third harmonic (f_3) is again predicted and defined by Equation 7–7 as

$$f_3 = 3c/2L$$

Furthermore, the wavelength for a standing wave that is propagated at the third resonance in a half-wave resonating tube is also given by Equation 7–8 as

$$\lambda = 2L/3 \text{ or simply } \lambda = 2/3L$$

In conclusion, the wavelength of the third resonance or third harmonic frequency (f_3) in a half-wave resonating tube is equal to $2/3$ the length (L) of the tube, as illustrated in the third panel down in Figure 5–15 (B). As exactly described above for string resonances, if the harmonic progression for the half-wave tube resonances were to be continued beyond the third resonance, increasingly more complex standing wave patterns would emerge. With each additional harmonic resonance, the standing wave pattern within the

tube would include one additional displacement node and one additional displacement antinode than the preceding harmonic. With each additional harmonic resonance, an additional half wavelength ($\lambda/2$) of a standing wave would be squeezed into the length of the tube, as illustrated in the fourth and fifth panels in Figure 5–15 (B).

Quarter-Wave Resonating Tubes

Quarter-wave resonances are generated in air-filled tubes that are open at one end and closed at the other (see Figure 5–15 column A). The simplest standing wave pattern that can be generated in a tube with only one end open will be created when the tube is vibrated at the fundamental or the first (harmonic) resonant frequency (f_0) of the tube. This quarter-wave resonance pattern is illustrated in the first panel of Figure 5–15 (A), and again in Figure 7–17 panel F. Again, bear in mind that the standing waves illustrated are depicted as transverse standing wave (string wave) patterns. The quarter-wave resonance pattern generated at the f_0 of the tube is characterized by a displacement antinode (half loop) at the open end and a displacement node at the closed end of the tube. The closed end of the tube acts like the fixed end of a string where there is zero displacement; therefore, a displacement node must always be in that location. A displacement antinode must always be located at the open end of the quarter-wave resonating tube, where air molecules can move freely and there is maximum displacement (Giancoli, 2005). As illustrated in the first panel of Figure 5–15 (A) and again in Figure 7–17 panel F, because the distance between the displacement antinode and the closed end of the tube is only one-fourth the wavelength (λ) of the standing wave (for the f_0 of the tube), only one fourth of the wavelength of the standing wave (or the f_0) is able to fit within the length of the tube at any given moment. Therefore, since the tube length (L) = $\frac{1}{4} \lambda$ of the standing wave, the wavelength (λ) of the first resonant frequency that generates a quarter-wave resonance pattern must have a wavelength that is $4L$. Summarily, the first resonance (or f_0) of a quarter-wave resonating tube is a sinusoidal frequency that generates a corresponding sinusoidal standing wave with a wavelength (λ) that is equal to four times the length (L) of the tube, or simply $4L$. Hence, in terms of defining the wavelength of the f_0 for any quarter-wave resonating tube (a tube open at one end and closed at the other), $\lambda = 4L$.

As before in descriptions of half-wave tube resonances and the resonances of strings, if the length of any quarter-wave resonating tube is known, the wavelength of the tube's fundamental frequency can always be determined. It again follows that if the wavelength of the fundamental frequency for any quarter-wave resonating tube is known, the actual fundamental frequency for the tube can additionally be determined. Because the wavelength of the f_0 for any quarter-wave resonating tube is defined as $\lambda = 4L$, Equation 7–9 may now be applied:

$$f_0 = c/4L \qquad (7\text{–}9)$$

Once more, the speed of sound (c) is 344 m/s (MKS) and 34,400 cm/s (CGS), as provided in Chapter 6 (Table 6–8).

As before in descriptions of half-wave tube resonances and the resonances of strings, additional quarter-wave resonant standing wave patterns will emerge at the harmonic resonances of the tube and will most often appear when the amount of air pressure applied to the inside of the tube is increased. However, unlike the half-wave tube resonances and the resonances of strings described above, the harmonic resonances of quarter-wave resonating tubes will correspond to integer odd-numbered multiple frequencies of the fundamental frequency of vibration. This means that for quarter-wave resonating tubes, the lowest and first resonant frequency, or first resonance, will still correspond to the fundamental frequency, or to the first harmonic of the fundamental frequency ($1 \times f_0$). However, the next lowest resonant frequency, or second resonance, corresponds to the third harmonic of the fundamental frequency or $3 \times f_0$. Likewise, the next lowest resonant frequency, or third resonance, corresponds to the fifth harmonic of the fundamental frequency or $5 \times f_0$, and so forth. Each odd-numbered harmonic frequency will of course generate a unique standing wave pattern. For quarter-wave resonating tubes, the additional odd harmonic frequencies can also be predicted, by taking these somewhat unusual tube properties into account and by using Equation 7–10, where f refers to frequency, n refers to the nth odd harmonic (i.e., first, third, fifth, seventh, ninth, etc.), and c of course refers to the speed of sound in air:

$$fn = nc/4L \qquad (7\text{–}10)$$

Therefore, the fundamental frequency or first harmonic resonance of a quarter-wave resonating tube may be expressed as

$$f_1 = 1c/4L$$

The wavelength for any standing wave that is propagated in a quarter-wave resonating tube with a length (L) is now given by Equation 7–11, where n refers to the nth odd harmonic (i.e., first, third, fifth, seventh, ninth, etc.):

$$\lambda = 4L/n \qquad (7\text{–}11)$$

Hence, the wavelength of the first resonance in a quarter-wave resonating tube was already defined as

$$\lambda = 4L$$

Quarter-wave resonances that occur at the third harmonic frequency (second resonance) will generate the fixed waveform pattern illustrated in the second panel down in Figure 5–15 (A), and in Figure 7–17 panel H. The quarter-wave resonance pattern generated at the third harmonic (f_3) of the tube is again characterized by a displacement antinode (half loop) at the open and a displacement node at the closed end of the tube. One additional displacement node and displacement antinode also appear inside the tube, as illustrated in the second panel down in Figure 5–15 (A), and in Figure 7–17 panel H. As before, because the distance between the displacement antinode and the closed end of the tube is three fourths the wavelength (λ) of the standing wave generated by the third harmonic, three fourths of the wavelength of the standing wave is able to fit within the length of the tube at any given moment. Therefore, since the tube length (L) = ¾ λ of the standing wave, the wavelength (λ) of the third resonant frequency that generates a quarter-wave resonance

pattern must have a wavelength that is 4/3 L. Summarily, the third harmonic (or f_3) of a quarter-wave resonating tube is a sinusoidal frequency that generates a corresponding sinusoidal standing wave with a wavelength (λ) that is equal to 4/3 times the length (L) of the tube, or simply 4/3L. In terms of defining the wavelength of the f_3 for any quarter-wave resonating tube, $\lambda = 4/3L$.

Applying Equations 7–10 and 7–11, for a quarter-wave resonating tube, the third harmonic (f_3) is also predicted, and defined by Equation 7–10 as

$$f_3 = 3c/4L$$

Furthermore, the wavelength for a standing wave that is propagated at the third harmonic in a quarter-wave resonating tube is also given by Equation 7–11 as

$$\lambda = 4L/3 \text{ or simply } \lambda = 4/3\ L$$

Hence, the wavelength of the third harmonic (f_3) or second resonance in a quarter-wave resonating tube is equal to 4/3 the length (L) of the tube, as illustrated in the second panel down in Figure 5–15 (A), and in Figure 7–17 panel H.

Finally, quarter-wave resonances that occur at the fifth harmonic frequency (third resonance) will generate the fixed waveform pattern illustrated in the third panel down in Figure 5–15 (A). The quarter-wave resonance pattern generated at the fifth harmonic (f_5) of the tube is again characterized by a displacement antinode (half loop) at the open end and a displacement node at the closed end of the tube. Two additional, evenly spaced displacement nodes and displacement antinodes also appear inside the tube, as illustrated in the third panel down in Figure 5–15 (A). Once again, because the distance between the displacement antinode and the closed end of the tube is 1¼ or five fourths the wavelength (λ) of the standing wave generated by the fifth harmonic, 1¼ or five fourths of the wavelength of the standing wave is able to fit within the length of the tube at any given moment. Therefore, since the tube length (L) = 5/4 λ of the standing wave, the wavelength (λ) of the fifth resonant frequency that generates a quarter-wave resonance pattern must have a wavelength that is only 4/5L. Summarily, the fifth harmonic (or f_5) of a quarter-wave resonating tube is a sinusoidal frequency that generates a corresponding sinusoidal standing wave with a wavelength (λ) that is equal to 4/5 times the length (L) of the tube, or simply 4/5L. In terms of defining the wavelength of the f_5 for any quarter-wave resonating tube, $\lambda = 4/5L$.

Again, applying Equations 7–10 and 7–11, for a quarter-wave resonating tube, the fifth harmonic (f_5) is also predicted, and defined by Equation 7–10 as

$$F_5 = 5c/4L$$

Furthermore, the wavelength for a standing wave that is propagated at the fifth harmonic in a quarter-wave resonating tube is also given by Equation 7–11 as

$$\lambda = 4L/5 \text{ or simply } \lambda = 4/5L$$

In conclusion, the wavelength of the fifth harmonic (f_5) or third resonance in a quarter-wave resonating tube is equal to 4/5 the length (L) of the tube, as again illustrated in the third panel down

in Figure 5–15 (A). If the harmonic progression for the quarter-wave tube resonances was to be continued at odd-numbered harmonics beyond the fifth harmonic, increasingly more complex standing wave patterns would emerge. With each additional odd harmonic, the standing wave pattern within the tube would include one additional displacement node and one additional displacement antinode than the preceding odd harmonic. Furthermore, with each additional odd harmonic, an additional quarter wavelength ($\lambda/4$) of a standing wave would be squeezed into the length of the tube, as illustrated in the fourth and fifth panels in Figure 5–15 (A).

Displacement and Pressure

A column of air within a tube resonator is often set into resonance with a driving force of air that is blown either into or across one of the open ends of the tube. The driving force alters the flow of air within the tube and sets up predictable interference patterns of air displacement within the resonator, referred to as longitudinal standing waves. In Chapter 4, pressure was introduced (Equation 4–8) as

$$\text{Pressure} = \text{force} \div \text{area}$$

or simply, pressure was defined as a force that is distributed over some area or volume of matter. The driving force of air blown either into or across one of the open ends of the tube resonator also creates variable but consecutive locations in the tube where the air is either compressed or expanded (rarefactions). At locations in the tube where the air is compressed, the pressure is made higher (more positive) relative to the atmospheric pressure. At locations in the tube where the air is expanded, the pressure is made lower (more negative) relative to the atmospheric pressure. Therefore, displacement refers to the flow or motion of the air within the tube and may be compared to the variations or fluctuations in pressure that occur during tube resonance. Finally, recall from Chapter 5 (see Figure 5–16A) that in any vibrating object, displacement and pressure are out of phase with each other, such that pressure leads displacement by 90° of phase.

Displacement nodes and displacement antinodes were illustrated in Figure 5–15 (columns A and B) and in Figure 7–17, panels E–H for both half- and quarter-wave tube resonators. Recall that the longitudinal standing wave patterns of air displacement within these tubes were conveniently depicted as transverse standing wave (string wave) patterns. By definition, at each of the resonant tube locations where displacement nodes exist, the air within the tube is not free to move and therefore, displacement is zero. Recall that for quarter-wave resonating tubes, a displacement node must always be found at the closed end of the tube, because the closed end of a quarter-wave resonating tube acts like the fixed end of a string resonator (Giancoli, 2005). At each of the resonant tube locations where displacement antinodes exist, the air within the tube is free to move, such that both positive and negative displacement is at a maximum. Recall that for quarter-wave resonating tubes, a displacement antinode must always be found at the open end of the tube where particle movement is free to vary.

In addition to the displacement nodes and displacement antinodes found in half-wave and quarter-wave resonating tubes, sound waves propagated in tube resonators also generate nodes and antinodes that correspond to pressure. A pressure node is a resonant tube location characterized by relatively zero change in pressure. That is, at each of the tube locations where pressure nodes exist, pressure does not fluctuate from equilibrium but instead remains the same, or unchanged from the outer atmospheric pressure. A pressure antinode is a resonant tube location characterized by maximum pressure fluctuation. That is, at each of the tube locations where pressure antinodes exist, the pressure is free to fluctuate maximally, from well above (positively) to well below (negatively) the outer atmospheric pressure. Displacement waves that generate nodes and antinodes, and pressure waves that generate nodes and antinodes are all sinusoidal waves that vibrate with the same period, frequency, and wavelength. However, just as pressure leads displacement by 90°, in half-wave and quarter-wave resonating tubes, pressure nodes lead displacement nodes by 90° of phase, and pressure antinodes lead displacement antinodes by 90° of phase.

Because the pressure waves lead the displacement waves by 90° of phase during half-wave and quarter-wave resonances, the displacement nodes will be found in the same locations within resonating tubes as the pressure antinodes. Likewise, the displacement antinodes will be found in the same locations within resonating tubes as the pressure nodes. At each resonant tube location where a displacement node exists, the amount of displacement of the air within the tube is zero but pressure will be free to fluctuate maximally. Recall again, that for a quarter-wave resonating tube, a displacement node is always to be found at the closed end of the tube. Therefore, a pressure antinode will also exist at the closed end of a quarter-wave resonating tube. Likewise, at the fundamental frequency of a half-wave resonating tube, a corresponding pressure antinode will also exist at the same location at the center the resonating tube, as the displacement node illustrated previously in the first panel of Figure 5–15 (B), and in Figure 7–17 panel E. Of course, with the addition of displacement nodes at each of the higher harmonic frequencies, additional pressure antinodes will emerge simultaneously within the standing wave patterns of both half-wave and quarter-wave resonating tubes.

At each resonant tube location where a displacement antinode exists, the air within the tube is free to displace maximally but pressure does not change from equilibrium. Recall that at the fundamental frequencies of quarter-wave and half-wave resonating tubes, displacement antinodes are located at the open ends of the tubes, as illustrated in the first panel of Figure 5–15 (A), the first panel of Figure 5–15 (B), and in panels E and F of Figure 7–17. Therefore, because the open ends of tube resonators are always "open" to the outer atmosphere, pressure nodes should also exist at these locations. This is because the pressure within the tube at these locations will not fluctuate but instead will remain the same as the outer atmospheric pressure (Giancoli, 2005). Naturally, with the addition of displacement antinodes at each of the higher harmonic frequencies, additional pressure nodes will emerge simultane-

ously within the standing wave patterns of both half-wave and quarter-wave resonating tubes.

Odd and Integer Harmonics

As indicated in the sections above, unlike the resonances of strings and of half-wave resonating tubes, the harmonic resonances of quarter-wave resonating tubes are restricted to the odd-numbered multiples of the fundamental frequency of vibration. That is, quarter-wave resonating tubes are incapable of producing integer (both even and odd) numbered harmonic resonance. In other words, even-numbered harmonics cannot exist as standing waves in half-wave resonating tubes. Why should this be the case? Look again at the collective standing wave patterns illustrated in Figure 5–15 (columns A and B), for both quarter wave and half resonances, respectively. It is important to note that in all the standing wave patterns shown, independent of the type of tube, the distance or length between each of the displacement nodes and each of the displacement antinodes is always equal to one-fourth (¼) of a standing wave (wavelength) cycle. For instance, examine the first half-wave resonance pattern illustrated in column B of Figure 5–15, labeled *first harmonic*. The standing wave envelope extends from antinode (open end) to node (¼) to antinode (open end; ¼). Therefore, the length of the standing wave that defines the fundamental frequency (f_0) corresponds to a ¼ + ¼ or to a half-wave of resonance. Because the f_0 is defined by a half-wave of resonance, the harmonics of f_0 must also be defined by multiples of a half-wave of resonance. That is, each additional half-wave of resonance that can fit into the tube will also define the next higher harmonic.

Now examine the second half-wave resonance pattern illustrated in column B of Figure 5–15 that is labeled the *second harmonic*. The standing wave envelope now extends from antinode (open end) to node (¼) to antinode (¼) to node (¼) to antinode (open end; ¼). Therefore, the length of the standing wave that defines the second harmonic corresponds to a ¼ + ¼ + ¼ + ¼, or to one full wave of resonance. Because the fundamental frequency (f_0) was defined by a half-wave of resonance, the next higher harmonic of the f_0 should be defined by the next whole number multiple of a one-half wave of resonance capable of squeezing inside the tube. Since one full wave of resonance does fit into the tube, and is equal to 2 × ½, the next higher harmonic should be defined as 2 × f_0 which is the manner in which the second harmonic is defined. The same reasoning may be applied to each of the remaining half-wave resonance standing wave patterns illustrated in column B of Figure 5–15. That is, the third harmonic is defined by three half-waves, the fourth by four half-waves, and the fifth by five half-waves, and so forth. Each harmonic progression, therefore, represents an integer whole multiple of the first half-wave of resonance.

The harmonic progression that defines half-wave resonant tubes may now be compared to the harmonic progression that defines quarter-wave resonant tubes. Examine the first quarter-wave resonance pattern illustrated in column B of Figure 5–15, labeled first harmonic. The standing wave envelope extends from node (closed end) to antinode (open end; ¼), Therefore, the length of the standing wave that defines the fundamental frequency (f_0) corresponds to a ¼, or to a quarter wave of resonance. Because the f_0 is defined by a quarter wave of resonance, the harmonics of f_0 must also be defined by multiples of a quarter wave of resonance. That is, each additional quarter wave of resonance that can fit into (or in this case fill) the tube will also define the next higher harmonic.

Now examine the second quarter-wave resonance pattern illustrated in column A of Figure 5–15 that is labeled the *third harmonic*. How is it that the illustration came to be labeled as the third harmonic and not as the second harmonic? Note that the standing wave envelope now extends from node (closed end) to antinode (¼) to node (¼) to antinode (open end; ¼). Therefore, the length of the standing wave that defines the third harmonic corresponds to a ¼ + ¼ + ¼ or to a (¾) three quarter-wave of resonance. Because the fundamental frequency (f_0) was defined by a quarter wave of resonance, the next higher harmonic should be defined by the next whole number multiple of a one-quarter wave of resonance that fits into the tube. Since three quarter-waves of resonance fit into the tube, and are equal to 3 × ¼, the next higher harmonic is defined as 3 × f_0 which is the manner in which the third harmonic (not the second) is defined. But what happened to the second harmonic?

A second harmonic in a quarter-wave resonating tube would have been defined as two quarter-waves of resonance. However, the quarter-wave resonating tube is too long for only two quarter-waves of resonance. As illustrated in column A of Figure 5–15, the quarter-wave resonating tube is one quarter-wave longer than two quarter-waves of resonance. In addition to this, two quarter-waves of resonance require and are characterized by a node that is surrounded at each end by an antinode. However, a node that is surrounded at each end by an antinode describes a tube that is open at both ends and not just one. Alternatively, two quarter-waves of resonance could also be defined by an antinode that is surrounded at each end by a node. However, an antinode that is surrounded at each end by a node describes a tube that is closed at both ends. Such a tube would have very little practical use in terms of resonance. Summarily, it is impossible for even-numbered harmonics to be generated from a tube in which there is always a displacement node at one end (closed end), and a displacement antinode at the other end. Therefore, even-numbered harmonics cannot exist as standing waves in tubes that are closed at one end and open at the other end. That is, even-numbered harmonics cannot exist as standing waves in quarter-wave resonating tubes (Giancoli, 2005). Finally, for the remaining quarter-wave resonance (standing wave) patterns illustrated in column A of Figure 5–15, it should be intuitively clear that the fifth harmonic is defined by five quarter-waves, the seventh by seven quarter-waves, and the ninth by nine quarter-waves. Each harmonic progression represents an odd integer whole multiple of the first quarter-wave of resonance.

Common Tube Resonators

As indicated in the sections above, the creation of standing wave patterns in a reverberant sound-field is often prob-lematic and steps are often taken to prevent their occurrence. However, just the opposite is true for musical instruments. The overall perception of pitch for any stringed, woodwind, or brass musical instrument is usually determined by the lowest resonant frequencies of either its strings or of its tube resonances. The lowest resonant frequency is, of course, the fundamental frequency. In terms of stringed instruments, recall from the sections above that the distinct advantage of generating standing wave patterns at the f_0 of a string is that the string will then resonate with very large and sustained amplitude and will generate a distinctly audible sound at the same frequency that the string is resonating. Woodwind and brass instruments, on the other hand, can be defined as either half-wave or as quarter-wave tube resonators. For instance, the piccolo and flute are examples of half-wave resonating woodwind instruments, whereas the clarinet, oboe, bassoon, and English horn are examples of quarter-wave resonating woodwind instruments. Other wind instruments like pipe organs make use of both types of tube resonators, whereas the trumpet, trombone, tuba, French horn, and saxophone are all examples of quarter-wave resonating brass instruments. Recall from the sections above that the distinct advantage of generating a standing wave pattern at the f_0 of a tube resonator is that the tube will then resonate with very large and sustained amplitude, and will generate a distinctly audible sound through one of the open ends of the tube, at the same frequency that the tube is resonating. In any resonating system such as an instrument that gives rise to musical sounds, the fundamental frequency and one or more of its higher harmonics will usually be generated, simultaneously. This is the case whether the sounds are generated by the strings on a violin, guitar, or piano, or the by the air within an instrument that is defined by tube resonances. However, even though strings and both types of tube systems can be made to vibrate at a variety of frequencies, only the frequencies that correspond to standing waves will persist (Halliday et al., 2011). Therefore, the standing wave patterns generated by the strings, or by the tube resonances of musical instruments, are absolutely essential for such instruments to function properly.

Tube Length

From the equation that defines the fundamental frequency (f_0) of a half-wave resonating tube,

$$f_0 = c/2L \qquad (7\text{--}4)$$

as well as from the equation that defines the fundamental frequency of a quarter-wave resonating tube,

$$f_0 = c/4L \qquad (7\text{--}9)$$

it should be evident that the fundamental frequencies of tube resonators are inversely proportional to the overall lengths of the tubes. That is, the longer the length of the vibrating air column, or simply, the longer the length of a given tube, the lower will be the fundamental frequency of the tube. In any woodwind or brass musical instrument, the overall length of the instrument reflects the range of frequencies over which the instrument is designed to resonate.

Higher frequencies are implied by an instrument that has a smaller length and a reduced overall size. Lower frequencies are implied by an instrument that has a longer length and greater overall size. In order to produce very high pitches, pipe organs make use of pipes that vary in length from only a few centimeters. Pipe organs also utilize pipes that vary in length from 5 m or more in order to achieve very low pitches (Giancoli, 2005). In addition, the various notes on woodwind instruments are achieved by functionally shortening the length of the tube length of the instrument. This is accomplished by systematically uncovering the openings that are located along the length of the instrument. In many brass instruments, tube length is manipulated by pushing down on valves that open additional lengths of tubing. In addition to valves, a (sliding) trombone uses a telescopic sliding mechanism that varies the overall length of the tube resonator and therefore, alters the overall pitch of the sound that is produced.

The External Auditory Canal

The *external auditory canal* (Chapter 10), properly referred to as the *external auditory meatus* or simply as the *external ear canal*, receives sounds from the environment and conducts these environmental sounds to the *tympanic membrane*. It is therefore one of many conductive components of the (peripheral) auditory system. The external ear canal is also an example of a quarter-wave resonating tube and the closed end of the canal tube is the tympanic membrane. The length of the average adult external auditory canal is approximately 0.025 m (MKS) or 2.5 cm (CGS). The ear canal, however, is not a straight tube and is not a perfectly cylindrical structure. Instead, it is a tube that has two curves that form an elongated "S", such that if the "S" were to be viewed, it would be lying on its side (Musiek & Baran, 2007). Nevertheless, the external auditory canal does act like a quarter-wave resonating band-pass filter. However, unlike the description of band-pass filter functions provided earlier in this chapter, the external auditory canal does not suppress or eliminate select frequencies of sound (except perhaps at $2f_0$). Instead, the resonances of the external auditory canal emphasize, accentuate, or simply add energy at the frequency that corresponds to the length of the standing waves that define its particular fundamental frequency (f_0). Recall again that the distinct advantage of generating a standing wave pattern at the f_0 of a tube resonator, such as the external auditory canal, is that the tube resonator will then resonate with very large and sustained amplitude. Therefore, like the standing wave patterns generated by strings, or by the resonances of woodwind or brass musical instruments, the standing waves generated within the external auditory canal are absolutely essential for the canal to function properly. Using the approximate length measurements provided above for an adult external auditory canal, of 0.025 m (MKS) or 2.5 cm (CGS), and the appropriate MKS (344 m/s) and CGS (34,400 cm/s) values for the speed of sound, a close approximation of the fundamental frequency of the adult external auditory canal may be computed, once again using Equation 7–9:

$$f_0 = c/4L \qquad (7–9)$$

$$f_0 \text{ (MKS)} = 344/0.1 = 3440 \text{ Hz}$$

$$f_0 \text{ (CGS)} = 34{,}400/10 = 3440 \text{ Hz}$$

While a good approximation, some degree of deviation from this value of 3440 Hz should be expected, since the closed end of the external auditory canal is composed of the tympanic membrane. Because the tympanic membrane and parts of the external auditory canal itself (the outer one-third) have a degree of compliance, not all of the sound energy will be reflected throughout the tube resonator in the form of standing waves. Some of the energy will be lost by absorption or lost as it is directly transmitted into the middle ear, resulting in some degree of signal damping. The effective or functional (not physical) resonating length of the tube will be somewhat modified. Consequently, the external auditory canal will resonate over a relatively wider range of frequencies (as opposed to the more restricted value suggested above) that would be predicted if the canal were actually a hard walled enclosure, open at one end and closed at the other (Musiek & Baran, 2007).

The Vocal Tract

The resonating cavities of the *vocal tract* include all of the air spaces that extend above the larynx, from the glottis (the space between the vocal folds) to the lips. The vocal tract is yet another example of a quarter-wave resonating tube, and the closed end of the tract is represented by the closed glottis during vocal fold adduction (during phonation). The resonating compartments of the vocal tract are inclusive of the laryngopharynx, the oropharynx, and the oral cavity. The nasopharynx, with its production of nasalized anti-resonances when the velum (soft palate) is lowered, will not be included in the present discussion. The vocal tract receives complex periodic glottal pulse waves from the vocal folds. The glottal pulse waves occur at the fundamental frequency of vibration of the vocal folds. Additional harmonics are generated for each integer whole numbered multiple (both even and odd numbered) of the fundamental frequency. Hence, the complex periodic glottal pulses generated by the vocal folds act as a source (the driver), setting the vocal tract (the load) into quarter-wave resonances. As a quarter-wave resonating filter, the vocal tract adds energy in the form of standing wave patterns at its particular fundamental frequency (f_0). Moreover, the vocal tract generates additional standing wave patterns that correspond to odd-numbered harmonic multiples of the f_0, while suppressing all of the even-numbered harmonic multiples. The standing wave patterns generated at the f_0 together with several of the odd-numbered harmonics are transmitted together in an upward direction through the vocal tract, and into the oral cavity. Once more bear in mind that with the production of each progressively higher harmonic, beginning in this case with the third harmonic resonance, the amount of energy observed at each progressively higher harmonic will be substantially reduced due to an increased opposition to resonance, as discussed in Chapter 5. Notwithstanding, the production by the vocal tract of these higher, odd harmonic standing wave resonances, is absolutely essen-

tial, not only for the perception of the various vowel sounds, but also for their production during voiced speech. Hence, the standing waves generated within the vocal tract are once again essential for the proper function of the vocal tract.

The length of the average adult male vocal tract is approximately 0.17 m (MKS) or 17.0 cm (CGS). Like the ear canal, the vocal tract is not a straight tube, and in adults, the oral cavity is located at a right angle (90°) to the pharynx. The vocal tract is not a straight tube and is not a perfectly cylindrical structure. It varies along its length and is not uniform in its cross-sectional area. Finally, the vocal tract is not a hard walled enclosure. The soft tissue of the vocal tract is fairly compliant and provides some energy absorption. Nevertheless, the lowest frequency of resonance may be determined for the vocal tract using the approximate length measurements provided above for an adult male, employing lengths of 0.17 m (MKS) or 17.0 cm (CGS), and the appropriate MKS and CGS values for the speed of sound. A close approximation of the fundamental frequency (f_0) of the adult male vocal tract is easily computed using Equation 7–9:

$$f_0 = c/4L \qquad (7\text{–}9)$$

$$f_0 \text{ (MKS)} = 344/0.68 = 506 \text{ Hz}$$

$$f_0 \text{ (CGS)} = 34{,}400/10 = 506 \text{ Hz}$$

Therefore, the lowest resonant (first resonance) or fundamental frequency for a quarter-wave resonating tube, approximately 17.0 cm in length, such as the length of the average adult male vocal tract is approximately 500 Hz. Relatively speaking, a shorter vocal tract would also be expected to generate a first resonance or fundamental frequency that is higher in frequency. This is because the fundamental frequency of any tube resonator is inversely proportional to the overall length of the tube. However, because the vocal tract is a quarter-wave resonating tube, it will also generate standing wave patterns that correspond exclusively to odd-numbered harmonic multiples of its f_0. Recall from a previous discussion of quarter-wave resonating tubes, that the lowest resonant frequency, or first resonance of a quarter-wave resonating tube always corresponds to the fundamental frequency, or to the first harmonic of the fundamental frequency ($1 \times f_0$). The next lowest resonant frequency or second resonance corresponds to the third harmonic of the fundamental frequency, or simply $3 \times f_0$. Likewise, the third resonance corresponds to the fifth harmonic of the fundamental frequency, or simply $5 \times f_0$. What if each of the resonances (i.e., the first, second, third, fourth, etc.) were to be given a different names, other than calling them *resonances*? Regardless of the names given, each would still correspond to an odd-numbered harmonic of f_0.

Formant Frequencies

Vocal tract resonances are called *formants*, or simply *formant frequencies*. The first formant (F_1) of a vocal tract is equal to the first resonance of the vocal tract. That is, the first formant frequency is also the fundamental frequency, or first harmonic of the fundamental frequency ($1 \times f_0$). Not only is the F_1 the lowest frequency of resonance of a vocal tract, it is the first odd harmonic of the fundamental frequency

of a vocal tract. The next odd harmonic of a vocal tract, or $3 \times f_0$, is equal to the second resonance of the vocal tract, and is therefore called the second formant (F_2). Similarly, the next odd harmonic of a vocal tract, or $5 \times f_0$, is equal to the third resonance of the vocal tract and is called the third formant (F_3). Sometimes even a fourth resonance ($7 \times f_0$) or fourth formant (F_4) may be observed in the spectral analysis of a vocal tract resonance. However, and as indicated above, with the production of each progressively higher harmonic, the amount of energy that can be observed will be substantially reduced. To summarize, formant frequencies, numbered 1, 2, 3, 4, and so forth, correspond to the odd-numbered harmonic resonances of the vocal tract. Ideally, if the 17-cm vocal tract happened to be a straight, hard walled tube enclosure, perfectly cylindrical and uniform in its cross-sectional area, the numerical spacing between the formant frequencies would likely correspond to the straightforward (odd) harmonic progression indicated by the following:

First Formant (F_1) = 500 Hz

Second Formant (F_2) = 1500 Hz

Third Formant (F_3) = 2500 Hz

There might even be resonances at the F_4 equal to 3500 Hz. The spacing of the formant frequencies as indicated might even come close to being approximated in a completely neutral vocal tract position. In a completely neutral position, the tongue and lips would need to be completely at rest. In that regard, neutrality of vocal tract shape may be achieved with the production of the "schwa" vowel sound. The schwa is the sound of the "a" in the words "about" or "among." However, in almost all instances during speech production, the vocal tract is a dynamic resonating system that is constantly changing internally in its shape and size. Much of the internal change in shape that occurs is the result of the rapid set of movements of a very important oral articulator, the tongue. Tongue elevation, fronting, depression, and retraction all produce changes in many of the effective oral resonating areas of the vocal tract. Lip protrusion also lengthens the oral resonating cavity, as well as the entire vocal tract and causes a lowering in frequency of all the formants. Therefore, with the production of each vowel sound, a unique, yet predictable and relatively fixed pattern of formant spacing is achieved. However, in terms of the respective energy and spectral composition of each formant, the first formant (F_1) is always lower in frequency and greater in energy than the second formant (F_2), which is always lower in frequency and greater in energy than the third formant (F_3), which is always lower in frequency and greater in energy than the fourth formant (F_4).

Chapter Summary

- Acoustics was defined in this chapter as a study of the waveform properties of sound, or, as the properties that define the behavior of sound in a sound-field.
- Wavelength (λ) was defined in this chapter as the physical distance that a waveform travels over the course of one completed cycle, measured in centimeters/cycle (CGS) or meters/cycle (MKS).
- In this chapter, wavelength (λ) computations were provided for a range of frequencies propagated in either an air or a water medium.
- In this chapter, transverse wave motion was defined as motion in which the direction of the particle vibration within a particular medium is at right angles (90°) or is perpendicular to the direction of the waveform that is being propagated through the medium.
- In this chapter, longitudinal wave motion was defined as motion in which the direction of the particle vibration within a particular medium is parallel to the direction of waveform propagation through the medium, and sound produces longitudinal wave fronts (wave motion) in all directions.
- The fate of sound in a sound-field is largely dependent upon the proximity and/or the distance that objects and/or listeners are from the source of the sound.
- In a diffuse, highly reverberant, and highly reflective sound-field with reflective boundaries (barriers) that offer an infinite amount of impedance, the inverse square law as defined in Chapter 6 will not apply to sound propagation. All of the energy of the incident waveform

will be reflected away from the reflective boundary and all of the sound energy will be retained within the original medium.

- If the impedance offered by a reflective barrier (or second medium boundary) is *not* infinite, then the amplitude intensity of the reflected wave will be less than the amplitude intensity of the incident wave.

- Opposition to sound transmission will exist at any boundary between different sound transmitting media, distinguished each by their own separate characteristic impedances.

- In this chapter, the separate characteristic impedances of different transmitting media such as air and water were again utilized from Chapter 5. Equations were provided so that the degree (or percentage) of airborne sound reflected from a secondary boundary, such as water, could be mathematically determined. Of the total sound energy originating in an air medium, 99.9% is reflected off of water and is retained within the air.

- When transferring airborne sounds into a freshwater medium, approximately 30 dB IL or 30 dB SPL of the airborne sound is lost from the air (medium) and is therefore transmitted from the air into the freshwater medium.

- Sound wave absorption is the acoustic equivalent of damping and is inversely proportional

to sound wave reflection. If the total incident sound energy is neither reflected by nor transmitted through a second medium, then the total energy of an incident sound has been completely absorbed by the second medium.

- Absorption results in a reduction in signal amplitude and not in signal frequency or wavelength, and the magnitude of sound wave absorption was quantified in this chapter by the absorption coefficient.

- In this chapter, diffraction was defined in this chapter as the wavelength-dependent phenomenon in which waves bend and/or scatter around obstacles. Wave diffraction and scattering was also defined as a universal property of all types of waves. Diffraction occurs only for the energy carried by the sound waves, and not for the energy carried by the material particles that make up the medium. Several examples were provided in this chapter that illustrated wave diffraction and wave scattering effects around the head.

- Sound-shadow effects were defined in this chapter as the wavelength-dependent phenomena resulting from sound wave transmission across a barrier with a finite size, where most of the incident sound wave energy is reflected off the surface of the barrier. Several examples were provided in this chapter that illustrated sound-shadow effects around the head.

■ The Doppler effect was defined in this chapter as a motion-related, wavelength-related phenomenon in which the wavelengths for light- and sound-emitting objects become shorter as objects rapidly travel toward us, and become longer as objects rapidly travel away from us.

■ The Doppler effect for sound was defined in this chapter as a motion-related, wavelength-related, and therefore, a frequency and (perceptual) pitch-related phenomenon in which the pitch of sound-emitting objects becomes higher for objects that rapidly travel toward us, and becomes lower for objects that rapidly travel away from us.

■ Shock waves were defined in this chapter as the motion-related phenomenon known as sonic booms that occur when the speed of a sound-emitting object (or any object) in a medium exceeds the speed of sound in the medium within which it is moving.

■ Wave refraction was defined in this chapter as the change in the direction of a wave front that occurs when changes are made in the transmitting medium through which the waveform is propagating. Wave refraction for sound is commonly observed when an incident sound wave passes from one medium into a second medium, and the speed of sound within the two media is not equal. Sound refraction also occurs as a function of changing environmental atmospheric temperature gradients.

■ The principle of superposition was presented in this chapter and stated that when two separate waveforms overlap, the shape of the resultant waveform will be the result of the algebraic sums of the two individual waveforms. Waveforms that combine according to this principle are said to interfere with each other, and the phenomenon is called interference.

■ Constructive interference occurs when the amplitudes of the composite waveform are larger relative to the constituent waveforms. Destructive interference occurs when the amplitudes of the composite waveform are cancelled or are reduced, relative to the constituent waveforms.

■ Whenever incident and reflected waves occupy the same space (medium) at the same time, incident and reflected sound waves produce wave interference patterns. Interference occurs only for the energy carried by the sound waves, and not for the energy carried by the material particles that make up the medium.

■ The principle of resonance introduced in Chapter 5 was reintroduced in this chapter. The principle states that when a periodically vibrating force is applied to an elastic system, the elastic system will be forced to vibrate, and will initially vibrate under forced vibration at the frequency of the force that is being applied.

- In this chapter, the mass of an enclosed volume of air within a bottle or tube resonator was referred to as an acoustic inertance. Because the same volume of air is also elastic and compressible, the volume of air was also referred to as an acoustic compliance. The fundamental frequency of resonance of the enclosed volume of air will be inversely proportional to both the acoustic inertance and to the acoustic compliance of the air within the bottle or tube resonator.

- Standing wave interference patterns for transverse and longitudinal wave motion were described and illustrated in this chapter. Standing waves occur when incident and reflected waves are generated at precisely the same frequency and amplitude, and travel within the same medium in opposite directions.

- Standing waves are produced at the resonant frequencies (or at resonance) of strings and air-filled tubes as discussed in this chapter. Furthermore, they derive their name from the observation that they appear to be standing still and do not propagate longitudinally.

- Displacement nodes (standing wave areas that correspond to destructive interference) and displacement antinodes (standing wave areas that correspond to constructive interference) for transverse standing waves were described and illustrated in this chapter.

- In this chapter, half-wave resonating standing wave patterns were described and illustrated for strings and for air-filled tubes open at both ends. Quarter-wave resonating standing wave patterns were also described and illustrated for air-filled tubes open at only one end.

- Half-wave resonating tubes produce standing wave patterns for integer (both even and odd) numbered harmonic frequencies. Quarter-wave resonating tubes only produce standing wave patterns for odd-numbered harmonic frequencies. Even-numbered harmonics cannot exist as standing waves in quarter-wave resonating tubes, which by definition, are closed at one end and open at the other end.

- Pressure nodes (standing wave areas that correspond to zero changes in pressure) and pressure antinodes (standing wave areas that correspond to maximum pressure fluctuation) for transverse standing waves were additionally described in this chapter. In half-wave and quarter-wave resonating tubes, pressure nodes lead displacement nodes by 90° of phase, and pressure antinodes lead displacement antinodes by 90° of phase.

- In this chapter, the external auditory canal (external auditory meatus) and the vocal tract were both defined as quarter-wave resonating tubes. Vocal tract resonances are called formants, or formant frequencies, and numbered are 1, 2, 3, 4, and so forth, and they correspond to the odd-numbered harmonic resonances of the vocal tract.

Chapter 7 Questions

1. Why is it that AM radio signals can be picked up from behind a large hill while FM radio signals cannot?

2. Differentiate between transverse and longitudinal wave motion in relation to the direction of travel of the overall waveform.

3. What type of motion should be imparted to a horizontally stretched coiled spring, such as a Slinky, to produce a transverse wave? A longitudinal wave?

4. Explain why relatively little effort is required to obtain large amplitudes during forced vibration when an object is made to resonate at its natural or fundamental frequency.

5. Why do you suppose that that piano strings that are made to resonate for the notes having lowest frequencies on a piano have extra wire wrapped around them?

6. If you are standing around a corner on one side of a building, explain why you can hear the sounds from the other side of the building but you cannot be hit by a baseball that is thrown from the other side of the building.

7. What is meant by a *blue shift* for sound? What is meant by a *red shift* for sound?

8. How does wavelength vary with frequency? How does wavelength vary with period?

9. What relationships exist between wave speed, wave frequency, and wavelength?

10. Why is a standing wave problematic in a sound-field situation but absolutely essential for the resonances of a string or air-filled tube?

11. Why is there a Doppler effect when the source of a sound is stationary (not moving), but the listener is in motion? In which direction (toward or away from the sound source) should the listener rapidly move in order to hear a higher pitch? In which direction to hear a lower pitch?

12. In which direction, toward the ground or away from the ground, is sound refracted when there is a positive temperature gradient (temperature inversion)? In which direction is sound refracted when there is a negative temperature gradient? Explain.

References

American National Standards Institute. (2010). *American National Standards specification for audiometers* (ANSI S3.6-2010). New York, NY: Author.

Durrant, J. D., & Feth, L. L. (2013). *Hearing sciences: A foundational approach.* Upper Saddle River, NJ: Pearson Education.

Giancoli, D. C. (2005). *Physics: Principles with applications* (6th ed.). Upper Saddle River, NJ: Prentice Hall.

Halliday, D., Resnick, R., & Walker, J. (2011). *Fundamentals of physics* (9th ed.). Hoboken, NJ: Wiley.

Hamill, T. A., & Price, L. L. (2014). *The hearing sciences* (2nd ed.). San Diego, CA: Plural.

Hewitt, P. G. (2010). *Conceptual physics* (11th ed.). Upper Saddle River, NJ: Pearson Education.

Musiek, F. E., & Baran, J. A. (2007). *The audi-tory system: Anatomy, physiology and clinical correlates.* Upper Saddle River, NJ: Pearson Education.

Silman, S., & Emmer, M. B. (2012). *Instrumentation for audiology and hearing science.* San Diego, CA: Plural.

Speaks, C. E. (1999). *Introduction to sound: Acoustics for the hearing and speech sciences* (3rd ed.). San Diego, CA: Singular.

Chapter 8

Psychoacoustics

The first law of psychophysics that was initially put forth by the Pythagorean School in 300 BC stated that the length of a plucked string is related to its pitch, such that, reducing the length of the string to half of its original length raises the pitch by one octave (von Békésy, 1967, p. 125). Explicit in the writings of Aristotle (384–322 BC) is the notion that knowledge comes to the "mind" by way of the senses (Hirsh, 1952, p. 8). By the middle of the fifth century BC the belief was widely held that the senses somehow mirrored the external world by the principle of likeness. According to this principle, perception arises because activity in the external environment is met by activity within the sense organ of a corresponding kind: that is, like is perceived by like.

Gulick, 1971, p. 5

Alphabetized Listing of Key Terms Discussed in Chapter 8

absolute threshold

audiogram

audiometer

audiometric zero

auditory adaptation

auditory fatigue

average normal threshold

backward masking

barks

beat frequency

beats

binaural advantage

binaural fusion

binaural hearing

binaural sound lateralization

binaural sound localization

binaural summation

broadband noise

critical bandwidth

critical duration

critical ratio

decibels of hearing level (dB HL)

decibels of sensation level (dB SL)

dichotic listening

difference limen

difference limen for frequency (DLF)

differential threshold

diotic listening

direct masking

duplex theory

equal-loudness level contours

equal-pitch contours

equivalent rectangular bandwidth (ERB)

Fechner, Gustav Theodor

Fechner's law

Fletcher, Harvey

Fletcher-Munson curves

flutter

forward masking

fractionation method

hearing level (HL)

interaural difference in intensity (IID; ILD)

interaural difference in phase (IPD)

interaural difference in the time of arrival (ITD)

just noticeable difference (JND)

level-per-cycle (LPC)

limen

loudness

loudness level contours

loudness scaling

low pitch

masked threshold

masking

masking patterns

mels of pitch

method of adjustment

method of limits

method of magnitude production

minimum audibility curve (MAC)

minimum audibility field (MAF) curve

minimum audibility pressure (MAP) curve

missing fundamental frequency

monaural hearing

monaural localization

Munson, Wilden A.

narrow-band noise

periodicity pitch

permanent threshold shift (PTS)

phons of loudness level

pitch

precedence effect

probe stimulus

psychoacoustics

psychophysics

pure tone

pure tone audiometer

pure tone average (PTA)

relative difference limen (DL)

remote masking

repetition pitch

residue pitch

roughness

sensation level (SL)

simultaneous masking

sones of loudness

spectral pitch

spectrum level

speech reception (recognition) threshold (SRT)

Stevens, Stanley Smith (S.S.)

Steven's law

suprathreshold

temporal masking

temporal summation

temporary threshold shift (TTS)

threshold

threshold adaptation

threshold shift

threshold of audibility

time-intensity tradeoff

unmasked threshold

upward spread of masking

virtual pitch

Weber, Ernst Heinrich

Weber fraction

Weber ratio

Weber's law

white noise

wide-band noise

Psychophysics

Recall from Chapter 3 that the discipline of psychophysics has historically existed as an outgrowth of sensory psychophysiology, which is a branch of experimental psychology (Boring, 1957). Also recall that Gustav Theodor Fechner (1801–1887) is credited as the founder of experimental psychology and for originally establishing (in 1860) the methodological foundations for the discipline of psychophysics (Boring, 1957). Fechner's goal was to establish or discover the relationships that exist between sensory experience, which is purely subjective, and the measureable objective events in the physical world. Hence, the events of interest in psychophysics are the sensations and the perceptions, and the systematic measurement and scaling of their magnitudes (Hirsh, 1952). Unlike the objective, mostly linear and at times logarithmic mathematical measures of physical stimuli that have been covered in the preceding chapters, sensations and perceptions are uniquely subjective and are almost entirely nonlinear. As indicated in Chapter 3, the subject matter and goals of psychophysics have traditionally been to discover the orderly relationships that exist between the quantifiably linear physical dimensions or attributes of stimuli and the scaling rules that determine the degree to which these physically quantified values correspond to nonlinear psychological experience. Fechner's work included the establishment of methods for ascertaining the lower limit of sensitivity for a stimulus, and Fechner was the first to propose that the magnitude of a subjective sensation could be computed from objective measurements of physical stimuli and behavioral responses, as indicated by threshold judgments, observed in the form of a behavioral response to those stimuli (Boring, 1957). Discoveries made in the field of psychophysics have provided the necessary connections between linear mathematical measures of physical stimuli and nonlinear subjective, experiential variables such as those associated with sensations and perceptions. Such discoveries have made it possible to develop, for purposes of quantification and comparison, fairly accurate measurement scales that have helped to define sensory and perceptual experiences.

Psychoacoustics

Psychoacoustics was introduced in Chapter 3 as a branch of psychophysics. Psychoacoustics, which is a subdivision of psychophysics, deals with the quantified physical values associated with sound and the degree to which those physical values correspond to the scaling rules that are used to measure the psychological experience of sound that is often referred to as *hearing*. Of central interest in the study of psychoacoustics is the measurement of the subjective attributes of "loudness" and "pitch" and the scaling rules that determine the degree to which these subjective dimensions correspond with their respective physical correlates, intensity (power and pressure) and frequency. The concept of an auditory threshold and the methods used to obtain an absolute and/or a differential auditory threshold are also the methods used to measure the subjective dimension of loudness. Threshold-related concepts, and the methods used to determine thresholds are the focus of the sections that follow. Although the concept of loudness is addressed briefly in what follows, psychoacoustic measures of loudness, loudness level and pitch will be dealt with a little later in the chapter.

Threshold Revisited

Recall from Chapter 6 that a *threshold* was conventionally defined as the least amount or level of any kind of environmental stimulus that can be detected, on the average, by an individual or by a group of individuals. In the present context, an auditory threshold represents the least level of loudness of an auditory stimulus that can be detected, on the average, by an individual or group of individuals. Loudness may be defined as that subjective dimension or attribute of an auditory perception or experience that is correlated with, but is not equal to, the physical dimension of intensity. Recall again that physical dimension of sound intensity was defined in Chapter 6, in terms of units of power and/ or pressure. Therefore, even though loudness is most often viewed as the psychoacoustic correlate of sound intensity, loudness should not be used as a synonym for intensity. Loudness may change even though intensity remains constant. Loudness may be organized on a scale that extends from very weak (soft) or very quiet, to loud or very loud (Hirsh, 1952).

The use of the term *threshold* often falsely implies the existence of a discrete point along a physical continuum, such as stimulus intensity, that must either be reached or breached before a given stimulus can be perceived. It is false to assume that above a certain threshold point, an individual always responds and below the same threshold point, the individual never responds (Durrant & Feth, 2013). Threshold, as defined in this chapter, is based strictly on a behavioral response to a particular stimulus; hence, auditory threshold judgments made on the part of the listener are purely subjective in nature and reflect an ability to perceive some degree of the loudness of a stimulus. Consequently, the only way to affirm that a threshold has been reached at any particular moment after the presentation of an auditory stimulus is by an affirmative behavioral response that is generated by a listener.

An auditory threshold is usually defined by the least amount of a signal that is required to evoke a response from a listener. Hence, the presentation level (signal intensity) of a stimulus must be adequate enough in both signal strength and in subjective loudness to motivate the listener to produce a behavioral response. If the intensity values of the stimulus are too low, the listener will not respond and the signals are then said to have been presented at subthreshold or subliminal levels. The term *limen* in the word subliminal refers to the threshold (Boring, 1957). When obtaining thresholds, it is often difficult to determine what "loudness criterion" the listener is using, moment to moment, to judge whether a stimulus is loud enough (or not) to warrant a response. Consequently, the "true" threshold will vary, not only between listeners, but moment to moment within each listener. Threshold variability that exists between listeners may be attributed to individual differences in sensitivity. The internal or within-listener variance that exists, however, is often due to a number of subjective factors. These factors include the moment-to-moment fluctuations that occur in the listener's physiological state of arousal, the listener's emotional state of motivation, the listener's level of attention, or any and all of these factors in combination.

Also recall from Chapter 6 that the method of presentation of the sound, the instructions given, and the methods used to determine or measure a threshold for any particular individual, represent additional sources of variability that must also be specified. Furthermore, in determining the auditory threshold for a pure tone, all other parameters of the stimulus, such as stimulus duration, stimulus frequency, starting phase, and distance from the sound source must also be held constant (Licklider, 1958). In sum, a strict interpretation of the term threshold as consisting of a discrete point along a physical continuum should be avoided (Durrant & Feth, 2013). The most accurate estimate of an auditory threshold will be obtained by the repeated sampling of responses at or near the adjusted limits of the listener's approximate hearing thresholds. This means that a meaningful threshold measurement cannot be made with any single presentation of a stimulus. Instead, meaningful auditory threshold measurements across a range of frequencies will require many stimulus presentations, administered at several points in time. For this reason, a threshold is most often statistically defined as the value of the stimulus that, on the average, elicits an affirmative response over a specified percentage of stimulus presentations (Hirsh, 1952). As a direct result of the psychophysical methods

established by Fechner in 1860, two types of threshold have received considerable attention in the years that followed. These methods were the difference threshold, characterized as the smallest amount of detectable (intensity or frequency) change in a stimulus, and the absolute threshold, defined as the lowest absolute value of a stimulus that is detectable.

Absolute Threshold Revisited

Recall from Chapter 6 that obtaining an absolute auditory threshold requires that the subject is able to perceive the sound, physically able to respond at any moment to the sound by confirming either its presence or its absence (in absolute terms), and consciously willing or behaviorally disposed to respond to the sound. Once these criteria are met, the test methods used to obtain a measure of the absolute threshold for a particular pure tone frequency will provide an answer to the question "was the stimulus loud enough to be present, or was it absent?" Absolute thresholds are often obtained using a combined ascending and descending *method of limits*. The method of limits is one of several (at least seven) classical psychophysical methods that were established by Fechner (Boring, 1942). The term *absolute* refers to the kind of (absolute) threshold response that is expected from the listener with each stimulus presentation when this method is employed. The concept of an absolute threshold response is defined, more often than not, by the method and the procedures used to obtain the response. The method of limits is the psychophysical procedure in which an investigator gradually increases and/ or gradually decreases the perceptual dimension of loudness (by manipulating the signal intensity) in successive and discrete serial steps, until a critical stimulus level is reached. Each time the critical stimulus level is reached, the listener will change his or her perceptual judgment. The procedure may begin with the presentation of a series of discrete supraliminal (above threshold) intensities that are systematically diminished by a consistent and specified amount, until the listener reports no degree of loudness perception. The intensity at which the listener reports that the audible stimulus (tone) has become inaudible as the intensity is decreased, is recorded. The procedure then continues with the presentation of a series of subliminal (below threshold) intensities that are systematically increased by a consistent and specified amount, until the listener reports the perception of some small degree of loudness. As the intensity is increased, the level at which the listener reports just hearing the stimulus (tone) as the sound begins to emerge from silence, is also recorded. Hence, in each case, the behavioral change in the listener's response is recorded, indicating a loudness perception that ranges from absolutely inaudible to absolutely audible, or vice versa (Hirsh, 1952). That is, the absolute presence or the absolute absence of the perceived stimulus, as determined by the listener, will be indicated by the listener's response each time a stimulus is presented, and the two absolute response options will always consist of "yes" or "no." Sets of signal intensity increments (ascending) and signal intensity decrements (descending) that are successively and gradu-

ally presented to the listener are often collectively referred to as a series of ascending and descending runs, respectively. Several ascending and descending runs are presented to the listener over time so that half of the absolute threshold measures are acquired when the intensity is decreased from stimulus levels that are above threshold, and the other half are acquired when the intensity is increased from stimulus levels that are below threshold. For any given frequency of interest, the lowest intensity level resulting in an affirmative response by the listener at least 50% of the time across both ascending and descending runs, is usually taken as a measure of the listener's absolute threshold (Boring, 1942). Use of the standard procedures outlined in the method of limits often results in the acquisition of absolute thresholds that tend to be measurably lower (sensitivity is greater) during the descending runs compared to those obtained during the ascending runs (Hirsh, 1952). In an attempt to improve test reliability, several modified versions (Gelfand, 2001), including one preferred version of the method of limits have been adopted for use during audiometric testing, when absolute hearing thresholds are acquired (Hall, 2014). Absolute thresholds obtained in this manner are then taken as a valid index of a listener's "auditory thresholds" and therefore the listener's hearing sensitivity.

The Threshold of Audibility

As indicated in the preceding sections, for any individual or group of subjects, the intensity level at which a sound stimulus first becomes audible is a level that is referred to as the auditory threshold. The auditory threshold is usually taken to mean the softest or faintest level of loudness, on the "average," that is required for the detection of what is usually, a pure tone. Recall that auditory sensitivity is inversely related to auditory threshold. That is, lower auditory thresholds are correlated with greater levels of auditory sensitivity, and vice versa. This means that auditory thresholds obtained with the least amount of acoustic intensity (watts of power) and/or pressure, are thresholds that are indicative of greater auditory sensitivity.

As far back as the middle of the nineteenth century, investigators in the field of experimental psychology were concerned with determining the sensory and perceptual performance of the average, normal adult human being. As important now as it was then, is the concept of "average normal absolute hearing thresholds." For instance, in "normal hearing" human subjects, that is, individuals in which normal hearing has been determined, and under optimal sound-field conditions, we may want to know, on the average, what are the lowest intensity (dB IL) or sound pressure levels (dB SPL) at which sounds across a fairly wide range of frequencies (pure tones) are "expected" to become (just) audible? Stated subjectively, we may want to know, on the average, what is the lowest loudness level at which sounds, across a fairly wide range of frequencies (pure tones) are "expected" to be detected? First, what exactly is meant by the expression, "optimal sound-field conditions"? An optimal sound-field condition obviously calls to mind the environment that is often found within a free sound-

field, or, within the closest approximation to a free-field which is the virtual free sound-field of an anechoic chamber, as illustrated in Chapter 6. What precisely is meant by the added assumption of "normal hearing sensitivity"? How is normal hearing sensitivity determined? Normal hearing sensitivity is usually inferred when hearing sensitivity, as determined by the acquisition of absolute threshold responses, is "excellent" and is observed to be within "normal and acceptable auditory limits." When hearing sensitivity is excellent, the first assumption is that an auditory system (or systems) under scrutiny, is free of disease. That is, from the outer ear to the cerebral auditory cortex, the assumption is that for any given sample of listeners whose auditory systems have been characterized as exhibiting excellent sensitivity, the same listeners are said to have auditory systems that are functioning optimally.

An important question still needs to be answered. What exactly is meant by the use of the term "normal and acceptable auditory limits" and how are these threshold limits defined? The concept of normal and acceptable auditory limits pertains to the average normal absolute hearing thresholds observed at select frequencies from across the audible range of possible frequencies. Thresholds are obtained from large samples of listeners drawn from a population of possible listeners. Hence, normal and acceptable auditory threshold limits must be inferred statistically from frequency-specific thresholds sampled from a population, using adequate sampling methods. Consequently, it follows that the intensity (or sound pressure) levels at which sounds are expected to become just audible, or just loud enough on the average, across a select range of pure tone frequencies, represents the set of average, normal, and acceptable auditory limits that generally define "the threshold of audibility." Hence, and to reiterate, the threshold of audibility is determined at select frequencies across the audible range of frequencies. As indicated in Chapter 6, the audible range of frequencies extends from a lower frequency limit of 20 Hz to an upper frequency limit of 20 kHz. The threshold of audibility is also synonymous with the threshold for loudness and, obviously as well, the threshold for hearing.

Why is it so important to define and quantify a threshold of audibility across the audible range of frequencies? An established set of normal hearing thresholds provides the necessary standards essential in the development of comparative norms, used as the foundation for evaluating hearing sensitivity across (ideally) all individuals within a population. Meaningful clinical diagnoses are absolutely dependent upon the availability of a reasonable estimate of what is "normal" with which what is "abnormal," may be contrasted (Hirsh, 1952). A good place to begin to define the average normal hearing threshold or threshold of audibility (or of loudness) is to once again be familiar with the least amount of acoustic intensity (watts of power) and/or pressure that is actually required, on the average, in order to reach an auditory threshold, as outlined in Chapter 6. Quantities of acoustic intensity that represent good approximations to the threshold of audibility for a 1000-Hz pure tone were 10^{-12} watts/m² (MKS), and the CGS equivalent of 10^{-16} watts/cm². Both of these quantities of acous-

tic intensity were used as reference values for decibel computations measured in terms of intensity level (dB IL), and therefore, both represent 0 dB IL. As for pressure, MKS sound pressure quantities were also provided in Chapter 6 as good approximations to the threshold of audibility for a 1000-Hz pure tone. Recall that these quantities were 0.00002 newtons (N)/m², also expressed in scientific notation as 2×10^{-5} N/m². Recall also that since 1 N/m² = 1 pascal (Pa) of pressure, it also followed that the same MKS sound pressure value is expressed as 0.00002 Pa, or in scientific notation as, 2×10^{-5} Pa. However, a zero is typically added in the negative sixth decimal place of 0.00002 Pa, resulting in an equivalent value of 0.000020 Pa, or in essence, 20×10^{-6} Pa, which is more commonly expressed as 20 micro (μ) Pa, or conveniently as 20 μPa. Furthermore, an equivalent CGS quantity of pressure was additionally provided (Chapter 6) as a good approximation to the threshold of audibility for a 1000-Hz pure tone. This CGS quantity of pressure was 0.0002 dynes/cm², which was also expressed in scientific notation as 2×10^{-4} dynes/cm². Finally, call to mind that the two MKS and the onc CGS quantities of pressure were also used as reference values for decibel computations measured in terms of sound pressure level (dB SPL), and therefore, all three represent 0 dB SPL.

The Minimum Audibility Curve (MAC)

How has the threshold of audibility or loudness been measured across the range of perceptible frequencies? Formal experiments to determine the threshold of audibility were initially conducted in the 1930s (Fletcher & Munson, 1933; Sivian & White, 1933) and again in the 1950s (Dadson & King, 1952; Robinson & Dadson, 1956) using pure tone signals. Two general methods have come to be used in measures that determine the threshold of audibility across the human audible frequency spectrum. Both methods employ pure tones with durations that are at least 250 to 300 ms (Hall, 2014). One measurement method establishes absolute thresholds at each frequency by measuring the sound pressure level at some point close to the entrance of, or better still, within the external ear canal, using a very small "probe" microphone (Moore, 2012). The pure tones are delivered to the listener by headphone or by insert phones. Ideally, measurements are made as close to the tympanic membrane as possible. The exact position of the microphone must, in all cases, be specified. This is because slight changes in microphone position can markedly affect absolute thresholds that are obtained at high frequencies. The absolute threshold measurements obtained by this "real ear" measurement method, as compared to the use of "artificial ear" (6 cc or 2 cc steel walled) coupling devices (Durrant & Feth, 2013), will yield more accurate threshold of audibility values for monaural (one ear) listening. Threshold of audibility values for monaural (one ear) listening obtained from real ear measurements, made with miniature probe microphones, and sounds that are delivered by insert phones, may be used to very accurately (Hall, 2014) generate what is known as the minimum audibility curve (MAC) for pressure, or simply the minimum audibility pressure (MAP)

curve (Figure 8–1). The other measurement method determines the threshold of audibility (or loudness) by the delivery of pure tones through a loudspeaker in a virtual free sound-field (anechoic chamber). In this measurement method, the listener does not wear headphones but directly faces a loudspeaker located within a sound-field. Listener and loudspeaker are separated by a distance of about 1 m (Hall, 2014). The actual sound pressure measurements that produce a behavioral response are made after the listener is removed from the sound-field. The microphone of a sound level meter (see Figures 6–2A and 6–2E) is then placed at the same location in the sound-field that was occupied by the listener's head (Moore, 2012).

Absolute threshold measures obtained by this method give rise to the threshold of audibility for binaural (two ears) listening and generate what is known as the minimum audibility curve (MAC) for the sound-field, or simply the minimum audibility field (MAF) curve (see Figure 8–1). Again, bear in mind that both curves represent average absolute threshold data obtained from large samples of young healthy listeners, all of whom have normal hearing sensitivity. It is also noteworthy that individual listeners with normal hearing sensitivity may have absolute thresholds that deviate by as much as ±20 dB from the average (mean) at a given frequency (Moore, 2012).

As illustrated in Figure 8–1, the MAF curve additionally indicates that lower thresholds and greater hearing sensitivity are obtained in the sound-field, when both ears are uncovered (binaural listening). That is, each frequency-specific absolute threshold, as indicated by each point located on the MAF curve

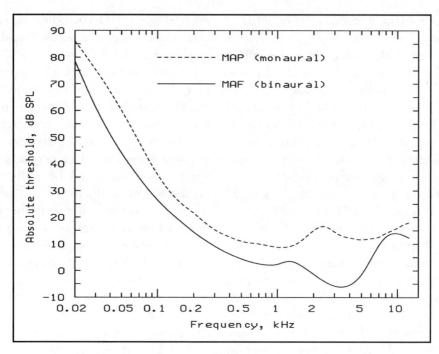

Figure 8–1. Minimum audibility curves (MACs) plotted as a function of frequency. The solid curve provides an example of the minimum audibility field (MAF) curve obtained under binaural listening conditions in an anechoic (sound-field) test chamber. The dashed curve provides an example of the minimum audibility pressure (MAP) curve obtained under monaural listening conditions recorded from a real ear using a small probe microphone. In addition, the threshold of audibility for both the MAP and MAF curves also signify equal loudness level judgments made across the audible frequency spectrum. Reproduced from Moore, B. C. J. (2012). *An introduction to the psychology of hearing* (6th ed.). Leiden, the Netherlands: Brill Publishing, by permission of the author.

is observed at a relatively lower sound pressure level (dB SPL) compared to the absolute thresholds (each point) depicted by the MAP curve. The reason for the greater hearing sensitivity under binaural listening conditions is primarily due to the observation that listening with two ears is approximately equivalent to the effects of doubling the intensity level (power) or the sound pressure level of a signal. Recall from Chapter 6 that there is a gain of 3 dB when either the intensity level (power) or the sound pressure level of a signal is exactly doubled. However, when the threshold of audibility values for monaural (one ear) listening are obtained from

real ear measurements, made with miniature probe microphones and sounds that are delivered by insert phones as described above, observed MAP curve values will very closely approximate MAF curve values, with differences of less than 3 dB SPL for octave and interoctave (between octave) frequencies from 500 to 2000 Hz (Hall, 2014). Figure 8–1 also illustrates that the shapes of the MAP and MAF curves differ. The difference observed in the shapes of the two curves is partly due to the fact that the head, the pinnae, and the external auditory canal (Chapter 10) produce resonances that affect sound-field measurements. For instance, note that the MAF curve indicates a distinct dip (increased sensitivity) at 3000 to 4000 Hz, and a peak (decreased sensitivity) at about 8000 to 9000 Hz. The dips and peaks reflect the broad resonances created by the pinna and external auditory canal (Moore, 2012).

What is most obvious from Figure 8–1 is that the MAP and MAF curves both indicate that the threshold of audibility, in terms of absolute threshold sound pressures (dB SPL), is not linearly equivalent across the audible frequency spectrum of 20 Hz to 20 kHz. That is, absolute thresholds are higher, and subsequently sensitivity is lower for the very low and for the very high frequencies. Put simply, the human auditory system is not equally sensitive across the audible frequency spectrum of 20 Hz to 20 kHz. This means that maintaining a threshold of audibility across the audible frequency spectrum requires greater amounts of sound pressure at the very low and at the very high frequencies. Upon inspection of both curves, it appears that the inner ear may be equally sensitive to many of the frequencies located above 500 Hz up to about 1500 Hz, and more sensitive to higher frequencies from 2000 Hz up to about 5000 Hz. The range of frequencies from 500 to 5000 Hz, are also the frequencies that are critical for the comprehension of speech. Both threshold of audibility curves also indicate that the sensitivity of the inner ear is appreciably decreased and subsequently, the threshold of audibility is higher for the successively lower frequencies found below about 500 Hz.

The lower frequency regions of both thresholds of audibility curves are also reminiscent of the dB-A weighting network built into sound level meters (SLMs) that was illustrated in Chapter 6 (see Figure 6–2B). Recall that this weighting curve was originally used in order to take into account the relatively poorer auditory sensitivity for the relatively weaker in intensity and lower in frequency environmental sounds, based on the human threshold of audibility. More will be said later in the chapter relating the dB-A weighting scale to the subjective dimension of loudness. Finally, it should be noted that the shape of the MAF curve, and therefore the threshold of audibility across individual listeners can vary markedly at 1000 Hz and at higher frequencies, with the greatest amount of individual variability observed at frequencies above 6000 Hz (Moore, 2012).

Figure 8–2 again illustrates the MAF curve plotted across a range of pure tone frequencies. As indicated, the threshold of audibility is lowest across a midrange of frequencies extending from about 500 Hz up to about 5000 Hz, indicating greater hearing sensitivity at these frequencies. The MAF also indicates that maximum auditory sensitivity can be found at or near 1000 Hz, extending upward to about 4000 Hz. Therefore, on the average, a minimal amount of sound pressure would be required for a normal hearing listener to just detect the presence of these pure tone frequencies. As illustrated in Figure 8–2, absolute thresholds at these frequencies should approximate 0 dB SPL (0 dB IL), or less. Finally, if it is also assumed that listeners, on the average, use the same loudness criterion to judge whether a stimulus is loud enough (or not) to warrant an absolute threshold response across the range of audible frequencies, then loudness level judgments at each of the frequency locations along the threshold of audibility should all be equal. That

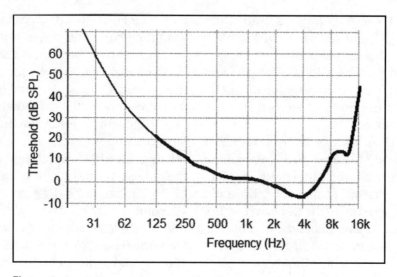

Figure 8–2. Minimum audibility field (MAF) curve plotted as a function of frequency, once again illustrating the threshold of audibility. As previously illustrated in Figure 8–1, the MAF curve is obtained under binaural listening conditions in an anechoic (sound-field) test chamber. The threshold of audibility for the MAF curve also signifies equal loudness level judgments made across the audible frequency spectrum. From T. A. Hamill and L. L. Price (2014), with permission.

is, the threshold of audibility for both the MAP and MAF curves also signifies equal loudness level judgments made across the audible frequency spectrum. This means that although the physical intensity required for an absolute threshold response varies across each frequency, each of the separate physical intensities is equated with respect to the psychological perception of loudness that each generates.

The Threshold of Audibility: Relationship to the Pure Tone Audiogram

Looking once again at Figures 8–1 and 8–2, it should again be emphasized that the threshold of audibility, as determined by absolute threshold sound pressure (dB SPL) values, is not linearly equivalent across the audible frequency spectrum of 20 Hz to 20 kHz. As indicated above, the loudness perception of a pure tone is affected not only by physical intensity or sound pressure, but also by the frequency of the pure tone. That is, absolute threshold values, stated in terms of dB IL or dB SPL will vary as a function of frequency, due to the fact that the human auditory system is not equally sensitive across the audible frequency range of 20 Hz to 20 kHz. Recall as well from the section above that maintaining a threshold of audibility across the human audible frequency range of pure tones will require the application of differing amounts of sound pressure as the frequency of the stimulus is altered or manipulated. The device that has the capability of systematically delivering pure tones over a range of calibrated frequencies and intensities is the audiometer.

The Audiometer

An audiometer (Figure 8–3) is an electronic device that is used to evaluate absolute hearing thresholds for pure tones and thresholds for speech. As illustrated in Figure 8–3, the audiometer is a device that has more testing options than those discussed in the present chapter. The *pure tone audiogram* (Figure 8–4) is a graphic, linear summary that is used to depict absolute hearing threshold test results that are obtained with the use of a pure tone audiometer. The term *pure tone audiometer* is used in the present context to refer to that part of the total circuitry of the audiometer that functions to deliver a range of calibrated and specified pure tone frequency sounds to the listener, over a range of calibrated and specified intensity levels. The pure tone audiometer essentially consists of a pure tone generator (pure tone oscillator) and a signal attenuator dial (shown as the *intensity control* in Figure 8–3) that is linearly calibrated on the face of the audiometer, in decibels of hearing level

(dB HL). The significance of the term *hearing level* is addressed below. The pure tone audiometer also has an interrupter (shown as the *present button* in Figure 8–3) that permits each pure tone stimulus to be delivered over a brief and specified duration of time, as needed. The standard pure tone audiometer will generate and, through a set of transducers, will deliver to the listener, pure tones that range over the octave frequencies, from 125 (or 250 Hz) to 8000 Hz. Octave notation was addressed in Table 5–3B (see Chapter 5). Recall that these audiometric frequencies normally consist of 250, 500, 1000, 2000, 4000, and 8000 Hz. The typical pure tone audiometer also generates and delivers the five interoctave frequencies of 750, 1500, 3000, and 6000 Hz. The set of transducers that plug into the pure tone audiometer include headphones or insert phones, bone oscillators, and sound-field speakers. The intensity of the pure tones delivered to the listener is controlled by the calibrated signal attenuator. The attenuator alters the voltage delivered to the listener in a

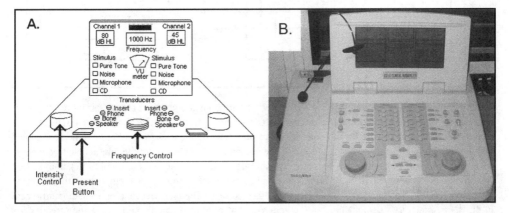

Figure 8–3. A. Parts of an audiometer showing that the device has more testing options than those discussed in this chapter. **B.** A Grason-Stadler 61 audiometer. From T. A. Hamill and L. L. Price (2014), with permission.

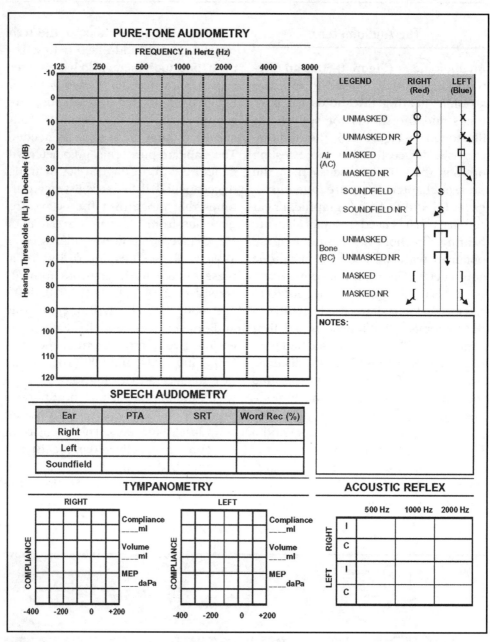

Figure 8–4. The pure tone audiogram is used during pure tone audiometry to record absolute thresholds obtained over a range of pure tones that are generated by a pure tone audiometer and delivered to the listener through a set of transducers. The audiometric octave pure tone frequencies from 125 to 8000 Hz are shown horizontally from left to right across the top of the audiogram. Not shown are the interoctave frequencies. Along the ordinate, stimulus intensity is linearly calibrated in decibels of hearing level (dB HL), and is often represented by successive 5 or 10 dB HL increments beginning at the top of the audiogram, with the lowest intensity level corresponding to −10 dB HL. The threshold of audibility, corresponding to audiometric zero (0 dB HL) is shown as a straight line (with a zero slope) at each of the audiometric pure tone frequencies that are tested. Reprinted from F. E. Musiek, J. A. Baran, J. B. Shinn, and R. O. Jones (2012), with permission.

manner that takes into account the normal, established threshold of audibility, as well as the electroacoustic limitations of the particular transducer that is being used. With respect to the electroacoustic limitations of transducer devices, the reader is referred to the calibration tables provided elsewhere (see Silman & Emmer, 2012). Hence, if the attenuator remains at a setting of *audiometric zero*, which is the same as 0 dB HL on the audiometric dial, the actual voltage delivered from the audiometer to the transducer will not remain constant each time a different frequency is selected for its presentation to the listener. Instead, the output intensity to the transducer will vary with each frequency, in accordance with the sound pressure levels or intensity levels specified by the threshold of audibility, as illustrated by the MAP curve, as well as the electroacoustic specifications of the transducer that is in use. The significance of audiometric zero is addressed in terms of the pure tone audiogram in the sections that follow. Bear in mind once again that the observed threshold values depicted in the MAP curve closely approximate the threshold values depicted in the MAF curve, with differences of less than 3 dB SPL for octave and interoctave frequencies from 500 to 2000 Hz when sounds are delivered to the listener by insert phones (Hall, 2014; Silman & Emmer, 2012). Therefore, with the attenuator dial set to 0 dB HL, the audiometer will automatically add and deliver the appropriate (threshold) physical intensity that is required for any audiometric frequency that is selected. The audiometer will also generate and deliver the appropriate frequency related increments in signal intensity as the attenuator dial is increased in 5 to 10 dB steps, up to the upper stimulus output limits of the audiometer, or about 115 dB HL.

The Pure Tone Audiogram

As indicated above, the pure tone audiogram is a graphic, linear summary that is used to depict absolute hearing threshold test results over a range of pure tones that are generated by a pure tone audiometer, and delivered to the listener through a set of transducers. As illustrated in Figure 8–4, audiometric octave and interoctave pure tone frequencies, from 125 to 8000 Hz are depicted horizontally from left to right across the top of the audiogram. Interoctave frequencies are not illustrated. Along the ordinate, stimulus intensity is linearly calibrated in decibels of hearing level (dB HL) and is represented by successive 5 or 10 dB HL increments, beginning at the top of the audiogram. Therefore, hearing level values located nearer to the top of the audiogram indicate lower pure tone thresholds and greater hearing sensitivity. Note that the lowest intensity level is −10 dB HL indicating thresholds that are very low and hearing sensitivity that is elevated. Conversely, elevations in absolute hearing thresholds, and hence, reduced amounts of hearing sensitivity at each of the audiometric pure tone frequencies on the pure tone audiogram may be described as a hearing loss. Hearing loss is then plotted for each ear, from the top of the audiogram to the bottom.

Audiometric Zero

The pure tone audiogram (see Figure 8–4) is distinguished by the fact that what had previously been a curvilinear threshold of audibility for physical intensity (dB SPL) as indicated in Figures 8–1 and 8–2, is now depicted as a straight line (with a zero slope) across each of the audiometric octave and interoctave pure tone frequencies. That is, the curvilinear threshold of audibility is linearly depicted on the pure tone audiogram, as *audiometric zero*. Recall once again that the amount of actual sound pressure (dB SPL) required for average normal absolute threshold responses, as indicated by the MAP and MAF threshold of audibility curves, varies with frequency. Given that absolute thresholds across the range of audiometric frequencies correspond to different sound pressure values, it would be much more convenient to somehow specify the threshold of audibility along a linear, rather than along a curvilinear matrix. For this reason, each of the different, frequency-related sound pressure level values obtained from the original (MAP) threshold of audibility curve is assigned a starting value of 0 dB HL on the pure tone audiogram. As indicated in Chapter 6, all scales of measurement need a starting point, and zero is an excellent place to begin any measurement scale. Therefore, the threshold of audibility across the audiometric frequencies is represented linearly, as audiometric zero. Because the same reference value (0 dB HL) is used at every frequency to represent the average normal hearing sensitivity, otherwise known as the threshold of audibility, deviations in normal hearing sensitivity are easily and conveniently specified at each frequency, as linear deviations from audiometric zero. That is, the amount of hearing loss for a particular listener is typically expressed at

each frequency in terms of how many decibels (dB HL) above 0 dB HL are required in order to reach the listener's absolute hearing thresholds. Summarily then, the threshold of audibility corresponds to audiometric zero which is a strictly linear audiometric reference that refers to an audiometer attenuator dial reading of 0 dB HL across the audiometric test frequencies. Deviations in hearing sensitivity across the range of audiometric frequencies are conveniently expressed in decibel units of hearing level (dB HL) and are easily quantified in reference to audiometric zero. What precisely is the meaning of the term *hearing level*?

Decibels of Hearing Level (dB HL)

From the preceding sections, it should be apparent that when the magnitude of a sound is specified in decibels, such as intensity (dB IL), sound pressure (dB SPL), or hearing (dB HL), it is customary to use the term *level* to refer to the magnitude of the sound. The threshold of audibility for both the MAP and MAF curves was said, in the above sections, to signify equal loudness level judgments made across the audible frequency spectrum, and as indicated above, the threshold of audibility corresponds to audiometric zero (0 dB HL) for each of the audiometric pure tone frequencies. Recall as well that the actual physical intensities required for absolute threshold responses that correspond to audiometric zero naturally vary with each frequency. Although each audiometric threshold at 0 dB HL corresponds to a different amount of actual sound pressure, each is nevertheless equally or just barely audible. Therefore, all of the physical intensities that correspond to the threshold of audibility (and audiometric zero) for each of the audiometric frequencies are equated with respect to the psychological perception of loudness that they generate. All are equated not only with respect to their loudness level, but with respect to their actual hearing level. Hence, for the audiometric pure tone frequencies, it may be said that each of the various sound pressure values that correspond to audiometric zero have the same *hearing level* (Gelfand, 2001). The use of the term dB HL may also be specified in terms of *hearing threshold level* (HTL).

It was made apparent in Chapter 6 that whenever decibel measurements are used, the quantities are meaningless unless the reference level values for each decibel computation are also specified. That is, all decibel measurements require the specification of a reference level value. To be sure, recall that decibel computations in terms of intensity level (dB IL) were performed employing either an MKS or a CGS reference level value for acoustic intensity, expressed in terms of units of power (watts) per area. Decibel computations in terms of sound pressure level (dB SPL) were also performed employing either one of two MKS or CGS reference level values for pressure. These reference level values were expressed either directly in terms of pressure (pascals), or as pressure defined in terms of units of force (newtons or dynes) per area. It should also be apparent that decibels expressed in terms of hearing level (dB HL) also have a starting (reference) level value consisting of a nonabsolute zero. Hence, as with the two previous decibel scales described in Chapter 6, dB HL is yet another example of an

interval scale of measurement. What then is the reference level value for dB HL? As indicated in the sections above, the reference level value for all absolute threshold measures obtained by the use of an audiometer, expressed in terms of dB HL, and recorded on an audiogram is, of course, audiometric zero (0 dB HL).

In the acquisition of audiometric pure tone thresholds, both the audiometer dial and the audiogram are calibrated in decibels of hearing level, hence hearing performance, with respect to absolute thresholds, and hearing sensitivity is always defined in terms of dB HL. The absolute thresholds (the observed quantities) that are acquired at specified audiometric test frequencies in terms of dB HL are evaluated relative to the reference level of 0 dB HL. As in the expression of zero decibels of acoustic intensity level (0 dB IL) and/or zero decibels of sound pressure level (0 dB SPL) discussed in Chapter 6, an absolute threshold of 0 dB HL at any particular frequency or frequencies quite obviously means, "no change from the reference." If a listener happens to show evidence of audiometric pure tone thresholds across a range of frequencies that is 50 dB HL, then the listener's auditory thresholds are, in essence, said to be elevated by 50 dB above the reference (0 dB HL), or above the threshold of audibility for that range of frequencies. In the same way, a listener exhibiting hearing thresholds across a range of audiometric frequencies of −10 dB HL would be said to exhibit hearing sensitivity that was 10 dB greater than the average, or 10 dB greater than the reference value of 0 dB HL for that range of frequencies. It would also mean that the listener's absolute thresholds for that range of frequencies are 10 dB lower than the average normal hearing thresholds.

Decibels of Sensation Level (dB SL)

As indicated above and in Chapter 6, all decibel measurements are computed relative to a reference value that must also be specified. The preceding sections have addressed issues relating to the definition and measurement of threshold, absolute threshold, and the threshold of audibility. However, not all sounds are intended to be presented, measured, or specified at threshold or at absolute threshold levels, given that sounds are often presented at levels above threshold or above the absolute threshold. Those that are, often are said to be presented at suprathreshold levels. When responses are quantified at suprathreshold levels, it is more convenient to use thresholds (as in speech) or absolute thresholds (as in pure tones) as reference level values. Therefore, suprathreshold levels of sound are often specified in terms of decibels of sensation level (dB SL), and the reference level for dB SL is defined by an initial threshold (as in speech) or absolute threshold response at a particular frequency, in a particular ear for an individual listener (Licklider, 1958). For instance, if an absolute threshold obtained at the audiometric pure tone frequency of 2000 Hz in the right ear is 10 dB HL, and the same pure tone is to be presented to the same ear at 40 dB SL, then the 2000 Hz pure tone would need to be delivered to that ear at an audiometric dial reading of 50 dB HL. That is, a 50 dB HL pure tone stimulus is 40 dB SL for an absolute threshold of 10 dB HL. At the same frequency, a 75 dB HL stimulus is also 40 dB SL

for an absolute threshold of 25 dB HL. Likewise, 40 dB HL is 20 dB SL for an absolute threshold of 20 dB HL. It also stands to reason that for any audiometric pure tone frequency, dB SL is equal to dB HL when the absolute threshold at the particular frequency is 0 dB HL. That is, for a given ear and at any audiometric pure tone frequency, 50 dB SL is equal to 50 dB HL when the absolute threshold for a particular frequency in the same ear is 0 dB HL. Likewise, 5 dB SL is 5 dB HL for an absolute threshold of 0 dB HL.

The reference level for dB SL may also be defined by an average of the absolute thresholds at several (usually three) audiometric pure tone frequencies, obtained in the same ear. For instance, if the absolute thresholds at 500, 1000, and 2000 Hz in the left ear were 15 dB HL, 10 dB HL, and 5 dB HL, respectively, then the average of the three absolute thresholds ([15 + 10 + 5]/3) would be equal to 30 dB HL/3 or simply 10 dB HL. An average of the absolute thresholds for a particular ear that is computed in this manner is referred to as a three-frequency *pure tone average* (PTA). Hence, in the above example, the left-ear three-frequency PTA is equal to 10 dB HL. Additional sounds may then be presented to the same ear at specified suprathreshold levels expressed as decibels of sensation level (dB SL), referenced (relative) to the PTA. Finally, the reference level for presentations made in terms of dB SL may also be defined by the "threshold for speech with comprehension," which is often called the "speech reception (recognition) threshold (SRT)." The SRT, like the PTA, is a measure that is obtained in each ear. Additional sounds may then be presented to either ear at specified suprathreshold levels, expressed as dB SL referenced (relative) to the SRT.

Loudness Scaling

From the sections above, recall that the threshold of audibility is also synonymous with threshold judgments that are made with respect to loudness, and loudness refers to that part of an auditory experience that is most often defined as the subjective, psychological correlate of sound intensity. Any behavioral measure of an absolute threshold is based on a response to a subjective experience that is directly dependent upon the perceived loudness of a stimulus. However, the perception of loudness will depend not only on the intensity of the stimulus, but also on the frequency of the stimulus as illustrated in Figures 8–1 and 8–2. Because the absolute threshold represents the least level of intensity (or pressure) that is required to generate the lowest perception of loudness for a stimulus, the threshold of audibility was a logical place to begin scaling procedures related to the subjective experience called loudness.

Historically, the scaling of loudness has been fraught with difficulty. In terms of estimating the relationship between physical intensity and the perception of loudness, problems involving the validation of loudness functions and translating from psychological to physical measurement scales created more predicaments than were warranted by the potential for obtaining unambiguous results (Moore, 2012). A compromise of sorts was therefore reached with the concept of the *loudness level* (Hirsh, 1952). The loudness level as a measure of the relative loudness of sounds was originally developed by Harvey Fletcher and Wilden A. Munson in the 1930s. The perception of loudness is obviously affected by frequency, as indicated by both the MAP and MAF threshold of audibility curves (see Figures 8–1 and 8–2). Conceived in an effort to elucidate the degree of influence that frequency has on the perception of loudness, the concept of the loudness level was developed as a straightforward solution to the inherent difficulties that existed in loudness scaling. As an added note, as research director at the Bell Telephone Laboratories in 1922, Harvey Fletcher (1884–1981) also played a key role in the development of the pure tone audiometer (Boring, 1942).

Rather than attempting to measure the loudness of pure tones in absolute terms, the units of loudness level developed by Fletcher and Munson (1933) specified the physical intensity that was required in the presentation level in order for a comparison pure tone to sound equal in loudness to a 1000-Hz pure tone. A 1000-Hz pure tone was always used as the standard of reference. The *method of adjustment*, yet another classic psychophysical method, was found to be useful in determining at what level two sounds with different frequencies could be equated in terms of their loudness. In general, the listener was asked to vary some physical attribute of a stimulus, such as the intensity of one signal, until a subjective dimension of the stimulus, such as loudness, appeared to be equal to that of a standard reference stimulus. With both the 1000-Hz standard and the comparison tone presented alternately (rather than simultaneously), the listener was required to manually adjust the intensity level (and therefore the loudness) of the comparison pure tone until it matched the loudness of the 1000-Hz standard. The 1000-Hz standard was presented during each test trial at a fixed intensity level. Fletcher and Munson (1933) required listeners to make loudness judgments (matches) while situated in a virtual free sound-field (anechoic chamber) and facing the direction of the sound source. Judgments were made between the 1000-Hz standard and about 10 other pure tones, over a range of 62 to 16,000 Hz. Loudness matches were also made across several intensities of the 1000-Hz standard. The range over which the stimulus intensities varied extended from inaudibility to intensity levels that were great enough to elicit unpleasant tactile sensations. Fletcher and Munson referred to these much higher intensities as the *threshold of feeling*. In this way, sets of parallel curvilinear lines (contours) were generated and collectively called *equal-loudness level contours* or *Fletcher-Munson curves*. The equal-loudness level contours presented in Figure 8–5

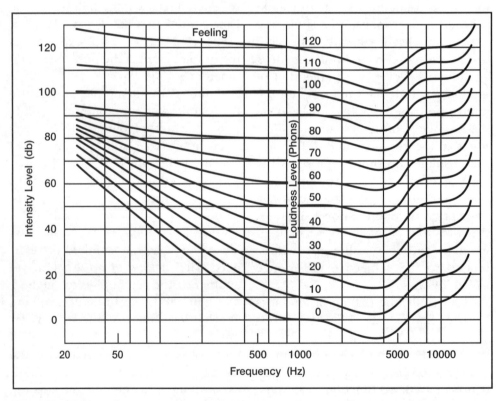

Figure 8–5. Equal-loudness level contours illustrating the relationship between loudness level measured in phons, physical intensity (*along the ordinate*) measured in decibels, and frequency (*along the abscissa*). The contours represent changes in intensity required by the average hearing listener for loudness to remain constant as frequency changes. The threshold of audibility corresponds to the 0-phon contour that extends horizontally across the range of frequencies indicated from left to right along the abscissa. Both the threshold of audibility and the 0-phon line also correspond to audiometric zero (0 dB HL) illustrated in Figure 8–4. From Frederick N. Martin, and John Greer Clark. (2015). *Introduction to audiology* (12th ed.), © 2015. Reprinted and electronically reproduced by permission of Pearson Education, Inc., Upper Saddle River, NJ.

are based on the earlier data of Fletcher and Munson (1933) and on the later work of Robinson and Dadson (1956).

Summarily, the equal-loudness level contours as illustrated in Figure 8–5 represent changes in the physical intensity (shown on the ordinate) that are required by the average normal hearing listener, to maintain a perception of equal loudness as frequency along the abscissa, changes. The audible frequency range as illustrated extends both below and above 1000 Hz. The perceived loudness at each frequency is compared to the perceived loudness of a standard 1000-Hz pure tone. The standard 1000-Hz pure tone depicted in Figure 8–5 is presented at fixed increments of 10 dB. Note that the lower-most equal-loudness level contour (marked by a zero) in the set of Fletcher-Munson curves corresponds to the MAF threshold of audibility curve illustrated in Figure 8–2. The meaning of the zero will be made clear in the sections that follow. The threshold of audibility and each subsequent parallel contour found directly above it reflects the fact that the perception of loudness is frequency dependent. If this were not so, each of the Fletcher-Munson curves, including the threshold of audibility, would not be curves at all, but would be represented linearly from left to right, by the horizontal lines provided in the linear matrix. That is, if physical intensity and the perception of loudness were linearly (and equivalently) related across the audible range of frequencies, the result would be loudness level lines (not contours) that would resemble the audiogram shown in Figure 8–4. The audiogram would therefore be calibrated in dB SPL or dB IL, and not in dB HL. Instead, each loudness level contour corresponds to

a fixed number of loudness level measurement units. The single measurement unit of loudness level is called the *phon*. Loudness level is therefore scaled in units of phons. Each loudness level contour corresponds to the fixed and specified number of phons assigned to it, based on loudness judgments relative to a 1000-Hz reference, independent of frequency or stimulus intensity.

The Phon: Phons of Loudness Level

As defined in the above sections, the equal-loudness level contours depicted in Figure 8–5 illustrate loudness judgments made across a range of comparison pure tone frequencies, and indicate the physical intensity in decibels (on the ordinate) at which each pure tone frequency (on the abscissa) is judged to be as loud as a 1000-Hz standard. The parallel set of equal-loudness level contours shown in Figure 8–5 represents loudness level, ranging from 0 to 120 phons. Hence, each loudness level contour corresponds to a specified number of phons, and pure tones that are judged to have the same loudness level, independent of their individual frequencies and stimulus intensities are assigned the same number of phons.

The set of parallel equal-loudness level contours illustrated in Figure 8–5 is best understood by first noting that the vertical line extending upward from the 1000-Hz reference standard, shown on the abscissa, intersects each successive 10-phon loudness level contour at increments of 10 dB marked by the decibel scale on the ordinate. The vertical line that extends upwardly from the 1000-Hz reference initially intersects the "0-phon" contour, with both the line and contour horizontally intersecting the ordinate scale at 0 dB. Hence, 0-phons of loudness level may be defined as the loudness level of a 1000-Hz pure tone standard presented at 0 dB. 0-phons is also the loudness level of every other pure tone frequency specified along the abscissa that can be shown by a vertical line that extends upward from the abscissa, to intersect the 0-phon contour. That is, every pure tone frequency that falls along the 0-phon line in this manner is equal in loudness level (with 0-phons), independent of the amount of physical intensity required to maintain equal loudness with the 1000-Hz standard. Inspection of the 0-phon contour of Figure 8–5 clearly indicates that maintaining equal loudness across the audible frequency spectrum requires relatively greater amounts of physical sound intensity for very low and very high frequencies. For instance, looking at Figure 8–5, a 50-Hz pure tone needs to be presented at approximately 55 dB in order to be equal in loudness to a 1000-Hz pure tone (standard) presented at 0 dB and at their respective intensities, both pure tones are equal to 0-phons of loudness level. A 100-Hz pure tone must be presented at approximately 24 dB to be equal in loudness to a 1000-Hz pure tone presented at 0 dB, and at their respective intensities, both pure tones are equal to 0-phons of loudness level. Likewise, a 250-Hz pure tone must be presented at approximately 13 dB to be equal in loudness to a 1000-Hz pure tone presented at 0 dB, and at their respective intensities, both pure tones are equal to 0-phons of loudness level. At the other end of the spectrum, a 7000-Hz pure tone must be presented at approximately 5 dB to be equal in loudness to a 1000-Hz pure tone presented at 0 dB, and once again,

at their respective intensities, both pure tones are equal to 0-phons of loudness level. On the 0-phon contour, it also appears that maintaining equal loudness for frequencies located well above 500 Hz, up to about 1500 Hz is achieved at about the same number of decibels as the 1000-Hz standard, whereas relatively less intensity is required in order to maintain equal loudness for frequencies that range from 2000 Hz upward to about 5000 Hz. For example, a 3000-Hz pure tone presented at approximately −5 dB is equal in loudness to a 1000-Hz pure tone presented at 0 dB. Hence, at their respective intensities, both pure tones are equal to 0-phons of loudness level. It should be apparent that the 0-phon contour closely corresponds to the threshold of audibility illustrated in Figures 8–1 and 8–2. Recall once more that under ideal stimulus conditions, the threshold of audibility values for the MAP curve will closely approximate those of the MAF curve (Hall, 2014). Therefore, the threshold of audibility corresponds to equal loudness level judgments made across the audible range of frequencies. The absolute threshold at one frequency is, and should be, as subjectively loud as the absolute threshold at another frequency, independent of the amount of physical intensity required for a normal absolute threshold response. Finally, because the 0-phon contour corresponds closely to the threshold of audibility, it should also correspond to audiometric zero (0 dB HL) illustrated in Figure 8–4.

Looking again at the vertical line extending upward from the 1000-Hz reference standard in Figure 8–5, it should be obvious that the line intersects each consecutive and parallel loudness level contour (from 10-phons to 120-phons) at precise increments of 10 dB on the ordinate. At each intersection, the physical intensity measured in dB IL or dB SPL for the 1000-Hz standard is also equivalent to the number of phons of loudness level. It also follows that the loudness level in phons that is specified for each contour is defined by the loudness level of the 1000-Hz pure tone standard that the contour intersects. Hence, the number of phons for any given 1000-Hz standard, as well as for any given loudness level contour, is arbitrarily equated with the decibel value of the 1000-Hz standard that intersects, and therefore, defines the contour. Simply put, at 1000 Hz, measures of SPL and units of phons are identical. Consequently, 10-phons of loudness level is defined as the subjective loudness of a 1000-Hz pure tone presented at 10 dB, whereas 20-phons of loudness level is defined as the subjective loudness of a 1000-Hz pure tone presented at an intensity of 20 dB, and so on. For any particular pure tone judged to be as loud as a 1000-Hz pure tone presented at x number of dB SPL, the same pure tone will have a loudness level of x number of phons. For instance, if a pure tone of any particular frequency is presented at a specified intensity and is judged to have a loudness level of 40-phons, then the same pure tone at the specified intensity may be said to be as loud as a 1000-Hz pure tone presented at 40 dB. Take as an example from the illustration of Figure 8–5, if a 50-Hz pure tone presented at 75 dB is judged to have a loudness level of 40-phons, then the same 50-Hz pure tone may be said to be as loud as a 1000-Hz pure tone presented at 40 dB. As yet another example, a 10-kHz pure tone presented at 40 dB would be judged as equally loud to a 1000-Hz pure tone presented at 30 dB; therefore, both pure tones have a loudness level of 30-phons. Summarily, the loudness level in phons of any pure tone is equal to the physical intensity (dB IL or dB SPL) of a 1000-Hz pure tone standard to which the pure tone sounds equal to in loudness. A pure tone represented on any single equal-loudness level contour will have the same phons of loudness level as the number of decibels in physical intensity of the 1000-Hz pure tone that intersects the contour. Finally, while the equal-loudness level contours illustrated in Figure 8–5 are depicted in 10-phon increments, from 0 to 120-phons, conceivably an infinite number of loudness level contours would actually exist between the threshold of audibility and the 120-phon contour.

At relatively low sound intensities (<50 dB), the equal-loudness level contours are all similar in shape to the threshold of audibility curve. The shapes of the equal-loudness contours have actually been used in the design of the filtering (weighting) characteristics found in sound level meters (SLMs). Recall from the sections above that the dB-A weighting network that is built into SLMs is similar in shape to the threshold of audibility (0-phon curve). It happens that the shape of the dB-A network is designed intentionally to approximate the shape of the 40-phon loudness level contour. Recall from Chapter 6 that the A-weighting network is the most commonly used SLM network in the assessment of noise levels, particularly in industrial and other high-noise-generating settings. At relatively low intensities, lower frequencies contribute little to the total loudness of complex sounds. Hence, the A-weighting network is designed to significantly de-emphasize most frequencies that fall below 1000 Hz. Recall as well that the A-network has a slight positive bias, or an increased detection sensitivity for some of the mid-frequencies located above 1000 Hz (Gelfand, 2001). At relatively higher stimulus intensities, all frequencies contribute more or less equally to the total loudness of complex sounds, and as illustrated in Figure 8–5, at relatively higher sound intensities, the equal-loudness level contours essentially flatten out across the range of frequencies. Hence, at higher sound intensities, the more linear weighting characteristics of the SLM "C-network" are employed. Alternatively, the SLM B-weighting network is often used at intermediate levels of sound intensity and since it is based on the 70-phon equal-loudness level contour (Moore, 2012).

As indicated above, the shape of each equal-loudness contour is similar to that of the threshold of audibility (0-phon curve) at relatively low stimulus intensities. However, at higher intensities of the stimulus, all of the contours become progressively flatter and linear across the range of frequencies. The flattening is most apparent at the 100-phon (100 dB) contour, as illustrated in Figure 8–5. The flattening of the contours at the higher intensity levels indicates that the dynamic range and the rate in the growth of loudness are both frequency dependent.

For instance, the dynamic range is greatly reduced (compressed) in decibels, from the threshold of audibility (0-phon contour) to the 100-phon contour for the lower frequencies, when compared to the mid- to higher frequencies. The reduced dynamic range

also indicates that with increasing increments of physical intensity, there is a rapid rate in the growth of loudness for the lower frequencies when compared to the loudness growth rates for the mid- to higher frequencies. The rapid growth of loudness for the lower frequencies will also be reflected by the relatively narrower spacing observed between each of the 10-phon equal-loudness level contours (see Figure 8–5) as the contours extend into the lower frequencies. The significance of the frequency-related differences in spacing between equal-loudness level contours will be addressed in the sections that follow.

The phon has been defined as the unit of loudness level that provides a measure by which pure tones, presented across a range of frequencies, can be equated in terms of their loudness, based on a 1000-Hz standard of reference delivered at a fixed intensity. However, with the dimension of frequency held constant, loudness judgments in the form of (vertical) comparisons between equal-loudness contours are also important. These types of loudness comparisons are customarily obtained before and after changes are made in the magnitude of the stimulus. Comparisons made of the relative loudness between same-frequency stimuli as physical intensity is manipulated, will be the focus of the sections that follow.

Differential Threshold

The differential threshold refers to the least, the smallest change, or the smallest difference in a physical dimension or attribute of a stimulus that can be detected between two comparative stimuli. It is an amount, in terms of intensity or frequency, that two comparison stimuli need to differ before a noticeable change, either in their intensity or their frequency, can be detected. The differential threshold, defined as the smallest perceptible difference, either in intensity (loudness) or frequency (pitch) between two comparison stimuli (two sounds), is often called the *difference limen* (DL). As indicated earlier in the chapter, the term *limen* is the German name for threshold, and DLs are equated with, and are therefore equal to, the concept of a *just noticeable difference* (JND) (Boring, 1957). The method of limits, also addressed earlier, is a classic psychophysical procedure that is often used in the determination of differential thresholds. For instance, an investigator will gradually increase or gradually decrease the difference between two stimuli on some physical dimension or attribute. The investor then records the change in the listener's response which has a range of options that can only extend from inaudible to audible, or vice versa (Hirsh, 1952). The task at hand in determining the differential threshold is to locate on the continuum of stimulus increments the point that divides the specified increments or dimensional changes (Δ) into two classifications: those to which the listener responds and those to which the listener does not respond (Stevens, 1958). An accurate determination of the DL will depend as much upon the measurement procedures that are followed by the investigator, as by the criterion that are used to define a greater than chance probability of responding. The DL is usually defined as the stimulus difference that produces consistent responses 75% of the time,

but other criteria, such as 71% or 79% have been used (Moore, 2012). Like the absolute threshold, the DL is a vague point that is obscured by variability and is empirically determined only by the use of adequate sampling procedures. The DL must also be defined as a statistical quantity since no stimulus difference is always just noticeable. That is, a difference may be noticed as often as it is not noticed (Boring, 1942).

Ernst Heinrich Weber: Weber's Law

In 1834, the German psychologist Ernst Heinrich Weber (1795–1878) first described a relationship between judgments made by an observer and variations that existed in the physical magnitude of a stimulus (Boring, 1942). In one set of experiments, Weber presented a reference weight to a subject who was then required to hold the weight in one hand. The subject was presented with another (comparison) weight to hold in the other hand. The comparison weight was either lighter or heaver than the reference weight, and the subject was asked to judge whether the comparison weight was indeed lighter or heavier than the reference weight. If the reference weight was, for instance, 5 grams, a comparison weight of 4 grams was never judged to be heavier than the reference. However, when the comparison weight was 5.1 grams, the subject reported that the comparison weight was heavier than the reference weight, on a significant number of trials. Therefore, the JND or DL was judged to be 0.1 gram. When Weber used a 50-gram weight as a reference, a 51-gram comparison weight was then judged to be heavier than the reference weight on a significant number of trials. In this situation, the JND was judged to be 1.0 gram. Obviously, the physical size of the JND was not the same under either condition. Nevertheless, while both JND values varied absolutely as a function of the different reference weights, both JNDs represented equal percentages of their respective reference values. That is, in either case, the JND represented 2% of the total weight. To be sure, 2% of 5 grams is equal to 0.1 gram, and 2% of 50 grams is equal to 1.0 gram. Hence, according to Weber, a JND could be given by a constant and determinable ratio between two stimuli (Boring, 1942).

In terms of the JND for sound, the symbols ΔI and ΔF are often used to specify the actual physical difference (or change) in intensity or the difference in frequency, respectively, that is needed in order to perceptually detect a difference (in either of these physical dimensions) whenever a listener is presented with two comparison stimuli. In terms of the intensity of sound, the size of ΔI will depend on the magnitude of I, where ΔI is the stimulus increment for the JND and I represents the stimulus from which the increment is measured. Therefore, the *relative DL* takes into account both the JND and the starting value, and hence, the relative DL is the ratio of the DL to the absolute magnitude of the stimulus to which it is related (Hirsh, 1952). The relative DL is equal to $\Delta I/I$ which has been called the *Weber fraction* or the *Weber ratio*. Recall from Chapter 6 that the same ratio was used (see Equation 6–9) in the expression of decibels of intensity level, such that dB IL = 10log ($\Delta I/I$). It was Weber who formulated the law that maintains that the ratio of a JND (or DL) and a reference is defined by a constant.

Weber's law states that a JND in any stimulus dimension is obtained from constant increments in the stimulus when those increments are expressed as ratios of two attributes. The two attributes are the magnitude of change and the absolute magnitude from which the change was made (Hirsh, 1952). Therefore, Weber proposed that JNDs for loudness would grow relatively (as a ratio) in proportion to the preceding (lower) stimulus, starting point, or baseline. Weber's law may be expressed as a ratio ($\Delta I/I$) that is equivalent to a constant (K) in which ΔI, again, is the stimulus increment for the JND and I is the stimulus from which the increment is measured, or simply,

$$\Delta I/I = K \text{ (for a JND)} \qquad (8–1)$$

For wide-band noise and band-pass–filtered noise, the smallest detectable intensity change is approximately a constant fraction of the intensity of the stimulus, and therefore, for these types of sound stimuli, $\Delta I/I$ is generally constant (Moore, 2012). For wide-band noise, the constant has a value that is about 0.5 to 1.0 dB, and this constant is maintained from about 20 dB above threshold (SL) to 100 dB SL (Miller, 1947). Hence, for wide-band noise, Weber's law covers a wide range of intensities. However, for pure tones, the Weber fraction is constant over only a very small range of the stimulus magnitudes. For pure tones presented at extreme magnitudes (either very low intensities and/or very high intensities), the Weber fraction can only be approximated and is therefore not a constant. The Weber fraction is therefore intensity dependent and appears to work best for the middle ranges of intensity

(Viemeister & Bacon, 1988) up to about 100 dB SPL, provided that the duration of each stimulus is greater than 200 ms. This observation has been referred to as a "near miss" to Weber's law (Moore, 2012).

Fechner's Law

Fechner's work was compelled by his intent to define the relationship between stimuli and sensations (as indicated by the responses) using a numerical formula. The foundation of Fechner's law was built upon the work of Weber, who, as indicated above, had observed that in order for an incremental stimulus to appear just noticeably different from a preceding stimulus, the necessary increment needed to be a constant fraction (ratio) of the original stimulus. Fechner integrated Weber's law to derive what he thought was a measure of the proportionality between the perceived magnitude of a sensation (loudness) and the SPL of the stimulus. Fechner not only had to believe in the validity that a JND between two magnitudes of a given stimulus is a constant percentage of the stimulus of lower magnitude (Weber's law) but had to additionally postulate the subjective equality of all JNDs, which he therefore did (Stevens, 1958). Hence, Fechner assumed that all JNDs were subjectively equal, that each DL represented an equal increment in loudness, and that the JND could be used as a basic measurement unit for a sensory scale relating the magnitude of sensations to the physical magnitudes of the same stimuli (Boring, 1957). He believed that sensations could only be measured indirectly and hoped to measure them (indirectly) by adding together equal numbers of differential increments or DLs (JNDs). Fechner therefore proposed that a scale could be formulated by the accumulation or summation of all the measureable JNDs ($\Delta I/I$'s) or DLs, beginning at the absolute threshold (Hirsh, 1952). That is, he proposed that by counting up all the JNDs, starting from the absolute threshold, the points on a scale of sensation could be obtained, which he called S. Fechner summarized his thinking with a formula in which S was taken as the magnitude of sensation in appropriate physical units of the stimulus, such as signal intensity or signal frequency, and I was defined as the physical dimension or attribute of the stimulus. When I is the stimulus intensity, I is measured in terms of the absolute threshold and as the reference measurement (Boring, 1942). That is, I was equal to $(x + a)$, where x is the physical magnitude of the reference stimulus and a is the absolute threshold for the stimulus. Finally, K represents a constant of proportionality that varies with the particular sense modality (Boring, 1957). Therefore, when I refers to the stimulus intensity, the formula, as given by *Fechner's law* (Equation 8–2) states that the perceived intensity (loudness, or S) of any given stimulus is proportional to the logarithm of the magnitude of the physical stimulus. That is, S indicates the value of the sensation that would be produced by a physical stimulus, with intensity x. In sum, according to Fechner's law, the response of human organisms to stimuli will vary as a function of the logarithms of those stimuli (Hirsch, 1952), or

$$S = K \log (I) \qquad (8\text{--}2)$$

where: $I = (x + a)$

According to the formula, loudness grows in proportion to the logarithm of the magnitude of the stimulus. This would suggest, for instance, that the loudness of a 1000-Hz pure tone delivered at 40 dB IL or SPL should be doubled in its loudness by the addition of a second 1000-Hz pure tone delivered at 40 dB. Recall once again from Chapter 6 that there is a gain of 3 dB when either the intensity level (power) or the sound pressure level of a signal is exactly doubled. Hence, the formula predicts that a 43 dB 1000 Hz pure tone should be twice as loud as one that is 40 dB, or in essence, a 3 dB or 3-phon increase is required for loudness to double.

As indicated above, Fechner's formula depended on the validity of Weber's law, upon which it was based. Because Weber's law is imprecise, the psychological scale that Fechner's law defined must also be imprecise. Very few sensory attributes obey the logarithmic principles of Fechner's law (Durrant & Feth, 2013). This is because the JNDs for the loudness judgments of pure tones, as well as subjective judgments of weight, brightness, and taste, are not equal in subjective magnitude (Stevens, 1958). As we will see in the sections that follow, Fechner's law overestimates the growth in loudness for pure tones. A 3-dB or 3-phon increase is an inadequate level of stimulus increment for loudness to double. Nevertheless, linear relationships, albeit those depicted on a semilog plot such as the kind that Fechner endeavored to establish between JNDs and the logarithm of the magnitudes of stimuli, are of great value to hearing science as they are often used to demonstrate that the value of one variable is proportional to some transformation of another variable. Recall that in the Fechner formula (see Equation 8–2) I is equal to $(x + a)$, such that x is the physical magnitude of the reference stimulus while a is the absolute threshold for the stimulus. A slight numerical transformation of I to (x/a), where x becomes the physical magnitude of the observed stimulus and a becomes the absolute threshold for the stimulus and the reference stimulus, now generates a familiar formula. The formula for the decibel presented in Chapter 6, where dB IL or SPL are both equal to the product of a constant value and the logarithm of the ratio of an observed physical quantity divided by a reference quantity, represents a numerical transformation that is identical to the Fechner equation, in that it predicts a direct proportional relationship between the magnitude of hearing sensation and acoustic intensity level (or sound pressure level), in decibels (Durrant & Feth, 2013).

Stanley Smith (S. S.) Stevens: Stevens Power Law

As indicated in the previous section, Fechner believed that sensations could only be measured indirectly. Hence, Fechner's method of adding JNDs was an indirect method of loudness scaling. S. S. Stevens (1906–1973) rejected the assumption that all JNDs are subjectively equal and proposed a more direct method for scaling sensory magnitude (1936). Fechner's formula resulted in interval scale of loudness measurement, and Stevens was determined to develop a ratio scale of loudness measurement. Recall that both the interval and the ratio scale of measurement are addressed in detail in Chapter 2. In Steven's experiments, a listener might be presented with a tone and asked to adjust a second tone until it appeared to be twice as loud as the first. The second tone would then be used as the reference for another (third) tone, also adjusted by the listener until it was judged to be half as intense as the previous second tone. The procedure was repeated several times, and each time the actual physical intensity of the tone was recorded. This more direct approach to loudness scaling is the *fractionation* method, a psychophysical method that was quite different from Fechner's indirect method of adding JNDs (Stevens, 1958). The fractionation method is also similar to the "method of magnitude production" in which the listener is asked to adjust the level of a tone until it has a specified loudness, either in absolute terms or relative to that of a standard, so that is twice as loud, half as loud, four times as loud, and so forth (Moore, 2012).

Based on an average of the results obtained by the fractionation method, a graph that related relative loudness to SPL could be plotted. According to Stevens, loudness is related to intensity exponentially and not logarithmically as Fechner had suggested. This relationship is known as Stevens' power law (Equation 8–3). In short, the power law states that the magnitude of a perception is equal to the product of an exponential (power) function of the magnitude of the stimulus and a constant of proportionality. According to Steven's power for sound, the magnitude of a perception (perceived loudness L) is equal to the product of an exponential (power) function of the magnitude of the stimulus (physical intensity I) and k, which is a scaling factor or constant of proportionality depending on the measurement units that are used.

$$L = kI^{0.3} \qquad (8\text{–}3)$$

The power law of Equation 8–3 states that the loudness (L) of a given sound is proportional to its intensity (I) raised to the (exponential) power of 0.3. The exponent refers to the power or the slope of the loudness function when plotted in log-log coordinates (Durrant & Lovrinic, 1995), such that a slope of 1.0 would indicate a one-to-one relationship between loudness and stimulus magnitude. Rather than being expressed in units of intensity (IL), the power law shown as Equation 8–3 may also be expressed as sound pressure (SPL) by recalling again the relationship between intensity and pressure provided in Chapter 6 by Equation 6–6:

$$I = P^2 \qquad (6\text{–}6)$$
$$P = \sqrt{I}$$

Therefore, expressed in terms of sound pressure, the power law shown as Equation 8–4 states that the loudness of a given sound is proportional to its pressure (P) raised to the power of 0.6.

$$L = k \, (P^2)^{0.3} \qquad (8\text{–}4)$$
$$L = kP^{0.6}$$

A slope in the loudness function of 0.3 for intensity and/or a slope of 0.6 for pressure indicate that the perception of loudness increases at a slower rate than the rate of increase in physical intensity, or pressure. Finally, under ideal environmental testing conditions, listeners are able to detect changes in intensity of a pure tone that are as small as 1 dB, provided that the pure tone is presented at a level that is greater than 20 dB SPL (Hamill & Price, 2014).

The Sone: Sones of Loudness

Stevens (1936) was the first to name the unit of loudness perception (L) the "sone." One sone of loudness is arbitrarily defined as the loudness of a 1000-Hz pure tone, delivered binaurally (from a frontal direction) in a virtual free-field (anechoic chamber) to listeners with average normal hearing sensitivity, at a level of 40 dB SPL, or 40 dB SL referenced to the threshold of audibility curve (0-phons) as illustrated in Figure 8–5. Therefore, one sone of loudness is also equal to 40-phons of loudness level (Stevens & Davis, 1938), and all values found along the 40-phon loudness level contour of Figure 8–5 represent 1 sone of loudness. In order to avoid confusion, it is important at this juncture to maintain the distinction between the use of the term loudness when referring to sones, and loudness level when referring to phons. In this context, it is important to remember that the phon, used as a measure of loudness level, is a unit of measure that is directly related to the physical intensity of a 1000-Hz reference standard.

A simple approximation to the power law is conventionally acknowledged such that for every 10-phon increase at 1000 Hz, there is a doubling of sones of loudness. Recall from the sections above that for a 1000-Hz pure tone, the number of phons of loudness level is also equivalent to the number of decibels. That is, at 1000 Hz, measures of SPL (of IL) and units of phons are identical. According to the power law, there is a doubling of sones of loudness at 1000 Hz for each 10-dB increment in the stimulus indicating a twofold increase in loudness for every 10-fold increase in stimulus intensity, or for every 10-fold increase in phons. Steven's power law suggests that equal ratios of sensation correspond to equal ratios of the physical stimulus. Loudness appears to grow more slowly, doubling with each 10-dB (or 10-phon) increase, rather than with each 3-dB increase as predicted by Fechner's simple logarithmic relationship.

The sone scale continues to be the most widely preferred method for measuring loudness, and the power law provides fairly accurate results for frequencies that cover a range of about 400 to 5000 Hz. Figure 8–6 illustrates the relationship on the average, between loudness, measured in sones and loudness level measured in phons, for a 1000-Hz pure tone presented binaurally in a virtual free-field to listeners with average normal hearing sensitivity. The relationship between phons of loudness level (LL) and sones of loudness (L) is also easily demonstrated (Durrant & Lovrinic, 1995) using Equation 8–5 which may be derived from Equations 8–3 and 8–4:

$$L = 2^{(LL - 40)/10} \qquad (8\text{–}5)$$

For instance, that 40 phons of loudness level are equal to one sone is demonstrated by

$$L = 2^{(40-40)/10}$$

which is equal to 2^0
which is then equal to 1.

That 50 phons of loudness level are equal to two sones, is also demonstrated by

$$L = 2^{(50-40)/10}$$

which is equal to 2^1
which is then equal to 2.

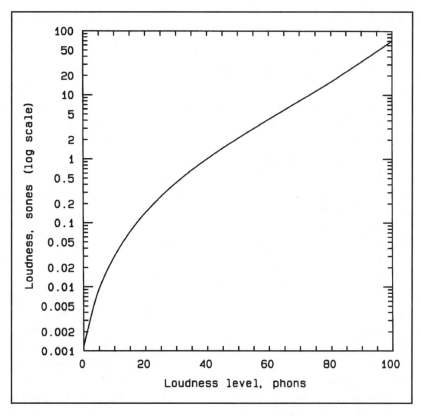

Figure 8–6. The relationship between loudness in "sones" and loudness level in "phons" for a 1000-Hz pure tone presented binaurally in a virtual free-field (anechoic chamber) to listeners with average normal hearing sensitivity. Reproduced from Moore, B. C. J. (2012). *An introduction to the psychology of hearing* (6th ed.) Leiden, the Netherlands: Brill, by permission of the author.

That 60 phons of loudness level are equal to four sones, is additionally demonstrated by

$$L = 2^{(60-40)/10}$$

which is equal to 2^2 which is then equal to 4.

That 70 phons of loudness level are equal to eight sones, is further demonstrated by

$$L = 2^{(70-40)/10}$$

which is equal to 2^3 which is then equal to 8, and so forth.

The rather simple relationship between loudness and stimulus intensity that is provided by the power law is not maintained or approximated for levels of sound that fall below 40 dB SPL, and/or for stimulus intensities that are close to absolute threshold. This relationship is, in point of fact, only valid for levels above 40 phons (or 40 dB SPL) and deviations from the prediction that loudness will double for every 10-phon (or 10-dB) increase, can be dramatic below 40 phons (Durrant & Feth, 2013). At lower stimulus intensities, the magnitude of the sensation of loudness changes more rapidly with each increment in sound level than what is predicted by Steven's law (Moore, 2012). Finally, the power law cannot be applied to complex sound stimuli.

As indicated in the preceding sections, the rate in the growth of loudness for pure tones is frequency dependent. Hence, the relationship between loudness and stimulus intensity that is provided by the power law is also not maintained for lower frequencies, such as those that fall below about 400 Hz. This will become obvious by once again examining the equal-loudness level contours illustrated in Figure 8–5. Consider that for every 10-phon increase across the range of frequencies, there is a doubling of sones of loudness. For frequencies falling at or near 1000 Hz, each 10-phon increase and subsequent doubling of sones of loudness corresponds to an increase in stimulus magnitude of 10 dB, as predicted by Steven's power law. However, each 10-phon increase and subsequent doubling of sones of loudness for frequencies falling (far) below 400 Hz will correspond to only a 5- or 6-dB increment in stimulus intensity. This is indicated by the relatively narrower spacing between each of the 10-phon contours of Figure 8–5 as the contours extend into the lower frequencies. The spacing between each of the loudness level contours at the much lower frequencies no longer corresponds to a spacing difference of 10 dB on the ordinate. This means that sones of loudness for lower frequencies will grow more rapidly and with fewer increments in the intensity of the stimulus when compared to the growth of loudness that occurs for the mid-frequencies.

The Loudness of Complex Signals

Complex sounds, whether periodic or aperiodic, are perceived to be louder than simple pure tones delivered at equal amounts of signal intensity. As several pure tones are added together to create a complex sound, the total energy in the complex sound will be greater than the energy of any one of the single pure tone components, and loudness should also be expected to increase. Since the early investigations of Fletcher and Munson (1937), it has been clear that the growth of loudness in sones for complex sounds is much more rapid, compared to the growth of loudness for pure tones, relative to signal intensity. For example, a broadband noise is likely to be judged twice as loud as a 1000-Hz pure tone delivered at the same intensity level. Speech sounds are always judged to be louder than individual pure tones when delivered at the same intensity level. The loudness of a complex sound depends, in large part, upon the spectral distribution of its component frequencies. When the frequency components of a complex sound are widely separated, the total loudness of the complex sound is equal to the sum of the loudness (in sones) of the separate component frequencies. When each of the component frequencies of a complex sound are similar, or closer in frequency, the total loudness of the complex sound is less than the sum of the loudness of the separate component frequencies, but still greater than the loudness of a single pure tone delivered at the same intensity level. The observation that the loudness of complex sounds is not always the simple summation of loudness from each of the separate components, led Fletcher (1940) to speculate that the peripheral auditory system (inner ear) is composed of a bank of band-pass auditory filters consisting of a series of overlapping pass-bands. When the separate components of a complex sound are close together in frequency, these (inner ear) auditory filters overlap, resulting in a less-than-linear summation of loudness. When the same numbers of components of a complex sound are not close together in frequency, the auditory filters that contribute to loudness do not overlap, resulting in the (greater) linear summation of the loudness of the separate components within the signal. This possibility that auditory filters existed in the inner ear led Fletcher to the concept of the *critical bandwidth*. Critical bands will be discussed later in the sections that follow.

Pitch

The great acoustic event of the seventeenth century was Galileo's discovery of the dependence of pitch upon frequency (Boring, 1942). Pitch may be defined as that subjective dimension or attribute of an auditory perception or experience that is correlated with, but is not equal to, the physical dimension of frequency. Because pitch is the subjective psychological correlate of frequency, as frequency is made to increase or decrease, pitch will also increase or decrease, respectively, in spite of the fact that frequency and pitch are not equal. Pitch is often organized on a subjective scale that extends from pitches

that are perceptually low, and are therefore associated with lower frequency sounds, to pitches that are perceptually high, and are associated with higher frequency sounds. The origin of this low-high dimension is uncertain. Perhaps the use of the words low and high to characterize pitch merely reflect an inherent knowledge of the relationship of the frequencies that give rise to such perceptions. Musical notation places notes on the staves such that higher frequency notes always appear above lower frequency notes. Whatever the reason for describing pitch on a low-high dimension, from the preceding chapters, it is clear that while the physical dimensions of acoustic intensity, sound pressure, and frequency can be measured directly, the perception of pitch, as with the perception of loudness, cannot be measured directly. Notwithstanding, even though pitch is a qualitative subjective dimension, it does have numerical properties, but like loudness and intensity, no simple linear or logarithmic relationship exists between pitch scales and frequency scales.

Signal Duration and Pitch

From the preceding sections, the perception of loudness appears to be optimally experienced for sounds that are at least 200 to 250 milliseconds (ms) in duration. Because pitch and frequency are correlates, the perception of *tonality* implies that a listener is detecting the presence of pitch. However, the sensation of pitch is not followed instantaneously by the immediate onset of a pure tone. A quality of pitch that is stable and recognizable requires some amount of minimal tonal duration. That is, before a pure tone frequency can perceptibly acquire a tonal quality, there is a frequency-related minimum duration of time that is required for the signal to remain on. Regardless of frequency, tonal durations of only a few milliseconds produce the perception of a click. The generation of broadband clicks and tone bursts was presented in some detail in Chapter 6. As the duration of the tone is lengthened from that of a click, a tonal quality begins to emerge. Because lower frequencies have longer wavelengths and longer periods, they should require longer durations before the appropriate numbers of cycles are produced that would enable an appreciation of tonality. Pure tones with frequencies less than 1000 Hz require a duration of at least three to nine periods in length before the tone can take on the quality of pitch (Yost, 2007). The general principle seems to be that below 1000 Hz, the *critical duration* for a stable perception of pitch consists of a fixed number of cycles, on the order of 6 ± 3 (Turnbull, 1944). Lower frequencies such as a 50-Hz pure tone would require at least 60 ms of signal duration, whereas a 500-Hz pure tone would require at least 15 ms of signal duration to reach tonality (Gelfand, 2001). A 1000-Hz pure tone may require at least 10 to 12 ms to reach full tonality, whereas the critical duration for the perception of pitch for frequencies that are above 1000 Hz appears to consist of a fixed length of time, which is about 10 ms regardless of frequency. Longer durations only lead to greater stability in pitch judgments, and full tonality for most pure tone frequencies is reached with durations of about 250 ms or greater.

Differential Thresholds for Pitch

The differential threshold was defined above as the least, the smallest change, or the smallest difference in a physical dimension or attribute of a stimulus that can be detected between two comparative stimuli. In terms of frequency, it is an amount that two comparison stimuli need to differ before a noticeable change in their frequency can be detected, or discriminated. With respect to pitch, an ability to discriminate different pure tone frequencies is directly dependent upon the ability to detect changes in the perceived pitch, as frequency is either changed or manipulated. One of the most common methods of obtaining a measure of frequency discrimination requires the presentation of two successive and continuous pure tones, each slightly different in frequency. The listener is required to judge whether one or the other of the two is higher in pitch. The presentation of the pure tones is randomized from trial to trial. The smallest detectable changes in frequency, or the ability to discriminate the frequencies of two different pure tones based on perceived differences pitch, are referred to as the difference limens for frequency (DLFs). The DLF is usually taken as the lowest separation in frequency, or fewest number of Hz at which the listener is able to achieve a certain percentage of correct responses, such as 75% (Moore, 2012). A second method of obtaining a measure of frequency discrimination uses pure tones that are frequency modulated at a low rate. Recall that frequency modulated (FM) waveform signals were discussed in Chapter 6 and that warble tones were provided as an example of a frequency modulated pure tone. This second method requires the presentation of two successive and continuous pure tones, one modulated and the other unmodulated, and the listener is required to differentiate between the two. The least amount of modulation required for the detection of the modulation, based on fluctuations in pitch, is then determined. This measure of frequency discrimination is called the frequency modulation detection limen (FMDL). A summary of the results of seven investigations employing both methods of frequency discrimination, using pure tone stimuli presented at 40 dB SPL, was provided by one group of investigators (Wier, Jesteadt, & Green, 1977), and later replicated (Sek & Moore, 1995). Their data describing the DLF, specified as a change in frequency (ΔF), were plotted against the frequency standard (F) depicted on the abscissa. When the DLF was plotted logarithmically such that log (DLF) fell on the ordinate, and frequency on the abscissa was transformed to the square root ($\sqrt{F}$) of the standard frequency, the data describing the DLF as a function of frequency resulted in the production of a horizontal, upward sloping linear function. While the theoretical significance of the linearity observed following the data transformation in this investigation remains unclear, what is clear is that the DLF expressed in Hz tends to be smallest for the lower frequencies and increases monotonically with increasing frequency (Sek & Moore, 1995). At 40 dB SPL, the DLF at 500 Hz is about 1 Hz, at 1000 Hz it is about 2 Hz, at 2000 Hz it is about 4 Hz, at 4000 it jumps to about 13 Hz, and at 8000 Hz the DLF may be as great as 60 Hz (Wier et al., 1977). However, even at moderate levels of intensity (60 to 70 dB SPL)

the DLF at 1000 Hz is still only about 2 to 3 Hz. FDMLs vary less as a function of frequency compared to DLFs, when expressed either in Hz, or as a proportion of the center frequency (Sek & Moore, 1995). Finally, DLFs increase significantly at levels that are close to threshold intensities, whereas both DLFs and FMDLs tend to get smaller as the sound level increases (Nelson, Stanton, & Freyman, 1983). That is, DLFs and FMDLs improve at greater intensities of the stimulus (Moore, 2012). The relationship between signal frequency, signal intensity, and DLFs is illustrated in Figure 8–7.

Intensity Level and Pitch

While it is obvious that loudness will increase or decrease as physical intensity increases or decreases, it is also true that loudness may change when frequency is changed, even though physical intensity remains constant. This should be obvious from the equal-loudness contours (see Figure 8–5) that indicated reduced sensitivity and greater thresholds at the lower frequencies. While it is also obvious that the perception of pitch increases or decreases when frequency increases or decreases, perhaps it is not so obvious that pitch can also change when physical intensity is changed, even though frequency remains constant (Hirsh, 1952). While the pitch of a pure tone is primarily affected by its frequency, the physical intensity, or sound pressure level of the pure tone also plays a role in pitch. On the average, the pitch of pure tones with frequencies that fall below 2 kHz will progressively decline with increasing stimulus levels, and the

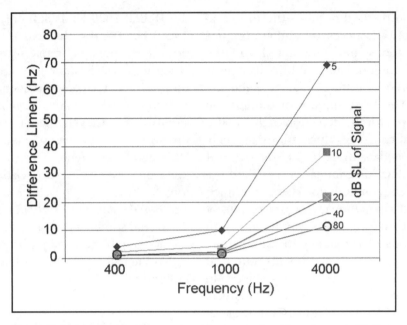

Figure 8–7. Relationship between signal frequency, signal intensity, and difference limens for frequency (DLFs). Data are presented from Wier et al., 1977. From T. A. Hamill and L. L. Price (2014), with permission.

pitch of pure tones with frequencies that fall above 4 kHz will progressively increase with increasing stimulus levels (Moore, 2012).

Historically, the most widely cited observations relating sound level to pitch are those of S. S. Stevens and were based on data obtained from a single listener (Stevens, 1935). Stevens successively presented two pure tones, each with slightly different frequencies, and required his listener to adjust the intensity of one pure tone until its pitch matched the other. Employing 11 standard frequencies, ranging from 150 Hz to 12 kHz, Stevens was able to generate a family of *equal-pitch contours*. In the Steven's investigation, in order to maintain an equal perception of pitch for frequencies falling either below or above 2 kHz, the actual frequency of the matching pure tone had to be altered (adjusted) as a function of increasing stimulus intensities. In general, the mid-frequencies were shown to exhibit relatively stable pitches independent of stimulus intensity. The low and high frequencies exhibited pitches that were shifted downward and upward, respectively, as a function of increasing intensity. That is the higher or the lower in frequency the pure tone, the more dramatic was the change in pitch as a function of increasing intensity. Lower frequency pure tones became lower in pitch as their intensity was increased, and higher frequency pure tones became higher in pitch as their intensity was increased, though this relationship was not linear. Subsequently, the required amount of adjustment in frequency was greatest for the much lower (500 to 150 Hz) and for the much higher (8 to 12 kHz) frequencies, as the effects of intensity on pitch were most pronounced at these extreme frequencies. For instance, in order to maintain a constant perception of pitch across a range of approximately 70 dB SL, the frequency of a 500-Hz pure tone had to be adjusted by as much as 4% in order to offset the changes (lowering) in pitch that resulted with an increase in stimulus intensity. Similarly, a 300-Hz pure tone had to be adjusted by as much as 6% and a 150-Hz pure tone had to be adjusted by as much as 10%. These required adjustments in frequency suggested that pitch decreased at 500, 300, and 150 Hz by as much as 4%, 6%, and 10%, respectively, as a function of increased intensity. Because the pitch of lower frequencies gets lower with increased intensity, in actuality, these adjustments in frequency meant that the original starting frequencies, in cycles per second at 500, 300, and 150 Hz had to be increased by as much as 20, 18, and 15 Hz, respectively, in order to maintain a constant sensation of pitch for those frequencies as a function of increased intensity. At the other end of the frequency spectrum, in order to maintain a constant perception of pitch across a range of approximately 50 to 70 dB SL, the frequency of a 4-kHz pure tone had to be adjusted by as much as 2.5% in order to offset the changes (increases) in pitch that resulted with an increase in stimulus intensity. Similarly, a 5-kHz pure tone had to be adjusted by as much as 8% and an 8-kHz pure tone had to be adjusted by as much as 14%. These required adjustments in frequency also suggested that pitch increased at 4, 5, and 8 kHz by as much as 2.5%, 8%, and 14%, respectively, as a function of increased intensity. Because the pitch

of higher frequencies gets higher with increased intensity, in actuality and as before, these adjustments in frequency meant that the original starting frequencies, in cycles per second at 4, 5, and 8 kHz had to be decreased by as much as 100, 400, and 1120 Hz, respectively, in order maintain a constant sensation of pitch for those frequencies as a function of increased intensity.

These early observations of Stevens (1935), based on data obtained from a single listener, indicated that the effects of stimulus intensity on pitch were rather large. However, much less pronounced effects were observed in subsequent investigations using larger samples of subjects (Gulick, 1971; Verschuure & van Meeteren, 1975). For pure tones that have frequencies that fall between 1 and 2 kHz, increasing levels of stimulus intensity are associated with pitch changes that are less than 1%. For pure tones having higher and lower frequencies, the changes in pitch can be larger, up to 5%, with considerably large individual differences (Moore, 2012).

The Mel: Mels of Pitch Perception

As indicated at the beginning of the chapter, of particular interest in the study of psychoacoustics is the measurement of pitch and the scaling rules that determine the degree to which the subjective dimension of pitch corresponds with the physical correlate of pitch, which is frequency. Unlike loudness, pitch is a qualitative attribute that does not vary along a single and predictable dimension of magnitude (greater to lesser), as does the attribute of loudness. One pitch is not judged as either greater or lesser in magnitude to another pitch, and when frequency is manipulated, one pitch is substituted for another. When assigning a pitch value to a specified sound, it is generally understood that the sound in question will be assigned the same subjective pitch value as the pure tone frequency that corresponds to that pitch. However, because lower frequency pure tones get lower in pitch as their intensity is made to increase, and higher frequency pure tones get higher in pitch as their intensity is made to increase, any conclusions regarding the scaling of pitch must also include a consideration of the intensity of the stimuli. Pitch, therefore, has been rather difficult to scale.

Once again, employing the direct method of fractionation enabled Stevens to establish a psychological scale for pitch. The listener was required to adjust the frequency of a comparison tone until its pitch appeared to be twice or half that of a comparison standard tone whose frequency and intensity were predetermined by an investigator (Stevens, Volkmann, & Newman, 1937). The psychological pitch function that Stevens established in 1937 was later modified (Stevens and Volkman, 1940), and the subjective unit of pitch perception was named the *mel*. The term *mel* was derived from the word "melody" because the melody of a song is composed of sounds with different pitches. Variations in pitch create the perception of melody. Stevens arbitrarily assigned a pitch value to the mel that was equal to one-thousandth the pitch of a 1000-Hz pure tone presented at 40 dB SPL (or 40 dB SL). Hence, and by definition, 1000 mels are assigned a pitch value that is equal to the perceived pitch of a 1000-Hz pure tone presented at 40 dB

SPL, or at 40-phons of loudness level. Recall that a 1000-Hz pure tone presented at 40-phons of loudness level is also equivalent to 1 sone of loudness. Hence, 1000 mels also correspond to a pitch that is equal to a 1000-Hz pure tone presented at 1 sone of loudness.

Accordingly, and by definition, a pure tone judged to have a pitch value that is twice as high as a 1000-Hz pure tone presented at 40-phons of loudness level, will have a pitch of 2000 mels. Similarly, a pitch value that is judged as three times as high as a 1000-Hz pure tone will have a pitch that is 3000 mels. However, as illustrated in Figures 8–8 and 8–9, the frequencies that correspond to a given number of mels of pitch do not themselves bear the same simplistic numerical relationships. A doubling of pitch from 1000 to 2000 mels of pitch corresponds to a frequency of 3 kHz, not to a frequency of 2 kHz. A doubling of frequency from 1000 Hz to 2 kHz yields a pitch value of only 1500 to 1600 mels. Likewise, a tripling of pitch from 1000 to 3000 mels corresponds to a frequency of 10 kHz, and not to a frequency of 3 kHz, which again, has a pitch of only 2000 mels. In addition, and as illustrated in Figures 8–8 and 8–9, a pure tone judged to have a pitch value that is half as high as a 1000-Hz pure tone presented at 40-phons of loudness level will have a pitch of 500 mels. However, 500 mels of pitch will correspond to a frequency of only 400 Hz, and not 500 Hz. A halving of frequency from 1000 to 500 Hz yields a pitch value of about 700 mels. In a similar way, if the pitch value of a 10-kHz pure tone is 3000 mels, halving of the frequency to 5 kHz does not result in a halving of pitch to 1500 mels. The pitch value of a 5-kHz pure tone is 2500 mels, not

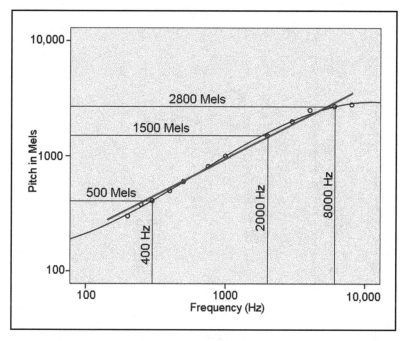

Figure 8–8. The relationship between perceived pitch in mels (*ordinate*) and frequency in Hz (*abscissa*). By definition, 1000 mels of pitch perception are equal to the pitch of a 1000-Hz pure tone presented at 40 dB SPL, or at 40-phons of loudness level. A doubling of frequency results in a less than doubling of pitch in mels, but a doubling of pitch in mels corresponds to a greater than doubling of frequency. A halving of frequency results in a less than halving of pitch in mels, but a halving of pitch in mels corresponds to more than a halving of frequency. From T. A. Hamill and L. L. Price (2014), with permission.

1500 mels. Recall again that in order to obtain a pure tone that is half as high in pitch (1500 to 1600 mels) as a 10-kHz pure tone, the frequency would need to be reduced from 10 to 2 kHz, as illustrated in Figures 8–8 and 8–9. Finally, as illustrated in Figure 8–9, it is important to note that the entire frequency range of hearing, from 20 to 20,000 Hz, composed of approximately 19,800 frequencies, is compressed by the human auditory system into a range composed of only 3500 mels of pitch (Stevens & Volkmann, 1940). The mel scale is still highly used by acoustical engineers and speech scientists. However, the validity of the scale is often questionable in that

pitch judgments are often influenced by the particular order of presentation, the reference standards that are selected (the methods), and the subjects that are selected for use (Moore, 2012).

The Pitch of Complex Signals

For a pure tone, pitch is directly related to the repetition rate of the waveform of the stimulus (cycles per second), and this of course corresponds to the frequency. For a complex periodic signal, pitch will often correspond to the lowest frequency in the waveform, which by definition is the fundamental frequency

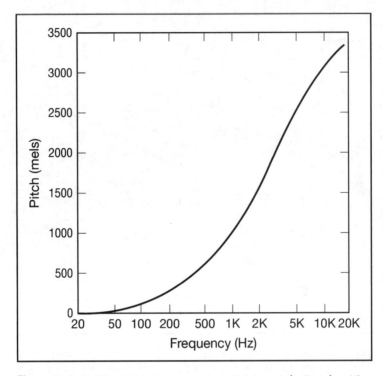

Figure 8–9. Relationship between perceived pitch in mels (ordinate) and frequency in Hz (abscissa) illustrating compression of the range of audible frequencies into just 3500-mels of pitch perception. (Based on the data of Stevens and Volkmann, 1940). From Durrant, John D.; Feth, Lawrence L., *Hearing Sciences: A Foundational Approach*, 1st Edition, © 2013. Adapted by permission of Pearson Education, Inc., Upper Saddle River, NJ.

or first harmonic resonance, as discussed in Chapters 6 and 7. The pitch that is associated directly with the frequency composition of a pure tone or the fundamental frequency of a complex periodic sound is often called the *spectral pitch* of the sound (Yost, 2007). As indicated in Chapter 6, the pitch of a complex signal may also correspond to a fundamental frequency for which no spectral energy is actually present. If the waveform representing the fundamental frequency in a complex sound were to be omitted from the harmonic series, the resulting complex composite periodic waveform would still have the same repetition rate (frequency and

period) as the *missing fundamental*, or in the present case, the *missing fundamental pitch*. Once again as an example, if a composite complex periodic signal were composed of only 1000, 1200, and 1400 Hz, a psychological perception of pitch would be perceived by a listener that would correspond to a frequency of 200 Hz. Clearly, 200 Hz is not contained within the composite spectrum of these three frequencies. It is in fact missing but will be perceived as long as all the remaining frequencies in the complex sound represent harmonics of 200 Hz. Recall that this phenomenon has been called by many names, such as the *residue pitch*, the *periodic-*

ity pitch, the *virtual pitch,* and by yet another name, the *low pitch* (Moore, 2012). A phenomenon related to periodicity pitch is *repetition pitch* which is the perception of pitch that occurs when a sound is pulsed, or gated rapidly and abruptly by switching on, and then rapidly and abruptly switching off an acoustic signal. If a high-frequency tone is interrupted every 10 ms (which is the equivalent period of a 100-Hz pure tone), the listener will often perceive a pitch that corresponds to a 100-Hz pure tone (Thurlow & Small, 1955). However, the mechanisms involved in the perceptual phenomenon of resolving a missing fundamental frequency or resolving the periodicity of a signal, are far from simple. Listeners can also quite easily detect the high pitches of high-frequency (aperiodic) voiceless consonant sounds, and the lower pitch of a broadband noise. The spectral content of the signal and/or the periodicity pitch (temporal structure) alone cannot account for the pitch perception of all types of complex sounds. For example, a complex tone composed of the frequencies 400, 500, 600, 700, 800, and 900 Hz will likely generate a residue pitch that corresponds to a 100-Hz pure tone. Suppose that each frequency component is elevated in frequency by 25 Hz, such that the complex tone consists instead of the frequencies 425, 525, 625, 725, 825, and 925 Hz. Each component is equally spaced by 100-Hz intervals, but 25 Hz and not 100 Hz now represents the fundamental frequency in this series. However, the pitch of the residue would correspond to a 104-Hz pure tone, in spite of the fact that 104 Hz is not the frequency of the missing fundamental, nor is it the frequency of the spacing between the component

pure tones (Yost, 2007). In addition, a missing fundamental frequency in a single complex sound may result in the simultaneous production of several pitch residues that correspond to the lower harmonic frequencies of the harmonic series.

Schouten (1970) proposed that the residue pitch in a complex sound is produced by the upper harmonics of the sound that are not well resolved, separated, or discriminated by the peripheral auditory system. Hence, they interfere with the periodic vibration patterns generated by the lower harmonics, on the basilar membrane (BM) within the inner ear (Chapter 10). The residue pitch is therefore determined by the time pattern of the waveform at the location on the BM where the upper harmonics interfere. A residue pitch may be heard even when there are no individual components that are clearly resolved, as with complex aperiodic sounds. However, even when the fundamental component of a complex tone is present, the overall pitch of the tone is often determined by harmonics other than the fundamental frequency. The residue pitch may instead be perceived through auditory neural channels that normally respond to the high- or middle-frequency components of a complex signal (Moore, 2012). Accordingly, the low or residue pitch is usually close to but not equal to the pitch of the fundamental component and represents the pitch that is normally heard when listening to complex sounds.

It appears that in addition to a dependence upon the spectral content and temporal structure of complex sounds, the pitch of complex sounds often depends upon a number of other parameters. These include parameters such as the number of frequency components in the overall signal, as well as the spread or distribution of the component frequencies and the degree of frequency overlap in the bank of band-pass auditory filters found along the length of the BM, as originally proposed by Fletcher (1940). The ability to determine the pitch of a complex sound is directly dependent upon the frequency selectivity of the auditory system, and frequency selectivity has been defined as the ability of this system of auditory filters to resolve the components of a complex sound. The frequency selectivity within this system of filters also goes hand-in-hand with the auditory system's inherent limitations in its ability to resolve the components of a complex sound (Durrant & Feth, 2013). This point brings us back once again to the concept of auditory signal processing, signal filtering, and to the concept of the *critical band* or the *critical bandwidth*.

The Critical Band

As originally proposed by Fletcher (1940), critical bands are a collection of overlapping band-pass filters located along the length of the basilar membrane (BM) within the inner ear (Licklider, 1958). Each critical band is composed of a center frequency, centrally located in the pass band of an auditory band-pass filter. At each location along the BM there is a corresponding center frequency for each separate band-pass filter and each center frequency also corresponds to the fundamental frequency at that location. Furthermore, each center frequency and band-pass filter will respond similarly to a limited range of frequencies. Therefore, surrounding every frequency, or center frequency of interest along the length of the BM is a critical band or range of frequencies that when stimulated will respond in a manner that is characteristic of the properties of the center frequency. The BM responds to the center frequency and to the range of frequencies as defined by the critical band. Also when stimulated, this critical band of frequencies will respond in a manner that is characteristically different from the frequencies that happen to fall just outside of the critical band. The auditory system processes, interprets and therefore treats each center frequency, and all the frequencies that fall within a critical bandwidth of the center frequency, differently than it treats the frequencies that fall just outside of each critical band. Critical bands should therefore be thought of as a series of pass-bands that overlap on a smooth continuum, such that there is a critical band for each and every conceivable center frequency (Gelfand, 2001). This would of course suggest a nearly infinite number of critical bands. In addition, the bandwidths of the auditory filters are proportional to their center frequencies, such that they grow increasingly broader as their center frequencies increase. As illustrated in panel A of Figure 8–10, only at the frequencies located below approximately 200 Hz are the critical bandwidths nearly constant. At a center frequency of 200 Hz, the critical band is about 100-Hz wide and widens as frequency increases. At a center frequency of 1000 Hz, the critical band is 160-Hz wide. It is 1000-Hz wide at 5000 Hz, and at 16 to 20 kHz, it is the widest (about 3500 Hz). It also

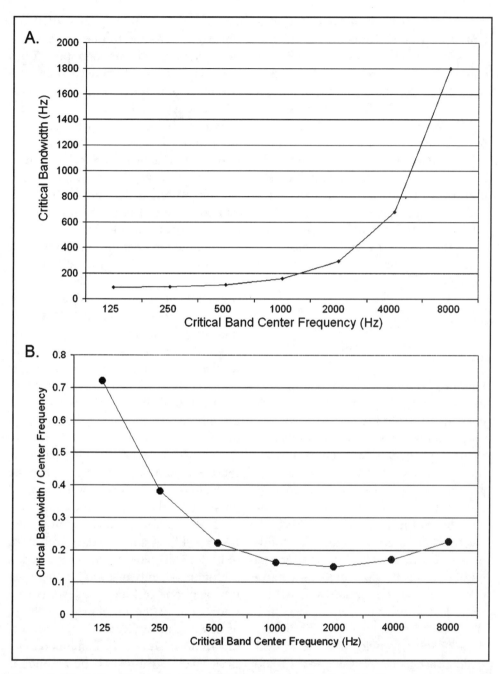

Figure 8–10. A. The critical bandwidth (*ordinate*) increases as a function of the frequency at the center of the band (*abscissa*), or the center frequency. The critical bandwidths of the auditory filters are proportional to their center frequencies, such that they grow increasingly broader as their center frequencies increase. **B.** The ratio of the critical bandwidth and center frequency (*ordinate*) plotted as a function of the center frequency (*abscissa*). From T. A. Hamill and L. L. Price (2014), with permission.

appears that each critical band is equivalent to a constant distance along the BM of approximately 1.2 mm. The apparent equivalence for all center frequencies is maintained except for those frequencies that fall below 200 Hz and for those that fall above 16 kHz, wherein the limiting frequencies are separated by more than 1.2 mm (Gulick, 1971). For each center frequency, the relationship between the critical bandwidth and the center frequency may also be illustrated as a ratio. Panel B of Figure 8–10 also illustrates the ratio of the critical bandwidth and center frequency as a function of the center frequency.

Loudness Summation and the Critical Band

Loudness summation may be taken to mean the addition of sones of loudness. Recall from the previous section that the auditory system interprets and treats each center frequency, and all the frequencies that fall within a critical bandwidth of the center frequency, differently than it treats the frequencies that fall just outside of each critical band. The critical band for loudness refers to the band of frequencies within which the loudness of a band of continuously distributed sound, presented at a constant sound pressure level, will be experienced, independent of the bandwidth of the critical band (Yost, 2007). Hence, for a fixed number of frequency components, the critical bandwidth represents the limits within which loudness is invariant. As an example, take a complex sound, presented at a given stimulus intensity, and composed of just two frequencies that are separated in frequency by only

10 Hz, such as 1000 Hz and 1010 Hz, for instance. As the frequency distance between the two component pure tones is slowly increased from 10 Hz as the two pure tones are moved further apart in frequency, the loudness of the complex tone (in sones) will remain constant until the separation between the two tones reaches a critical distance, separation, or width. Beyond this critical separation, as defined by the limits or boundaries of the critical band, the complex sound will become louder, in spite of the fact that the signal intensity has not changed (Gelfand, 2001).

The example provided above may be best illustrated by supposing that the two pure tones (1000 and 1010 Hz) in this complex signal are each presented at 40 dB SPL (or 40-phons of loudness level each). Because the two pure tones are separated by less than a critical bandwidth, the auditory system will treat them both as if they were the same frequency, only doubled in sound pressure (or intensity). As indicated in Chapter 6, there is a gain of 3 dB when either the intensity level (power) or the sound pressure level of a signal is exactly doubled. Hence, for these two pure tones, there will be a combined, overall IL or SPL of 43 dB. For frequencies that fall within the vicinity of 1000 Hz, the number of phons of loudness level is also equivalent to the number of decibels, as once again indicated in the preceding sections. Hence, the combined loudness level of these two pure tones is 43-phons. Also in the sections above, the relationship between phons of loudness level (LL) and sones of loudness (L) was demonstrated (Durrant & Lovrinic, 1995) using the following equation:

$$L = 2^{(LL - 40)/10} \qquad (8–5)$$

Hence, in this example, the expected number of sones of loudness (L) should be equal to

$$2^{(43-40)/10} \text{ or } 2^{0.3}$$
which is equal to 1.23 sones

Beyond the critical separation, as defined by the limits or boundaries of the critical band, the complex sound composed of the two signals in the present example will become louder. Assuming that the two tones in the present example are still equal in loudness level (40 phons each), the two tones combined will produce a complex tone that will approach twice the loudness of either component alone (Durrant & Lovrinic, 1995). Once again applying Equation 8–5, the two tones will be equivalent to

$$2^{(43-40)/10} + 2^{(43-40)/10} \text{ or}$$
$$2^{(40-40)/10} + 2^{(40-40)/10}$$

which is equivalent to

$$2^{(0)} + 2^{(0)} \text{ or simply}$$
$$1 + 1 \text{ which equals 2 sones}$$

In the present example, a loudness that approaches 2 sones, representing the sum of the individual sones for the two pure tones that fell outside of the same critical band (or within different critical bands), is much greater than the 1.23 sones of loudness that resulted when the two pure tones fell within the same critical band. The same loudness phenomenon also occurs by taking a narrow-band of noise, concentrated around a center frequency, and presented at a constant intensity level. Provided that no additional frequency components are added to the noise,

as the band of noise gets increasingly wider from the center frequency, the loudness of the noise will remain the same until the boundaries of critical bandwidth are reached and exceeded. The noise then becomes increasingly louder as the critical bandwidth is exceeded (Gelfand, 2001). Additionally, as indicated above, complex sounds are always perceived to be louder than simple pure tones delivered at equal amounts of signal intensity. As several pure tones are added together to create a complex sound, the total energy in the sound will be greater than the energy of any one of the single pure tone components, and loudness should also be expected to increase. However, with each additional frequency component that might be added to a complex sound, there will be far less loudness summation as long as each added component falls within the critical band, as defined by a given center frequency. This modest growth in loudness will stand in direct contrast to the loudness summation that would result if the additional frequency components added to a complex signal were to fall outside the specified critical bandwidth.

Such examples serve to demonstrate that when the separate components of a complex sound are close together in frequency, such that the critical bands overlap, there is a less-than-linear summation of loudness. When the same numbers of separate components of a complex sound are not close together in frequency, the auditory filters (critical bands) that contribute to loudness do not overlap, resulting in the (greater) linear summation of the loudness of the separate components within the signal. Complete loudness summation will occur only when the frequency difference between two sounds or between the components within a complex sound, exceed the boundaries of a specified critical bandwidth (Durrant & Lovrinic, 1995). Consequently, with each additional frequency component that might be added to a complex sound, there will be far greater loudness summation if each added component falls outside of the critical band, as defined by a given center frequency. For precisely this reason, only narrow-bands of noise are used during clinical testing procedures involving the masking of pure tones and speech (using speech noise). White noise (wide-band noise), or broadband noise when it is passed through a headphone transducer, is always an unacceptable choice for masking pure tones and speech. This is because wide-band noise produces unnecessary amounts of loudness summation and often, added amounts of annoyance. Wide-band noise is also inefficient as a masking stimulus, since the energy that falls outside of the critical band of the signal that is to be masked (the probe stimulus) provides only negligible masking effects, as addressed in the sections below.

Pitch and the Critical Band

The actual physiological basis for frequency resolution by the auditory system remains an uncertainty. Historically, formulating a comprehensive theory of pitch perception has resulted in a great deal of difficulty. Nevertheless, a cascaded collection, or bank of band-pass filters located along the length of the basilar membrane (BM) consisting of a series of overlapping pass-bands would seem to be the type of mechanism well suited to perform a frequency analysis of the components within a complex sound. The system of overlapping filters or critical bands is likely to be the primary mechanism that defines the frequency and pitch resolving capacity of the auditory system. In contrast to loudness, which appears to be coded by a much less precise and more diffuse arrangement of locations along the BM, pitch appears to be coded by a series of specific, finely spaced BM locations. When a critical band is used in reference to pitch, it is often defined as one "bark." That is, the perception of pitch may be described using the bark scale in which 1 bark is equal to the frequencies that make up one critical band. Across most of the auditory frequency range, a critical band is also equivalent to a constant number of mels of pitch perception, and 1 bark is equivalent to about 100 mels. Furthermore, 1 bark corresponds to about 1 mm along the BM (Moore, 2012). Listeners' responses to complex stimuli will differ, depending upon whether the components of the sound fall within one critical band or are spread over a number of critical bands. In this way, the pitch of a sound may also vary as a result of the bandwidth. As the bandwidth of a noise is narrowed, the noise assumes a more tonal quality and will elicit a stronger perception of pitch. The value of the critical band should not be taken as complete measure of the auditory filter but instead as a rough approximation of its bandwidth. The auditory filter should be thought of as a weighting function that can characterize frequency selectivity according to a particular center frequency. Psychophysically then, the excitation patterns of the BM in the processing of pitch may be defined as the output of each auditory filter that occurs as a function of its center frequency (Moore, 2012).

Masking

Masking is defined as the process by which the threshold of audibility of one sound (the sound to be masked) is raised or increased by the presence of another sound (the masking sound). Masking refers to the temporary loss in sensitivity to one sound most often, but not always, during the simultaneous presentation of another sound (the masker). By this definition, masking occurs concurrently with the presentation of a second stimulus. This distinction helps to differentiate masking from *auditory fatigue*, which is the temporary loss in sensitivity to one stimulus following an exposure to a second stimulus. The term *simultaneous masking* is used to describe the masking that occurs when the masker is present over the full duration of the presentation of the probe stimulus. Simultaneous or concurrent masking occurs whenever a part of the auditory system that normally responds to one stimulus is simultaneously activated by a second stimulus. The amount by which the threshold of audibility of one sound is increased by the simultaneous presence of another sound (the masker) is usually quantified in decibels. The signal that is to be masked is often called the *probe stimulus*, and the *unmasked threshold* is the threshold of the probe stimulus in a condition of quiet, or in the absence of the masker. In a typical masking procedure, the unmasked threshold of the probe stimulus is initially determined. Following this, the

masker is then simultaneously added to the probe stimulus. The masker is very often but not always, a type of noise. The degree of masking that occurs is determined by the amount by which the probe stimulus is elevated or shifted from its unmasked threshold as a result of the simultaneous presence of the masker. In order to determine the amount of threshold elevation or shift, the threshold of the probe stimulus is re-established or retested in the presence of the masker. The observed change in the unmasked threshold of the probe stimulus that occurs in the presence of the masker is often referred to as the *threshold shift*. In general, the greater the intensity of the masker, the greater is the threshold shift. The new and shifted threshold level of the probe stimulus is called the *masked threshold*, and it is the stimulus level at which the probe stimulus is just audible in the presence of the background of the masker. As an example, if the unmasked threshold of a probe stimulus is 10 dB HL and if retesting the threshold of the probe in the presence of a masking stimulus results in a masked threshold of 60 dB HL, then the masker is said to have caused a threshold shift of 50 dB, from 10 to 60 dB. The masker may be said to have provided 50 dB of masking. How well or how effectively (and efficiently) a masker is able to mask a particular probe stimulus will depend upon both the intensity of the masker, as indicated above, and upon the frequency of the masker relative to the frequency of the probe stimulus.

It has been known for a number of years that a signal is most easily masked by sounds that have frequency components that are close to, or the same as, those within the signal that is to be masked. Wegel and Lane (1924) published the first systematic investigation of the masking of one pure tone by another pure tone. This type of masking procedure is often referred to as *tone-on-tone masking*. They measured the magnitude of threshold elevations (dB SL) for a number of probe stimuli with frequencies, ranging from 400 to 4000 Hz. The threshold elevations in the probe stimuli were determined in the presence of a 12-kHz masking tone, presented at either a low intensity level of 44 dB SL or a high-intensity level of 80 dB SL. By plotting threshold elevations, or masked thresholds on the ordinate and frequency on the abscissa, they derived a series of nearly bell-shaped masking patterns. The nearly bell-shaped masking patterns exhibited steep symmetrical slopes on both the low-frequency and high-frequency sides of the curves, but only when the masking stimulus was presented at the low intensity level of 44 dB SL. In general, the amount of masking increased as the intensity of the masking stimulus increased. Although the 44 dB SL masker resulted in symmetrical threshold elevations, these elevations, and therefore the effects of masking, were restricted to the range of probe frequencies that fell between 600 and 2400 Hz. That is, greater masking resulted for pure tones that were closer in frequency to the frequency of the masker, compared to the amount of masking that was provided at more distant frequencies. Their tone-on-tone masking experiments demonstrated that the greatest amount of masking occurs when the masking stimulus and the probe tone are identical or nearly identical in frequency.

In addition, the more intense masking stimulus (80 dB SL) in the Wegel and Lane investigation (1924) gave rise to asymmetrical masking patterns such that the slope of the upper frequency limit was extended indefinitely. That is, at the higher masking level, the masking effect spread into the higher, 4000-Hz frequency range, and did not fall off with increasing frequencies, as compared to the masking effects observed with the lower intensity masker. It has been noted that the results of this early investigation were complicated by the occurrence of *beats*. Beats occurred when the signal and the masker (both tones) were close together in frequency. The phenomenon of beats will be discussed later in this chapter. In an attempt to reduce the occurrence of beats, subsequent investigations employed narrowbands of noise in place of either the signal, or the masker (Greenwood, 1961; Moore, Alcántara, & Dau, 1998). Because narrow-band noise exhibits inherent fluctuations in amplitude that render it difficult to detect beats, noise is generally preferred for use as a masking stimulus (Kluk & Moore, 2004). The data obtained from these ensuing investigations essentially replicated the earlier observations of Wegel and Lane (1924). On the low frequency sides of the bell-shaped masking patterns, steep slopes of between 80 and 240 dB/octave have been observed using pure tone maskers, and slopes of between 55 and 190 dB/octave have been observed using narrow-bands of noise as maskers. On the high-frequency sides of the masking patterns, the slopes were generally less steep and become shallower at the higher masking intensity levels. If the level of a low-frequency masker was increased by 10 dB, the masked threshold of a high-frequency signal was elevated by more than 10 dB, such that the amount of masking grew nonlinearly on the high-frequency side (Moore, 2012). That is, lower frequency signals were found to mask higher frequency signals. However, increasing the level of a low-frequency masker had very little masking effect at frequencies located below the frequency of the masker.

An Upward Spread of Masking

The tendency of lower frequency signals, especially noise, to mask higher frequency signals is called an "upward spread of masking." It is very difficult however, for high-frequency tones and higher frequency noise to mask lower frequency signals. The upward spread of masking phenomenon reflects, and is a direct result of, the base-to-apical directional excitation pattern of the "traveling wave" within the cochlear partition of the inner ear (Chapter 10). For lower frequency sounds in general, and for lower frequency masking stimuli in particular, the envelope of the traveling wave rises gradually on the basal, high-frequency side of its peak, and then falls off abruptly on the apical, lower frequency side of the peak. When the intensity of the low-frequency masker is increased, the excitation pattern becomes larger and the envelope on the lower frequency side of the traveling wave encompasses the excitation patterns of higher frequency signals, resulting in the masking of higher frequencies. The leading side of the traveling wave of a high-frequency masker, however, is unable to encompass the excitation patterns of lower frequency signals because the traveling wave peak always falls off abruptly on its apical side (Gelfand, 2001). Finally, masking

can be said to reflect the limits of frequency selectivity and resolution of the auditory filter. If the selectivity of the auditory system is insufficient to separate the signal from the masker, then masking occurs (Moore, 2012). Consequently, masking has been used as a method to quantify auditory frequency selectivity.

Masking and the Critical Band

It is presently known that surrounding every pure tone is a critical band of frequencies that provides maximum masking "efficiency" with minimum sound pressure. Narrowing the noise band to less than the critical bandwidth will require a greater masking intensity to mask a given level of a pure tone. Adding frequencies outside of the critical band will increase the loudness of the noise masker but will not increase masking effectiveness or efficiency. Only the sound energy from the noise (masker) that then falls within a critical band of the pure tone to be masked (the signal) will provide effective masking. Therefore, masking efficiency is decreased as the bandwidth of the noise is either widened with or widened without the addition of frequency components, as the frequency components begin to fall outside of the critical band of the pure tone, or probe stimulus.

In the now classic investigation of Fletcher (1940), thresholds for detecting pure tones were measured as a function of the changing bandwidth of a noise masker. The term *critical* was used by Fletcher to indicate the bandwidth that was critical for masking. The term critical also refers to a measure of the *effective bandwidth* of the auditory filter for masking (Moore, 2012). The noise in Fletcher's experiments was always centered at the frequency of the pure tone, and the spectrum density (level-per-cycle) of the noise was held constant. Because the spectrum level for each frequency in the noise masker was proportionally reduced, the overall level of the masker was kept at a constant. Fletcher found that the masked threshold for a pure tone kept increasing (shifting) as the bandwidth of the masking noise was made wider, even though the overall intensity level of the noise was held constant. However, once a certain bandwidth was reached, or once the boundary of the critical band for the pure tone's center frequency was reached, additional widening of the noise spectrum did not contribute further to the masking effects. That is, the threshold of the pure tone at that critical boundary was no longer shifted and the masked threshold of the pure tone did not change. Fletcher (1940) first observed that once the bandwidth of the noise exceeded the signal's critical bandwidth, further increments in the bandwidth of the masker did not increase the amount of noise passing through the filter and, therefore, did not contribute to masking. The energy that falls outside of the critical band provides only negligible masking effects. Wide-band noise is therefore a poor choice for masking pure tones because it is both inefficient and unnecessarily loud (Gelfand, 2001). Only a portion of the energy within the wide-band noise masker, that portion that is restricted to frequencies that fall within a critical band of the pure tone's (probe tone's) center frequency, will contribute effectively to masking. This range of frequencies, by definition, is also called

the effective bandwidth (Moore, 2012). *Direct masking* is the term used to describe masking that occurs when the probe stimulus and the masker contain common frequencies such that the frequencies of the masker fall to within one critical bandwidth of the filter's center frequency, as defined by the frequency of the probe stimulus. *Remote masking* is the term used to describe masking that occurs when the probe stimulus and the masker share no frequencies in common, as defined by the critical band of the probe stimulus. It is believed that remote masking occurs when the effective vibrating component (the cochlear partition) of the inner ear system is overdriven by high levels of signal intensity and the masking energy is transferred to its lower frequency regions, by distortion (Durrant & Feth, 2013).

The Equivalent Rectangular Bandwidth (ERB)

If a wide-band noise is to be used as a masking stimulus, it is of interest to know how much of the noise is actually needed to mask a pure tone of a specified frequency. In an attempt to simplify his experimental results, Fletcher (1940) assumed that the shape of the auditory filter within the inner ear could be approximated as a simple rectangle, with a flat peak and vertical (absolute) roll-off rates. Fletcher assumed that the shape of the auditory filter could be approximated by the shape of an ideal filter. Recall from Chapter 6 that with ideal filters, all the frequency components located within the pass-band are passed faithfully, whereas all of the frequencies located outside of the pass-band are eliminated. In fact, the concept of a critical band is often used hypothetically to imply the existence of a rectangular filter. Fletcher, however, was well aware that the auditory filters within the inner ear are not rectangular in shape (Moore, 2012). The auditory filter (critical band) is not rectangular in shape. Instead, it has a rounded peak and sloping roll-off rates, as illustrated by the shaded area shown in Figure 8–11.

The earlier tone-on-tone investigations indicated that not all frequencies within a critical band are of equal importance in terms of their masking efficiency. The equivalent rectangular bandwidth (ERB) of the auditory filter is a measure or estimate of the critical bandwidth, and estimates of the effective bandwidth of the auditory filter are often based on its ERB. By definition, the ERB is the bandwidth of an ideal rectangular filter that would have the same filtering effects and peak transmission as an auditory filter that passes the same total power for a wide-band noise. Furthermore, the average value of the ERB at moderate intensity levels for normal hearing listeners is denoted as the ERB_N, and by definition, the ERB_N is the average value of the equivalent rectangular bandwidth at moderate sound levels for normal hearing listeners (Moore, 2012). Those frequencies closest to the center frequency appear to be more important in terms of masking efficiency. The area within the rectangle that is shown in Figure 8–11 is equivalent to the area of the filter that is shaded. The rectangle that is superimposed on the shaded area of the filter provides a convenient means of describing the outer boundaries of the filter by making it easier to define the

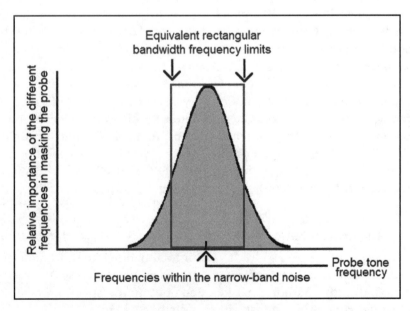

Figure 8–11. The equivalent rectangular bandwidth (ERB) illustrating the relative importance within the critical band of different frequencies within a noise masker, when masking a probe stimulus. The ERB is about 10% to 17% of the center frequency for most frequencies. From T. A. Hamill and L. L. Price (2014), with permission.

effective lower and upper bandwidth frequencies of the critical band (Hamill & Price, 2014).

The formula that relates the ERB_N to frequency may be found elsewhere (Glasberg & Moore, 1990). In short, ERB_N values for auditory filters are typically computed at between 10 and 17% of the center frequency. For instance, the ERB_N for a center frequency of 1000 Hz is between 130 and 150 Hz. The ERB_N for the center frequency of 1000 Hz has a bandwidth that spans from a low frequency of between 925 and 935 Hz, up to 1065 to 1075 Hz (Hamill & Price, 2014). An increase in frequency from a low of about 925 to 935 Hz, to 1065 to 1075 Hz represents a measurement step of 1-ERB_N (Moore, 2012). The ERB_N is conceptually similar to the bark scale described above and to the mel scale of pitch, although it differs slightly in its numerical values. The critical band or ERB_N also corresponds to a constant distance along the BM, which in humans is about 0.9 mm independent of the center frequency. Since the auditory filter is not linear, its shape will vary with the intensity level of the noise that is used to measure it. At moderate intensity levels, the auditory filter is generally symmetrical. At high intensity levels, the filter becomes broader or less steep, especially on its low-frequency side (Glasberg & Moore, 2000).

The Critical Ratio

Another measure that reflects the limited effective bandwidth of a noise masker is the *critical ratio*. The critical ratio is an indirect measure of the critical bandwidth, and it is usually defined by and determined with wide-band noise. Recall that wide-band noise exhibits equal amounts of energy per cycle, or equal amounts of energy per frequency. The critical ratio is the value that is used to determine the bandwidth of a wide-band noise that is just effective in masking a probe stimulus (Durrant & Feth, 2013). Fletcher (1940) initially used the critical ratio as a method for computing the critical bandwidth, as both the critical ratio and critical bandwidth reflect the same underlying mechanisms involved in frequency resolution by the auditory system. According to Fletcher (1940), at the masked threshold, the power of the signal is equal to the power of the noise falling within the critical band that masks it. If the total power within the critical band does not equal the power of the masked signal at threshold, then the critical ratio is not valid (Yost, 2007). The critical ratio is obtained by simply taking the difference in decibels between the masked threshold of the probe stimulus and the level-per-cycle of the (wide-band noise) masking stimulus. Recall from Chapter 6 that the spectrum level or level-per-cycle (LPC) was defined as the average intensity or average noise power in a band of noise (called the unit bandwidth) that is 1 Hz wide (Yost, 2007). The LPC in decibels was computed by taking the total power of the noise (TP) in decibels and subtracting from it, the value that was equal to $10 \times \log$ of ΔF, where ΔF was equal to the overall range or total bandwidth of frequencies contained within the noise. The formula for computing the spectrum level, or LPC was then given by

$$LPC = TP - 10 \times \log \Delta F \qquad (6\text{--}18)$$

For the present, the *LPC* is simply defined as the total power (in decibels) of the noise masker (*TP*), minus 10 × the logarithm of the overall bandwidth (Δ*F*) of the same, noise masker.

Under the assumption that at the masked threshold, there is equal power in both the pure tone that is being masked (dBs), and in the effective (relevant) bandwidth of noise (*LPC*) that is just able to mask it, then at the masked threshold, the power of the signal (dBs) is equal to the power of the noise (*LPC*) inside of the critical band (*CBW*), or according to Fletcher (1940), dBs = *CBW* × *LPC*. Consequently, *CBW* = dBs/*LPC*. That is, the critical band for masking is a critical ratio, and the critical bandwidth can be estimated as a signal-to-noise ratio, represented as

$$dBs /LPC \qquad (8\text{--}6)$$

The critical ratio is then defined as the power in decibels at the masked threshold of the probe stimulus (dBs), minus the *LPC* in dB of the masker, or

$$dBs - LPC \qquad (8\text{--}7)$$

For instance, if the masked threshold of a 1000-Hz probe stimulus is 58 dB when the wide-band masking noise is 40 dB, the critical ratio is 58 − 40 = 18 dB. This corresponds to about 63.1 Hz when converted back to frequency (Hawkins & Stevens, 1950), as illustrated in Figure 8–12. This means that when a wide-band noise is used to mask a 1000-Hz probe stimulus, the only part of the noise that is actually

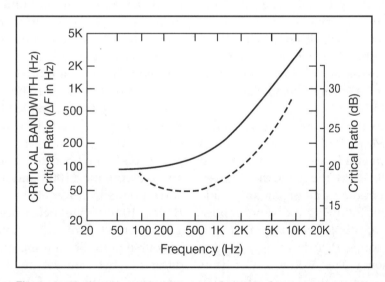

Figure 8–12. Estimates of the critical ratio (*dotted line*) and the critical bandwidth (*solid line*). The critical ratio is plotted as a function of both bandwidth (Δ*F*) on the left ordinate, or decibels on the right ordinate, and the probe stimulus frequency at the center of the band, as shown on the abscissa. The critical bandwidth is also plotted as a function of the probe stimulus frequency at the center of the band. Reproduced with permission from Zwicker, E., Flottrop, G., and Stevens, S. S. (1957). Critical bandwidth in loudness summation. *Journal of the Acoustical Society of America, 29,* 548–557. Copyright 2015, Acoustical Society of America.

effective as a masker is a 63-Hz-wide band of noise surrounding the 1000-Hz center frequency (Gelfand, 2001). As illustrated in Figure 8–12, the critical ratio, as with the critical band, varies with frequency. The critical bandwidth is about 2.5 times larger than the critical ratio, and the critical ratio is about 0.4 times the value of the critical band (Scharf, 1970). While the critical band and critical ratio appear to yield different measurement estimates, the two measures are in fact, in agreement (Durrant & Lovrinic, 1995).

Beats, Flutter, Roughness, and the Critical Band

When two pure tones are presented simultaneously to a listener, and the two tones are similar in frequency such that they fall within a critical band of each other, it is very often the case that the two-tone complex will not be perceived as having a steady, unwavering loudness.

Instead, the loudness of the complex signal will periodically vary, such that it fades in and fades out, or waxes and wanes. *Beats* are the name that is given to the periodic variations in amplitude that result following the superimposition of two simple harmonic quantities, or pure tones, that differ only slightly in frequency. The production of beats is a reflection of the degree of overlap between the excitation patterns along the basilar membrane (BM) occurring within one critical bandwidth, as a result of stimulation by the tonal components within the signal. Beats are also a manifestation of just how imperfect the BM functions as a frequency (spectrum) analyzer (Durrant & Lovrinic, 1995).

First, for any two pure tones (F_1 and F_2) combined to a complex signal, the total frequency of the signal that is created is equal to the mean of the frequencies of the two pure tones, or simply [(F_1 + F_2)/2]. For instance, for a complex signal composed of an F_1 of 1000 and an F_2 of 1002 Hz, the composite signal will have a pitch that corresponds to a frequency of 1001 Hz. As a second example, a complex signal composed of an F_1 of 1000 and an F_2 of 1010 Hz results in a complex signal with a pitch that corresponds to a frequency of 1005 Hz. In both of these examples, the amplitude of either of the complex signals will fluctuate (wax and wane) at a regular and repetitious rate. The rate of this amplitude modulation is equivalent to ($F_2 - F_1$), or simply a rate that equals the positive (or absolute) difference in frequency between the two component pure tones. This then, is the phenomenon known as beats, and the rate of this modulation in amplitude is known as the *beat frequency*. The beat frequency in the first example (1000 and 1002 Hz) corresponds to a frequency of 2 Hz. Hence, two beats will occur per second. The beat frequency in the second example (1000 and 1010 Hz) corresponds to a frequency of 10 Hz. Hence, 10 beats will occur per second. The observed amplitude modulation is of course periodic, and the greater the difference between the two tones, the faster will be the rate of the beats, and the higher will be the beat frequency.

Beats occur due to the slight phase differences in the two, nearly identical-in-frequency components, as the two components combine and interact inside of one critical bandwidth. As discussed in Chapter 6, such amplitude fluctuations in a composite waveform are the direct result of the interactions (constructive and destructive) that occur as the nearly overlapping areas of compression and rarefaction periodically interact at precise moments in time, as both pure tones are propagated. The most pronounced beating sensation for a continuously presented complex sound is usually heard at a rate that is equivalent to 3 to 5 Hz, provided that the amplitudes of the two pure tones are equal (Yost, 2007). As the frequency difference between the two pure tones is increased, beyond about 10 Hz, the smooth fluctuations in amplitude that characterize beats will give way to intermittent or pulsating fluctuations, called *flutter*. As the frequency difference increases to approximately 30 or 40 Hz, flutter will change to *roughness*. The complex signal will sound like a single tone but with an unpleasant (rough) sound quality. At some point the listener is able to perceive the presence of the two pure tones as a complex periodic sound, producing a steady, unwavering perception of loudness. This occurs when the two pure tones are finally separated in frequency by approximately one critical bandwidth (Durrant & Lovrinic, 1995).

The Temporal Aspects of Hearing

Recall from earlier in this chapter that in determining the auditory threshold for a pure tone, all other parameters of the stimulus, such as stimulus duration, stimulus frequency, starting phase, and distance from the sound source must also be held constant. Of interest in the current section is stimulus duration, which is an important factor in determining the threshold for a sound such as a pure tone. As indicated in previous sections of this chapter, the threshold for a sound is not affected by its duration unless the duration is shorter than approximately 300 ms (Gelfand, 2001). As the duration of a pure tone becomes progressively shorter than 200 ms, the signal's intensity must be progressively increased in order to maintain an equality of loudness. Intensity is a measure of energy per unit time. It is the total energy of the sound that determines its threshold (Moore, 2012). Summarily, the perception of loudness at threshold levels appears to be optimally experienced for sounds that are at least 200 to 250 ms in duration, and for durations that are equal to or that roughly exceed approximately 300 to 500 ms, the sound intensity required for a threshold response is independent of signal duration. The loudness of sounds presented at suprathreshold levels also appears to increase with an increase in stimulus duration. At relatively low intensity levels above threshold (30 dB SL), loudness seems to be complete within a duration of 10 ms or less. However, the duration of time required to reach a sensation of full loudness will decrease as the intensity of the stimulus is increased (Durrant & Lovrinic, 1995). Furthermore, as indicated in the above sections, pitch perception that is stable and recognizable will also require a minimum duration of onset time. Recall, this critical duration is longer for frequencies below 1000 Hz, often requiring a fixed number of cycles, or what amounts to durations that are often three to nine periods in length. Additionally, recall that the critical duration is about 10 to 12 ms for a 1000-Hz pure tone, and is about 10 ms for all other frequencies above 1000 Hz, and that the perception of pitch is optimally experienced for sounds that are at least 200 to 250 ms in duration.

Temporal Summation

The dependence of both loudness and pitch upon stimulus duration indicates that the auditory system integrates or summates the power of an auditory stimulus over time. Earlier investigations conducted in the 1940s suggested that insofar as the detection of short duration signals over a reasonable range of stimulus durations is concerned, the auditory system seems to integrate signal energy over time (Garner & Miller, 1947). An experienced listener can observe an improvement in threshold of about 2 or 3 dB for every doubling of the duration of the signal. This equates to about a 10-dB threshold improvement for every 10-fold increase in signal duration, such as when the duration increases from 10 to 100 ms (Durrant & Feth, 2013). The effect of the 10-fold increase in stimulus duration on a measure of threshold can be counteracted by a 10-dB reduction in stimulus intensity. Likewise, the effect of a 10-fold decrease in stimulus duration on a measure of threshold can be counteracted by a 10-dB increase in stimulus intensity. This phenomenon is known as temporal summation or temporal integration and reflects the capacity of the auditory system to integrate energy within a relatively short time frame that is roughly one-third of a second, or within 300 ms. As an example, if a listener's threshold is 15 dB for a pure tone that is 250 ms in duration, reducing the duration of the stimulus by a factor of 10 (to 25 ms),

will result in a threshold that increases by a factor of 10. In this example, it will increase to 25 dB. In the same way, if a listener's threshold is 25 dB for a pure tone that is 25 ms in duration, increasing the duration of the stimulus by a factor of 10 (to 250 ms) will result in a threshold that decreases by a factor of 10. In this example, it will decrease to 15 dB. A similar relationship seems to apply to the perceived loudness of suprathreshold-level sounds. A 25-ms pure tone presented at 40 dB will sound as loud as the same pure tone at 50 dB if the duration is increased by a 10-fold factor, from 25 to 250 ms (Gelfand, 2001).

Temporal Masking

Masking was previously described as a temporary loss in sensitivity to one sound (the probe stimulus) that was most often, but not always caused by the simultaneous presentation of another sound (the masker). In the preceding sections, masking was considered in terms of two sounds presented simultaneously (overlapping in time) into one ear, or monaurally. The term simultaneous (or concurrent) masking was used to describe the masking that occurs when the masker is present (and heard) over the full duration of the presentation of the probe stimulus. However, masking has also been shown to occur if the signal or probe stimulus is presented just after or just before the masker. The probe stimulus used in many of these investigations often consisted of a very brief signal, such as a click (Wilson & Carhart, 1971). Nonsimultaneous masking is the term often used to describe the masking that occurs when the masker and the probe stimulus are not present at the same moment in time, and therefore do not overlap temporally. Hence, nonsimultaneous masking is conveniently called *temporal masking* to refer to the masking effects that occur between a probe stimulus and a masker when the two sounds are not presented simultaneously. The two basic types of temporal masking that are often distinguished are *forward masking* and *backward masking*.

Forward Masking

In forward masking, the onset of the probe stimulus occurs with a tempo-ral delay that follows the offset of the masking stimulus that precedes it. That is, the masking stimulus is presented first and then it is terminated, then the probe stimulus follows, as illustrated in panel A of Figure 8–13. Because the masker temporally precedes the probe, it may be thought of as reaching forward in time following its offset, to mask the probe. Forward masking, like adaptation and fatigue (discussed below), is a conceptually distinct temporal event in which the threshold of a probe stimulus is elevated by a sound (the masker) that temporally precedes it. However, forward masking is distinguished from adaptation and fatigue

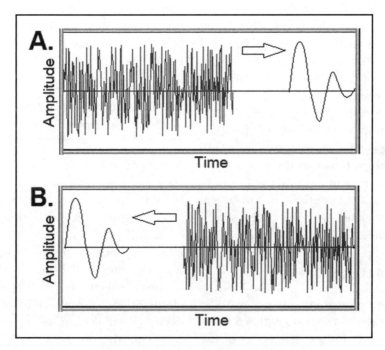

Figure 8–13. A. Components involved in forward masking in which the offset of the noise masker precedes the onset of the click (probe) stimulus over a specified duration of time, which is usually ≤200 ms. The click (probe) stimulus is rendered inaudible when it follows the noise. **B.** Components involved in backward masking in which the offset of the click (probe) stimulus precedes the onset of the noise masker over a specified duration of time, which may be ≤20 or 25 ms. The click (probe) stimulus is rendered inaudible when it is followed by the noise. From T. A. Hamill and L. L. Price (2014), with permission.

principally by the fact it is observed using maskers with brief durations of only a few hundred milliseconds (Moore, 2012). Forward masking is also limited to probe stimuli that are presented up to, but not exceeding durations of about 200 ms following the termination of the masking stimulus. Beyond approximately 200 ms, there is no forward masking, regardless of the intensity level of the masker, and the amount of forward masking is greatest when the duration (or delay) between the offset of the masker and the onset of the probe stimulus is shortened (Moore & Glasberg, 1983). In contrast to simultaneous masking in which there is a fairly constant signal-to-masker ratio, a given increment in the level of the masker is not associated with equal increments in the amount of forward masking. For instance, an increase in the level of the masker of 10 dB may only correspond to an increase in the masked threshold of only 3 dB. Finally, like simultaneous masking, forward masking is affected by the overlapping relationships between the frequencies of the probe stimulus and the frequencies of masker, as defined by the critical band associated with the probe stimulus (Moore, 2012).

Backward Masking

In backward masking, the onset of the masking stimulus occurs with a temporal delay that follows the offset of the probe stimulus that precedes it. That is, the probe stimulus is presented first and then it is terminated, then the masking stimulus follows, as illustrated in panel B of Figure 8–13. Because the masker temporally follows the probe, it may

be thought of as reaching backward in time following its onset, to mask the probe. The phenomenon of backward masking is not only poorly understood, but the amount of backward masking seems to be inversely related to the amount of practice and experience the listeners have received. Experienced listeners often show little evidence of backward masking (Oxenham & Moore, 1994). When backward masking is observed, it is usually limited to masking stimuli that are presented up to, but not exceeding durations of about 20 to 25 ms following the termination of the probe stimulus. However, the sometimes large backward masking effects observed with inexperienced listeners may simply reflect the degree of confusion exhibited by these listeners in differentiating between the signal and the masker (Moore, 2012).

Auditory Adaptation and Auditory Fatigue

A property that is common to sensory systems occurs when a system is exposed to a stimulus, with either a sufficiently prolonged duration and/or a sufficient intensity level. When either or both of these conditions are met, changes will occur in the overall responsiveness of the system. The changes in system's responses can occur either during, or at some time following the presentation of the prolonged and/or intense stimulus. In the auditory system, for instance, some of the changes that can occur during the presentation of a prolonged auditory stimulus would include a reduction in the perceived magnitude of the prolonged stimulus, and/or a total inability to perceive the prolonged stimulus over the duration of its presentation. Other changes that can occur in the auditory system, during the presentation of an intense auditory stimulus, may include shifts (increases) in absolute threshold. Such changes may only become apparent after the termination of the intense stimulus and would not be immediately apparent over the duration of the presentation of the stimulus. Changes in the response of the auditory system, occurring either during or after the presentation of a stimulus, relate to two time-dependent or temporally related auditory phenomena. These two phenomena are referred to as *auditory adaptation* and *auditory fatigue.*

Auditory Adaptation

Adaptation in general is a normal physiological process that occurs in all sensory systems and is best defined as an adjustment of the nervous system to unchanging, relatively low-intensity stimuli, or to an unchanging environment. The response of a sensory system to a steady-state, low-intensity stimulus declines as a function of time until the response reaches a steady value, during which the energy expended by the system is just balanced by the metabolic energy that is available to sustain the system (Moore, 2012). Auditory adaptation occurs when a threshold or near threshold-level stimulus is presented over a prolonged duration of time. During its presentation, there is either a reduction in the perceived magnitude of the stimulus, or the auditory stimulus becomes completely inaudible over the duration of its presentation. Auditory

adaptation occurs only for low-intensity level pure tones, presented at or near threshold, or below about 30 dB SL. The greatest degree of auditory adaptation usually occurs within durations of about 1 or 2 min, and within even shorter durations if the pure tone is high in frequency (Scharf, 1983). Compared to low-to-mid-frequency pure tones, marked adaptation occurs for pure tones having frequencies close to the upper high-frequency limits of hearing. When presented at low-to-moderate intensity levels, such high-frequency signals often become completely inaudible during prolonged exposure (Bacon & Viemeister, 1994). Furthermore, auditory adaptation occurs much more reliably for pure tones that have a constant, sustained amplitude. If a signal is sufficiently amplitude modulated, as when two, similar in frequency pure tones are producing beats, adaptation effects may disappear completely (Scharf, 1983). In addition, adaptation can be reversed by momentarily terminating the sustained stimulus. Intermittent pure tones presented for short durations, such as 200 ms, for instance, to a normal hearing listener will not result in adaptation effects (Bray, Dirks, & Morgan, 1973).

Finally, *threshold adaptation*, or the adaptation associated with threshold levels of a stimulus, occurs when a threshold level stimulus is presented over a prolonged duration of time. Threshold adaptation usually occurs within durations of about 1 min. When an adapted pure tone is increased in intensity by 5 dB SL, the pure tone will return to audibility and will often continue to persist as long as the listener has normal hearing. For listeners with retrocochlear disease, it may be necessary to increase the intensity of an adapted pure tone by 20 or 30 dB SL before an uninterrupted auditory perception can be achieved (Jerger & Jerger, 1975)

Auditory Fatigue

Fatigue in general results from the introduction of a stimulus into a system, such that the stimulus that is introduced is considerably greater than the amount of stimulation that is normally required to sustain a physiological response. In terms of the auditory system, prolonged exposure to sustained, suprathreshold levels of sound that are either painful or obnoxiously loud can deplete the auditory system's capacity for maintaining hearing sensitivity. When such an exposure takes place, it may be said that auditory fatigue has occurred and that the auditory system has essentially been overworked. Auditory fatigue often produces a transient increase in the normal auditory threshold for sound. Hence, auditory fatigue does not and will not occur from the presentation of threshold levels of sound stimuli. Like forward masking, auditory fatigue represents a temporary loss in auditory sensitivity to one stimulus, following an exposure to another stimulus that temporally precedes it. Unlike the effects of masking, however, the effects of fatigue on the auditory system will change over time, sometimes well after the fatiguing sound has been terminated (Hirsh, 1952). Auditory fatigue, together with the accompanying transient changes in auditory thresholds, may additionally be accompanied by a temporary (acute) *tinnitus*. Tinnitus has been defined as a phantom perception of sound (a ringing

or a buzzing) that occurs in the absence of an actual external sound source, and both acute and chronic forms of tinnitus often begin with stressful acoustic overstimulation of the auditory (inner ear) system (Sahley, Hammonds, & Musiek, 2013).

Auditory fatigue is typically measured as a function of the transient negative changes in auditory sensitivity (or temporary increases in absolute threshold) that are observed after the fatiguing stimulus has been terminated. Auditory fatigue is therefore reflected by the difference in decibels between the thresholds of audibility that are obtained immediately following an exposure to a fatiguing acoustic signal and the thresholds obtained before such stimulation (Hirsh, 1952). The temporary loss of sensitivity resulting from auditory fatigue is often called a *temporary threshold shift* (TTS), and the TTS is often used as an index of the degree of auditory fatigue. Immediately following an exposure to a prolonged and fatiguing auditory stimulus, the amount of the TTS is usually at a maximum. The amount of fatigue, measured as a function of the TTS, is usually less (in decibels) for an exposure to lower intensity sound levels. The amount of the TTS will increase rapidly when the intensity level of the fatiguing stimulus reaches approximately 90 or 100 dB SPL. Hence, the degree or amount of a TTS generally increases as the intensity of the fatiguing stimulus also increases (Davis, Morgan, Hawkins, Galambos, & Smith, 1950). For exposure levels that are above 90 to 100 dB SPL, the degree of a TTS rises rapidly (Davis et al., 1950; Hirsh & Bilger, 1955) which has been taken to suggest that the auditory fatigue has changed to a condition that is more permanent and pathological. Exposure to levels of sound that are above 110 to 120 dB SPL may produce permanent hearing losses, especially if the exposure is of long duration (Moore, 2012).

At lower exposure intensities, the TTS occurs at thresholds for frequencies that are close to, or that correspond in frequency with those of the fatiguing stimulus. As the intensity of the fatiguing stimulus increases, the frequency range over which the exposure effects occur also increases, or spreads (Hood, 1950). At high exposure intensities, the greatest degree of TTS often occurs for thresholds at frequencies that are higher than the frequency of the fatiguing (exposure) stimulus. The maximum degree of TTS occurs about one-half octave or more above the frequency of the exposure stimulus (Davis et al., 1950). At high-intensity levels, the TTS will grow rapidly when the affected frequency is higher than the frequency of the exposure stimulus (Hirsh & Bilger, 1955). Finally, the effects of auditory fatigue are generally more pronounced for the higher frequencies. Fatigue and the accompanying TTSs, will generally involve reductions in hearing sensitivity for frequencies that fall above 1000 Hz. When the fatiguing stimulus is broadband noise, maximum TTS typically results for pure tone frequencies that fall between 2 and 6 kHz (Hood, 1950). Permanent hearing loss resulting from exposure to intense sounds tends to be greatest across this range of frequencies. In addition, the amount of auditory fatigue, as indexed by the TTS, generally increases (in decibels) with increased exposure duration (Davis et al., 1950;

Hood, 1950). To summarize the effects of duration on the TTS, the degree of fatigue remains small and stable as exposure durations increase from 0.1 to approximately 5 s. As exposure durations are increased to 10 s, up to as long as 1 min, fatigue, as measured in decibels, increases linearly. Above 1 min, as durations increase to as high as 64 min, fatigue increases much more rapidly as a function of duration (Hirsch, 1952).

The word "temporary" in TTS implies that absolute thresholds return to their pre-exposure values following a sufficient lapse of time. Because the auditory system often recovers, fatigue has at times been thought to represent a type of adaptation mechanism in response to potentially damaging sounds. However, recovery from auditory fatigue is never instantaneous (Durrant & Lovrinic, 1995). Because the auditory system often recovers, the degree of TTS also tends to decrease with increasing amounts of recovery time (Hirsh, 1952) though recovery times tend to vary considerably. The amount of recovery time needed will depend upon the parameters of the exposure, such as the duration and the intensity of the fatiguing stimulus, as well as upon the type and frequency of the fatiguing stimulus. The recovery process from a TTS may be quite rapid, or it may take minutes or even hours for thresholds to return to their pre-exposure values. If the amount of the TTS is as great as 40 to 50 dB, following, for instance, an exposure to a very intense sound, recovery time may be longer, requiring up to 16 hr or more (Ward, Glorig, & Sklar, 1958). However, even full recovery of absolute thresholds from a TTS, back to pre-exposure threshold levels does not necessarily indicate that there has been no auditory neural damage. Longer recovery times for the TTS may still indicate the presence of permanent damage. Significant amounts of auditory neural damage have been demonstrated in animals experiencing a TTS, following even a moderate exposure to noise (Kujawa & Liberman, 2009). If a sustained, suprathreshold level of sound is sufficiently intense and sufficiently prolonged in duration, full recovery of absolute thresholds to pre-exposure levels will not occur, and the shift in threshold may be permanent (Davis et al., 1950). The TTS may change to a permanent threshold shift (PTS). A PTS represents a permanent change in auditory thresholds resulting from prolonged or repeated exposure to intense and sufficiently prolonged and intense suprathreshold auditory stimuli, to the extent that a full recovery of absolute thresholds to pre-exposure levels is not possible. Finally, it is important to note that sounds that are intense enough to produce permanent or even temporary changes in auditory thresholds are not found in nature, but are instead a direct result of human technology (Durrant & Feth, 2013).

| Binaural Hearing |

Binaural hearing is the general term used to describe the nature and the effects of listening to sounds using both ears, rather than just one ear (Gelfand, 2001). That is, binaural hearing refers to those situations in which sound is delivered to both ears, compared to *monaural hearing* that refers to situations in which sound is delivered to

only one ear. When two identical stimuli are delivered binaurally through headphones, the term that is used to describe this condition is *diotic listening*. When two stimuli are delivered binaurally through headphones, and both stimuli are distinctly different, the term that is used to describe this condition is *dichotic listening*. In Chapter 7, a monaural listening condition was said to exist when a speaker (in a sound-field) was located at either a 45° incidence, or a 90° incidence, or using the illustration provided in Figure 8–14, at a horizontal azimuth of either 270° (left ear) or 90° (right ear) relative to the (stationary) head of the listening subject. In the sections that follow, a monaural listening condition will refer to situations in which headphones are worn and sounds are delivered to only one ear at a time. Also in Chapter 7, a binaural listening condition was said to exist when a speaker (in a sound-field) was located at a 0° incidence (directly

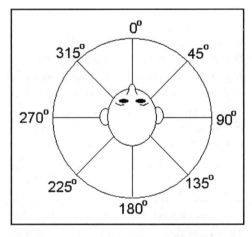

Figure 8–14. Various locations of a sound source for sounds presented in a sound-field. Directions or locations are expressed in degrees of azimuth in a horizontal plane that circles the head to the right. From T. A. Hamill and L. L. Price (2014), with permission.

in front), or at 0° of azimuth (see Figure 8–14), relative to the (stationary) head of the listening subject. In the sections that follow, a binaural listening condition will refer to situations in which headphones are worn and sounds are delivered to both ears simultaneously. A binaural listening condition will also refer to situations in which headphones are not worn, and sounds are delivered in a sound-field from any one of a variety of directions. Sounds may be delivered from any direction to both ears, where direction is expressed in degrees of azimuth in a horizontal plane that circles the head, as shown in Figure 8–14.

Binaural Summation

Recall from Chapter 6 that a gain of 3 dB occurs when either the intensity level (power) or the sound pressure level of a signal is exactly doubled. This is generally called *binaural summation*. What has been referred to as the *binaural advantage* amounts to 3 dB improvement in absolute thresholds when pure tones are delivered binaurally rather than monaurally, through headphones. The 3-dB difference between the absolute thresholds obtained binaurally, as compared to monaurally, does not vary in any systematic way as a function of frequency (Hirsh, 1952). The 3-dB advantage for binaural thresholds also applies when the stimulus is wideband noise (Pollack, 1948). In order for a monaural pure tone to sound as loud as the same binaural pure tone at near threshold levels, it must be elevated in intensity by about 3 dB and a given pure tone stimulus will sound louder when it is delivered binaurally through headphones. Finally, difference limens

(DLs) for both intensity and frequency are also larger, and are therefore poorer, when stimuli are delivered monaurally, compared to when the stimuli are presented binaurally. DLs obtained for monaurally compared to binaurally delivered stimuli are greater by a factor of 1.65 to 1 for intensity and 1.44 to 1 for frequency. (Jesteadt, Wier, & Green, 1977). Therefore, differential sensitivity is enhanced under binaural listening conditions.

Binaural Fusion

Another manifestation of binaural summation is *binaural fusion*. Binaural fusion refers to the phenomenon in which the separate signals from each ear are perceived not as two separate auditory experiences, but as a single, fused auditory image or experience that originates from one apparent source (Durrant & Lovrinic, 1995). Different environmentl sounds can often impinge upon each ear and even sounds that are similar that reach both ears are rarely identical, due to the effects of diffraction and head shadow as addressed in Chapter 7. Under standard listening conditions, a fused auditory image is usually perceived as originating from a source that is located outside of the head. When, however, sounds are delivered through headphones, the fused auditory image is usually perceived as originating from a source that is located inside of the head. Comparative differences that may exist between the two ears, in terms of the sound that reaches each ear either from the environment or when delivered through headphones, will affect the extent to which the sounds are fused into a single auditory image. Between-ear differences that may exist will also affect the apparent location of the fused image (Durrant & Lovrinic, 1995).

Binaural Sound Localization

The ability to localize the sources of environmental sounds has considerable survival value. The ability to localize a sound source greatly aids in determining the locations of objects that should either be sought after and approached, or by contrast, avoided completely. The ability to localize the source of an environmental sound also aids in determining the appropriate direction of visual attention. Sound localization in general refers to judgments that are made in terms of the direction and distance of a sound source (Moore, 2012). The most reliable perceptual cues used in the localization of sounds will depend upon a bilateral comparison of the differences in the signals that reach the two ears, but the perceptual cues that allow for sound localization often vary. Environmental sounds that impinge upon both ears will often arrive sooner in one ear rather than reaching both ears simultaneously. Hence, between-ear or interaural differences in either the time of arrival or the intensity of signals will often exist and such differences can often be used to determine the location of a sound source. The ability to locate the source of a sound will also depend upon the type and the frequency of the sound in question. For simple sinusoidal pure tones, there are two possible perceptual cues that will greatly assist in the location of the source of the sound. The effectiveness with which either of the two per-

ceptual cues actually functions in the localization of environmental sounds will largely be dependent upon the relationship that exists between the width of the human head and the wavelength of the incident waveform. One of the two perceptual cues will depend upon *diffraction* and the between-ear or interaural differences that exist in the time of arrival (ITD) of the signal. For pure tones, the occurrence of an ITD is also equivalent to a difference in phase between the two ears, which is often referred to as an interaural difference in phase (IPD). For low-frequency pure tones, the IPD provides useful and unequivocal information about the location of a sound. For higher frequencies, the IPD is rather ambiguous (Moore, 2012). The second of the two perceptual cues will depend upon *head-shadow effects* and the interaural differences that exist in the intensity of the signal (IID), or, when specified in decibels, the interaural level difference (ILD). Recall from Chapter 7 that diffraction produces little or no head-shadow effects and that the head-shadow effect produces little or no diffraction. In terms of binaural sound localization, differences in interaural intensity (IID) are the more important perceptual cues for localizing higher frequencies, while interaural differences in the time of arrival (ITD) and/or phase (IPD) are the more important perceptual cues for localizing lower frequencies (Stevens & Newman, 1936). This differentiation of perceptual cues in relation to sound localization is called the *duplex theory* of hearing. The duplex theory dates back to Lord Rayleigh (1907) who also firmly established the important role played by phase in sound localization.

The Interaural Difference in the Time of Arrival (ITD)

The interaural difference in the time of arrival, or ITD, as indicated above, is largely dependent upon the waveform diffraction of low-frequency signals by the human head. The diffraction effects associated with low-frequency signals were introduced in Chapter 7. Recall that when an incident wave encounters a finite barrier such as a head, and the barrier has a width that is less than the wavelength of the incident wave front, the sound wave that is transmitted will be diffracted or bent around to the opposite side of the barrier (or head), in all directions. This is illustrated once again in Figure 8–15. Because sounds composed of lower frequency components have longer wavelengths, the lower frequencies are more likely to bend or diffract around the head, by comparison to sounds with higher frequency compo-

nents. Assuming again that the human head is approximately 23 cm in width, ear-to-ear, the frequencies that would or would not be expected to diffract can again be computed using Equation 7–1:

$$\lambda = c/f \qquad (7-1)$$

For an incident pure tone, approaching the head from either the right or the left side only, or from 90° or 270° of azimuth, as illustrated in Figure 8–14, and having a wavelength of about 23 cm/cycle, we can once again solve for frequency (f) using the CGS speed of sound (see Table 6–8) in the following way:

$$23 \text{ cm cycle} = 34{,}400 \text{ cm/s}/f$$

$$f = 1500 \text{ cycles/s}$$

Because low-frequency pure tones have longer wavelengths and lead to diffraction effects, they often arrive later in

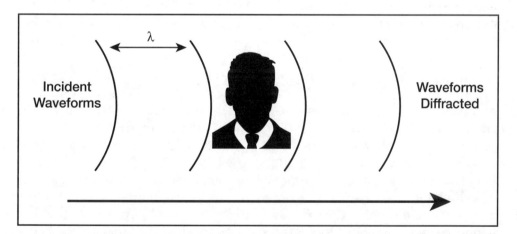

Figure 8–15. Perceptual cues for the localization of low-frequency sounds depend upon interaural differences in the time of arrival of signals (ITDs) and/or interaural differences in phase (IPDs), and both depend on waveform diffraction around the human head. In general, signals having wavelengths (λ) of 23 cm (approximate width of the human head) or greater will result in waveform diffraction on the side of the head facing away (or opposite) from the source of the incident waveform. Hence, frequencies that are below approximately 1500 Hz will be diffracted.

time on the side of the head with the ear that faces away from the incident sound source. Hence, the localization of sounds with frequencies that fall below approximately 1500 Hz should largely depend upon ITDs. Because the average distance from ear-to-ear is 23 cm, and because sound requires about 0.03 ms to travel 1 cm, the ITD will range from 0 ms (for 0° or 180° of azimuth) to a maximum of about 0.67 to 0.69 ms, when delivered at azimuths of either 90° or 270°, using the azimuth locations provided in Figure 8–14 (Moore, 2012). Again, referring to the azimuth locations shown in Figure 8–14, an incident tone presented at an azimuth of 90° will require 0.67 to 0.69 ms to reach the left ear, and an incident tone presented at an azimuth of 270° will require 0.66 to 0.69 ms to reach the right ear. For other azimuths, the time disparities will of course be less. Pure tones presented at azimuths of either 45°, 135°, 225°, or 315° will require less time, or approximately 0.37 ms to reach the opposite ear (Fedderson, Sandel, Teas, & Jeffress, 1957).

The Interaural Difference in Phase (IPD)

As indicated above, the interaural differences in the time of arrival, or the ITDs of a pure tone, will produce interaural differences in phase, or IPDs. The IPD is in fact a manifestation of the time-of-arrival of the signal and is actually a more important cue that ITDs for low-frequency pure tone sound localization (Moore, 2012). This is because time disparities, in general, introduce phase differences in propagated waveforms and a maximum time disparity (ITD) of 0.67 to 0.69 ms will introduce a maximum

amount of phase difference in the ear opposite the sound source. For a given pure tone stimulus, the amount of the difference in phase that reaches the two ears will depend on the horizontal azimuth of the sound (which will determine the amount of the ITD) and the period of the pure tone, which is a direct reflection of the frequency of the pure tone. The IPD can be computed using Equation 8–8 where P is equal to the period in milliseconds of the pure tone, 360 refers to the number of degrees in one cycle, and ITD is equal to the interaural time disparity, also in milliseconds, that will of course be a function of the horizontal azimuth of the incident sound (Fedderson et al., 1957), or

$$IPD = [1/(P \div ITD)] \times 360$$
$$(8–8)$$

For instance, if the ITD is 0.5 ms at the horizontal azimuth of 60° or 300° (see Figure 8–14), then the IPD for a 200-Hz pure tone, with a period of 5 ms, can be computed. Therefore, $[1/(5 \div 0.5)] \times 360$ is equal to an IPD of 36°, which is one-tenth of a cycle of phase difference. If the azimuth changes to 90° or 270°, a new IPD can be computed for the same 200-Hz frequency. For instance, when the ITD is 0.67 ms at a horizontal azimuth of 90° or 270°, then the IPD for the same 200-Hz pure tone is computed by $[1/(5 \div 0.67)] \times 360$, which is equal to an IPD of 48° of phase.

As yet another example, if the ITD is 0.27 ms at a horizontal azimuth of 30° or 330° (see Figure 8–14), then the IPD for a 500-Hz pure tone, with a period of 2 ms, can also be computed. Therefore, $[1/(2 \div 0.27)] \times 360$ is equal to an

IPD of 48.6° of phase. If the azimuth again changes to 90° or 270°, a new IPD can be computed for the same 500-Hz frequency, using once again the ITD of 0.67 ms. Hence, [1/(2 ÷ 0.67)] × 360 is equal to an IPD of 120.6° of phase, which is a fairly large phase disparity. While there is no abrupt upper limit in the frequency at which phase differences are no longer useful between the two ears, ambiguities in the ability to localize low-frequency pure tones, based on the IPD, begin to occur for frequencies of about 725 Hz, or when the period of the pure tone is about twice the maximum possible ITD (Moore, 2012). For example, a 725-Hz pure tone has a period of about 1.38 ms which is almost twice the maximum possible ITD of 0.67 to 0.69 ms. With an azimuth of 90° or 270°, the IPD for a 725-Hz pure tone may be determined by [1/(1.38 ÷ 0.67)] × 360, which is equal to an IPD of 178°, or approximately 180° of phase difference. This means that the same waveform reaches each of the two ears in opposite phase. The location of the sound source becomes ambiguous because the auditory system cannot determine whether the sound reaching either ear is either one-half-cycle ahead (leading) or one-half-cycle behind (lagging) the other ear in phase. Movements of the head or movements of the sound source may help resolve the ambiguity (Moore, 2012). Phase differences and the ability to localize pure tones based on IPD become highly ambiguous for frequencies at, or much above 1500 Hz. Indeed, 0.67 ms is the period of a 1500-Hz pure tone. Once again, if we apply Equation 8–8, then [1/(0.67 ÷ 0.67)] × 360 computes to 360°, indicating that with a maximum time disparity

of 0.67 ms occurring at 90° or 270° of azimuth, there should be no interaural phase difference occurring between the two ears at 1500 Hz.

The Interaural Difference in Intensity (IID)

The interaural difference in signal intensity, or the IID, as indicated above, is largely dependent upon the head-shadow that is cast (by the head) for high-frequency signals. Head-shadow effects associated with high-frequency signals were also introduced in Chapter 7. The head-shadow effect is once again illustrated in Figure 8–16. Recall that high frequencies by comparison to low frequencies have wavelengths that are short relative to the size of the head, and therefore, for these types of sounds a head-shadow is cast on the side of the head with the ear that faces away from the sound source. Because high-frequency pure tones have shorter wavelengths that lead to the production of head-shadow effects, there will be a significant reduction in the intensity level of the waveforms that are perceived on the side of the head for the ear that faces away from the incident sound source, especially when the sound is presented at 90° or 270° of azimuth (see Figure 8–14). Hence, the localization of sounds with frequencies approximately at or above 1500 Hz should largely depend upon IIDs. It is therefore obvious that in most instances ITDs and IIDs (or IPDs) are not equally effective at all frequencies.

While the duplex theory works well for pure tones, it is not as accurate a predictor for complex sounds. However, for complex environmental sounds, a multiplicity of cues will often help to

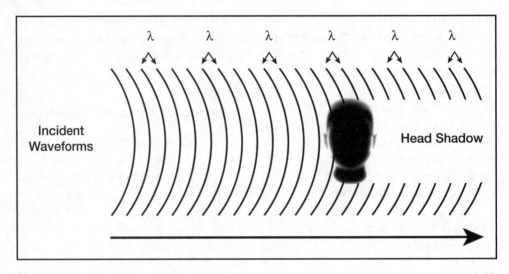

Figure 8–16. Perceptual cues for the localization of high-frequency sounds depend upon interaural differences in the intensity of signals (IIDs) that also depend on the production of head-shadow effects on the opposite side of the head. In general, signals having wavelengths (λ) of less than 23 cm (approximate width of the human head) will result in the production of a head-shadow on the side of the head facing away (or opposite) from the source of the incident waveform. Hence, frequencies that are above approximately 1500 Hz will produce a head-shadow.

improve the accuracy of judging their location. The various frequencies that may exist in a complex sound are often attenuated and/or delayed by varying amounts before the sound reaches the ear. The amount of relative attenuation and/or delay will depend not only upon the interactions between the separate wavelengths within the sound and the size of the head, but also on wavelength interactions that occur with the various parts of both pinnae, the nose, and the torso of the body. Such interactions are likely to produce phase alterations, as well as spectral variations in the overall sound that reaches the two ears.

Environmental sounds normally impinge upon each ear from all directions, not just from locations that are easily defined in the horizontal plane. The directionality of an environmental sound source is uaually described three dimensionally, not just one dimension-

ally as previously shown in Figure 8–14. In addition to a horizontal plane, there is a frontal plane which is located at right angles to the horizontal plane and encircles the head from top to bottom, as well as from side to side. A median plane can be described as well, and is also located at right angles to the horizontal and frontal planes. The median plane encircles the head from top to bottom, as well as front to back. Sound locations in the median plane are equidistant from the two ears and are usually described in degrees of elevation. All sound locations in the median plane have 0° of azimuth and all locations in the horizontal plane have 0° of elevation. A sound with a 0° azimuth and 0° elevation will be located directly in front of the head. A sound with a 180° azimuth and 0° elevation will be located directly behind the head. A sound with a 0° azimuth and 90° of elevation will be located directly above the head. Sound localization errors often occur when attempts are made to determine whether a sound is approaching from in front, behind, from above, or from below the horizontal (Stevens & Newman, 1936). No interaural differences can be said to exist in the horizontal plane when the sound source is directly in front of, or behind the listener, because these locations are approximately equidistant from the two ears. In such circumstances, movements of the head and/or of the sound source may help to remove such ambiguities as median plane localizations that often depend upon spectral variations resulting from the combined effects of the pinna, head, and torso (Moore, 2012).

Listeners are relatively poor at judging the distance of a sound source for very distant sounds. For distant sources of sound, IIDs may be as large as 10 to 20 dB for the 4 to 6 kHz range of frequencies (Fedderson et al., 1957). However, reflected sounds from nearby nonabsorbent surfaces located in the environment that arrive earlier in time may also provide important cues in determining the distance and approximate locations of distant sound sources. The greater the distance a sound source is from a listener, the greater will be the ratio of the intensity level of reflected sounds relative to the intensity levels of the direct or incident sounds that reach the listener. As a listener moves closer to a distant sound source, the intensity level of the reflected sounds become progressively lower relative to the increasingly higher levels of the direct or incident sounds (Hirsh, 1952). When the sound source is very close to the head, however, considerable IIDs may exist even for low frequencies

(Brungart & Rabinowitz, 1999). Hence, IIDs can at times be detected over the whole audible frequency range. In practice, however, IIDs that are sufficiently large enough to provide useful perceptual cues to sound localization usually occur only for higher frequencies (Moore, 2012).

The Precedence Effect

Because of the complex waveform patterns created as sound waves are reflected from nonabsorbant enviromental surfaces, environmental sounds can impinge upon each ear from all directions, often making it difficult to locate the source of an incident sound. In most listening environments, some degree of sound reflection is expected. In other listening environments, relatively greater amounts of reverberation or echo may be experienced. With greater amounts of reverberation there is an even greater potential of impeding sound localization abilities. In spite of such difficulties, however, listeners are still quite able to localize a sound source in reverberant sound-field settings. This is because the incident waves are often the most intense, but more importantly, the incident waves arrive at the ears first, before the reflected waves. The auditory system then processes the information from the incident wave front and suppresses all other information relating to the reflected waveform locations carried by the reflected waveforms that follow. The incident waveform, therefore, dominates in establishing the location of the sound source. Because the incident or first waveform from a sound source arrives at the ears first, it may be said to take precedence over all other incoming waves, in terms of sound localization processing. Hence, this phenomenon is called the *law of the first wave front,* the *Haas effect,* or the *precedence effect* (Blauert, 1997; Moore, 2012).

Monaural Sound Localization

Monaural sound localization or localization that occurs by the use of just one ear is also possible, though the localization that occurs with two ears is several times more precise. Acuity for localizing sounds will always be greatest in the horizontal (azimuth) plane (Moore, 2012). However, monaural intensity differences may at times be useful for monaural sound localization in the horizontal plane. In the absence of bilateral temporal cues, the combined effects of moving the pinna and the head toward and then away from the source of a sound can alter the intensity of the sound reaching the functional ear by virtue of the head-shadow effect. Hence, monaural localization judgments made in the horizontal plane most often rely upon monaural intensity discrimination (Durrant & Lovrinic, 1995). There is also considerable evidence that monaural judgments are quite accurate for localizing sounds in the median plane (Moore, 2012). Recall that sounds presented in the medial plane have 0° of horizontal azimuth. The localization of sounds based upon judgments made in the median plane is often referred to as *vertical localization.* Vertical localization, as well as judgments made for the localization of sounds presented to the front and to the back of the head, appear to depend at least in part, upon the pinnae. In general, it appears that the cavities of the pinnae modify the

spectra of incoming sounds in conjunction with the angle of incidence of the sound wave relative to the head. The incident sound entering the external ear canal not only arrives directly from the sound source but also arrives as one or more reflected sounds from the surface of the pinna, producing a series of sharp spectral peaks and dips (Watkins, 1978). The head and pinna together constitute a complex directional-dependent sound filter (Moore, 2012). Spectral changes produced by the head and pinnae are then used to judge the location of a sound source in the median plane (Blauert, 1997). The shorter wavelengths that characterize frequencies that are above 6 kHz appear to be especially important for monaural vertical localization, as these frequencies appear to produce complex interactions with the small surface features of the pinnae. The median plane vertical localization of noise also seems to be greatest for wide-band noise (Gardner & Gardner, 1973) suggesting that the spectral information provided by the pinnae is usually most effective when the source of the sound contains spectral energy that covers a wide frequency range. In addition, the median plane vertical localization of narrow-bands of noise seems to be greatest for center frequencies of 8 to 10 kHz (Gardner & Gardner, 1973). The median plane vertical localization of either a narrow-band of noise with a center frequency of 8 kHz or even 10 kHz depends on frequency and not on the actual direction of the sound source. Both types of sound will be localized to a point above the head, regardless of their actual position (Blauert, 1970). While the spectral changes produced by the pinnae appear to be limited to frequencies above 6 kHz, modifications of the stimulus spectrum may also occur at much lower frequencies due to the spectral contributions from the head and torso (Moore, 2012).

Binaural Sound Lateralization

Binaural sound lateralization refers to judgments that are made with respect to the location of a sound source, when sounds are delivered through headphones. When sounds are delivered through headphones, the fused auditory image is usually perceived as originating from a source that is located somewhere inside of the head. Unlike localization, in which a sound may be perceived to originate from any direction or distance, most lateralized sounds are perceived as originating from somewhere along an imaginary line that joins the two ears (Moore, 2012). Binaural sound lateralization is the perception generated that a binaurally fused image is originating from one ear or from the other. The same time (phase) and intensity principles that applied to binaural sound localization will also apply to binaural sound lateralization. Indeed, and consistent with the duplex theory, increasing the intensity or advancing the phase or time of arrival of the onset of a tone at one ear relative to the other through headphones will create a perception such that the apparent source of the sound will move toward the ear that received the greater intensity or the earlier time of arrival (Hirsh, 1952). For instance, when a single pure tone having a fixed frequency, time of arrival (or phase) and intensity are delivered diotically through headphones to both ears, the location of the sound source is perceived to be at the center, or in the middle, of the head. If the same pure tone is delivered diotically through headphones to both ears, and the signals differ only by intensity such that the tone delivered to the right ear is slightly greater in intensity than the same tone delivered to the left, the fused auditory image will shift to the right or will appear to have originated from the right ear where the intensity was greater. Hence, the fused auditory image lateralizes to the ear in which the sound is perceived to be louder. If the same pure tone is again delivered diotically through headphones to both ears, and the signals differ only with respect to their time of arrival and/or phase such that the tone delivered to the right ear arrives earlier and/or leads the same tone delivered to the left ear in phase, the fused auditory image will again shift to the right, or will appear to have originated from the right ear, where the signal arrived sooner. Once again, the fused auditory image lateralizes to the ear in which the sound arrives sooner or leads the other in phase. Binaural sound lateralization can therefore be described as a laboratory or controlled version of binaural sound localization (Moore, 2012). In investigations of binaural sound lateralization, thresholds for detecting changes in the ITD under headphones have been observed to be as low as 10 micro-seconds (at 900 Hz), corresponding to a horizontal azimuth of about 1°, or about 3° of phase. Thresholds also tend to increase slightly at lower frequencies. Above 900 Hz, ITD thresholds increase substantially and at frequencies above 1500 Hz, changes in the ITD cannot be detected (Yost, 1974, 2007). Thresholds for detecting changes in the IID (or ILD) under headphones can also be as low as 1 dB across a wide range of frequencies but tend to worsen slightly at frequencies near 1000 Hz (Yost & Dye, 1988). Recall from above that IIDs are also detected when a low-frequency environmental sound source is located very close to the head (Brungart & Rabinowitz, 1999).

Finally, in binaural sound lateralization tasks, there is often a demonstrable *time-intensity trade-off* such that the lateralization of a diotically presented, fused auditory image toward an ear that received the signal sooner in time (or phase-led), may be offset by increasing the intensity of the signal presented to the opposite ear. That is, at times it may be possible to trade an ITD for an IID. For instance, when identical clicks are presented diotically by headphones, the location of the sound source is usually perceived as the center or the middle of the head. If the time of onset of the click is the same as is presented to the left ear but is made to lead the click presented to the right ear by 100 micro-seconds, then the auditory image will shift or lateralize from the center of the head to the left ear. If the click presented to the right ear is then made more intense, the auditory image may again shift or lateralize back toward the right, so that it is once again centered. The amount of the difference in time (ITD) needed to offset a 1-dB difference in intensity level (IIL) at the two ears is often described as the *trading ratio* (Moore, 2012).

Chapter Summary

- Psychoacoustics was defined historically in this chapter as a branch of psychophysics.

- Psychoacoustics addresses the quantified physical values associated with sound and the degree to which those physical values correspond to the scaling rules that are used to measure the psychological experience of sound.

- Threshold was again defined in this chapter as the least amount or level of an environmental stimulus that can be detected, on the average, by an individual or by a group of individuals.

- An auditory threshold was defined in this chapter as the least level of loudness of an auditory stimulus that can be detected, on the average, by an individual or group of individuals.

- An auditory threshold was also defined in this chapter by the least amount of a signal that is required to evoke a response from a listener.

- Absolute (auditory) threshold was defined in this chapter by the methods and the procedures used to obtain an "absolute" response from a listener.

- The threshold of audibility was defined in this chapter as the average normal hearing threshold or set of average, normal, and acceptable auditory limits that generally define the limits of hearing sensitivity.

- The threshold of audibility was also defined in this chapter as the intensity (or sound pressure) levels at which sounds are expected on the average, to become just audible or just loud enough across a select range of pure tone frequencies.

- The threshold of audibility was additionally defined in this chapter as the threshold for loudness, as well as the normal threshold for hearing.

- Loudness was defined as that subjective dimension or attribute of an auditory perception or experience that is correlated with, but not equal to, the physical dimension of intensity.

- The threshold of audibility that is determined monaurally using miniature probe microphones and sounds delivered by insert phones was defined in this chapter as the minimum audibility curve (MAC) for pressure, or simply the minimum audibility pressure (MAP) curve.

- The threshold of audibility that is determined binaurally by the delivery of pure tones through a loudspeaker in a virtual free sound-field (anechoic chamber), was defined in this chapter as the minimum audibility curve (MAC) for the sound-field, or simply the minimum audibility field (MAF) curve.

- In this chapter, it was emphasized that the threshold of audibility is not linearly equivalent across the audible frequency spectrum of 20 Hz to 20 kHz because the human auditory system is not equally sensitive across the same audible frequency spectrum.

- As illustrated in this chapter, the curvilinear threshold of audibility is linearly depicted on the pure tone audiogram, as audiometric zero.

- Decibels of hearing level (dB HL) were defined in this chapter as a method of equating each of the different physical intensities for each audiometric pure tone frequency such that each sound pressure value corresponding to the threshold of audibility (audiometric zero) has the same hearing level and therefore generates the same psychological perception of loudness. Hence, the reference for a particular auditory stimulus that is expressed in terms of dB HL is audiometric zero.

- Decibels of sensation level (dB SL) were defined in this chapter as a method of quantifying or specifying suprathreshold levels of stimuli in relation to a particular threshold (as in speech) or absolute threshold (as in pure tones). The reference for a particular auditory stimulus that is expressed in terms of dB SL is the threshold level of the stimulus.

- The inherent difficulties that existed historically in early attempts at loudness scaling led to the development of the concept of the loudness level, and to the creation of equal-loudness level contours (Fletcher-Munson curves).

- Equal-loudness level contours were conceived in an effort to elucidate the degree of influence that frequency has on the perception of loudness.

- In this chapter, the phon was defined as the single measurement unit of loudness level, providing a measure by which pure tones presented across a range of frequencies can be equated in terms of their loudness, based on a 1000-Hz standard of reference delivered at a fixed intensity.

■ Each loudness level contour corresponds to the fixed and specified number of phons assigned to it, based on loudness judgments relative to a 1000-Hz reference, independent of frequency or stimulus intensity.

■ The 0-phon contour of the equal-loudness level contours corresponds to the threshold of audibility, and also corresponds to audiometric zero (0 dB HL).

■ The reduced dynamic range with increasing increments of physical intensity as illustrated by the equal-loudness level contours is indicative of the rapid rate in the growth of loudness for lower frequencies when compared to the loudness growth rates for the mid to higher frequencies.

■ Differential threshold was defined in this chapter as the least, the smallest change or the smallest difference in a physical dimension or attribute of a stimulus that can be detected between two comparative stimuli.

■ In this chapter, the differential threshold was used synonymously with the terms difference limen (DL) and/or just noticeable difference (JND).

■ In this chapter, Weber's law was presented. It states that a JND in any stimulus dimension is obtained from constant increments in the stimulus when those increments are expressed

as ratios of the two attributes composed of the magnitude of the change and the absolute magnitude from which the change was made.

■ In this chapter, Fechner's law was presented. It states that the perceived intensity of any given stimulus is proportional to the logarithm of the magnitude of the physical stimulus.

■ In this chapter, Steven's power law was presented. It states that the magnitude of a perception is equal to the product of an exponential (power) function of the magnitude of the stimulus and a constant of proportionality.

■ The *sone* was first proposed as a unit of loudness by S. S. Stevens and was arbitrarily defined as the loudness of a 1000-Hz pure tone presented at an intensity of 40 dB, or at a loudness level of 40-phons, from a frontal direction in a virtual free-sound-field (anechoic chamber).

■ Excluding pure tones with intensities below 40 dB SPL (40-phons) and/or pure tone frequencies below 400 Hz, for every 10 dB, and corresponding 10-phon increase in loudness level, there is a doubling of sones of loudness.

■ For low-intensity (near threshold) and/or low-frequency pure tones, the magnitude of the sensation of loudness in sones grows rapidly with fewer increments in stimulus intensity, than predicted by Steven's power law.

■ The perception of loudness with respect to threshold levels is optimally experienced for sounds that are at least 200 to 250 ms in duration.

■ In this chapter, pitch was defined as that subjective dimension or attribute of an auditory perception or experience that is correlated with, but is not equal to, the physical dimension of frequency. As frequency is made to increase or decrease, pitch will also increase or decrease, respectively, in spite of the fact that frequency and pitch are not equal.

■ Pitch perception that is stable and recognizable requires a minimum duration of time for the signal to remain on. This critical duration is longer for frequencies below 1000 Hz requiring a fixed number of cycles. It is about 10 to 12 ms for a 1000-Hz pure tone, and is about 10 ms for all other frequencies above 1000 Hz.

■ Difference limens for frequency (DLFs) that are expressed in Hz, determined at 40 dB SPL and measured as changes in pitch, tend to be smallest for the lower frequencies. DLFs increase monotonically with increasing frequencies above 2000 Hz and also increase significantly at levels that are close to threshold intensities.

■ The perception of pitch is optimally experienced for sounds that are at least 200 to 250 ms in duration.

■ Pitch changes when physical intensity is changed, even though frequency remains constant. The pitch of pure tones with frequencies below 2 kHz progressively decline with increasing stimulus levels, and the pitch of pure tones with frequencies that are above 4 kHz progressively increases with increasing stimulus levels.

■ In this chapter, the mel was defined as a standard unit of pitch equal to one-thousandth the pitch of a 1000-Hz pure tone presented at 40 dB SPL (or 40 dB SL), such that 1000-mels are assigned to the value that is equal to the perceived pitch of a 1000-Hz pure tone presented at 40 dB SPL, or at 40 phons of loudness level.

■ In this chapter, 1000 mels were also defined as the pitch value that corresponded to a 1000-Hz pure tone presented at 1-sone of loudness.

■ In this chapter, it was shown that doubling of frequency results in a less than doubling of pitch in mels, but a doubling of pitch in mels corresponds to a greater than doubling of frequency. Moreover, a halving of frequency results in a less than halving of pitch in mels, but a halving of pitch in mels corresponds to more than a halving of frequency.

■ In this chapter, it was shown that the entire frequency range of hearing, from 20 Hz to 20,000 Hz is compressed, by the human auditory system, into a range of only 3500 mels of pitch.

■ In this chapter, the pitch perception of complex sounds was described in terms of spectral pitch, periodicity pitch, residue pitch, virtual pitch, low pitch, and repetition pitch.

- The low or residue pitch is usually close to, but not exactly equal to the pitch of the fundamental component of a complex signal and probably represents the pitch that is normally heard when listening to complex sounds.

- In this chapter, critical bands were defined as a collection of overlapping band-pass filters located along the length of the basilar membrane (BM) within the inner ear.

- When stimulated, each critical band responds in a manner that is characteristic of the properties of the center frequency. The bandwidth of each critical band is proportional to the value of the center frequency and grows increasingly broader as the frequency value of the center frequency increases.

- In this chapter, the critical band for loudness was defined as the band of frequencies within which the loudness of a band of continuously distributed sound, presented at a constant sound pressure level, will be experienced in a manner that is independent of the bandwidth of the critical band. For a fixed number of frequency components, the critical bandwidth represents the limits within which loudness is invariant.

- The perception of pitch may be described using the bark scale in which 1 bark is equal to the frequencies that make up one critical band or the equivalent of 100 mels of pitch, which corresponds to about 1 mm along the inner ear, basilar membrane.

- Although the mechanisms involved in pitch perception are not fully understood, the processing of pitch may be defined as the output of each auditory filter that occurs as a function of its center frequency.

- Masking was defined in this chapter as the process by which the threshold of audibility of one sound is raised or increased by the presence of another sound. How effectively a masker is able to mask a particular sound will depend upon the intensity and the frequency of the masker.

- When the masking of one sound occurs concurrently with the presentation of a second sound, the greatest amount of masking occurs when the masking stimulus and the probe tone are identical or nearly identical in frequency.

- The upward spread of masking was defined in this chapter as the tendency of lower frequency signals, especially noise, to mask higher frequency signals.

- Only that portion of the energy within a wide-band noise masker that is restricted to within a critical band of the center frequency of a pure tone (probe stimulus) that is to be masked, will contribute effectively to masking.

- Estimates of the effective bandwidth of the auditory filter (the critical band) are often based on its equivalent rectangular bandwidth (ERB), defined in this chapter as the bandwidth of an ideal rectangular filter that would have the same filtering effects and peak transmission as an auditory filter that passes the same total power for a wide-band noise.

- In this chapter, the critical ratio was defined as the value used to determine the bandwidth of a wide-band noise that is just effective in masking a probe stimulus, and is computed by taking the difference in decibels between the masked threshold of a probe stimulus and the level-per-cycle (LPC) of a wide-band noise masker.

- Beats were defined in this chapter as the periodic variations in amplitude (amplitude modulation) that result following the superimposition of two simple harmonic quantities, differing only slightly in frequency. The rate of the modulation in amplitude is known as the beat frequency.

- Beats reflect the degree of overlap between the excitation patterns along the basilar membrane (BM) that occur within one critical bandwidth. An increase in the frequency separation between the two pure tone components will give way to the perception of flutter and then to roughness.

- Loudness and pitch both depend upon stimulus duration, indicating that the auditory system integrates or summates the power of an auditory stimulus over time.

- Nonsimultaneous masking or temporal masking was defined in this chapter as the masking that occurs when a masker and a probe stimulus are not presented at identical moments in time, and hence, do not overlap temporally. The two basic types of temporal masking described in this chapter were forward masking and backward masking.

- With forward masking, the onset of a probe stimulus occurs with a temporal delay that follows the offset of a masking stimulus that precedes it. With backward masking, the onset of the masking stimulus occurs with a temporal delay that follows the offset of a probe stimulus that precedes it.

- Auditory adaptation was defined in this chapter as a normal physiological process that occurs as the auditory system adjusts in response to an unchanging, and relatively low-intensity auditory stimulus. Threshold adaptation was defined in this chapter as the adaptation associated with a threshold level of a stimulus.

- Auditory fatigue was defined in this chapter as a response by the auditory system to prolonged, sustained suprathreshold levels of sound that far exceed the normal amount of stimulation that is normally required to sustain the physiological response of hearing.

- Auditory fatigue (from a fatiguing auditory stimulus) depletes the auditory system's capacity for maintaining hearing sensitivity and often results in a temporary threshold shift (TTS).

- A temporary threshold shift (TTS) was defined in this chapter as the transient negative changes in auditory sensitivity observed following an exposure to a fatiguing stimulus. The TTS is often used as an index of the degree of auditory fatigue. Following a TTS, absolute thresholds eventually return to their pre-exposure values following a sufficient lapse of time.

- A permanent threshold shift (PTS) was defined in this chapter as a permanent change in auditory thresholds resulting from prolonged or repeated exposure to an intense and sufficiently prolonged and intense suprathreshold auditory stimulus, to the extent that a full recovery of absolute thresholds to pre-exposure levels is not possible.

- Binaural hearing was defined in this chapter as the nature and the effects of listening to sounds using both ears, rather than just one ear. Monaural hearing was defined in this chapter as the listening that occurs when sound is delivered to only one ear. Diotic listening was defined in this chapter as listening to two identical sound stimuli that are delivered binaurally through headphones. Dichotic listening was defined in this chapter as listening to two distinctly different sound stimuli that are delivered binaurally through headphones.

- Binaural summation was defined in this chapter as the gain of 3 dB that occurs when either the intensity level (power) or the sound pressure level of a signal is exactly doubled, and when applied to absolute thresholds, is referred to as the binaural advantage.

- Binaural fusion was defined in this chapter as the phenomenon in which the separate signals from each ear are perceived as a single, fused auditory image or experience that originates from one apparent source.

- Sound localization was defined in this chapter as judgments made in terms of the direction and distance of a sound source, and the most reliable perceptual cues used in sound localization will depend upon a bilateral comparison of the differences in the signals that reach the two ears.

- In binaural sound localization, differences in interaural intensity (IID) are the more important perceptual cues for localizing higher frequencies (>1500 Hz), while interaural differences in the time of arrival (ITD) and/ or phase (IPD) are the more important perceptual cues for localizing lower (<1500 Hz) frequencies. This is known as the duplex theory of hearing.

- Monaural sound localization judgemnets made in the horizontal plane will at best rely upon monaural intensity differences provided by movements of the head, whereas monaural cues provided by the pinnae and head are quite accurate for determining the vertical localization of sounds in the median plane.

■ The ability to locate environmental sounds is accurate for judgments made on the horizontal plane (azimuth), is fairly accurate for judgments made on the vertical plane (elevation), and is the poorest for distance.

■ In this chapter, the precedence effect was defined as the auditory phenomenon whereby the processing of the localization of an incident waveform in a reveberrant sound-field takes precedence over the sound localization processing of the reflected waveforms.

■ Binaural sound lateralization was defined in this chapter as judgments made with respect to the location of a sound source when sounds are delivered through headphones. Consistent with the duplex theory, the same time (phase) and intensity principles that apply to binaural sound localization also apply to binaural sound lateralization.

Chapter 8 Questions

1. The threshold of audibility as indicated by the MAF curve should approximate:
   (a) audiometric "zero" across the frequency range of 250 Hz through 8 kHz
   (b) the average normal hearing thresholds for humans
   (c) 0 dB SPL at 1000 Hz using both ears
   (d) 0-phons of loudness level across the range of frequencies
   (e) all of the above

   It should be apparent in this question that the answer is (e).

2. Equal-loudness level contours indicate that for ____ frequencies ____ of loudness grow more rapidly with ____ increments in the intensity of the sound.
   (a) the mid-range of; sones; equal
   (b) very low; sones; fewer
   (c) very high; phons; larger
   (d) very low; mels; fewer

   It should be apparent in this question that the answer is (b).

3. In the equation: $[L = 2^{(LL - 40)/10}]$ the L refers to ____ and the LL refers to ____, respectively.
   (a) phons; sones
   (b) mels; sones
   (c) sones; phons
   (d) loudness summation; mels

   It should be apparent in this question that the answer is (c).

4. When using the equation: $[L = 2^{(LL - 40)/10}]$, L is equal to ____ if LL is equal to ____, respectively.
   (a) 32; 90
   (b) 1; 40
   (c) 4; 60
   (d) all of the above

   It should be apparent in this question that the answer is (d).

5. 60-phons is always equal to ____ sones, and a 30-phon increase from 5 sones results in ____ sones.
   (a) 4; 40
   (b) 8; 80
   (c) 2; 20
   (d) 3; 30

   It should be apparent in this question that the answer is (a).

6. A 20-phon increase from 2 sones results in ____ sones, and a 200-Hz pure tone presented at 60 phons is equivalent in loudness level to a ____ Hz pure tone presented at ____ dB SPL.
   (a) 16; 200; 60
   (b) 32; 1000; 60
   (c) 32; 1000; 20
   (d) 64; 200; 60

   It should be apparent in this question that the answer is (b).

7. 1000-mels of pitch will correspond to a sound presented at:
   (a) 40 dB SPL at 1 kHz
   (b) 40-phons of loudness level at 1 kHz
   (c) 1 sone of loudness at 1 kHz
   (d) all of the above

   It should be apparent in this question that the answer is (d).

8. The human auditory system compresses the entire frequency range of hearing into exactly:
   (a) 20 Hz to 20 kHz
   (b) 3500 sones of loudness
   (c) 3500 mels of pitch perception
   (d) 3500 phons of loudness level

   It should be apparent in this question that the answer is (c).

9. The equal-pitch contours described in this chapter suggest that as signal intensity is increased, pitch gets progressively ____ for frequencies ____ than 2000 Hz.
   (a) lower; lower
   (b) higher; higher
   (c) lower; higher
   (d) both (a) and (b) above

   It should be apparent in this question that the answer is (d).

10. A pitch that is twice that of a 1000-Hz pure tone presented at 40-phons of loudness level would have a pitch of:
    (a) a 2000 Hz pure tone
    (b) 80-phons
    (c) 2000 mels
    (d) 2 sones

    It should be apparent in this question that the answer is (c).

11. Which of the following is likely to produce the least amount of loudness summation?
    (a) a wide-band noise
    (b) a complex tone consisting of two pure tones
    (c) a vowel taken from speech
    (d) a narrow-band noise

    It should be apparent in this question that the answer is (b).

12. Two tones are presented together, each at 40 dB SPL. One is 1000 Hz and the other is 1015 Hz. The combined tones should:
    (a) have a loudness level of 43-phons
    (b) have a sound pressure of 43 dB SPL

(c) fall within a critical band of each other

(d) produce less than 1 sone of loudness

It should be apparent in this question that the answer is (d).

13. What occurs when the threshold of one sound is raised or elevated by the simultaneous presentation of another sound?

(a) masking

(b) fatigue

(c) summation

(d) adaptation

It should be apparent in this question that the answer is (a).

14. Temporal integration should be complete by ____ for an accurate measure and valid experience of an absolute threshold.

(a) 2 full seconds

(b) 200 ms

(c) 10 to 15 ms

(d) less than 10 ms

It should be apparent in this question that the answer is (b).

15. ____ can occur when a nonoverlapping masker precedes a probe stimulus in time, provided that the offset of the masker and onset of the probe occur within ____.

(a) Forward masking; 200 ms

(b) Backward masking; 200 ms

(c) Forward masking; 20 to 25 ms

(d) Backward masking; 20 to 25 ms

It should be apparent in this question that the answer is (a).

16. A most frequently used index of ____ following prolonged exposure to sounds that are presented many decibels above an auditory threshold, is indicated by a ____.

(a) threshold adaptation; temporary threshold shift (TTS)

(b) auditory adaptation; temporary threshold shift (TTS)

(c) auditory fatigue; temporary threshold shift (TTS)

(d) threshold fatigue; permanent threshold shift (PTS)

It should be apparent in this question that the answer is (c).

17. Which of these explanations best describes why humans are able to binaurally locate the direction of relatively higher frequency (>1500 Hz) signals in the environment?

(a) interaural time-of-arrival differences

(b) diffraction effects produced by lower frequency signals

(c) diffraction effects produced by higher frequency signals

(d) head-shadow effects produced by higher frequency signals

It should be apparent in this question that the answer is (d).

18. Binaural sound lateralization generally takes place ____, while binaural sound localization generally takes place ____, but both lateralization and localization work by ____ principles.

(a) with headphones; without headphones; completely different

(b) with headphones; without headphones; the same

(c) without headphones; with headphones; the same

(d) without headphones; with headphones; completely different

It should be apparent in this question that the answer is (b).

References

Bacon, S. P., & Viemeister, N. F. (1994). Intensity discrimination and increment detection at 16 kHz. *Journal of the Acoustical Society of America, 95,* 2616–2621.

Békésy, G. von (1967). *Sensory inhibition.* Princeton, NJ: Princeton University Press.

Blauert, J. (1970). Sound localization in the median plane. *Acustica, 22,* 205–213.

Blauert, J. (1997). *Spatial hearing. The psychophysics of human sound localization.* Cambridge, MA: MIT Press.

Boring, E. G. (1942). *Sensation and perception in the history of experimental psychology.* New York, NY: Appelton-Century-Crofts.

Boring, E. G. (1957). *A history of experimental psychology* (2nd ed.). New York, NY: Appelton-Century-Crofts.

Bray, D. A., Dirks, D. D., & Morgan, D. E. (1973). Perstimulatory loudness adaptation. *Journal of the Acoustical Society of America, 53,* 1544–1548.

Brungart, D. S., & Rabinowitz, W. M. (1999). Auditory localization of nearby sources. Head-related transfer functions. *Journal of the Acoustical Society of America, 106,* 1465–1479.

Dadson, R. S., & King, J. H. (1952). A determination of the normal threshold of hearing and its relation to the standardization of audiometers. *Laryngology and Otology, 46,* 366–378.

Davis, H., Morgan, C. T., Hawkins, J. E. Jr., Galambos, R., & Smith, F. W. (1950). Temporary deafness following exposure to loud tones and noise. *Acta Otolaryngologica, 88 (Suppl.),* 1–56.

Durrant, J. D., & Feth, L. L. (2013). *Hearing sciences: A foundational approach.* Upper Saddle River, NJ: Pearson Education.

Durrant, J. D., & Lovrinic, J. H. (1995). *Bases of hearing science* (3rd ed.). Baltimore, MD: Williams & Wilkins.

Fedderson, W. E., Sandel, T. T., Teas, D. C., & Jeffress, L. A. (1957). Localization of high-frequency tones. *Journal of the Acoustical Society of America, 29,* 988–991.

Fletcher, H. (1940). Auditory patterns. *Reviews of Modern Physics, 12,* 47–65.

Fletcher, H., & Munson, W. A. (1933). Loudness, its definition, measurement, and calculation. *Journal of the Acoustical Society of America, 5,* 82–108.

Fletcher, H., & Munson, W. A. (1937). Relation between loudness and masking. *Journal of the Acoustical Society of America, 9,* 1–10.

Gardner, M. B., & Gardner, R. S. (1973). Problems of localization in the median plane: Effect of pinnae cavity occlusion. *Journal of the Acoustical Society of America, 53,* 400–408.

Garner, W. R., & Miller, G. A. (1947). The masked threshold of pure tones as a function of duration. *Journal of Experimental Psychology, 37,* 293–303.

Gelfand, S. A. (2001). *Essentials of audiology* (2nd ed.). New York, NY: Thieme.

Glasberg, B. R., & Moore, B. C. J. (1990). Derivation of auditory filter shapes from notched-noise data. *Hearing Research, 47,* 103–138.

Glasberg, B. R., & Moore, B. C. J. (2000). Frequency selectivity as function of level and frequency measured with uniformly exciting notched-noise. *Journal of the Acoustical Society of America, 108,* 2318–2328.

Greenwood, D. D. (1961). Auditory masking and the critical band. *Journal of the Acoustical Society of America, 33,* 484–501.

Gulick, W. L. (1971). *Hearing: Physiology and psychophysics.* New York, NY: Oxford University Press.

Hall, J. W. (2014). *Introduction to audiology today.* Upper Saddle River, NJ: Pearson Education.

Hamill, T. A., & Price, L. L. (2014). *The hearing sciences* (2nd ed.). San Diego, CA: Plural.

Hawkins, J. E., & Stevens, S. S. (1950). The masking of pure tones and of speech by white noise. *Journal of the Acoustical Society of America, 22,* 6–13.

Hirsh, I. J. (1952). *The measurement of hearing.* New York, NY: McGraw-Hill.

Hirsh, I. J., & Bilger, R. C. (1955). Auditory-threshold recovery after exposures to pure tones. *Journal of the Acoustical Society of America, 27,* 1186–1194.

Hood, J. D. (1950). Studies in auditory fatigue and adaptation. *Acta Otolaryngologica, 92 (Suppl.),* 1–57.

Jerger, J., & Jerger, S. (1975). A simplified tone decay test. *Archives of Otolaryngology, 102,* 403–407.

Jesteadt, W., Wier, C. C., & Green, D. M. (1977). Comparison of monaural and binaural discrimination of intensity and frequency. *Journal of the Acoustical Society of America, 61,* 1599–1603.

Kluk, K., & Moore, B. C. J. (2004). Factors affecting psychophysical tuning curves for normally hearing subjects. *Hearing Research, 194,* 118–134.

Kujawa, S. G., & Liberman, M. C. (2009). Adding insult to injury: Cochlear nerve degeneration after "temporary" noise-induced hearing loss. *Journal of Neuroscience, 29,* 14077–14085.

Licklider, J. C. R. (1958). Chapter 25: Basic correlates of the auditory stimulus. In S. S. Stevens (Ed.), *Handbook of experimental psychology* (pp. 985–1039). New York, NY: Wiley.

Martin, F. N., & Clark, J. G. (2015). *Introduction to audiology* (12th ed.). Upper Saddle River, NJ: Pearson Education.

Miller, G. A. (1947). Sensitivity to changes in the intensity of white noise and its relation to masking and loudness. *Journal of the Acoustical Society of America, 191,* 609–619.

Moore, B. C. J. (1986). Parallels between frequency selectivity measured psychophysically and in cochlear mechanics. *Scandinavian Audiology Supplementum, 25,* 139–152.

Moore, B. C. J. (2012). *An introduction to the psychology of hearing* (6th ed.). Leiden, the Netherlands: Brill.

Moore, B. C. J., Alcántara, J. I., & Dau, T. (1998). Masking patterns for sinusoidal and narrow-band noise maskers. *Journal of the Acoustical Society of America, 104,* 1023–1038.

Moore, B. C. J., & Glasberg, B. R. (1983). Growth of forward masking for sinusoidal and noise maskers as a function of signal delay: Implications for suppression in noise. *Journal of the Acoustical Society of America, 73,* 1249–1259.

Musiek, F. E., Baran, J. A., Shinn, J. B., & Jones, R. O. (2012). Audiologic, vestibular, and radiologic procedures. *Disorders of the auditory system* (pp. 63–103). San Diego, CA: Plural.

Nelson, D. A., Stanton, M. E., & Freyman, R. L. (1983). A general equation describing frequency discrimination as a function of frequency and sensation level. *Journal of the Acoustical Society of America, 73,* 2117–2123.

Oxenham, A. J., & Moore, B. C. J. (1994). Modeling the additivity of nonsimultaneous masking. *Hearing Research, 80,* 105–118.

Pollack, I. (1948). Monaural and binaural threshold sensitivity for tones and for white noise. *Journal of the Acoustical Society of America, 20,* 52–57.

Rayleigh, L. (Strutt, J. W.). (1907). On our perception of sound direction. *Philosophical Magazine, 13*(Series 6; Issue 4), 214–232.

Robinson, D. W., & Dadson, R. S. (1956). A re-determination of the equal loudness relations for pure tones. *British Journal of Applied Physics, 7,* 166–181.

Sahley, T. L., Hammonds, M. D., & Musiek, F. E. (2013). Endogenous dynorphins, glutamate and *N*-methyl-D-aspartate (NMDA) receptors may participate in a stress-mediated Type-I auditory neural exacerbation of tinnitus. *Brain Research, 1499,* 80–108.

Scharf, B. (1970). Critical bands. In J. V. Tobias (Ed.), *Foundations of modern auditory theory* (pp. 157–202). New York, NY: Academic Press.

Scharf, B. (1983). Loudness adaptation. In J. V. Tobias & E. D. Schubert (Eds.), *Hearing research and theory* (Vol. 2, pp. 1–56). New York, NY: Academic Press.

Schouten, J. F. (1970). The residue revisited. In R. Plomp & G. F. Smoorenburg (Eds.), *Frequency analysis and periodicity detection in hearing.* Leiden, the Netherlands: Sijthoff.

Sek, A., & Moore, B. C. J. (1995). Frequency discrimination as a function of frequency, measured in several ways. *Journal of the Acoustical Society of America, 97,* 2479–2486.

Silman, S., & Emmer, M. B. (2012). *Instrumentation for audiology and hearing science.* San Diego, CA: Plural.

Sivian, L. J., & White, S. D. (1933). On minimum audible sound fields. *Journal of the Acoustical Society of America, 4,* 288–321.

Stevens, S. S. (1935). The relation of pitch to intensity. *Journal of the Acoustical Society of America, 6,* 150–154.

Stevens, S. S. (1936). A scale for the measurement of a psychological magnitude: Loudness. *Psychological Review, 43,* 405–416.

Stevens, S. S. (1958). Chapter 1: Mathematics, measurement, and psychophysics. In S. S. Stevens (Ed.), *Handbook of experimental psychology* (pp. 1–49). New York, NY: Wiley.

Stevens, S. S., & Davis, H. (1938). *Hearing: Its psychology and physiology.* New York, NY: Wiley.

Stevens, S. S., & Newman, E. B. (1936). The localization of actual sources of sound. *American Journal of Psychology, 48,* 297–306.

Stevens, S. S., & Volkmann, J. (1940). The relation of pitch to frequency. *The American Journal of Psychology, 53,* 329–353.

Stevens, S. S., Volkmann, J., & Newman, E. B. (1937). A scale for the measurement of the psychological magnitude of pitch. *Journal of the Acoustical Society of America, 8,* 185–190.

Thurlow, W. R., & Small, A. M. (1955). Pitch perception of certain periodic auditory stimuli. *Journal of the Acoustical Society of America, 27,* 132–137.

Turnbull, W. W. (1944). Pitch discrimination as a function of tonal duration. *Journal of Experimental Psychology, 34,* 302–316.

Verschuure, J., & van Meeteren, A. A. (1975). The effect of intensity on pitch. *Acustica, 32,* 33–44.

Viemeister, N. F., & Bacon, S. P. (1988). Intensity discrimination, increment detection, and magnitude estimation for 1-kHz tones. *Journal of the Acoustical Society of America, 84,* 172–178.

Ward, W. D., Glorig, A., & Sklar, D. L. (1958). Dependence of temporary threshold shift at 4 kc on intensity and time. *Journal of the Acoustical Society of America, 30,* 944–954.

Watkins, A. J. (1978). Psychoacoustical aspects of synthesized vertical locale cues. *Journal of the Acoustical Society of America, 63,* 1152–1165.

Wegel, R. L., & Lane, C. E. (1924). The auditory masking of one sound by another and its probable relation to the dynamics of the inner ear. *Physics Review, 23,* 266–285.

Wier, C. C., Jesteadt, W., & Green, D. M. (1977). Frequency discrimination as a function of frequency and sensation level. *Journal of the Acoustical Society of America, 61,* 178–184.

Wilson, R. H., & Carhart, R. (1971). Forward and backward masking: Interactions and additivity. *Journal of the Acoustical Society of America, 49,* 1254–1263.

Yost, W. A. (1974). Discrimination of inter-aural phase differences. *Journal of the Acoustical Society of America, 55,* 1299–1303.

Yost, W. A. (2007). *Fundamentals of hearing: An introduction* (5th ed.). San Diego, CA: Academic Press.

Yost, W. A., & Dye, R. (1988). Discrimination of inter-aural differences of level as a function of frequency. *Journal of the Acoustical Society of America, 83,* 1846–1851.

Zwicker, E., Flottrop, G., & Stevens, S. S. (1957). Critical bandwidth in loudness summation. *Journal of the Acoustical Society of America, 29,* 548–557.

Chapter 9

Nervous System Terminology: The Structure and Function of Neurons and the Cranial Nerves

The doctrine that had its foundation in the extensive studies of Santiago Ramón y Cajal, that was based on the staining methods developed by Camillo Golgi (the Golgi silver method), states that the individual neuron constitutes the genetic, anatomic, trophic and fundamental (functional) unit of the nervous system. This is known as the "neuron doctrine."

Carpenter & Sutin, 1983, p. 87

Alphabetized Listing of Key Terms Discussed in Chapter 9

abducens nerve

absolute refractory period

action potential

afferent

after-polarization

anions

anosmia

ansa cervicalis

anterior cranial fossa

anterograde propagation

antidromic propagation

aortic sinus reflex

association fibers

astrocytes

auditory-vestibular nerve

auricular nerve of cranial nerve X

axo-axonic

axo-dendritic

axo-somatic

axon

axon hillock

Bell's palsy

bipolar neuron

brain

brainstem

capsule

carotid sinus reflex

cations

Cajal, Santiago Ramón y

cell body

center for lateral gaze

center for vertical gaze

central nervous system (CNS)

cervical plexus

chemical synapse

chorda tympani nerve

choroid plexus

ciliary ganglion

orthodromic propagation	relative refractory period	superior ganglion of cranial nerve IX
osseous labyrinth	respiratory reflex	superior ganglion of cranial nerve X
peduncle	retch reflex	synapse
perikaryon	salivatory nucleus	synaptic cleft
peripheral nervous system (PNS)	saltatory conduction	telodendria
pharyngeal plexus	Scarpa's ganglion	temporal summation
piriform cortex	Schwann cell	tensor tympani muscle
polarized	sensory neurons	tensor tympani reflex
pons	skeletal neuromuscular junction	tensor veli palatini muscle
pontine tegmentum	slow potentials	terminal boutons
posterior cranial fossa	soma	terminal endplates
postsynaptic	spatial summation	tracts
presynaptic	spinal accessory nerve	trigeminal ganglion
pre-tectum	spinal cord	trigeminal nerve
principle sensory nucleus of cranial nerve v	spinal trigeminal nucleus of cranial nerve V	trigeminal neuralgia
projection fibers	spiral ganglion	trigger zone
pseudo-unipolar neuron	stapedius muscle	trochlear nerve
pterygopalatine ganglion	strabismus	unipolar neuron
receptor potential	submandibular ganglion	unmyelinated neurons
refractory period	superior colliculus	upper motor neuron
		vagus nerve
		vomit reflex
		white matter

The Neuron

The neuron is the single fundamental cell of the nervous system. Neurons are the basic units of the nervous system, numbering about 100 billion. Nervous tissue, which is composed mostly of neurons, is highly specialized for communication or signaling. It may be said that the fundamental task of the nervous system is signaling. In most but certainly not all neurons, signaling is accomplished through what is called a *chemical synapse*. This can be differentiated from another type of signaling mechanism, called an *electrical synapse*. Signaling through a chemical synapse occurs when an endogenous (natural) chemical messenger substance called a neurotransmitter is released from one neuron (the *presynaptic* neuron) into a very restricted physical space, called a *synaptic cleft* or simply, a *synapse*. Most neurotransmitters are small amine molecules, amino acids, or neuropeptides that are released from presynaptic *microvesicles* (see below). The neurotransmitter released into the synaptic cleft will be very close in physical proximity to the adjacent parts of another (or other) neurons, as well as parts of muscle cells (skeletal, smooth, and cardiac) and/or parts of organs. These neurons, muscle tissue, or organs that are located on the receiving side of the synapse are said to be located *postsynaptic* to the presynaptic neuron. Embedded within the plasma membrane (surfaces) of the adjacent parts of these (other) postsynaptic targets are specified (postsynaptic) binding-site receptor complexes that are linked to regulated transmembrane (across the membrane) carrier protein-channels. The neurotransmitter travels across the very short distance of the synaptic space and binds to the appropriate postsynaptic binding site-receptor complex. The binding site-receptor complex in this instance is linked to a chemically gated (regulated) or, as it is often called, a ligand-gated carrier protein channel. The binding of the neurotransmitter to the binding site-receptor complex results in a temporary conformational (shape) change in the ligand-gated carrier protein channel, causing it to temporarily open to allow ions to enter (or exit). Depending upon the charge (+ or −) of the ions that pass through the opened channel and into the postsynaptic target cells, the result of this synaptic interaction will be excitation, inhibition, or modulation (modification or

regulation) of the postsynaptic neuron, neurons, muscle cells, or organ cells.

In terms of neuron-to-neuron communication, each neuron may communicate directly with as many as 2000 other neurons, providing one trillion points of communication. Neurons comprise the cells of the central nervous system (CNS) and the peripheral nervous system (PNS). The boundaries of the CNS are the brain, the brainstem, and the spinal cord. The adult brain (with brainstem) weighs between 1200 and 1600 g. Since a gram is about 0.04 oz, the adult human brain therefore weighs about 48 to 64 oz, which amounts to about 3 or 4 lb. The human brain is rather gelatinous in its consistency in the living state and basically pours out of the skull if it is not, in advance, subjected to a chemical fixative.

Neurons of the CNS link the brain, brainstem, and spinal cord together, internally. Neurons of the CNS also link the brain, brainstem, and spinal cord to the skeletal muscles (somatic-motor or skeletal-motor), and to the smooth and cardiac muscle and soft tissue of the internal organs, such as glands (general visceral-motor), all of which are located outside of the CNS. Once the neural processes (axons) of these CNS (motor or efferent) neurons exit the CNS for their peripheral targets, they fall within the domain of the PNS. Indeed, all other neurons of the nervous system located outside of the three anatomical structures that define the CNS are said to be situated within the PNS. Many of the neurons of the PNS are sensory (or afferent) and link the peripheral sensory receptors (somato-sensory), as well as the internal sensory receptors of the internal organs (general visceral-sensory), to the brain, brainstem, and spinal cord. The CNS then processes and organizes all incoming sensory information so that only the important information from the external environment and/or the internal environments of the body is extracted.

Structure and Function of the Neuron

Like all living cells, neurons are microscopic. A simplified neuron is illustrated in Figure 9–1. When viewing the brain, the brainstem, or the spinal cord (the CNS), or when viewing the nerves and ganglion of the PNS (see below), what we are able to actually see without the aid of a microscope are large conglomerations of cell bodies and axons from thousands of individual neurons.

The Cell Body and the Dendrites

All neurons have a *cell body*, also called a *perikaryon* or a *soma*. The cell body, illustrated in Figure 9–1, contains the metabolic machinery (the organelles) of the cell, which includes of course, the nucleus. The cell body's primary concern is with the outgrowth and maintenance of the processes (axons and dendrites) and with their other metabolic functions, aside from membrane (signaling) activity. As in the nucleus of all cells, the nucleus within the cell body of a neuron contains the cell's deoxyribonucleic acid (DNA). DNA

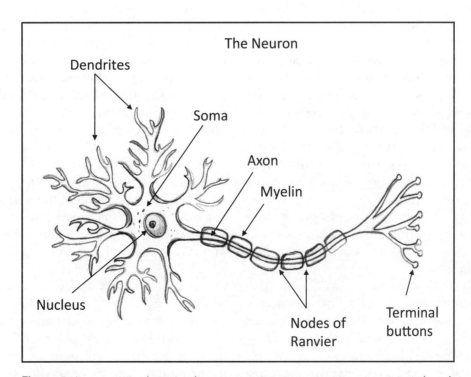

Figure 9–1. A simplified (multipolar) neuron. Labeled are the dendrites, the cell body (soma), the axon, the myelin that covers the axon, the nodes of Ranvier (interruptions in the myelin), and the terminal endplates or boutons (buttons). Not labeled are the axon hillock and initial segment. Courtesy of F. Musiek and the neuroaudiology lab, University of Connecticut.

contains the genetic code for the production (transcription) of endogenous (natural) proteins and enzymes from amino acids. Within the nucleus of a neuron, the DNA contains the genetic code for the production of endogenous enzymes and neurotransmitters. Large collections or conglomerations of cell bodies from specialized neurons located within the CNS are very often visible to the naked eye, as indicated above. Upon anatomical inspection, examination, or viewing, these clusters of cell bodies are collectively referred to as *nuclei*. A single large and visible collection of cell bodies from specialized neurons within the CNS is called a *nucleus*. The term *nucleus* is not to be confused with the microscopic organelle known as the DNA-containing nucleus that is found in all eukaryotic cells. In the CNS, specialized nuclei constitute a large part (not the total) of the so-called *gray matter* of the CNS. On the other hand, large collections or conglomerations of visible cell bodies from specialized neurons located within the PNS are called *ganglion* (or *ganglia*). Finally, cell bodies of neurons very often receive input from the axon terminals of other neurons. Such interactions are called *axo-somatic*.

Dendrites may branch outward from the cell body for short distances, resembling the extensions of trees or bushes, as observed in the microstructure of most motor neurons, as illustrated in Figure 9–1. Sometimes the dendrites are located some distance from the cell body and are joined to the cell body by a long dendritic extension or (peripheral) process, as observed in the microstructure of most bipolar and pseudounipolar (see below) sensory neurons. Functionally, the role of the dendrite is to direct the input from a stimulus toward the direction of the cell body. Dendrites of neurons very often receive input from the axon terminals of other neurons. Such interactions are called *axo-dendritic*.

The Axon Hillock and the Initial Segment

The *axon hillock* is a conical mass of specialized protoplasm that extends from the cell body and is the location of the junction of the cell body and the axon. The axon hillock is distinguished from the cell body by its complete absence of *Nissl bodies*. Nissl bodies are composed of rough or granular endoplasmic reticulum, owing to their content of free ribosomes. During enzyme or neurotransmitter translation, clusters of ribosomes (polyribosomes) are frequently observed as 3 to 10 ribosomes attached to a single messenger ribonucleic acid (mRNA). Obviously then, the axon hillock is not involved in the processing (translation) of enzymes or neurotransmitters. Anatomically, the axon hillock narrows distally into an area called the *initial segment* of the axon.

The initial segment is often the location and the generator site (*trigger zone*) for the production of the *action potential* that occurs when a neuron has reached its excitatory threshold. The excitability of the neuron is greatest at the neuron's trigger zone. The action potential may be defined as a reliable, depolarizing change in the plasma membrane potential along the axon. Whether the action potential does or does not occur will depend upon the amount of synaptic interaction that occurs at the dendrites and/or along the peripheral process of the dendrites, relative to the synaptic interactions that are occurring at the cell body. The initial segment and/or the subsequent trigger zone is the location in the neuron where electrical signals from the dendrites (in *bipolar* and in *pseudo-unipolar* neurons) and/or from the dendrites and cell body (in *multipolar* neurons) are integrated. Action potentials occur when a neuron has been activated, excited, or otherwise maximally depolarized. The definition of *depolarization* is provided in the sections below. Reaching the threshold for an action potential will depend upon the summation of adequate numbers of excitatory postsynaptic potentials (EPSPs) and their equivalent or analogous *receptor potentials* in sensory neurons, relative to the number of summated inhibitory postsynaptic potentials (IPSPs). This additive and subtractive processing occurs wherever and whenever the initial segment serves as a trigger zone. What is an EPSP? Each EPSP is a tiny, reversible depolarization. What is an IPSP? Each IPSP is a tiny, reversible hyperpolarization. The definition of *hyperpolarization* is also provided in the sections below. The majority of EPSPs (and receptor potentials) originate from the synaptic interactions that occur at the dendrites (axo-dendritic). The majority of IPSPs originate from the synaptic interactions that occur at the cell body (axo-somatic). Hence, at the initial segment of multipolar neurons, the processing and/or summating of all of the EPSPs relative to all of the IPSPs occurs. As a result, the likelihood of summating enough EPSPs or receptor potentials that push a neuron to its excitatory threshold and generating a full-blown action potential, becomes a statistical probability. Beyond the initial segment, the *axon* (or the peripheral processes

in many sensory neurons) will contain mitochondria, neurofilaments, microtubules, smooth (agranular) endoplasmic reticulum, and vesicles, but will contain no granular endoplasmic reticulum or ribosomes.

The Axon, Myelin, and the Terminal Endplate

The axon (see Figure 9–1) is a slender, often long process that arises proximally from the axon hillock and from its initial segment. The axon is responsible for propagating the action potential away from the initial segment and toward the *terminal endplates* or endings of the axon. Axons may receive input from the axons of other neurons. These interactions are called *axo-axonic*, and they typically result in neural-modulation (neuromodulation). Generally, axons may be myelinated or they may be unmyelinated. *Myelin* is a form of neural insulation. It is a white, fatty wrapping or covering composed of a biomolecular lipid leaflet sandwiched between monolayers of protein. Myelin (see Figure 9–1) is not found on cell bodies and technically is not found on the anatomically designated dendrites. Exceptions to this rule occur in bipolar and pseudo-unipolar sensory neurons. In these neurons, the long dendritic extension (peripheral process) located between the dendritic terminals and the cell body is myelinated. With certainty, however, myelin is never found on the dendritic terminals, within the dendritic zone (see below).

In the PNS, myelin is composed of Schwann cells. *Schwann cells* are named in honor of Theodore Schwann (1810–1882) who initially proposed that cells were the basic building blocks of life. Schwann cells in the PNS encapsulate only one axon at a time and seem to assist in the repair of damaged axons. Schwann cells promote the regrowth of neurons following axonal damage. In the CNS, myelin is composed of *oligodendrocytes*. Oligodendrocytes encapsulate about 15 axons at once and seem to inhibit the repair and the regeneration of damaged neurons in the CNS. Schwann cells of the PNS and oligodendrocytes of the CNS both represent a type of nonneural support cell. The nonneural support cells that are found within the interstitial tissue of the nervous system are known as *neuroglia*, which means nerve-glue. In general, neuroglia create a boundary between the neural elements and the blood vessels. Two categories of neuroglia are generally recognized. These are the *macroglia*, consisting of *astrocytes* and oligodendrocytes, and the *microglia*. The microglia cells are known simply as *glia* and include the *ependyma* and the *neurilemma cells*. The neurilemma cells are simply another name for the Schwann cells. The ependyma, however, refers to the thin epithelial membrane lining the ventricles of the brain, brainstem, and spinal cord. Modified ependymal cells are also known as the *choroid plexus*. The specialized cells of the choroid plexus within the ventricular system are directly responsible for the production of cerebrospinal fluid.

The myelin sheath that surrounds myelinated axons is not continuous along the full length of each axon but is interrupted at fairly regular intervals, as illustrated in Figure 9–1. These interruptions will appear as constrictions within the myelin sheath and are commonly known as the *nodes of Ranvier*. At each node, or break in the myelin sheath, the cell membrane of the axon, which is otherwise insulated, is more or less exposed to the surrounding extracellular fluids that surround all cells. Only neurons with myelinated axons will have nodes of Ranvier, whereas neurons with unmyelinated axons do not. The insulating myelin and the accompanying nodes greatly contribute to the increased conduction velocity that can only be observed in myelinated neurons. The action potential, as indicated by and defined as the depolarizing change in the plasma membrane potential along the axon, will appear to "jump" from node to node, skipping over the larger insulated areas, rather than proceeding in a uniform velocity along the entire length of the axon membrane, as would occur if no myelin were present. This type of node-to-node conduction is the result of the electrical resistance and capacitance properties of the myelin sheath and is called *saltatory conduction*. The term saltatory (or to saltate) literally means to hop or to dance. The presence of myelin also prevents the action potential current from leaking across the internodal (between nodes) membrane. By contrast, propagation of an action potential in unmyelinated neurons is a continuous and more time-consuming process. During action potential propagation in these neurons, the entire membrane surface of the exposed axon must slowly exchange ionic elements with the surrounding fluids. This much slower exchange of ions dramatically reduces conduction velocity; hence, the speed of signaling between unmyelinated neurons is much slower. The typical unmyelinated axon diameter is usually between 0.2 and 1 micron. A micron is one millionth (10^{-6})

of a meter. The typical action potential conduction velocity of an unmyelinated axon is about 0.2 to 2 m/s, but axon conduction velocities in these axons may range from 0.5 to 10 m/s. In contrast, the typical diameter of a myelinated axon is between 2.0 and 20 microns and the typical action potential conduction velocity in these axons may be anywhere from 12 to 120 m/s. However, myelinated axons can exhibit conduction velocities of as high as 150 m/s. Summarily then, myelinated axons have much faster conduction velocities than unmyelinated axons. Moreover, larger diameter axons also conduct action potentials more rapidly than smaller diameter axons. Hence, large-diameter myelinated axons will have the fastest conduction velocities.

As indicated above, large bundles or conglomerations of myelinated axons are very often visible to the naked eye. These bundles are often referred to as fibers, especially when reference is made to the fiber tracts within the CNS. Recall from above that neurons of the CNS link the brain, brainstem, and spinal cord together, internally. The fiber tracts of these neurons connect the parts of the CNS together. Therefore, these large groups of visible, myelinated axons located within the CNS are called *tracts,* and fiber tracts constitute the *white matter* of the CNS. Fiber tracts within the CNS are often referred to singularly as a particular *fasciculus,* a general region or a *funiculus,* a *capsule,* a *peduncle,* a *lemniscus,* or a *commissure.* Collectively, and more generally, these fiber tracts are typically classified as *projection fibers, association fibers,* or *commissural fibers.* Bundles or conglomerations of myelinated axons located within the PNS are also

very often visible to the naked eye. However, the myelinated (axon) fiber bundles located within the periphery are called *nerves.*

At the distal end of each axon, the axon breaks up into multiple but simpler branches (arborizations) or *telodendria* that ultimately end in axon terminals or terminal endings that are often called *terminal endplates* or *terminal boutons* (French for buttons), as illustrated in Figure 9–1. Within these terminal endplates are the *microvesicles* that contain the endogenous neurotransmitter (messenger) substances. The axon terminal with its neurotransmitter vesicles is said to be the presynaptic terminal. When the action potential arrives at the presynaptic axon terminal, the depolarization of the axon terminal activates (opens) voltage-gated (regulated) Ca^{++} carrier protein channels. These channels are, of course, embedded within the plasma membrane of the presynaptic axon terminal. When these channels open, extracellular Ca^{++} rapidly enters the axon terminal. This influx (inward flow) of extracellular Ca^{++} into the terminal is absolutely necessary for the presynaptic release of neurotransmitter. The Ca^{++} influx into the axon terminal causes the microvesicles that contain the neurotransmitter to migrate to the most distal end of the terminal. Here, they bind, dock, or fuse with the presynaptic terminal membrane. The synaptic vesicles then release their neurotransmitter contents into the synaptic cleft, by way of a simple cellular process called exocytosis. If there is or was a presynaptic axon terminal, then there must also be a postsynaptic target or set of targets, and the synapse or synaptic cleft is the physical space that exists between the two structures.

The Chemical Synapse and Postsynaptic Interactions

The chemical synapse is defined as a specialized morphological space within which the release of a chemical messenger substance by one neuron can influence the activity of another neuron, or some other target organ. To be sure, neurotransmitters, neuromodulators, or neurohormones are released from a presynaptic axon terminal into this physical space or synapse that separates the presynaptic terminal from the postsynaptic target cells. The synaptic space is only 10 to 20 nanometers (nm) across. Recall that 1 nm is equal to 10^{-9} m. It takes about 2 ms for the neurotransmitter to bridge this physical (spatial) gap. As indicated above, the neurotransmitter substance released into the synapse must migrate to and bind with a specific set of postsynaptic binding-sites on receptors linked to chemically gated (regulated) carrier protein channels. The direction of movement of the neurotransmitter is always unidirectional, toward the postsynaptic membrane. The postsynaptic membrane-bound carrier-protein channels will then temporarily open in response to the binding of the neurotransmitter, permitting the influx or even the efflux (outward flow) of a specific ion species. An exchange of ions between the postsynaptic target cell and its extracellular environment will occur each time the channels are temporarily opened. Recall again that the postsynaptic target may be the dendrites, the cell bodies, or the axons of other neurons or may be organ or muscle (skeletal, smooth, or cardiac) cells.

In terms of neuron-to-neuron interactions, axon terminals of a neuron often end in a series of synaptic interactions with another neuron's dendrites, as indicated above. The presynaptic release of an *excitatory neurotransmitter* into an axo-dendritic synapse usually results in the production of a postsynaptic EPSP. The production of an EPSP is the result of an influx of a specific set of positive (+) ions (or *cations*) into the plasma membrane of the postsynaptic dendrite. Examples of cations are sodium ions (Na^+), calcium ions (Ca^{++}), and potassium ions (K^+). Cations enter the postsynaptic dendrite by way of the temporarily opened (ligand-gated) membrane-bound carrier protein channels. The EPSP, therefore, is the result of a very slight and temporary depolarization of the postsynaptic plasma membrane and represents a very slight and temporary form of excitation. Similarly, axon terminals can often end in a series of synaptic interactions with the cell bodies of other neurons. A presynaptic release of an *inhibitory neurotransmitter* into an axo-somatic synapse usually results in the production of a postsynaptic IPSP. The production of an IPSP is the result of an influx of a specific set of negative (–) ions (or *anions*) into the plasma membrane of the postsynaptic cell body. One example of an anion is the chloride ion (Cl^-). Anions enter the postsynaptic cell body by way of the temporarily opened (ligand-gated) membrane-bound carrier protein channels. The IPSP, therefore, is the result of a very slight and temporary hyperpolarization of the postsynaptic plasma membrane and represents a very slight and temporary form of inhibition. Finally, the axon terminals may end in a series of synapses with another neuron's axons. These axo-axonic interactions may be excitatory or inhibitory. As indicated above, axo-axonic interactions are usually regulatory and involve neuromodulation at the site of the postsynaptic axon. Chemical synapses between neurons are directly involved in maintaining the plasticity of the brain (neural and synaptic plasticity) and are also very important for information processing, such as in learning and in memory retrieval. Chemical synapses are also important sites for the actions of drugs, or exogenous chemical substances. Finally, neural interactions with skeletal muscle, at the *skeletal neuromuscular junction*, are always excitatory. Neural interactions with both smooth and cardiac muscle can be either excitatory or inhibitory.

Generation of the Action Potential

As described above, neurons of the CNS link the brain, brainstem, and spinal cord to the skeletal muscles and to the smooth and cardiac muscle of the internal organs. Skeletal muscle is also called striated muscle or somatic muscle. These neurons are collectively called motor or *efferent* pathways and collectively they include both the upper and/or the lower *motor neurons*. The descending *upper motor neurons* are located entirely within the CNS. The axons of the *lower motor neurons* enter the periphery where they extend outward to innervate their targets. A common function of these neurons is to generate signals in the form of a universal code or language that can be converted, transformed, or otherwise transduced into the neural action patterns that characterize skeletal, smooth, or cardiac muscle. Neurons of the PNS also link the external peripheral sensory receptors of the skin and joints,

as well as the internal peripheral sensory receptors of the internal organs, to the brain, brainstem, and spinal cord. These are collectively called sensory or *afferent* pathways and/or *sensory neurons*. A common function of these neurons is to take the sensory receptor information from the environment, whether it is light, sound, smell, taste, hot, cold, touch, pressure, irritation, or pain, and/or the sensory receptor-information from internal body cavities, and convert, transform, or otherwise transduce this input into a universal code or language that the nervous system can interpret and understand. Independent of whether the universal language is carried by motor or by sensory neurons, the language takes the form of neural impulses, spikes, or action potentials.

What Is Neural Depolarization?

In the sections above, the term *depolarization* was associated with the notion of excitation, and with the production of EPSPs, whereas the term *hyperpolarization* was associated with the notion of inhibition, and with the production of IPSPs. What then does it mean for a cell to be *polarized*? A neuron (like all cells) is normally polarized relative to the extracellular fluid medium that surrounds all cells. This is because the insides of all cells are negatively charged relative to the surrounding fluid medium in which they live, although not all cells have the same negative resting membrane values. In general, neurons tend to have an intracellular transmembrane (across the plasma membrane) resting potential of about −70 mV. To *depolarize* a neuron means to partially (in the case of an EPSP) or completely (in the case of an action potential) unpolarize a neuron, or simply to make the inside of the neuron relatively less negative, but only temporarily. Hence, depolarization really means temporarily making the inside of the neuron slightly (EPSP) or significantly (action potential) more positive than −70 mV. In order for this to occur, cations must be allowed to enter through the regulated, carrier protein channels embedded within the semipermeable plasma membrane of the cell. In many but certainly not in all neurons, the depolarizing cation will be Na^+. However, Na^+ cannot randomly enter or exit from the cell. There are very few open (unregulated), resting protein channels for Na^+ since the influx of Na^+ must be tightly regulated. To hyperpolarize a neuron by an IPSP means to make the inside of the neuron slightly more negative (−75 or −80 mV) relative to its resting potential of −70 mV. In order for this to occur, anions must be allowed to enter through the regulated, carrier protein channels embedded within the semipermeable plasma membrane of the cell. In many but certainly not in all neurons, the hyperpolarizing anion is Cl^-. However, Cl^- is not able to randomly enter or exit from the cell since the influx of Cl^- is also tightly regulated. Hyperpolarizing a neuron continuously with IPSPs, will reduce the probability that the neuron will reach the excitatory threshold required to initiate an action potential. The excitatory threshold required for the generation of an action potential is typically 10 to 20 (or 15) mV above (less negative than) the neurons' resting membrane potential. Hence, if the resting potential for a neuron is −70 mV, then the action potential threshold

should be about −55 mV. As indicated below, when the action potential is activated, neural depolarization can reach as high as +30 to +40 mV and even higher at the peak of the action potential.

Slow Potentials: The Role of Excitatory Postsynaptic Potentials (EPSPs)

Each neuron-to-neuron synaptic interaction does not guarantee the generation of a postsynaptic action potential. As indicated in the sections above, neuron-to-neuron synaptic interactions generate postsynaptic EPSPs and/or IPSPs. Both EPSPs and IPSPs are referred to as *local potentials* or *slow potentials*. They are local potentials because they spread in all directions, but their spread is confined or localized and does not extend much beyond the point of their activation. They are slow potentials because their amplitudes are graded, such that they rely upon summation. Because each potential usually consists of only a few mV, the growth of their amplitudes will depend upon both *temporal summation* and *spatial summation*. If not reinforced through temporal and/or spatial summation, their amplitudes passively degrade over time. Their durations are also graded and will depend upon the strength of the stimulus. Finally, their polarity is either positive (EPSPs) or negative (IPSPs). As indicated above, excitatory neurotransmitters (ligands) open cation-specific carrier protein channels on postsynaptic dendrites and are largely responsible for the generation of EPSPs, while inhibitory neurotransmitters open anion-specific carrier protein channels on postsynaptic cell bodies and are largely responsible for the generation of IPSPs.

When excitatory neurotransmitters bombard postsynaptic dendrites, the subsequent generation of EPSPs in the postsynaptic plasma membrane is the direct result of the opening of many carrier protein channels for cations (usually but certainly not always Na$^+$). If and when the number of EPSPs and the subsequent postsynaptic influx of Na$^+$ exceeds and overtakes (in a timely manner), the passive compensatory efflux of K$^+$ through the resting (and always open) channels that exist for K$^+$ and/or the numbers of possible IPSPs, and subsequent influx of anions like Cl$^-$, then the neuron's action potential threshold is likely to be reached. If IPSPs are sufficient in number to offset the number of EPSPs, then the postsynaptic neuron will fail to reach its excitatory threshold and will remain hyperpolarized or inhibited. When the threshold for an action potential is eventually reached, it will be due to an accumulation of EPSPs owing to temporal and/or spatial summation. It will also be due to the large influx of cations entering the postsynaptic dendrites by way of the many, opened ligand-gated protein channels.

The Action Potential Threshold:
Role of the Voltage-Gated Na$^+$ Channels

What exactly is the nature of the action potential threshold? In actuality, it is the threshold that when reached will result in the opening of a type of carrier protein channel that is activated only by voltage changes that occur across the plasma membrane of the neuron. Up to this point, these carrier protein channels have been in their closed and resting state. However, in response to the transmembrane voltage changes created by the increased numbers of EPSPs and increased influx of Na$^+$, these carrier protein channels will open and are therefore known as voltage-gated (regulated) Na$^+$ channels. Recall the importance of the voltage-gated Ca^{++} carrier protein channels located within the axon terminals. As indicated above, these are activated (opened) in response to the depolarization of the axon terminal caused by the arrival of the action potential. The action potential threshold of a neuron is also the voltage threshold required to open the voltage-gated (regulated) Na$^+$ channels located at the trigger zone initially, and subsequently along the length of the axon. Their opening at the trigger zone initiates the action potential. The excitatory threshold of the voltage-gated Na$^+$ channels should be the same as the action potential threshold, which again is 10 to 20 (or 15) mV above (less negative than) the resting membrane potential of the neuron. If the resting membrane potential of a neuron is −70 mV, then the voltage-gated Na$^+$ channel threshold for the same neuron should again be about −55 mV, or identical to its action potential threshold. When the excitatory threshold is reached (or breached), the proximal-most voltage-gated Na$^+$ channels, located nearest and just distal to the axon hillock (in multipolar neurons) in the trigger zone of the initial segment will open. These channels will open en masse in an all-or-nothing (absolute) fashion. When this occurs, Na$^+$ influx will be maximal as the action potential begins to reach its maximum peak of depolarization. The action potential will then be propagated along the length of the axon to its terminals, as previously described.

The Influence of Myelin

Once the action potential is initiated, it will continue to propagate without decrement as it travels distally to the axon terminals. It will propagate and will be carried distally along the length of the axon by the successive opening (and closing) of voltage-gated carrier protein channels for Na^+. Because these channels are only located within the axon at regions that are exposed to the extracellular fluid medium, the action potential will propagate distally at each successive region of exposed axon. For neurons with myelinated axons, these exposed regions will correspond to the nodes of Ranvier, as discussed above. For neurons with unmyelinated axons, these exposed regions correspond to the entire length of the axon membrane. Action potentials still propagate without decrement in these kinds of neurons, but at much slower and uniform velocities along their unmyelinated axons.

Fast Potentials

Action potentials and EPSPs represent two forms of depolarization. However, in spite of their similarity, both are in fact quite different. First, unlike EPSPs (slow potentials), action potentials are referred to as *fast potentials*. This is because their amplitudes are not graded or small but instead occur in an all-or-nothing manner. Their amplitudes are also constant and are typically about 100 mV. In addition, their amplitudes do not rely upon any form of summation, and their durations are not graded, but are typically about 1 to 2 ms. Unlike EPSPs (and receptor potentials), action potentials are not local. They propagate

long distances, from the trigger zone within the initial segment, along the axon (or the peripheral process in sensory neurons), to the axon terminals. Rather than spreading in all directions from their point of origin, their travel is unidirectional from the trigger zone, or from the proximal to the distal-most part of the axon. This unidirectional propagation is called *anterograde propagation* or *orthodromic propagation*. In addition, action potentials do not passively degrade over time but are instead *self-propagating* along the entire length of the axon. The propagation of the action potential represents a form of self-perpetuating positive-feedback or feed-forward cycle. Finally, like EPSPs and receptor potentials, but unlike IPSPs, the polarity of action potentials is always positive. To summarize, in response to a presynaptic release of adequate amounts of an excitatory neurotransmitter at the synapse, postsynaptic ligand-gated carrier protein channels for Na^+ open in numbers that allow for an adequate summation of EPSPs. An adequate summation of EPSPs leads to a degree of postsynaptic depolarization that is sufficient to push the postsynaptic neuron (the voltage-gated Na^+ channels) to an excitatory threshold. Once this threshold is reached or breached, the voltage-gated carrier protein channels for Na^+ open and an action potential is generated. It is first generated at the initial segment (or the comparable trigger zone of a peripheral process) and is propagated distally without decrement to the axon terminals.

Stages of an Action Potential

The voltage-gated Na^+ channels responsible for the propagation of an action potential have three states of activity: the resting or closed state, the activated state, and the inactivated state. The inactivated state is also called a refractory state or more commonly the *refractory period*, and the refractory state has two stages: a *relative refractory period* and an *absolute refractory period*. Furthermore, channel inactivation, as in Na$^+$ channel inactivation is not the same as the closed, resting state of the Na$^+$ channel. Prior to the initiation of an action potential, the voltage-gated Na$^+$ channels are in their resting or their closed state. The probability of the channel being opened in this state is extremely low. The action potential is then initiated when the voltage potentials across the plasma membrane (and the voltage-gated Na$^+$ channels) are pushed to their threshold. Beginning at the initial segment (or comparable trigger zone) and continuing distally at each axonal location where voltage-gated Na$^+$ channel activation occurs, there will be a dramatic and explosive inward conductance (influx) of Na$^+$ as the action potential is both generated and propagated. At each successive location, most of the available extracellular Na$^+$ rushes (diffuses) into the axon in less than a millisecond. The inward diffusion of Na$^+$ is driven by the strong inward electrochemical and inward concentration gradients that exist for Na$^+$. Because the amplitude of the action potential is about 100 mV, the membrane potential at the action potential peak of depolarization can reach as high as +30 to +40 mV and even higher. As the action potential moves closer to its peak, two events will occur that will ultimately lead to the termination of the action potential. First, after about a millisecond or so in this mostly opened state, the voltage-gated Na$^+$ channels will spontaneously inactivate. Second, a set of voltage-gated K$^+$ channels that had previously been inactive are also activated in response to the membrane's depolarization at threshold. However, a significant duration of time will pass between the time of their activation and the time of their actual opening. That is, only after a latency of time has passed will these voltage-gated K$^+$ channels finally respond by opening. Therefore, these channels open more slowly or with a time delay in response to depolarization.

In terms of the first event that leads to the termination of an action potential, by the time the action potential has reached its peak, many of the voltage-gated Na$^+$ channels have already been spontaneously inactivated, as stated above. This inactivation of voltage-gated Na$^+$ channels leads to a refractory period. That is, Na$^+$ channel inactivation puts the voltage-gated Na$^+$ channels in a refractory state but not in a closed state. The total refractory period will last for several milliseconds. When these Na$^+$ channels do spontaneously inactivate, the inward Na$^+$ conductance is made to return to its normal nominal level. Because so many voltage-gated Na$^+$ channels are inactivated in the early stage of the refractory period, another action potential cannot be generated, no matter how large the stimulus. This early stage of the refractory period is called the absolute refractory period. The absolute refractory period changes to a relative refractory period, at which time some but not all of the voltage-gated Na$^+$ channels have returned (recovered) to their resting state and can now be opened. The recovered but relatively few-in-number voltage-gated

Na$^+$ channels can be re-opened, provided that the stimulus has a sufficiently high magnitude. Relative refractoriness really means relative to the intensity level of the stimulus and relative to the altered (higher) threshold at that particular moment in time. However, the reactivation of these channels is made difficult not only by the reduced numbers of recovered Na$^+$ channels and higher thresholds required for their re-opening, but also by the voltage-gated K$^+$ channels that are now opened, as indicated above and in greater detail, below. Any potential depolarizing effect resulting from an influx of Na$^+$ can be counteracted, offset, or neutralized by an even greater efflux of K$^+$. Overall, the existence of a refractory period limits the repetition rates of action potentials and limits the rate of signaling (spike discharges) from neurons. It also prevents action potentials from traveling backward and toward the cell body, an effect that is called *antidromic propagation*. When the membrane polarity diminishes to a level that is near to the original threshold level for the action potential, the voltage-gated Na$^+$ channels begin to change from a state of relative refractoriness to their resting or closed state.

In terms of the second event that leads to the termination of an action potential, the activation and the eventual opening of the slower-to-respond voltage-gated K$^+$ channels results in an outward conductance (efflux) of K$^+$ from the axon. K$^+$ rushes (diffuses) out of the axon, driven by its high outward concentration gradient, since it is no longer held inward by the relatively greater net negativity within the axon. This progressive, outward K$^+$ conductance is part of the neuron's repolar-

ization process and occurs as the voltage-gated Na$^+$ channels are entering into their relative refractory periods. Unlike voltage-gated Na$^+$ channels, voltage-gated K$^+$ channels do not inactivate but remain opened for as long as the plasma membrane of the axon is depolarized. As the voltage-gated Na$^+$ channels are changing from a state of relative refractoriness to their resting or closed state, voltage-gated K$^+$ channels continue to remain opened for a few milliseconds, causing a brief *after-polarization,* at which time the membrane potential very briefly falls (hyperpolarizes) below its normal resting potential, before again returning to -70 mV. The voltage-gated K$^+$ channels then close. This added repolarization allows the voltage-gated Na$^+$ channels to finally reset and return to their original resting state in readiness to respond to the next series of EPSP bombardments and the initiation of another action potential. The propagation of an action potential along the axon of a neuron ends with the release of a neurotransmitter from the axon terminals. To summarize, membrane depolarization that reaches threshold (from an accumulation of summated EPSPs) rapidly activates a positive feedback (feed-forward) cycle fueled by the voltage-dependent activation of an inward Na$^+$ conductance (through voltage-dependent Na$^+$ carrier protein channels). This is then followed by the slower activation of a negative feed-back cycle as the depolarization at threshold activates a slower-to-respond outward K$^+$ conductance (through voltage-dependent K$^+$ carrier protein channels) which helps to repolarize the membrane, as the action potential is terminated.

Types of Neurons

Neurons exhibit wide variations in their size. They also exhibit a nearly infinite variety in the arrangement or morphology of their processes (axons and dendrites). However, neurons that provide a common function or those that share a common locus within the nervous system often resemble each other in their structure. Hence, neurons are quite often classified according to the morphological arrangement and structure of their processes. Some of the terms used to describe and classify neurons are multipolar, bipolar, unipolar, or pseudo-unipolar. To begin with, the vast majority of vertebrate neurons are multipolar. The term *multipolar* implies that multiple dendritic projections arise from the cell body. *Multipolar neurons* can transmit both sensory and motor impulses and are characteristically found in the brain, brainstem, and spinal cord, and in the peripheral autonomic nervous system. The lower motor neurons that arise from the brainstem and spinal cord and innervate skeletal muscle are all mulipolar neurons. The neuron illustrated in Figure 9–1 resembles a multipolar neuron. The primary, secondary, and tertiary dendritic branches of some multipolar neurons may be elaborate and can enormously increase the total postsynaptic target surface that is available to other neurons. The Purkinje cells within the cortex of the cerebellum serve as an illustrative example of multipolar neurons having elaborate sets of dendritic branches. In the Purkinje cell, the dendrites are wide at their base and taper rapidly. The primary, secondary, and tertiary branches have a smooth surface, while more distal dendritic branches are beset with great numbers of dendritic spines or *gemmules*. Gemmules are locations where axons from other neurons seem to prefer to target, as they are areas that exhibit high concentrations of postsynaptic binding site-receptor complexes for ligand-gated carrier protein channels.

Bipolar neurons are usually sensory in function and transmit impulses generated by olfactory, visual, vestibular, and auditory receptor endings. The Type-I auditory (and vestibular) neurons of the eighth cranial nerve (Chapter 10) are bipolar neurons. Neurons that transmit information involving olfaction (smell) are also bipolar neurons. The cell body of bipolar neurons is centered between a long myelinated axonal process (the axon) and a long, myelinated dendritic process that is located distally to the dendritic zone. The *dendritic zone* is the receptive membrane region of the dendrite. The dendritic zone is unmyelinated. *Unipolar neurons*, alternatively, have a characteristic "T" shape, and true unipolar neurons are more commonly found in invertebrates. The unipolar neuron's cell body gives off a single combined axonal/dendritic process, resulting from the fusion of its two polar processes during development. At some distance from the cell body, the process divides into a set of dendrites and a central axon branch that enters into presynaptic relations with other neurons.

Finally, the *pseudo-unipolar neuron* has an appearance that is somewhat similar to that of a unipolar neuron. However, unlike the cell body of the bipolar neuron that is centered between its long myelinated axonal and long, myelinated dendritic process, the cell body of a pseudo-unipolar neuron is located to the side of, and is attached by a stalk to, both processes which appear to be fused or continuous. Early in development, pseudo-unipolar neurons begin as bipolar neurons, but during development the cell body expands asymmetrically, leaving behind a stalk from which both processes appear to emerge. The pseudo-unipolar neuron is typical of most cutaneous sensory neurons. It is the kind of neuron (cell body) typically found within both the dorsal root ganglion of the spinal cord and the mesencephalic nucleus of the trigeminal nerve (CN-V). The cell bodies of pseudo-unipolar neurons are also the type of neuron often found within the peripheral sensory ganglion of cranial nerves, which are associated almost exclusively with the brainstem.

As indicated above, neurons exhibit wide variations in their size. Cell bodies can range in size from 4 or 5 to 100 microns (10^{-6} of a meter) in diameter. In general, the size of the cell body of a neuron tends to be proportional to the length, diameter, and complexity of its dendritic branches, and to the numbers of terminal arborizations at the distal ends of its axon. Many axons are short, or approximately 1 mm or so in length. Some, like the large axons of pyramidal motor neurons that begin in the cerebral cortex and extend to the sacral spinal cord, are much longer. These axons can measure 1 m or more in length. These giant pyramidal motor neurons, with their pyramid-shaped cell bodies, originate in the precentral gyrus of the cortex, and their axons are part of the larger group of descending projection fibers known as upper motor neurons. Collectively, their axons descend as pyramidal motor neurons of the corti-

cospinal (cortex to spinal cord) or the corticobulbar (cortex to brainstem) fiber pathways (see below).

Neurons, both sensory (afferent) and motor (efferent), can also be classified in terms of the conduction velocity of their axons, which is directly related to the diameter of their axons, and whether or not their axons are myelinated. Hence, there is an A, B, and C-class of axon fibers. Both the A and B classes are myelinated, whereas the C class of fibers has no myelin. The A class of motor fibers is further divided into an A-alpha, A-beta, A-gamma, and an A-delta subclass of fibers, based on diameter and conduction velocity. For instance, the A-alpha neurons are the largest. The A-alpha motor neurons have large diameter axons, are multipolar, and have high conduction velocities that average about 50 to 120 m/s. Their cell bodies are located within the CNS (brainstem or spinal cord), and their axons extend outward into the periphery and terminate exclusively on skeletal muscle. The A-alpha motor neurons are the cranial motor (from the brainstem) and spinal motor (from the spinal cord) neurons that belong to the larger, lower motor neuron class of skeletal motor neurons. These lower motor neurons fall under the direct control of the upper motor neurons, which as indicated above, consist of the corticobulbar (cortex to brainstem) and corticospinal (cortex to spinal cord) motor pathways, all of which are made up of descending pyramidal (and extrapyramidal) motor fibers.

The cell bodies of the considerably smaller-in-diameter axons of the A-gamma motor neurons are also located in the CNS. Their conduction velocities are quite a bit slower, averaging about

40 m/s. These neurons are also classified as lower motor neurons. Their axons travel into the periphery where they terminate, innervating the intrafusal muscle fibers (the polar regions) of the muscle spindles that are embedded within the skeletal muscles. *Muscle spindles* are a type of receptor called a proprioceptor. Muscle spindles in particular respond to skeletal muscle stretch and participate in the regulation of fine motor coordination by way of their interactions with the A-gamma motor neurons. The A-gamma motor neuron interactions with muscle spindles are also responsible for the maintenance of skeletal muscle tone. These lower motor neurons principally fall under the control of the descending upper motor neurons that belong to the extrapyramidal motor system of fibers, also traveling within the descending corticobulbar and corticospinal fiber pathways. As yet another cell-type example, the cell bodies of the even smaller-in-diameter, axons of the A-delta motor neurons are also located within the CNS. Their conduction velocities are once again a bit slower, averaging about 15 m/s. These neurons once again represent a type of lower motor neuron. Their axons travel into the periphery and constitute the myelinated, preganglionic neurons of the autonomic nervous system. By contrast, motor neurons that constitute the autonomic postganglionic nerve fibers are the peripherally located, small diameter unmyelinated C-class of motor fibers, with conduction velocities of about 2 m/s.

Sensory fibers can also be specified for the A-class of neurons, specifically for the A-alpha, the A-beta, and the A-delta fibers. This classification scheme typically utilizes Roman numer-als and lowercase letters. For instance, the subtypes are typically labeled as Ia, Ib, II, III, or IV. The cell bodies of most sensory neurons are usually located within the peripheral ganglion associated with either the brainstem (as with the cranial nerves), or the spinal cord, as in the dorsal root ganglia associated with the spinal nerves. To begin with, the A-alpha sensory neurons are again very large in terms of cell size. They also have large-diameter axons with conduction velocities averaging about 120 m/s. The A-alpha-Ia neurons are the primary afferent neurons for the muscle spindles. Their dendrites are located within the central receptive regions of the muscle spindles. Together with the A-beta II sensory neurons (see below), they respond to skeletal muscle stretch and provide direct proprioceptive feedback to the dendrites and cell bodies of the A-alpha (skeletal) motor neurons located within the CNS. The A-alpha-Ib neurons are the afferent neurons for the *Golgi tendon organs.* Golgi tendon organs are the proprioceptors that respond to forces placed upon the muscle tendon during skeletal muscle contraction.

The slightly smaller-in-diameter axons of the A-beta-II class of sensory neurons exhibit conduction velocities of about 70 m/s. As indicated above, these neurons also innervate the muscle spindles and are referred to as the secondary muscle spindle afferents. This same class of neuron also conveys somatosensory information from cutaneous receptors found in the skin and joints, processing the sensations of touch, pressure, and vibration. The even smaller-in-diameter axons of the A-delta-III sensory neurons have conduction velocities of about 15 m/s, as indicated above. These neurons convey sensory information from cutaneous and thermoreceptors found in the skin and joints that process the sensations of touch, pressure, temperature, and thermal pain. The A-delta-III sensory neurons also convey information about sharp pain from cutaneous and deep, free-nerve endings. Finally, the small-diameter unmyelinated C-class of sensory fibers with very slow conduction velocities (2 m/s) convey information about slow, dull, aching, and/or burning pain and itch, from the cutaneous and deep, free-nerve endings.

The Peripheral Nervous System (PNS)

As indicated above, neurons of the nervous system that are located outside of the brain, brainstem, and spinal cord, or simply the three anatomical structures that define the central nervous system (CNS), are said to be situated within the peripheral nervous system (PNS). The PNS consists of 12 pairs of cranial nerves and 31 pairs of spinal nerves. Cranial and spinal nerves contain both sensory (afferent) and motor (efferent) neurons. As indicated above, sensory neurons of the cranial and spinal nerves link the peripheral sensory receptors, as well as the internal sensory receptors of the internal organs, to structures within the CNS. The PNS also includes the sensory receptors and ganglion of these peripheral neurons. Recall as well that motor or efferent neurons of the cranial and spinal nerves also link the CNS to the skeletal, smooth, and cardiac muscle of the internal organs. These peripheral nerve bundles were said to belong to the lower motor neurons. In most cases, the cell bodies and dendrites of the motor neurons that

comprise the cranial and spinal nerves will be located within the brainstem and spinal cord, respectively. It is only their axonal processes that extend outward into the periphery to innervate their targets. Branches of the cranial and spinal nerves infiltrate virtually all parts of the body, conveying signals to and from the CNS.

The Cranial Nerves

The 12 pairs of cranial nerves (CNs) function as modified spinal nerves and provide sensory (general and special) and motor innervation to the head, as well as to much of the neck. Their name *cranial* is derived from the fact that they emerge from the cranium, which may be contrasted to the spinal nerves that emerge from the spinal cord. The 12 pairs of CNs are labeled by Roman numerals, as I through XII, and can easily be visualized as they exit from or enter into the ventral surface of the brain, much of the ventral surface of the brainstem, and part of the upper cervical segments of the spinal cord. Their motor innervation includes the innervation that they provide to voluntary (skeletal) as well as to smooth or cardiac (involuntary autonomic) muscle. Sometimes the skeletal muscles that are innervated by certain of the cranial nerves (CNs-V, VII, IX, X, XI) are given a special name based on their embryological origin. The term *branchial* or *branchiomeric* is often attached to those skeletal muscles located within and near the head and neck. In humans and in other mammals, structures that develop into the gill arches (or branchial arches) in fish, develop instead into the various skeletal muscles associated with the larynx, the pharynx, the jaw, and the face. Hence, skeletal muscles of the larynx, pharynx, jaw, and face are often associated with their branchial or branchiomeric embryological origins. Functionally, however, branchiomeric muscles fall under the same voluntary control as skeletal muscles, and branchiomeric muscles are indeed identical to skeletal muscles.

In terms of the various cranial nerve functions that are provided, individual CNs may be purely motor in function (CNs-III, IV, VI, XI, XII), purely sensory in function (CNs-I, II, VIII), or mixed in function with both sensory and motor components (CNs-V, VII, IX, X). Some of these motor functions include chewing (CN-V), the control and modulation of swallowing (CNs-IX, X, XI, XII), voicing (CNs-X, XI), the movement of the eyes (CNs-III, IV, VI), the movement of the head (CN-XI), the movement of the tongue (CN-XII), the movement of the muscles of the face (CN-VII), and involuntary, autonomic parasympathetic functions involving the activation of smooth (CNs-III, VII, IX, X) and cardiac (X) muscle. Through their innervations, the CNs also provide special senses, such as the sense of smell (CN-I), the sense of vision (CN-II), the sense of hearing and balance (CN-VIII), and the gustatory sense, known as taste (CNs-VII, IX, X). They also function by carrying (cutaneous) somatic or what is called general-sensory (CNs-V, VII, IX, X) and visceral sensations, or what is called general visceral-sensory information (CNs-IX, X) from the head and neck, to the CNS.

Cranial Nerve (CN) I: The Olfactory Nerve

The first cranial nerve (CN-I) is the olfactory nerve. The word *olfactory* means "smell bearing." The olfactory nerve functions in carrying the special (afferent) sense of smell, enabling an organism to detect odors. Hence, CN-I is functionally classified as special-sensory. The CNS structures that process this special sense are collectively referred to as the rhinencephalon (nose brain). What is actually visualized on the ventral surface of the brain is not CN-I, but is in fact the olfactory CNS bulb and tracts for CN-I. The *olfactory bulb* is actually an outgrowth of the telencephalon (or forebrain). The olfactory bulb, which is located in the *anterior cranial fossa* of the cranium, is really a collection of olfactory nuclei where thin, unmyelinated olfactory axons ultimately terminate. These thin, unmyelinated olfactory bipolar neurons, numbering several million, arise from the olfactory mucosa, which is composed of epithelial tissue located on the lateral wall of the nasal cavity. This *olfactory epithelium* as it is called, is located in the nasal cavity just anterior and superior to the nasopharynx. Odorants can reach the olfactory epithelium by the oral route, or by the nasal route. The mucous-secreting epithelial tissue of the nasal mucosa contains the dendritic *odorant receptors* for these bipolar olfactory neurons. Odorants must diffuse across the mucous layer of the olfactory epithelium to activate the chemically sensitive cilia of these odorant receptors. Each neuron probably expresses only one type of odorant receptor. However, these odorant receptors can distinguish between thousands of odors at very low concentrations. There appears to be greater than 1,000 different types of odorant receptors, and some individuals can discriminate from 5000 to 10,000 different odors. Sensory endings of trigeminal nerve fibers (CN-V) are also found in the olfactory epithelium for the detection of noxious odors, like concentrated ammonia.

The very thin, unmyelinated axon processes of the olfactory bipolar neurons are collectively called *olfactory fila* or threads, and have very slow conduction velocities. Collectively, the olfactory fila constitute what would be called CN-I. These axons or threads collect into bundles as they pass superiorly through the tiny perforations in the *cribriform plates* of the ethmoid bone of the skull. The ethmoid bone is part of the floor of the anterior cranial fossa of the cranium. The perforated cribriform plates, therefore, separate the nasal and cranial cavities and provide a bony conduit for the olfactory axons as they enter the anterior cranial fossa of the cranium. Each bundle ends in the olfactory bulb, specifically in a set of nuclei found within the bulb. Each set of nuclei is called a glomerulus. The axon of each olfactory neuron will synapse in only one glomerulus and each glomerulus receives over 1,000 converging axons. However, each glomerulus receives input from only one type of olfactory odorant receptor. About 20 to 50 relay neurons leave each glomerulus, travel a very short distance, and synapse with the mitral cells within the olfactory bulb. Myelinated axons of the mitral cells become the olfactory tract that courses in a posterior direction along the ventral surface of the frontal lobes, terminating in the olfactory cortex. The olfactory cortex consists of a number of distinct areas, the largest of which is the *piriform cortex* of the medial temporal lobe. The piriform cortex is essentially the olfactory cortex. Unlike all other sensory systems, olfactory sensory information from olfactory fila (CN-I) reaches the telencephalon (olfactory cortex) without first terminating in the thalamus. Total damage to the olfactory nerve produces *anosmia* which is an inability to smell or detect odorants. Damage to this system can also produce associated problems with the sense of taste.

Cranial Nerve (CN) II: The Optic Nerve

The second cranial nerve (CN-II) is the optic nerve. The optic nerve functions in carrying the special (afferent) sense of vision, enabling an organism to visually detect objects in the environment. Hence, CN-II is functionally classified as special-sensory. Its role is to convey visual information from the light-sensitive photoreceptors within the retina, to the CNS. Visual input in the form of light enters the pupils of the eyes and passes (posterior) into the deep layers of the retina. Here, light energy is transformed or transduced into receptor potentials by the rods and cones that form the photoreceptor layer of the retina. In the retina, information from the rods and cones is then relayed forward (anterior) to the retinal bipolar cells, which are the primary sensory neurons of the visual system. The axons of the retinal bipolar cells then relay the information, again in an even further anterior direction, to the retinal ganglion cells which are the secondary sensory neurons of the visual system. The axons of the retinal ganglion cells converge toward the optic disc, located near the center of the retina where no photoreceptors exist, and exit the posterior of the eye as the optic nerve. In spite of the fact that the optic nerve consists of second-order axons that technically form a tract, that part of the tract that runs from the back of the eye to the optic chiasm is traditionally called the optic nerve. From the eye, each optic nerve passes in a posterior direction, exits from the orbit, and passes through the optic canal. At the distal end of the optic canal, the nerve enters the *middle cranial fossa* of the cranium, at the level of the diencephalon of the brain. Here, the optic nerves from both eyes join to form the *optic chiasma* or *optic chiasm*, which means *optic cross*. At the optic chiasm, approximately one-half of the axons of each optic nerve will cross, and will continue postchiasmatically as contralateral optic tract fibers. The remaining postchiasmatic fibers will continue on the ipsilateral side as uncrossed optic tract fibers. Optic fibers (axons) located posterior to the optic chiasm or postchiasmatically become fibers of the *optic tract*. Hence, only the optic fibers located anterior to the optic chiasm belong to the optic nerve.

At the optic chiasm, axons of retinal ganglion cells arising from the right hemi-retina (half-retina) of the left eye, and from the left hemi-retina of the right eye will cross to the other side. Therefore, axons arising from the medial-most hemi-retinas of both eyes cross the midline at the optic chiasm. Axons of retinal ganglion cells arising from the left hemi-retina of the left eye, and from the right hemi-retina of the right eye will not cross. That is, axons arising from the lateral-most hemi-retinas of both eyes do not cross the midline at the optic chiasm. Beyond the optic chiasm, both contralateral and ipsilateral fibers of both optic tracts continue in a posterior direction as they circle around the cerebral peduncles. Fibers of the optic tract then terminate, either in the right or the left *lateral geniculate body or nucleus* (LGN). The LGN are a set of paired thalamic nuclei located in the posterior ventral-lateral thalamus.

Neurons of the LGN project their axons outward from the thalamus and into the internal capsule (of fibers) that surrounds the thalamic nuclei. These fiber tracts course posteriorly, enter the cerebral hemispheres and terminate in the primary visual cortex located in the occipital lobes of either hemisphere. The primary visual cortex corresponds to Brodmann area 17. Integrated visual signals from the primary visual cortex are then sent by way of association fibers to the adjacent, visual association regions of the occipital lobe (Brodmann area 18) for interpretation, based on prior visual experience. Therefore, visual sensations that are generated in the left hemi-retina of each eye are processed in the primary visual cortex of the left cerebral hemisphere. Visual sensations that are generated in the right hemi-retina of each eye are processed in the primary visual cortex of the right cerebral hemisphere. Furthermore, the entire region in the environment from which light is received is called the visual field. Both eyes typically will focus on the same object in the environment and often view the same visual field, but from slightly different angles due to the physical separation between the eyes. The visual field is usually divided into a right and a left half. It is also divided into an upper and a lower half, therefore creating four quadrants. These quadrants are projected onto four corresponding quadrants of the retina. As the rays of light converge and pass through the pupil, the image of the visual field that is projected onto the retina is both upside-down and reversed, or backward. Light that is detected in the right visual field is picked up by the left hemi-retina of each eye, and is therefore processed in the primary visual cortex of the left cerebral hemisphere. Light that is detected in the left visual field is picked up by the right hemi-retina of each eye, and is therefore processed in the primary visual cortex of the right cerebral hemisphere.

Some of the neurons of the LGN project their axons into the upper-most part of the brainstem, known as the *midbrain*, where these axons then travel to the dorsal-most part of the midbrain. Here they terminate, either in the right or the left nucleus of the *superior colliculus*. The superior colliculi, therefore, are a set of paired nuclei located in the upper-most part of dorsal midbrain, an area known as the *midbrain tectum*. At this location, visual, auditory, and motor information may be integrated for the production of a startle, or orienting reflex, often referred to as the tectospinal reflex.

Axons of other LGN neurons reach another area of the midbrain located slightly rostral (superior) and anterior to the midbrain tectum. This area of the midbrain is referred to as the pretectum. Here, they terminate within either a right or a left, and mostly midline-located, Edinger-Westphal nucleus. This nucleus is one of six nearby nuclei that belong to CN-III (the oculomotor nerve). The Edinger-Westphal nucleus is strictly parasympathetic in function (general visceral-motor) and is part of the larger autonomic nervous system. In response to signals from the retina and as a reaction to light, the Edinger-Westphal nucleus mediates the ipsilateral lens-accommodation reflex and the pupillary-light reflex, as discussed below under the heading of CN-III.

Damage to any part of the visual system can produce visual deficits. The type and degree of the deficit will depend not only upon where but how extensive the damage happens to be.

Cranial Nerve (CN) III: The Oculomotor Nerve

The third cranial nerve (CN-III) is the oculomotor nerve. The oculomotor nerve functions primary in activating most of the skeletal (extraocular) muscles that move the eyes. The term *oculomotor* means *eye-mover*. CN-III is composed of a nearly paired set of six nuclei in total. The six, nearly paired set of nuclei of CN-III are located in the midbrain, in an area that is just ventral (anterior) to the cerebral aqueduct, and located at the same level as, but just rostral (superior) to the more dorsal, superior colliculus. This area is called the *midbrain tegmentum*. Five of the six nuclei give rise to lower motor neurons that course in a ventral (anterior) direction through the tegmentum. These lower motor neurons are therefore *general skeletal-motor* in function. The sixth nucleus, which is general visceral-motor in function, is located just rostral and dorsal to the complex of skeletal-motor nuclei of CN-III, in a region called the pre-tectum. This sixth nucleus is the Edinger-Westphal nucleus, and it is part of the parasympathetic division of the larger autonomic nervous system. Its preganglionic lower (visceral)-motor axons also course ventrally through the tegmentum and join up with axons from the other five skeletal-motor nuclei. The fibers then collectively emerge as CN-III from the ventral surface of the brainstem, at the junction of the midbrain and pons. Fibers of CN-III travel collectively through the middle cranial fossa of the cranium, and eventually enter the bony orbit for the eye. Hence, CN-III is classified as both skeletal-motor and as general visceral-motor in function.

Skeletal–Motor Function

CN-III provides mostly ipsilateral skeletal-motor innervation to four of the six extraocular muscles that move the eye, as illustrated in Figure 9–2. The extraocular muscles that are innervated by CN-III are the medial rectus, the superior rectus, the inferior rectus, and the inferior oblique. The medial rectus pulls or rotates the ipsilateral eyeball in a medial direction. The eyeball is therefore pulled inward or is adducted. The superior rectus primarily pulls or rotates the contralateral eyeball upward (elevation). Secondarily, it

rotates the top of the eyeball toward the nose or medially (intorsion), so that gaze is directed upward and inward, or medially. The inferior rectus primarily pulls or rotates the ipsilateral eyeball downward (depression). Secondarily, it rotates the top of the eyeball away from the nose or laterally (extorsion) so that gaze is directed downward and outward, or laterally. Finally, the inferior oblique primarily rotates the top of the ipsilateral eyeball away from the nose or laterally (extorsion). Secondarily it pulls or rotates the eyeball upward (elevation), and gaze is subsequently directed upward and outward, or laterally. CN-III does not innervate the remaining two extraocular muscles. These muscles are the superioir oblique, which is instead innervated by the fourth cranial nerve (CN-IV), and the lateral recus, which is innervated by the sixth cranial nerve

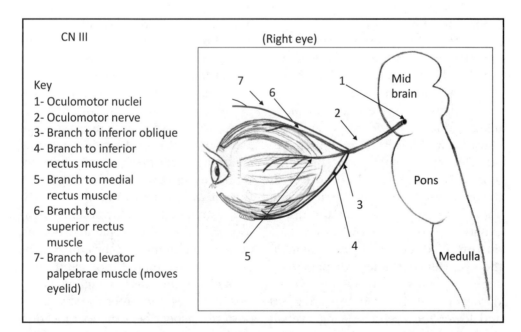

Figure 9–2. General skeletal-motor innervation of the extraocular muscles of the eye, all of which are controlled by the separate nuclei of the oculomotor nerve (CN-III). Courtesy of F. Musiek and the neuroaudiology lab, University of Connecticut.

(CN-VI). All of the extraocular muscles participate in both conjugate eye movements, as well as in convergent eye movements. Conjugate eye movements refer to the ability of the eyes to symmetrically track or follow an object in the visual field as it is moved left, right, up or down. Convergent eye movements refer to the ability of the eyes to symmetrically track or follow an object in the visual field as it is moved from far-to-near, near-to-far, relative to the midline of the face. In order to change visual fixation or to maintain fixation on an object that is moving, the eyes must move together as a pair, with a fine degree of precision. This requires a great deal of neural synchronization of the extraocular muscles to each eye. This can only be accomplished with the collective and synchronous control of cranial nerves III, IV, and VI by specialized regions within the brainstem, as well as by higher regulatory centers within the cerebral cortex.

The fifth skeletal-motor nucleus of CN-III is a ventral midline structure that bilaterally innervates the levator palpebrae superioris muscles (see Figure 9–2). This muscle does not move the eye but is instead responsible for elevating and lowering the upper eyelid. The levator palpebrae superioris muscle is synchronized to work with the extraocular muscles that elevate and lower the eye so that the upper eyelid can follow in the upward or downward direction of movement of the eye. Hence, the levator palpebrae superioris muscles raise the eyelids during eyeball elevation (upward gaze) and lower the eyelids during eyeball depression (downward gaze). The levator palpebrae superioris muscle is not involved in the corneal (eye-blink) reflex. Instead, this protective reflex is initiated by sensory input from the eye and/or its surrounding regions. These sensations are then carried by the sensory innervation provided by cranial nerve five (CN-V). The actual eye-blink is due to the contraction of the orbicularis oculi muscles. Motor innervation to these muscles is provided by cranial nerve seven (CN-VII).

General Visceral–Motor (Autonomic) Function

As indicated above, the sixth motor nucleus of CN-III is autonomic in function and is, therefore, general visceral-motor (efferent) in function. The Edinger-Westphal nucleus is a dorsal, nearly midline structure located just dorsal to the complex of skeletal-motor nuclei of CN-III, in the region of the midbrain called the pre-tectum. The pre-tectum is a midbrain region that is located between the superior colliculus and the caudal-most part of the thalamus (diencephalon). Recall that in response to light striking the retinal photoreceptors, the Edinger-Westphal nucleus responds to the inputs it receives from neurons of the LGN. Myelinated, preganglionic axons that arise ipsilaterally from this parasympathetic nucleus enter the bony orbit for the eye, together with the skeletal–motor axon fibers of CN-III. These preganglionic, lower motor neuron axon fibers then separate from the nerve and terminate in the *ciliary ganglion*. Unmyelinated postganglionic axons leave the ciliary ganglion as the ciliary nerves and enter the eye at its posterior aspect near the exit location of the optic nerve. The nerve fibers then travel to the anterior region of the eye and innervate both the constrictor pupillae and ciliary muscles. The constrictor pupillae is a smooth (sphincter) muscle that contracts in response to efferent signals from the ciliary nerves. Contraction of this pupillary sphincter results in a smaller pupil, or pupillary constriction, which helps to sharpen the image falling on the retina. The ciliary muscles attach to the lens of the eye and keep it relatively flat. In response to efferent signals from the ciliary nerves, the ciliary muscles contract and allow the curvature of the lens to increase. The added curvature or accommodation improves near-vision focus. The Edinger-Westphal nucleus therefore mediates the lens-accommodation reflex and the pupillary-light reflex. When bright light is presented to either eye, both reflexes will occur in the same eye. This is called the direct light reflex. However, when bright light is presented to either eye, both reflexes will also occur in the opposite eye. This is called the consensual light reflex. The consensual light reflex is made possible by additional interneurons located within the pre-tectal area that decussate or cross over to the other side of the midbrain. In sum, CN-II provides the sensory input, which is usually activated by the delivery of bright light to the retinal photoreceptors, and CN-III controls the smooth muscles that regulate pupillary constriction and lens accommodation.

Lower motor damage to CN-III can result in an inability to synchronize the eyes toward objects in the environment. This asynchronous eye turning is referred to as *strabismus*. Strabismus leads to the symptom of double vision which is called *diplopia*. Furthermore, inactivation of the levator palpebrae superioris will produce the symptom known as *ptosis*. Ptosis is the droop-

ing of an eyelid, characterized by an eyelid that covers half of one eye when the eyes are open. Finally, damage to the Edenger-Westphal nucleus or its axons leads to decreased parasympathetic (and subsequently increased sympathetic) tone in the ciliary nerves. This results in a loss of the pupillary light reflex, and a pupil or pupils that remain dilated. This symptom is known as *mydriasis*. Such damage or dysfunction may also create an inability to focus on near objects. Collectively then, all of the symptoms associated with CN-III damage or dysfunction are generally referred to as *oculomotor ophthalmoplegia*.

Cranial Nerve (CN) IV: The Trochlear Nerve

The fourth cranial nerve (CN-IV) is the *trochlear nerve*. Like CN-III, the trochlear nerve functions primarily in activating a specified set of skeletal muscles that move the eyes. Hence, CN-IV is functionally classified as general skeletal-motor. The term *trochlear* means "pulley." CN-IV is composed of only one pair of skeletal-motor nuclei. Hence, CN-IV innervates only one pair of extraocular muscles, as illustrated in Figure 9–3. The extraocular muscles that are innervated by CN-IV are the contralateral superior oblique muscles. The paired nuclei of CN-IV are located in the midbrain tegmentum at the same level as the more dorsally (in the tectum) located nuclei of the *inferior colliculus*. This location is just below the level of the skeletal-motor nuclei of CN-III. Like the motor nuclei of CN-III, the paired nuclei of CN-IV are situated near the midline of the midbrain tegmentum, just ventral (anterior) to the cerebral

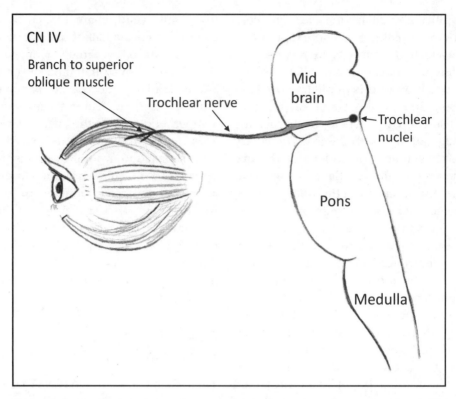

Figure 9–3. General skeletal-motor innervation of the single extraocular muscle of the eye that is controlled by the trochlear nerve (CN-IV). Courtesy of F. Musiek and the neuroaudiology lab, University of Connecticut.

aqueduct. Axons exit from the paired nuclei and travel in a dorsal (posterior) direction, around the cerebral aqueduct, and then decussate (cross over). Each of the paired nerves exits from the dorsal surface of the midbrain and then turns laterally. These lower motor neurons then circle back around the cerebral peduncles, traveling in a ventral (anterior) direction along the outer margins of the midbrain. Each CN-IV emerges ventrally in close proximity to CN-III and enters the bony orbit for the eye where it innervates the contralateral superior oblique muscle. The superior oblique primarily rotates the top of the contralateral eyeball toward the nose, or in a medial direction (intorsion). Sec-

ondarily, it pulls or rotates the eyeball downward (depression). Hence, gaze is directed downward and outward, or laterally. As with CN-III, lower motor damage to CN-IV often leads to asynchronous eye turning, or strabismus, followed by double vision or diplopia.

Cranial Nerve (CN) V: The Trigeminal Nerve

The fifth cranial nerve (CN-V) is the *trigeminal nerve*. The term *trigeminal* means "triplet" or "three twins." CN-V is generally responsible for providing sensory input to the CNS, such as tactile, proprioceptive, nociceptive (pain), and temperature information from all of the head and neck, the face, including all of the mouth and eyes. It is also responsible for providing motor innervation to the lower jaw (mandible), as well as to other skeletal-motor structures (see below). The large sensory and smaller motor roots of CN-V emerge from the left and right lateral surfaces of the area of the mid-pons. The sensory ganglion of CN-V is the most prominent in size of all the cranial nerves. The sensory ganglion of CN-V is often referred to as the trigeminal, the Gasserian, or the semilu-

nar ganglion. The large paired sensory ganglia occupy a cavity on either side called Meckel's cave located in the dura mater near the apex within the petrous (bone) division on either side of the temporal bone.

CN-V has three major divisions. These divisions are the ophthalmic (V_1), the maxillary (V_2), and the mandibular (V_3), as illustrated in Figure 9–4. Two of the three divisions (V_1 and V_2) carry only general-sensory information, while the third division (V_3) is mixed. The third

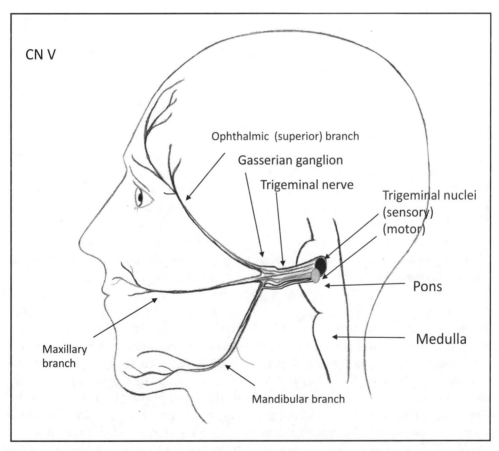

Figure 9–4. General-sensory innervation of the head and face is provided by the ophthalmic (V_1), the maxillary (V_2), and the mandibular (V_3) divisons of CN-V. Because the third division (V_3) is mixed, it also carries special-skeletal (branchial) motor fibers that innervate the muscles of mastication, the tensor veli palatini muscle, and the tensor tympani muscle of the middle ear. Courtesy of F. Musiek and the neuroaudiology lab, University of Connecticut.

division is composed of neurons that provide both general-sensory input and skeletal-motor output. Recall that skeletal muscles innervated by certain of the cranial nerves (CNs-V, VII, IX, X, XI) are often given the name of branchial or branchiomeric, based on their embryological origins. Hence, the motor functions provided by CN-V, as well as by CNs-VII, IX, X, XI, are often referred to as branchial-motor, branchial efferent, or more commonly as special-visceral efferent. However, use of the term *visceral-motor*, as in general visceral-motor, could easily be mistakenly associated with the involuntary control of smooth muscle, or of other internal (glandular) body tissues. Recall that branchiomeric muscles fall under voluntary control and are identical to skeletal (striated or somatic) muscles. Therefore, in the present context, innervation of the branchiomeric muscles by CN-V (as well as by CNs- VII, IX, X, XI) will be classified as special-skeletal (branchial) motor in function. Hence, general-sensory information is carried by all three divisions of CN-V. Special-skeletal (branchial) motor functions are also carried by the (mixed), third mandibular division, or V_3.

General–Sensory Function

To begin with, sensory innervation of the skin covering the upper face, the forehead, the scalp, the eye and its parts that include the iris, the upper eyelid, the conjunctiva (lining of eyelid), the dorsum of nose, the nasal mucosa, the ethmoid bone, the frontal sinus, the lacrimal (tear) glands, and parts of the dura mater, is carried by the peripheral neuron processes of the ophthalmic division (V_1) of CN-V that exit the skull through the superior orbital fissure, as they make their way to their cell bodies located within the trigeminal ganglion. Recall that sensory innervation of the cornea of the eye provides the stimulus input for the eye-blink/corneal reflex. Also indicated in previous sections, the motor output for the corneal reflex will be provided by CN-VII. Next, sensory innervation of the upper teeth and the upper gums, the upper lip, the skin on lateral and posterior sides of nose, the mucous membranes of the nose, the lower eyelids, the anterior part of the temple, the upper jaw (maxilla), the upper cheek, the roof of the mouth, the maxillary sinuses, the nasopharynx, and once again, parts of the dura mater, is carried by the peripheral neuron processes of the maxillary division (V_2) of CN-V that exit the skull through the foramen rotundum, as they make their way to their cell bodies located within the trigeminal ganglion. Finally, sensory innervation of the lower jaw (the mandible), the lower teeth and gums, the lower lip, the mucous membranes of the lower jaw, the external auditory canal, all lower parts of the face including the skin surfaces, the cheeks, the temporomandibular joint, the tympanic membrane, the pinna, the parotid salivary gland, the mastoid air cells, and for the third time, parts of dura mater, is carried by the peripheral neuron processes of the mandibular division (V_3) of CN-V that exit the skull through the foramen ovale, as they make their way to their cell bodies located within the trigeminal ganglion. The *lingual nerve* is also an important branch of V_3 as it innervates the anterior two-thirds of the ipsilateral tongue, as well as the ipsilateral floor of the mouth. The lingual nerve carries information related to the sensations of pain, pressure, and touch applied to the tongue and does not carry sensory information related to the special sensation of taste.

It should be evident that peripheral nerves from all three sensory divisions of CN-V converge at the trigeminal ganglion (see Figure 9–4). With the exception (see below) of the peripheral processes carried within V_3 that happen to be associated with pressure and stretch (proprioception), the neuron cell bodies of all the sensory neurons are located within the large, flattened crescent shaped trigeminal ganglion. The centrally projecting processes (axons) of the neurons within the trigeminal ganglion constitute the sensory root of CN-V. These axons pass into the lateral part of the mid-pons, and enter the *pontine tegmentum*. The pontine tegmentum is an area deep within the pons, located just ventral (anterior) to the cerebral aqueduct and fourth ventricle. Here, the sensory axons terminate within the *principal sensory nucleus of CN-V*. This nucleus is also known as the pontine trigeminal nucleus. The principal sensory nucleus of CN-V is the largest of the cranial nerve nuclei. It is vertically elongated at both of its ends. It blends into two long and slender nuclear subsets, one that extends caudally (downward) and one that extends rostrally (upward). Caudally, the principal sensory nucleus of CN-V extends from the pontine tegmentum, as far down as the second or third cervical spinal segment (C2 and C3). This caudal extension is called the *spinal trigeminal nucleus of CN-V*. The principal sensory nucleus of CN-V also extends rostrally (upward) as far as the rostral midbrain. This long, thin sickle shaped, rostral extension is called the *mesencephalic nucleus of CN-V*.

Recall that some of the cell bodies of the sensory neurons within V_3 are not localized within the trigeminal ganglion. The skeletal muscles of the mandible represent the muscles of mastication and the associated proprioceptors, embedded within these muscles, provide feedback for the control of the rate and degree of both biting and chewing. The peripheral neuron processes of primary and secondary afferents that innervate the embedded muscle spindles and the Golgi-tendon organs (proprioceptors) also travel with the collective mandibular division (V_3) as they exit the skull through the foramen ovale. These neurons additionally carry proprioceptive impulses from the teeth, the periodontium, the hard palate, and the joint capsules of the mandible. Peripheral sensory processes originating from the proprioceptors, however, travel past the trigeminal ganglion and pass directly into the lateral part of the mid-pons with the centrally projecting axons of V_3. These peripheral sensory processes enter the pontine tegmentum, turn in a rostral direction and make their way to the location of their cell bodies. That location happens to be within the mesencephalic nucleus. The mesencephalic nucleus consists of pseudo-unipolar neurons. The nucleus itself, which is a CNS structure, is homologous to the dorsal root ganglion of the PNS. Hence, the mesencephalic nucleus of CN-V is a ganglion of sorts that is located within the CNS. It is composed of the cell bodies of the sensory neurons associated with pressure and stretch (proprioception) that arise from the muscles of mastication and travel within the mandibular division (V_3), directly to the mesencephalic nucleus of CN-V. The central axons of the mesencephalic nucleus mostly project to the *motor nucleus of CN-V*, providing feedback control to the CN-V motor neurons that control the muscles of mastication. The mesencephalic nucleus also receives muscle spindle information from the extraocular muscles (of the eye). This system generally appears to consist of mechanisms that control for the precise force of a bite. Finally, both ipsilateral and contralateral ascending fiber tracts arise from the principal sensory nucleus of CN-V and the spinal trigeminal nucleus of CN-V, and carry information to higher centers of the CNS. These ascending fiber tracts include both the ventral and the dorsal trigeminothalamic tracts.

Special–Skeletal (Branchial) Motor Function

The motor nucleus of CN-V, also called the masticator nucleus, is located just medial to the principal sensory nucleus of CN-V within the pontine tegmentum (see Figure 9–4). Axons of the motor nucleus of CN-V course laterally through the pons and exit as small paired motor roots from the left and right lateral surfaces of the mid-pons. These lower motor neurons travel into the middle cranial fossa of the cranium and leave the cranium through the foramen ovale. Here, they unite with and travel alongside the sensory (afferent) branches of the mandibular division (V_3) of CN-V. Motor branches are then given off that innervate the *tensor veli palatini* muscle, the *tensor tympani* muscle, and the muscles of mastication. The muscles of mastication are the *medial* and *lateral pterygoid* muscles, the *masseter* muscles, and the *temporalis* muscles. Motor branches of V_3 also innervate the anterior belly of the digastric muscle by way of the mylohyoid branch of the inferior alveolar nerve. Contraction of the anterior belly of the digastric causes the hyoid bone to be drawn up and forward. The digastric muscles are considered to be suprahyoid or strap muscles.

The tensor veli palatini, which means tensor of the soft palate (velum), is found in the nasopharynx. As the name implies, it tenses the velum during swallowing and assists in the periodic opening of the Eustachian tube, during, for instance, swallowing. The tensor tympani muscle is located behind the anterior wall of the middle ear cavity. The tendon of the tensor tympani muscle enters the middle ear cavity through a small opening in its anterior wall. The muscle tendon attaches to the neck of the first of the three tiny middle ear bones (ossicles), which is the malleus. Reflexive contraction of the tensor tympani muscle from nonauditory stimuli causes the muscle tendon to pull on the malleus. Hence, the entire middle ear system, including the tympanic membrane, is temporarily made stiff or noncompliant. Reflexive contraction of the tensor tympani muscle occurs during chewing or biting. Stiffening of the middle ear system can prevent lower frequency energy (background noise) from entering the inner ear (cochlea), where it often leads to the masking of higher frequency sounds, such as consonants. Hence, the tensor tympani reflex resulting from motor activation by branches of CN-V can temporarily improve speech intelligibility in backgrounds of noise. Finally, as the name implies, the muscles of mastication are used for biting and for chewing.

Damage to the peripheral sensory branches of CN-V often results in a loss of sensation or anesthesia in the area of distribution of the nerve. Damage to or dysfunction of the peripheral sensory branches of CN-V more commonly results in *trigeminal neuralgia* (nerve pain) of unknown etiology, characterized by very brief periods of excruciating pain with the activation of a trigger zone. These split-second periods of neuralgia can also result in a loss of sensory input for the corneal reflex. Lower motor damage to CN-V often results in paralysis and eventual atrophy of the muscles of mastication on the affected side of the lesion, producing a decline in bite strength. Ipsilateral lower motor damage can also result in jaw imbalances during chewing.

Cranial Nerve (CN) VI: The Abducens Nerve

The sixth cranial nerve (CN-VI) is the *abducens nerve*. Like CN-IIIs and IV, the abducens nerve functions primarily in activating a set of skeletal muscles that move the eyes. Hence, CN-VI is functionally classified as general skeletal-motor. The term *abducens* means "puller away" or simply to "abduct." Like CN-IV, CN-VI is composed of only one pair of skeletal-motor nuclei. Hence, CN-VI innervates only one pair of extraocular muscles. The extraocular muscles innervated by CN-VI are the ipsilateral lateral rectus muscles, as illustrated in Figure 9–5. The paired nuclei of CN-VI are located in the pontine tegmentum, close to the midline and just ventral (anterior) to the fourth ventricle. Axons exit from the paired nuclei and travel in a ventral direction through the pontine tegmentum. These lower motor neurons then

emerge from the ventral surface of the brainstem, at the junction of the lower pons and the upper medulla, an area that is known as the pontomedullary junction. Each CN-VI enters the bony orbit for the eye where it innervates the ipsilateral lateral rectus muscle. The lateral rectus primarily pulls or rotates the eyeball away from the nose, or outward and away from the midline, in a lateral direction (abduction). Hence, gaze is simply directed outward, or laterally.

Conjugate eye movements made to the left and/or to the right in the horizontal plane of the visual field (lateral gaze) requires that the both the lateral and the medial rectus muscles work together as a pair. To track or follow a laterally moving object requires a fine degree of precision, or neural synchronization between the extraocular muscles controlled by CNs-III and VI. Recall from the sections above that this high level of collective and synchronous control can only be achieved by specialized regions within the brainstem, as well as by higher regulatory centers within the cerebral cortex. The control that is required for synchronized lateral gaze is coordinated by a combination of impulses from the pontine vestibular (for balance) nuclei and by the *center for lateral gaze* which is also located in the pontine tegmentum of the brainstem. The center for lateral gaze is also called the *paramedian pontine reticular formation* (PPRF). Higher centers of the CNS send signals to the PPRF that simultaneously activate the ipsilateral CN-VI nucleus and ipsilateral lateral rectus muscle, and the contralateral medial rectus muscle, by way of the contralateral CN-III nucleus. Signals reach the contralateral CN-III nucleus by way of a type of utility fiber pathway, called the

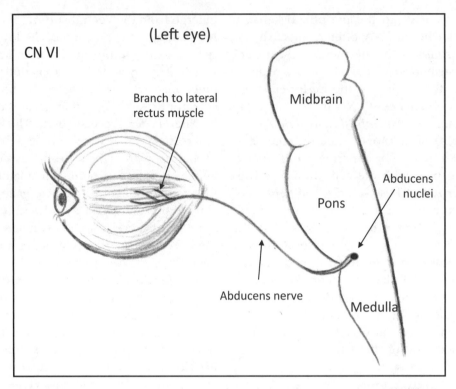

Figure 9–5. General skeletal-motor innervation of the single extraocular muscle of the eye that is controlled by the abducens nerve (CN-VI). Courtesy of F. Musiek and the neuroaudiology lab, University of Connecticut.

medial longitudinal fasciculus (MLF). The MLF is a ventral column of both ascending and descending fiber tracts that enables the "yoking" together of the extraocular muscles controlled by CNs-III, IV, and VI. The MLF ensures the synchrony and the coordination of all bilateral eye movements and is also intimately involved in brainstem pathways and systems that regulate balance. As with all lower motor damage to the nerves that innervate the extraocular muscles, lower motor damage to CN-VI (or paralysis if the ipsilateral lateral rectus muscle) leads to asynchronous eye turning and a condition known as medial strabismus. The ipsilateral (affected) eye cannot abduct past the midline position and deviates medially since there is no lateral rectus opposition to the tonic activity imposed by the medial rectus. As expected, medial strabismus will result in double vision, or diplopia. The location of the center for vertical gaze is, however, uncertain. However, it is believed to project to CNs-III and IV where it synchronizes the vertical movements of the eyes by yoking the extraocular muscles of CN-III (the superior and inferior rectus, and inferior oblique) with the superior oblique muscle of CN-IV.

Cranial Nerve (CN) VII: The Facial-Intermediate Nerve

The seventh cranial nerve (CN-VII) is often called the *facial nerve*. Indeed,

CN-VII is generally known for providing motor innervation to the muscles of the face, which collectively are known as the muscles of facial expression. However, the term *facial* implies that all of the functions provided by CN-VII involve those that are served by the facial motor nucleus of CN-VII and therefore, by the facial nerve division of CN-VII. Additional and important functions are provided by three divisions of CN-VII that are carried by the separate branches of the *nervus intermedius*, or the intermediate nerve division of CN-VII. These three additional functions are separate from, and have nothing to do with, functions provided by the facial nerve division of CN-VII. However, the facial nerve division is by far the largest division. Out of the necessity

to organize CN-VII by function and not strictly by anatomy, the name *facial-intermediate nerve* emerges. As in the case of the skeletal (branchiomeric) motor functions provided by CN-V (see above), to avoid confusion in the present context, the facial motor components of CN-VII will be referred to as special-skeletal (branchial) motor in function. Therefore, it may be said that the special-skeletal (branchial) motor division of CN-VII, is by far the largest division, as illustrated in Figure 9–6.

The remaining fibers belong to the intermediate nerve division of CN-VII. This division is responsible for special-sensory (taste), general-sensory and general visceral-motor (parasympathetic) functions, as illustrated in Figure 9–7. Facial motor neurons emerge from

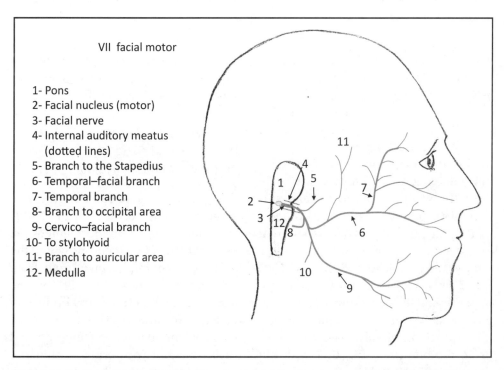

VII facial motor

1- Pons
2- Facial nucleus (motor)
3- Facial nerve
4- Internal auditory meatus
   (dotted lines)
5- Branch to the Stapedius
6- Temporal–facial branch
7- Temporal branch
8- Branch to occipital area
9- Cervico–facial branch
10- To stylohyoid
11- Branch to auricular area
12- Medulla

Figure 9–6. Special-skeletal (branchial) motor fibers of the facial-motor division of CN-VII, illustrating motor innervation of the muscles of facial expression and of the stapedius muscle of the middle ear. Courtesy of F. Musiek and the neuroaudiology lab, University of Connecticut.

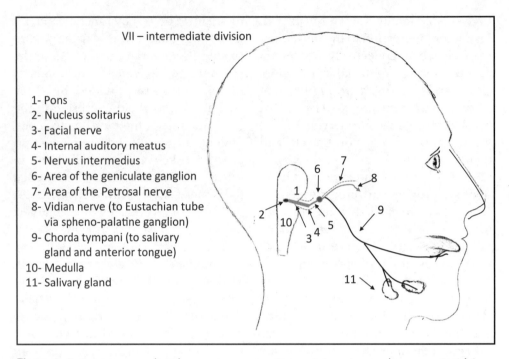

VII – intermediate division

1- Pons
2- Nucleus solitarius
3- Facial nerve
4- Internal auditory meatus
5- Nervus intermedius
6- Area of the geniculate ganglion
7- Area of the Petrosal nerve
8- Vidian nerve (to Eustachian tube
   via spheno-palatine ganglion)
9- Chorda tympani (to salivary
   gland and anterior tongue)
10- Medulla
11- Salivary gland

Figure 9–7. Special-sensory (taste), general-sensory, and general visceral-motor (parasympathetic) functions provided by the intermediate (nervus intermedius) division of CN-VII (see text). Courtesy of F. Musiek and the neuroaudiology lab, University of Connecticut.

the facial motor nucleus just medial to the intermediate division fibers of CN-VII. The intermediate division fibers are bound together and are separated from the facial nerve fibers, by a distinct sheath of connective tissue. The location of the emergence from the CNS of the combined facial-intermediate nerve is at the ventral (anterior)-lateral surface of the brainstem at the caudal most part of the pons. Recall from above that this area is known as the pontomedullary junction. The collective CN-VII emerges at a location just lateral to the more medially emerging CN-VI, and just medial to the more laterally emerging CN-VIII, or simply CN-VII emerges from the brainstem together with but between CNs-VI and VIII. The collective fibers of CN-VII that have emerged from the brainstem then enter the internal auditory meatus (canal) where they are accompanied by the special-sensory fibers of cranial nerve VIII.

Facial Nerve Division of CN-VII: Special-Skeletal (Branchial) Motor Function

The facial motor nucleus that gives rise to the facial nerve division of CN-VII is located in the pontine tegmentum. A small subset of the neurons within the facial nerve nuclei receive input from collateral branches given off by the nearby ascending tracts and brainstem nuclei of the auditory system. Axons of the facial motor nucleus emerge and travel dorsally (posterior) within the pons and toward the floor of the fourth ventricle. The axons loop in a lateral direction around the motor nucleus of

CN-VI and, in so doing, create a slight bulge in the floor of the fourth ventricle. The slight bulge is known as the *facial colliculus*. The axons then turn ventrally and emerge as lower motor neurons from the brainstem, as indicated above. These lower motor neurons then enter the petrous part of the temporal bone, by way of the internal auditory canal. The petrous part of the temporal bone is composed of a very high degree of bone density. That is, it is very hard. These lower motor neurons travel along the facial canal that runs along the posterior-medial wall of the middle ear space, where they turn laterally and caudally. Here, a set of collateral motor branches are given off that innervate the *stapedius muscle*.

The stapedius muscle is located behind the posterior wall of the middle ear cavity. The tendon of the stapedius muscle enters the middle ear cavity through a small opening in its posterior wall. The muscle tendon then attaches, either to the neck or to the posterior limb (crus) of the third and smallest of the three tiny middle ear bones (ossicles), which happens to be the stapes (see Figure 9–6). Reflexive contraction of the stapedius muscle in response to relatively loud auditory sounds causes the muscle tendon to pull on the stapes. Hence, the entire middle ear system, including the tympanic membrane, is temporarily made stiff or noncompliant. The activation of the reflex is highly reliable, and it is best observed with the delivery of pure tones presented at the threshold intensity (for the reflex) of 65 decibels of sound pressure (dB SPL), or even higher, and at frequencies of 500, 1000, and 2000 Hz. These three frequencies are often found in the vowel components of speech. The reflex is

commonly referred as the acoustic, the auditory, or the stapedius reflex, and the sound intensity required to elicit the reflex is commonly referred to as the auditory, the acoustic, or the stapedius reflex threshold. As described earlier for the tensor tympani muscle and tensor tympani reflex, a stiffening of the middle ear system in response to certain (speech) frequencies helps to prevent lower frequency energy (background noise) from entering the inner ear (cochlea), where it can lead to the masking of higher frequency sounds, such as consonants. Hence, as with the tensor tympani reflex which is mediated by motor innervation from CN-V, the stapedius reflex, which is mediated by motor innervation from CN-VII in response to relatively loud sounds, can temporarily improve speech intelligibility in backgrounds of noise.

The remaining fibers that define the facial division of CN-VII exit the facial canal and emerge from the skull through the stylomastoid foramen. Here, another set of collateral motor neurons are given off. These motor neurons innervate the stylohyoid muscle and the posterior belly of the digastric muscle. Both of these muscles are referred to as suprahyoid, or strap muscles, and they both serve to elevate the hyoid bone and the larynx. The fibers that remain pass through the parotid gland and supply all of the muscles of facial expression (see Figure 9–6). Recall that lower motor neurons fall under the direct control of upper motor neurons. Hence, voluntary movement of the facial muscles is made possible by innervations that are provided by the descending upper motor neurons that terminate within the brainstem facial nerve nuclei. This voluntary motor control is carried by the pyramidal motor neurons that originate in the pre-central gyrus of the cerebral cortex. The pre-central gyrus is also called the primary motor cortex. Therefore, voluntary movement of the facial muscles is made possible by the descending upper motor neuron fiber tracts of the pyramidal motor neurons that travel within the corticobulbar (cortex to brainstem) fiber pathways.

Lower motor neurons of the facial nerve nuclei that innervate the upper facial muscles, or simply those facial muscles located above the level of the nose, receive bilateral upper motor neuron innervation by way of the descending corticobulbar fiber pathways. Lower motor neurons of the facial nerve nuclei that innervate the lower facial muscles, or simply those facial muscles located at the level of the nose and below, receive only contralateral upper motor neuron innervation by way of the descending corticobulbar fiber pathways. Consequently, following unilateral upper motor damage (lesions), voluntary motor control is lost, but only for the lower facial muscles on the side of the face that is contralateral to the side of the lesion. Voluntary control of the upper facial muscles located on the same side of the lesion will continue to function because the lower motor neurons that control these muscles still receive ipsilateral, upper motor neuron input. The most common form of upper motor lesion involving CN-VII is usually the result of a cerebrovascular accident (stroke).

Damage to the facial nerve division of CN-VII results in characteristically distorted appearances of the face, both at rest and during attempts at voluntary motor movements. Lower motor damage (lesions) resulting from dysfunction or damage to the facial nerve nucleus, or its axons at any point along the course of the nerve, can also occur. A lower motor neuron lesion results in a loss of motor control in all of the muscles of the face located on the same side (ipsilateral to) as the lesion. Such a lesion that occurs at or beyond the level of the stylomastoid foramen is commonly known as a *Bell's palsy*. Unilateral atrophy of the muscles of facial expression results in marked facial asymmetry. For instance, the eyebrow droops, the corner of the mouth droops, and the lips cannot be closed tightly enough during eating to keep food in the mouth. There is also a loss of motor control to the orbicularis oculi muscles and therefore, a loss of the corneal (eye-blink) reflex.

Intermediate Nerve Division of CN-VII

Special-Sensory Function. As indicated above, the intermediate nerve division of CN-VII is responsible for carrying special-sensory information from special-sensory receptors that process the gustatory sense, known as taste. Special-sensory peripheral processes of CN-VII carry information from the taste buds (receptors) located on the lateral border of the anterior two-thirds of the ipsilateral tongue surface (see Figure 9–7). These receptors process the taste sensations for sweet, salty, and sour. Branches of these special-sensory fibers also carry information from taste receptors located on the hard and soft palate. Similar to the odorant receptors of CN-I, taste receptors, often called taste papillae, are modified epithelial cells that produce receptor potentials in response to chemical "tastants." The peripheral processes of these special-sensory neurons travel together with the general-sensory fibers of the lingual nerve.

Recall that the lingual nerve of CN-V also innervates the anterior two-thirds of the ipsilateral tongue, and floor of the mouth. The special-sensory peripheral processes then separate from the lingual nerve to join the *chorda tympani nerve*. The chorda tympani nerve courses in a posterior and horizontal direction through the middle ear cavity, to its posterior-medial wall. The chorda tympani nerve travels with neurons of CN-VII in the facial canal and enters the internal auditory canal within the petrous part of the temporal bone. The peripheral processes then make their way to their special-sensory cell bodies located within the *geniculate ganglion.* Axons arising from the geniculate ganglion enter the brainstem at the caudal border of the pons, together with other fibers of the intermediate division of CN-VII. The central projections travel dorsally to the lateral-rostral-most nucleus of the *tractus solitarius,* which is sometimes called the gustatory nucleus. The nucleus of the tractus solitarius (solitary nuclei and tracts) is long and slender and lines the borders of the fourth ventricle. Central axons arising from this nucleus project bilaterally to primary sensory nuclei in the thalamus. Second-order neurons arising from the gustatory nucleus also participate in reflexive salivation, swallowing, coughing, the gag reflex, and the retch reflex. Thalamic fibers then radiate upward to the gustatory cortex located in the postcentral gyrus as it extends into the superior *insular cortex,* or as it is called, the insula.

General-Sensory Function. The intermediate nerve division of CN-VII is also responsible for conveying general-sensory (somatosensory) information from cutaneous sensory receptors and nerve endings located in the contralateral external auditory canal, including the concha of the pinna, the external surface of the tympanic membrane, and the region just behind the contralateral pinna (see Figure 9–7). The sensory receptors, nerve endings, and general-sensory neurons of the intermediate nerve convey information involving deep pain and deep pressure. The seemingly redundant innervation provided by these fibers probably serves as a supplement to the general-sensory neurons of the mandibular (V_3) division of CN-V. The peripheral processes of these general-sensory neurons make their way to the petrous part of the temporal bone and to their general-sensory cell bodies, located within the *geniculate ganglion.* The general-sensory cell bodies within the geniculate ganglion are found alongside of the special-sensory cell bodies of the chorda tympani. Axons arising from the geniculate ganglion enter the brainstem at the caudal border of the pons together with other fibers of the intermediate division of CN-VII. The central projections then travel dorsally to the principle sensory nucleus of CN-V, where they terminate. The neurons of the CN-V nucleus that carry impulses from the general-sensory neurons of CN-VII, project caudally from the principle sensory nucleus of CN-V and into the network of fibers of the dorsal spinal trigeminal tracts. These tracts then terminate within the spinal trigeminal nucleus of CN-V.

General Visceral-Motor (Autonomic) Function. Finally, the intermediate nerve division of CN-VII is parasympathetic in function and is responsible for the motor control of the lacrimal (tear), the submandibular and the sublingual glands (salivary), as illustrated in Figure 9–7. It is also responsible for motor control of the nasal mucosa, the paranasal sinuses, and virtually all of the involuntary, secretory glands of the head, except for glands of the skin and the parotid (salivary) gland. Myelinated, preganglionic general visceral-motor axons of the intermediate nerve division of CN-VII arise from the *superior salivatory nucleus*. The superior salivatory nucleus is a collection of autonomic (parasympathetic) motor neurons scattered within the pontine tegmentum. Myelinated axons emerge from this nucleus, travel ventrally (anterior) within the pontine tegmentum, and then emerge as lower motor neurons from the caudal border of the pons, together with other fibers of the intermediate division of CN-VII. These general visceral-motor axons then enter the ipsilateral facial canal within the petrous portion of the temporal bone, where they split into two groups of preganglionic nerves. One group becomes the *greater superficial petrosal nerve*. The other group splits off and travels with the peripheral processes of the chorda tympani.

The greater superficial petrosal nerve exits from the petrous portion of the temporal bone, enters the middle cranial fossa of the cranium, and eventually makes its way to the pterygopalatine fossa, where it terminates within the *pterygopalatine ganglion*. Unmyelinated postganglionic axons then innervate the ipsilateral lacrimal glands, as well as the mucous membranes of the nose and palate, or the so-called palatine glands, where they stimulate secretion. The preganglionic general visceral-motor nerve of the chorda tympani joins the lingual nerve

of the mandibular (V_3) division of CN-V, and both fiber bundles travel together toward the floor of the oral cavity. Here, the general visceral-motor neurons of the chorda tympani terminate within the *submandibular ganglion*. Unmyelinated postganglionic axons then innervate the ipsilateral submandibular and sublingual glands, as well as minor glands found at the floor of the mouth, where they stimulate secretion. Hence, damage to the chorda tympani results in a loss of taste sensation from the anterior two-thirds of the tongue surface on the side of the tongue that is ipsilateral to the site of the lesion. Damage to the chorda tympani also results in a loss of the submandibular, the sublingual, and other parasympathetic glandular secretions, on the inside of the mouth that is ipsilateral to the site of the lesion.

Cranial Nerve (CN) VIII: The Vestibulo-Cochlear Nerve

The eighth cranial nerve (CN-VIII) is often called the *vestibulo-cochlear nerve* or the *auditory (cochlear) and vestibular nerve*. Hence, CN-VIII is special-sensory and is responsible for carrying two separate and distinct sensory systems to the CNS. These two special-sensory systems are hearing (audition) and balance (vestibular). Therefore, CN-VIII has an auditory division and a vestibular division, and is composed of an auditory nerve and a vestibular nerve, as illustrated in Figure 9–8. At first glance it may seem odd that two separate populations of special-sensory neurons should be part of the same, single, cranial nerve. Each of the separate nerves has separate peripheral sensory receptors, separate peripheral ganglion, and separate special-sensory

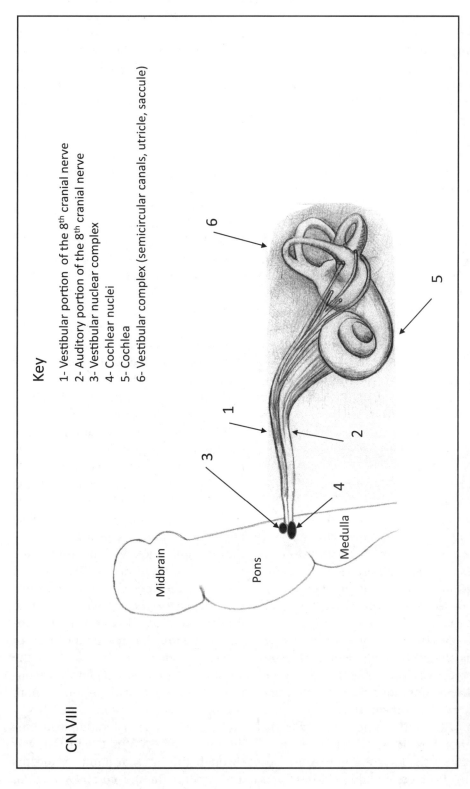

CN VIII

Key

1- Vestibular portion of the 8th cranial nerve
2- Auditory portion of the 8th cranial nerve
3- Vestibular nuclear complex
4- Cochlear nuclei
5- Cochlea
6- Vestibular complex (semicircular canals, utricle, saccule)

Midbrain

Pons

Medulla

Figure 9–8. Special-sensory neurons for balance (vestibular) and for hearing (auditory) which are functions that are both provided by the vestibulo–cochelear nerve (CN-VIII). Courtesy of F. Musiek and the neuroaudiology lab, University of Connecticut.

nuclei within the CNS. However, while distinctly different in function, the peripheral sensory receptors for both divisions of CN-VIII are housed within a common set of labyrinthine-inner ear structures, and both divisions share the same peripheral inner ear fluids. In addition, the peripheral processes and axons of both nerves travel together to the brainstem for most of their length (see Figure 9–8). Moreover, the axons of both enter the cranium through the same opening, and enter the brainstem at the same location.

As indicated above, the peripheral sensory receptors for both divisions of CN-VIII are housed within a common set of inner ear-labyrinthine structures. The labyrinthine structures are encased in the petrous part of the temporal bone, and are located on the floor of the left and right middle cranial fossae of the cranium. The petrous temporal bone is composed of the hardest bone found in the body. The inside of each labyrinthine structure consists of a delicate tubular, fluid-filled structure, called the *membranous labyrinth* that is essentially suspended in fluid within an outer (petrous) bony (osseous) labyrinth (see Figure 9–8) that precisely conforms in shape to the membranous labyrinth. Each labyrinthine structure therefore, is composed of a membranous labyrinth suspended within an *osseous labyrinth*. The sensory receptors for both divisions of CN-VIII are located in the specialized areas located on the inner walls of the membranous labyrinth. Special-sensory receptors for the auditory division of CN-VIII are housed within the anterior part of the labyrinthine structure, in a snail-shaped enclosure (see Figure 9–8) commonly referred to as the *cochlea*. Special-sensory receptors

for the vestibular division of CN-VIII are housed within the medial and posterior parts of the labyrinthine system. These special-sensory receptors for balance are located within two structures located in the labyrinthine area known the vestibule, and within structures located at the bases of the three, posteriorly located semicircular canals (see Figure 9–8).

Peripheral processes of primary sensory (bipolar) neurons for both the hearing and balance divisions of CN-VIII extend for only a short distance from their respective special-sensory receptors, and make their way to their respective cell bodies. The cell bodies of the special-sensory neurons for hearing are located within the central pillar of petrous bone called the *modiolus* that is located within the center of the spiraling cochlea. At each spiraling level of the cochlea, collections of auditory cell bodies within the modiolus are called the *spiral ganglion*. Collectively, throughout the modiolus, they constitute the spiral ganglia. Spiral ganglia axons travel uniformly from all levels of the cochlea, through the modiolus, and collect at the cochlear base where they eventually join with neurons of the vestibular divison of CN-VIII. The cell bodies of the special-sensory neurons for balance are located within the vestibular ganglion, also known as *Scarpa's ganglion*, located at the base of the semicircular canals. Axons of the vestibular ganglion then join with axons of the auditory division. Axons of both divisions collectively constitute CN-VIII and enter the internal auditory meatus alongside of CN-VII. CN-VIII travels through the internal auditory meatus and emerge in the *posterior cranial fossa* of the cranium. Collectively, fibers of CN-VIII enter the brainstem at the ventral (anterior)-lateral surface of the brainstem at the caudal most part of the pons, at a location that is lateral to the more medially emerging CN-VII. Recall again that this area is known as the pontomedullary junction. CN-VIII with its separate auditory and vestibular divisions is discussed in greater detail in Chapter 10.

Cranial Nerve (CN) IX:
The Glossopharyngeal Nerve

The ninth cranial nerve (CN-IX) is the *glossopharyngeal nerve*. The term glossopharyngeal means "tongue-pharynx," which simply means that the distribution of CN-IX involves the tongue and the pharynx. CN-IX has five functional components. These functions are special-skeletal (branchial) motor, general-visceral (autonomic) motor, general-visceral sensory, general-sensory, and special-sensory. CN-IX is related closely to the vagus nerve (CN-X). Both of these cranial nerves share common nuclei within the medulla and share common functional components. CN-IX is composed of a series of sensory and motor rootlets that emerge from the uppermost and lateral sides of the brainstem medulla. Finally, CN-IX has two sets of peripheral ganglia. These are the inferior (petrosal) ganglion and the superior ganglion of CN-IX.

Special-Skeletal (Branchial) Motor Function

Cortical motor commands carried by upper motor neurons descend along the corticobulbar fiber pathways and terminate bilaterally in the rostral part of the *nucleus ambiguus*. Hence, the nucleus

ambiguus is controlled bilaterally by descending upper motor neurons of the corticobulbar fiber pathway. The nucleus ambiguus is a motor nucleus composed of a column of cells located within the rostral medulla of the brainstem, in the brainstem reticular formation. Lower motor branchial-efferent fibers arise from the nucleus ambiguus and travel in a ventral-lateral direction. They then exit from the uppermost and lateral sides of the medulla together with the rootlets of the other divisions of CN-IX. CN-IX passes laterally through the posterior cranial fossa, exits the cranium through the jugular foramen, and eventually innervates the stylopharyngeus muscle and perhaps a part of the superior pharyngeal constrictor muscle as well. The stylopharyngeus muscle elevates and opens the pharynx during swallowing. The superior pharyngeal constrictor muscle pulls the upper pharyngeal wall forward and constricts the diameter of the upper pharynx during swallowing.

General Visceral-Motor (Autonomic) Function

Myelinated axons of preganglionic parasympathetic lower motor neurons arise from the inferior salivatory nucleus, located in the rostral medulla of the brainstem. These axons travel in a ventral-lateral direction and exit from the uppermost and lateral sides of the medulla together with the rootlets of the other divisions of CN-IX. CN-IX passes laterally through the posterior cranial fossa, exits the cranium through the jugular foramen, and travels to the surface of the promontory in the middle ear cavity. Here, the general visceral-motor fibers become the *lesser petrosal nerve.* This nerve travels back into the cranium and into the middle cranial fossa, eventually descends into the foramen ovale, and terminates in the *otic ganglion* located immediately below the foramen ovale. Unmyelinated postganglionic axons of the otic ganglion travel with a branch of CN-V (V_3) and innervate the ipsilateral parotid (salivary) gland located in the oral cheek.

General Visceral–Sensory Function

Peripheral processes of CN-IX neurons convey sensory impulses of tactile, thermal, and pain sensation from the mucous membranes of the posterior one third of the ipsilateral tongue, the palatine tonsils, and the Eustachian tube. As part of the *pharyngeal plexus* of nerves that supply the muscles of swallowing (deglutition), peripheral afferent processes of CN-IX neurons also innervate the levator veli palatini (velum), the uvula, the faucial pillars, and the posterior wall of the upper pharynx. As indicated in the sections that follow, the pharyngeal plexus also contains motor components from CNs-X and XI (see below). The peripheral sensory processes of CN-IX then make their way to their cell bodies, located within the inferior (petrosal) ganglion of CN-IX. Axons arising from the inferior ganglion of CN-IX then make their way into the cranium and enter the uppermost and lateral sides of the medulla, together with the rootlets of other divisions of CN-IX. The central visceral-sensory projections are then distributed to the upper portions of the nucleus of the tractus solitarius (the solitary nuclei and tracts) in the upper medulla.

The anterior faucial pillars are known as the palatoglossus or glossopalatine muscles. The posterior faucial pillars are also known as the palatopharyngeus or pharyngopalatine muscles. Sensory input from CN-IX, and the motor innervations from CNs-X and XI as part of the pharyngeal plexus (see below), enables both sets of faucial pillars to depress the velum. The anterior faucial pillars also elevate the tongue, whereas the posterior faucial pillars elevate the larynx. The levator veli palatini muscle, or elevator of the soft palate (velum), is found in the nasopharynx, together with the tensor veli palatini muscle. As the name implies, it elevates the velum during swallowing and assists the tensor veli palatini muscle in the periodic opening of the Eustachian tube during swallowing. In addition, contraction of the uvula causes the velum to shorten and to bunch up. Swallowing can be initiated by stimulation of the posterior one third of the tongue, but is most often triggered by stimulation of the tongue base just above the vocal folds. Tactile stimulation of the faucial pillars elicits the gag reflex, mediated of course by the general-visceral sensory neurons of CN-IX. The gag reflex is also elicited by tactile stimulation of the posterior pharyngeal wall (general-visceral sensory from CN-X) or base of the tongue (CN-IX). It can also be elicited by (bitter) taste, mediated again by CN-IX. Disturbances associated with lesions of this branch of CN-IX include the loss of the gag reflex.

Peripheral processes of CN-IX neurons also convey sensory impulses from the (stretch-activated) baroreceptors located in the sinuses of the carotid arteries, as part of the *carotid sinus reflex.* The carotid sinus is, in essence, located at the bifurcation of the common carotid artery into an external and an internal carotid artery. The carotid sinus reflex is an autonomic (parasympathetic) negative feedback mechanism that serves to lower blood pressure. The carotid sinus baroreceptors respond to increases in blood pressure, and the peripheral sensory processes of CN-IX are collectively referred to as *Hering's nerve*. Hering's nerve carries impulses away from the carotid sinus and toward its cell bodies that are also located within the inferior (petrosal) ganglion of CN-IX. Axons arising from the inferior ganglion of CN-IX then make their way into the cranium and enter the upper most and lateral sides of the medulla, together with the rootlets of other divisions of CN-IX. The central visceral-sensory projections are then again distributed to the upper portions of the nucleus of the tractus solitarius (the solitary nuclei and tracts) in the upper medulla. Second-order solitary neurons then excite the cells of the dorsal motor nucleus of the vagus nerve (CN-X) located in the dorsal medulla to bring about reductions in arterial pressure and heart rate. Motor neurons of the dorsal motor nucleus descend to laminar layer VII of the spinal cord where they inhibit the preganglionic neurons of the sympathetic nervous system, thereby reducing sympathetic tone, resulting in increased vasodilation. Preganglionic vagal motor neurons of the dorsal motor nucleus of CN-X also emerge from the lateral medulla and, by way of their unmyelinated postganglionic CN-X fibers, travel to the heart where they innervate the cardiac pacemaker cells to reduce heart rate (also see below). Disturbances associated with lesions of this visceral-sensory branch of CN-IX include loss of the carotid sinus reflex.

Peripheral processes of CN-IX neurons additionally convey sensory impulses from chemoreceptors that are also located in the sinuses of the carotid arteries, as part of the *respiratory reflex*. Carotid sinus chemoreceptors respond to an increase in blood levels of carbon dioxide (CO_2), a decrease in blood levels of oxygen (O_2), or an increase in blood acidity (low pH). The peripheral sensory processes of these CN-IX neurons carry impulses away from the carotid sinus and toward their cell bodies, also located within the inferior (petrosal) ganglion of CN-IX. Axons arising from the inferior ganglion of CN-IX then make their way into the cranium and enter the uppermost and lateral sides of the medulla, together with the rootlets of other divisions of CN-IX. The central visceral-sensory projections are then distributed to portions of the nucleus of the tractus solitarius. Second-order solitary neurons then relay the impulses to the lower lower-medullary respiratory centers in the brainstem and respiration rate is then increased.

General–Sensory Function

Peripheral processes of CN-IX neurons carry sensations of pain and temperature from the skin surfaces of the contralateral external auditory canal, the area behind the pinna, and the inner (medial) surface of the tympanic membrane. General-sensory information conveyed by these peripheral processes is carried toward their cell bodies, located within the superior ganglion of CN-IX. These general-sensory neurons of CN-IX again appear to provide a redundant supply of innervation, serving perhaps as a supplement to the general-sensory neurons of the mandibular (V_3) division of CN-V, as well as to the general-sensory neurons of the intermediate division of CN-VII. Axons of the general-sensory neurons within the superior ganglion of CN-IX enter the cranium through the jugular foramen, then enter the uppermost and lateral sides of the medulla, together with the rootlets of other divisions of CN-IX. The central projections then travel dorsally to the principal sensory nucleus of CN-V, where they terminate. The neurons of the CN-V nucleus that carry impulses from the general-sensory neurons of CN-IX, project caudally from the principle sensory nucleus of CN-V and into the network of fibers of the dorsal spinal trigeminal tracts. These tracts then terminate within the spinal trigeminal nucleus of CN-V. Disturbances associated with lesions of this general-sensory branch of CN-IX include *glossopharyngeal neuralgia* that resembles trigeminal neuralgia. This disorder is characterized by sudden attacks of excruciating pain that begin in the throat and radiate along the side of the neck, to regions in back of the mandible and behind the pinna. The pain is triggered by seemingly trivial stimuli such as coughing or swallowing.

Special–Sensory Function

Special-sensory, peripheral processes of CN-IX carry information from taste receptors located on the lateral border of the posterior one-third, or base of the ipsilateral tongue surface. These receptors process the taste sensation for bitter. Branches of these special-sensory fibers also carry information from taste receptors located on the ventral surface of the oropharynx. Similar to the odorant receptors of CN-I, taste receptors, or taste papillae are modified epithelial cells that produce receptor potentials in response to chemical "tastants." The peripheral processes of these special-

sensory neurons carry taste information toward their cell bodies, located within the inferior (petrosal) ganglion of CN-IX. Axons of the special-sensory neurons within the inferior ganglion of CN-IX enter the cranium through the jugular foramen, then enter the upper most and lateral sides of the medulla, together with the rootlets of other divisions of CN-IX. The central projections travel dorsally to the lateral-rostral-most nucleus of the tractus solitarius (the gustatory nucleus). Recall that the nucleus of the tractus solitarius (solitary nuclei and tracts) is long and slender and lines the borders of the fourth ventricle. Central axons arising from this nucleus project bilaterally to primary sensory nuclei within the thalamus. Second-order neurons arising from the gustatory nucleus also participate in reflexive salivation, swallowing, coughing, and the gag and retch reflexes. Thalamic fibers then radiate upward to the gustatory cortex located in the postcentral gyrus as it extends into the superior insular cortex, or as it is called, the insula.

Cranial Nerve (CN) X: The Vagus Nerve

The tenth cranial nerve (CN-X) is the *vagus nerve*. The term *vagus* is Latin and means "wanderer," which simply means that the distribution of CN-X is widespread. Fibers of the vagus nerve wander throughout the thoracic and abdominal cavities. The vagus is a complex branchiomeric cranial nerve that, like CN-IX, has five functional components. The functions of CN-X are special-skeletal (branchial) motor, general-visceral (autonomic) motor, general-visceral sensory, general-sensory and special-sensory. CN-X is related closely to the glossopharyngeal nerve (CN-IX). Both CN-IX and CN-X share common nuclei within the medulla (such as the nucleus ambiguus) and share common functional components. Like CN-IX, CN-X is composed of a series of sensory and motor rootlets that emerge from the uppermost and lateral sides of the brainstem medulla. Motor division axons (lower motor neurons) of CN-X exit from, and sensory division axons enter into the cranium by way of the jugular foramen. Finally, CN-X has two sets of peripheral (sensory) ganglia. These are the inferior (nodose) ganglion of CN-X and the superior ganglion of CN-X. The cell bodies of all general-visceral sensory and all special (visceral)-sensory neurons are located within the inferior ganglion of CN-X. The cell bodies of all general-sensory neurons are located within the superior ganglion of CN-X.

Special-Skeletal (Branchial) Motor Function

The nucleus ambiguus, which is a motor nucleus, is a column of cells located within the brainstem reticular formation, as indicated above. The nucleus ambiguus is shared by three cranial nerves. These are CNs-IX, X, and XI. Recall that rostral parts of this column of nuclei give rise to fibers of the glossopharyngeal nerve (CN-IX) that innervate the stylopharyngeus and parts of superior pharyngeal constrictor muscles, as discussed in the sections above. Caudal parts of the nucleus ambiguus will also give rise to the cranial division of the spinal accessory nerve (CN-XI), as discussed in the sections below. Recall from CN-IX that the nucleus ambiguus is controlled bilaterally by descending upper motor neurons of the corticobul-

bar fiber pathway. With respect to CN-X, the lower motor fibers that emerge from the nucleus ambiguus arch dorsally and join (travel) with motor fibers arising from the dorsal motor nucleus of CN-X. Recall that the motor nucleus of CN-X is located in the dorsal medulla within the floor of the fourth ventricle. Collectively these fibers emerge from the lateral surface of the medulla together with the rootlets of other divisions of CN-X. The lower motor neurons of the nucleus ambiguus split into three descending ipsilateral special-skeletal, or branchial motor divisions. These three branchial motor divisions of CN-X are the motor branch of the pharyngeal division, the external branch of the superior laryngeal division, and the motor branch of the inferior (or recurrent) laryngeal division.

Pharyngeal-Motor Division. The pharyngeal division of CN-X divides into a sensory and into a motor branch. The sensory branch of the pharyngeal division of CN-X is general visceral-sensory in function (see below). The motor branch of the pharyngeal division of CN-X is represented by the principal motor nerve of the pharynx. It enters the upper pharynx near the middle pharyngeal constrictor muscle and breaks up to form the network of nerves known as the pharyngeal plexus. The pharyngeal plexus innervates all of the skeletal muscles of the pharynx and soft palate (velum), except for the stylopharyngeus (CN-IX) and the tensor veli palatini (CN-V). It provides motor innervation to the muscles involved in swallowing (deglutition), such as the anterior faucial pillars (palatoglossus or glossopalatine muscles); the posterior faucial pillars (palatopharyngeus or pharyngopalatine muscles); the superior, middle, and inferior pharyngeal constrictors; the levator veli palatini; the uvula; and the salpingopharyngeus. The functions of several of these muscles were addressed previously in relation to CN-IX. The superior pharyngeal constrictor muscle, once again, pulls the upper pharyngeal wall forward and constricts the diameter of the upper pharynx during swallowing. The middle constrictor muscle narrows the diameter of the pharynx during swallowing. The inferior constrictor has two parts. These are the cricopharyngeus muscle that constricts the upper opening of the esophagus during swallowing, and the thyropharyngeus muscle that reduces the diameter of the lower pharynx during swallowing. Finally, the salpingopharyngeus muscle elevates the pharyngeal wall during swallowing.

Superior Laryngeal Division: External Branch. The superior laryngeal division of CN-X divides into an internal and an external branch. The internal branch of the superior laryngeal division of CN-X is general visceral-sensory in function (see below). The external branch of the superior laryngeal division of CN-X, which is motor in function, again innervates the inferior constrictor muscle(s) and contributes branches that enter into the pharyngeal plexus of nerves that innervate the muscles involved in swallowing. The external branch of the superior laryngeal division of CN-X also innervates the cricothyroid muscle, located on either side of the base of the larynx. The cricothyroid muscle, with its two components, the pars recta and pars oblique, serves as a vocal fold tensor.

Inferior (Recurrent) Laryngeal Division: Motor Branch. The inferior (or recur-

rent) division of CN-X divides into a sensory and into a motor branch. The sensory branch of the inferior laryngeal division of CN-X is general visceral-sensory in function (see below). The motor branch of the inferior division of CN-X innervates all of the intrinsic skeletal muscles of the larynx, except of course, the cricothyroid. As indicated above, the inferior division of CN-X is often generally called the recurrent laryngeal nerve. This is because the right recurrent laryngeal nerve vertically descends alongside of the right common carotid artery, cuts across the anterior surface of the right subclavian artery, and then loops behind the right subclavian artery at its junction with the right common carotid artery. It then ascends in a vertical direction and terminates in the larynx. The left recurrent laryngeal nerve vertically descends alongside of the left common carotid artery, cuts across the anterior surface of the left subclavian artery at its junction with the aortic arch, then loops behind the aortic arch and ascends in a vertical direction and terminates in the larynx. Hence, the nerve first descends, then ascends or recurs (returns), and is therefore recurrent.

Unilateral lower motor neuron damage to the special-skeletal (branchial) motor neurons of the recurrent division of CN-X, results in hoarseness or breathiness of the voice, or harsh distressing phonation (laryngeal stridor) due to inadequate adduction of the vocal folds. Bilateral paralysis of the recurrent laryngeal nerve with the vocal folds in the adducted position, is life threatening. Partial paralysis of the vocal folds increases the risk of aspirating solids and liquids during swallowing. Unilateral lower motor neuron damage to the pharyngeal division of CN-X produces difficulty in swallowing (dysphagia) due to an inability to adequately elevate the velum. The arch of the velum is often seen drooping on the affected side of the lesion, and the uvula will often deviate toward the unaffected side.

General Visceral-Motor (Autonomic) Function

The cell bodies of parasympathetic lower motor neurons of CN-X are located in the dorsal motor nucleus of CN-X, located dorsally in the medulla within the floor of the fourth ventricle.

Preganglionic myelinated axons arise from the motor nucleus of CN-X, traverse the spinal trigeminal nucleus and tract, and emerge from the lateral surface of the medulla together with the rootlets of other divisions of CN-X. Some preganglionic vagal motor neurons distribute ipsilaterally to the pharyngeal plexus by way of the pharyngeal and internal laryngeal branches of CN-X, where they activate (smooth muscle) secretory glands of the pharyngeal and laryngeal mucosa by way of their unmyelinated postganglionic axons. Other preganglionic vagal motor neurons emerge from the lateral medulla and, by way of their unmyelinated postganglionic CN-X fibers, distribute to the smooth and cardiac muscle and plexuses of the thoracic viscera, as well as to the smooth muscle and plexuses of the abdominal viscera. This parasympathetic innervation includes innervation to the lungs, the esophagus, the bronchial tree, the heart, the pancreas, the stomach, the kidneys, the liver, and the upper part of the gastrointestinal (upper GI) tract. Branches of this division of CN-X are also responsible for the overall parasympathetic effects on the heart discussed above, in reference to the carotid sinus reflex. Branches of this CN-X division serve as a common motor pathway for both the cardiac sinus reflex mediated by CN-IX (discussed above), and the aortic sinus reflex, mediated by the general-visceral sensory divisions of CN-X (discussed below). In both reflexes, activation of the dorsal motor nucleus of CN-X by second-order neurons of the solitary nucleus, brings about reductions in arterial blood pressure and heart rate. Recall that motor neurons of the dorsal motor nucleus also descend to laminar layer VII of the spinal cord and inhibit the preganglionic neurons of the sympathetic nervous system, thereby reducing sympathetic tone, resulting in increased vasodilation. Recall as well that preganglionic vagal neurons of the dorsal motor nucleus also emerge from the lateral medulla and, by way of their unmyelinated postganglionic CN-X fibers, travel to the heart and innervate the cardiac pacemaker cells to reduce heart rate.

Additional autonomic parasympathetic effects of CN-X include increased bronchial constriction, increased esophageal peristalsis, increased stomach and intestinal motility, and increased secretion of digestive enzymes and acids. Recall that tactile stimulation of the faucial pillars elicits the gag reflex, mediated of course by the general-visceral sensory neurons of CN-IX. The gag reflex is also elicited by tactile stimulation of the posterior pharyngeal wall (general visceral sensory from CN-X) or base of the tongue (CN-IX). It can also be elicited by (bitter) taste, mediated again by CN-IX. When activated by second-order neurons of the solitary nucleus and fasciculus of the medulla, neurons of the dorsal motor nucleus of CN-X can bring about the gag reflex. The gag reflex is characterized by abdominal muscular contraction, a temporary termination of respiration, an elevation of the velum, and both an elevation and a constriction of the pharynx. Disturbances associated with lesions of this visceral-motor branch of CN-X can again include loss of the gag reflex, but on the motor side of the gag reflex. Hyperactivity of the parasympathetic division of CN-X can also lead to an oversecretion of stomach acids and to gastric ulcers.

General Visceral–Sensory Function

There are three general visceral-sensory divisions of CN-X. These three divisions are the sensory branch of the pharyngeal division, the internal branch of the superior laryngeal division, and the sensory branch of the inferior (or recurrent) division. All general visceral-sensory divisions terminate in the nucleus of the tractus solitarius for the mediation of reflexes (by way of the dorsal motor nucleus of CN-X), and/or traverse the dorsal spinal trigeminal tracts and terminate within the spinal trigeminal nucleus of CN-V.

Pharyngeal-Sensory Division. Peripheral processes of the sensory branch of the pharyngeal division CN-X convey information that includes sensations of pain, from the ipsilateral base of the tongue, the upper and lower pharynx, the larynx, the trachea, the esophagus, and all of the thoracic (lungs and heart) and abdominal viscera, which includes the entire digestive system. These sensory neurons also carry sensations of hun-

ger, acid reflux (heartburn), and chest pain, including heart and lung pain. These general-visceral fibers of CN-X terminate either in the nucleus of the tractus solitarius for the mediation of reflexes (by way of the dorsal motor nucleus of CN-X), or traverse the dorsal spinal trigeminal tracts and terminate within the spinal trigeminal nucleus of CN-V.

Peripheral processes of the sensory branch of the pharyngeal division of CN-X also convey sensory impulses from the (stretch-activated) baroreceptors located within the arch of the aorta, as part of the *aortic sinus reflex.* Like the carotid sinus reflex, the aortic sinus reflex is part of an autonomic (parasympathetic) negative feedback mechanism that serves to lower blood pressure. Like the carotid sinus baroreceptors, the baroreceptors located in the aortic arch respond to increases in blood pressure. The peripheral processes of CN-X carry impulses away from the aorta and toward their cell bodies, located within the inferior (nodose) ganglion of CN-X. Axons arising from the inferior ganglion of CN-X then make their way into the cranium and enter the lateral sides of the medulla, together with the rootlets of other divisions of CN-X. The central visceral-sensory projections are then distributed to the upper portions of the nucleus of the tractus solitarius (the solitary nuclei and tracts) in the upper medulla. Recall that branches of the general-visceral (autonomic) motor neurons arising from the dorsal motor nucleus of CN-X serve as a common motor pathway for both the cardiac sinus reflex mediated by CN-IX (discussed above), and the aortic sinus reflex, mediated by general-visceral sensory divisions of CN-X. In both reflexes, neurons of the dorsal motor nucleus of CN-X bring about reductions in arterial pressure and heart rate, when activated by second-order neurons of the solitary nucleus. As also described for the carotid sinus reflex, motor neurons of the dorsal motor nucleus descend to laminar layer VII of the spinal cord to reduce sympathetic tone, resulting in increased vasodilation. Also, and as described for the carotid sinus reflex, preganglionic vagal neurons of the dorsal motor nucleus then emerge from the lateral medulla and, by way of their unmyelinated postganglionic CN-X fibers, innervate the cardiac pacemaker cells to reduce heart rate.

Peripheral processes of CN-X neurons also convey sensory impulses from chemoreceptors located within the arch of the aorta as an additional part of the respiratory reflex. This is similar to the part of the respiratory reflex that was mediated by the general-visceral sensory neurons of CN-IX. Like the carotid sinus chemoreceptors, aortic chemoreceptors respond to an increase in blood levels of carbon dioxide (CO_2), a decrease in blood levels of oxygen (O_2), or an increase in blood acidity (low pH). The peripheral sensory processes of these CN-X neurons then carry impulses away from the aorta and toward their cell bodies, which are located within the inferior (nodose) ganglion of CN-X. Axons arising from the inferior ganglion of CN-X then make their way into the cranium and enter the lateral sides of the medulla, together with the rootlets of other divisions of CN-X. The central visceral-sensory projections are then distributed to portions of the nucleus of the tractus solitarius. Second-order solitary neurons then relay the impulses to the lower-medullary respiratory cen-

ters in the brainstem, and respiration rate is increased.

Finally, peripheral processes of the sensory branch of the pharyngeal division CN-X convey negative feedback information from stretch-activated receptors located within the ipsilateral lobes of the lungs. Both the receptors and the sensory neurons of CN-X are activated when lung tissue is fully distended. The peripheral sensory processes of these CN-X neurons then carry impulses away from the lungs and toward their cell bodies, which are also located within the inferior (nodose) ganglion of CN-X. Axons arising from the inferior ganglion of CN-X then make their way into the cranium and enter the lateral sides of the medulla, together with the rootlets of other divisions of CN-X. This feedback information is then relayed to the lower-medullary respiratory centers in the brainstem, resulting in the termination of the inspiration cycle of respiration, preventing overinflation of the lungs.

Superior Laryngeal Division: Internal Branch. Peripheral processes of the internal branch of the superior laryngeal division of CN-X provide sensory innervation of the ipsilateral mucous membranes located above the vocal folds in the supraglottic region of the larynx. This includes the mucous membranes located at the epiglottis, and at the very base of the tongue. The peripheral processes make their way to their cell bodies, which are located within the inferior (nodose) ganglion of CN-X. Axons arising from the inferior ganglion of CN-X then travel into the cranium and enter the lateral sides of the medulla, together with the rootlets of other divisions of CN-X. These general-visceral fibers either terminate in the nucleus of the tractus solitarius for the mediation of reflexes (by way of the dorsal motor nucleus of CN-X), and/or traverse the dorsal spinal trigeminal tracts and terminate within the spinal trigeminal nucleus of CN-V.

Inferior (Recurrent) Laryngeal Division: Sensory Branch. Peripheral processes of the sensory division of the recurrent (inferior) laryngeal nerve of CN-X provide sensory innervation of the ipsilateral mucous membranes located below the vocal folds, in the subglottic region of the larynx. The peripheral processes make their way to their cell bodies, also located within the inferior (nodose) ganglion of CN-X. Axons arising from the inferior ganglion of CN-X then travel into the cranium and enter the lateral sides of the medulla, together with the rootlets of other divisions of CN-X. These general-visceral fibers either terminate in the nucleus of the tractus solitarius for the mediation of reflexes (by way of the dorsal motor nucleus of CN-X), and/or traverse the dorsal spinal trigeminal tracts and terminate within the spinal trigeminal nucleus of CN-V.

General-visceral sensory neurons of CN-X are involved in several reflexes. For instance, and as indicated above, tactile stimulation of the posterior pharyngeal wall and activation of general-visceral sensory neurons of CN-X can elicit the gag reflex. Recall that the gag reflex is mediated by neurons of the solitary nucleus and fasciculus of the medulla, which then activates the dorsal motor nucleus of CN-X. Hence, disturbances associated with lesions of this branch of CN-X can again include loss of the gag reflex. The cough reflex is usually initiated by a noxious stimulus presented to the pharynx, larynx, or bronchial airway. General-visceral sensory neurons of CN-X relay such information to the nucleus of the tractus solitarius within the medulla. Interneurons then activate the expiration (respiratory) center in the (reticular formation) medulla, resulting in the contraction of the abdominal muscles necessary for the expiration needed for coughing. The nucleus ambiguus and dorsal motor nucleus of CN-X are also activated. They initiate the reflexive, vocal fold (glottal) adduction prior to the forced and active exhalation that is needed to dislodge the irritant from the airway. Retching or the retch reflex, is an involuntary attempt at vomiting. Vomiting or the "vomit reflex" refers to the oral expulsion of the gastrointestinal contents. Vomiting leads to the emptying of highly acidic stomach contents into the esophagus and oral cavity. It may be triggered by odors (CN-I), by tastes (CNs-VII, IX, or X), or by gastrointestinal distress, carried by the general-visceral sensory neurons of CN-X. It may also be triggered by a vestibular dysfunction (CN-VIII) or by distressing visual input (CN-II). In fact, any or all types of stimuli can stimulate the retch/vomit reflex, by activating the retching center located in the (reticular formation) medulla, found near the dorsal motor nucleus of CN-X. The vomit reflex is rather complex and requires the synchronization of a few of the separate divisions of CN-X. For instance, it involves vocal fold adduction, relaxation of the upper and lower-esophageal sphincters, elevation of the larynx and velum, and depression of the epiglottis, all of which is accompanied by the protrusion of the tongue (CN-XII).

General-Sensory Function

Peripheral processes of CN-X carry sensations of pain, touch, and temperature from the skin surfaces of the posterior wall of the contralateral external auditory canal and the skin surface of back of the pinna, as the auricular nerve of CN-X. The auricular nerve also elicits a cough reflex when the skin surface within the deeper, inner two-thirds of the external ear canal is touched. Pain, touch, and temperature are also carried by general-sensory fibers of CN-X that innervate the external (lateral) surface of the tympanic membrane. Nausea and vomiting can also be triggered if the tympanic membrane is touched by an external stimulus. The general-sensory neurons of CN-X again appear to redundantly innervate the same skin areas covered by the general-sensory neurons of the mandibular (V_3) division of CN-V, the general-sensory neurons of the intermediate division of CN-VII, and the general-sensory neurons of CN-IX. Separate general-sensory fibers of CN-X also innervate the posterior part of the dura mater. Recall that much of the dura mater is also innervated by the three sensory divisions of CN-V. General-sensory information conveyed by these peripheral processes is carried toward their cell bodies, located within the superior ganglion of CN-X. Axons of the general-sensory neurons within the superior ganglion of CN-X enter the cranium through the jugular foramen, and then enter the lateral sides of the medulla, together with the rootlets of other divisions of CN-X. Axons of some of the general-sensory neurons terminate within the nucleus of the tractus solitarius for the mediation of reflexes by way of the dorsal motor nucleus of CN-X. Many others, however, traverse the dorsal spinal trigeminal tracts and terminate within the spinal trigeminal nucleus of CN-V.

Special-Sensory Function

Special-sensory, peripheral processes of CN-X carry information from taste receptors located on the epiglottis and parts of the laryngopharynx. The peripheral processes of these special-sensory neurons carry taste information toward their cell bodies, located within the inferior (nodose) ganglion of CN-X. Axons of the special-sensory neurons within the inferior ganglion of CN-X enter the cranium through the jugular foramen, and then enter the lateral sides of the medulla together with the rootlets of other divisions of CN-X. The central projections travel dorsally to the lateral-rostral-most nucleus of the tractus solitarius (the gustatory nucleus). Central axons arising from this nucleus project bilaterally to primary sensory nuclei in the thalamus. Thalamic fibers then radiate upward to the gustatory cortex located in the postcentral gyrus extending into the superior insular cortex, or as it is called, the insula.

Cranial Nerve (CN) XI: The Spinal-Accessory Nerve

The eleventh cranial nerve (CN-XI) is the *spinal accessory nerve* which is composed of two divisions, both of which are considered to be special-skeletal (branchial) motor in function. The two divisions of CN-XI are the cranial (internal) division and the spinal (external) division. Collectively, the lower motor neurons of both divisions of CN-XI emerge from the lateral surface of the medulla just caudal to the lowest trunks of CN-X. They then exit the cranium through the jugular foramen together with the rootlets of CNs-IX and X.

Cranial–Motor (Internal) Division

The cranial-motor division of CN-XI arises from the caudal-most parts of the nucleus ambiguus, located, as indicated previously, in the caudal medulla. Recall that the nucleus ambiguus is a nucleus that is shared by three cranial nerves, namely CNs-IX, X, and XI, and that the nucleus ambiguus is controlled bilaterally by descending upper motor neurons of the corticobulbar fiber pathway. Within the jugular foramen, lower motor neurons of the cranial-motor division of CN-XI join with lower motor neurons of the motor branch of the inferior (recurrent) division of CN-X. Collectively, these lower motor neurons of CN-X and XI, originating from the nucleus ambiguus, innervate all of the intrinsic skeletal muscles of the larynx, except of course, the cricothyroid.

Some of the lower motor neurons of the cranial-motor division of CN-XI also join with the lower motor neurons of the pharyngeal division of CN-X, as part of the pharyngeal plexus. Recall that motor neurons of the pharyngeal plexus innervate all of the skeletal muscles of the pharynx and soft palate (velum), except for the stylopharyngeus (CN-IX) and the tensor veli palatini (CN-V). Hence, as part of the pharyngeal plexus, CN-XI together with CN-X, provide motor innervation to the muscles involved in swallowing (deglutition).

Spinal–Motor (External) Division

The spinal-motor division of CN-XI arises from the spinal (motor) nucleus

of CN-XI, located in the rostral-most regions of the spinal cord. The spinal nucleus of CN-XI is composed of a column of cell bodies situated in the ventral horn of the upper five or six cervical spinal segments (C_2 through C_5 or C_6) of the spinal cord. The spinal nucleus of CN-XI lines up, approximately, with the caudal pole of the nucleus ambiguus. However, the spinal nucleus of CN-XI is controlled by descending contralateral upper motor neurons of the corticospinal fiber pathway, specifically, neurons within the descending lateral corticospinal tract. Axon rootlets from the spinal nucleus emerge as lower motor neurons from C_2 through C_5 or C_6 along the lateral aspect of the spinal cord, between the dorsal and ventral roots. These rootlets will include motor branches of the *cervical plexus*, arising from cervical spinal levels C_1 to C_4. The rootlets of the spinal motor nucleus then unite and form a common trunk called the spinal (external) motor division of the accessory nerve. The fiber rootlets traveling within the spinal-motor accessory nerve ascend along the exterior of the spinal cord and enter the skull through the foramen magnum. They then unite at the lateral surface of the medulla, with fibers of the cranial (internal) division accessory nerve prior to exiting the skull through the jugular foramen as one anatomically unified CN-XI. Fibers of the spinal-motor and cranial-motor divisions of CN-XI then pass through the jugular foramen, together with lower motor neurons of the motor branch of the inferior (recurrent) division of CN-X, and the rootlets of CN-IX. Within the jugular foramen, the spinal-motor division of CN-XI separates from the other lower motor neurons and travels in a posteromedial direction to the styloid process where some fibers descend and innervate the sternocleidomastoid muscle. The remaining spinal-motor neurons of CN-XI pass laterally about 5 cm above the clavicle to the anterior border of the trapezius muscle. These remaining spinal-motor neurons of CN-XI then innervate the trapezius muscle.

The sternocleidomastoid muscle has two heads, both of which originate on the mastoid process. One head of the sternocleidomastoid muscle inserts onto the sternum, and the other head inserts onto the clavicle. The term *cleido* stands for collarbone. The sternocleidomastoid muscle on the right rotates the head to the left, whereas the muscle on the left rotates the head to the right. Damage to the spinal-motor neurons that innervate this muscle results in an inability to rotate the head away from the side of the damage. The trapezius muscle forms much of the shoulder. The result of damage to the spinal-motor neurons that innervate the trapezius muscle is a restricted ability to elevate the arm or to shrug the shoulders. The shoulder may also droop on the side of the damage.

Cranial Nerve (CN) XII: The Hypoglossal Nerve

The twelfth cranial nerve (CN-XII) is the *hypoglossal nerve*. The name *hypoglossal* means "under the tongue." The hypoglossal nerve functions primary in moving the skeletal musculature of the tongue. Hence, CN-XII is functionally classified as general skeletal-motor. The nucleus of CN-XII (hypoglossal nucleus) is a long, slender column of motor neurons located in the medulla, caudal to the inferior olivary nucleus at the floor of the fourth ventricle. The hypoglossal nucleus of CN-XII is controlled by descending contralateral upper motor neurons of the corticobulbar fiber pathway. The hypoglossal nucleus of CN-XII also receives gustatory and tactile input from the nucleus of the tractus solitarius and sensory trigeminal nucleus, respectively, for the mediation of swallowing, sucking, and chewing reflexes. Axons from the hypoglossal nucleus pass ventrally and laterally toward the pyramidal motor fibers (rostral to their decussation) and emerge collectively as a set of rootlets from the most ventral surface of the rostral-to-mid lateral medulla. The lower motor neuron rootlets of CN-XII emerge from a location that is ventral to the emergence of CNs-IX, X, and XI. Axons of CN-XII exit the cranium through the hypoglossal foramen, located in the posterior cranial fossa. After exiting the cranium, CN-XII passes downward and laterally, eventually making its way to the intrinsic and extrinsic muscles of the tongue. CN-XII then divides and supplies motor innervation to both the intrinsic and most of the extrinsic muscles of the tongue.

The intrinsic tongue muscles are the superior longitudinal, the inferior longitudinal, the transverse and the vertical muscles of the tongue. The intrinsic tongue muscles affect the overall shape of the tongue and enable rapid, precise, and delicate movements of the tongue musculature. The extrinsic tongue muscles of the tongue are the genioglossus, the hyoglossus, the styloglossus, the chondroglossus, and the palatoglossus or glossopalatine muscles. The last set of extrinsic tongue muscles listed, however, is not innervated by CN-XII. Recall that the palatoglossus (anterior faucial pillars) muscles are innervated instead by the pharyngeal plexus. The extrinsic tongue muscles function to determine the gross position of the tongue musculature. The genioglossus muscle retracts, protrudes, and depresses the tongue musculature. The hyoglossus muscle pulls the sides of the tongue downward. The styloglossus muscle pulls the tongue musculature back and upward. Finally, the chondroglossus muscle depresses the tongue musculature. Recall from the above sections that innervation provided by the pharyngeal plexus enables the anterior faucial pillars to elevate the tongue musculature (and depress the velum).

Spinal motor fibers arising from cervical spinal levels C_1 to C_3 also mix with motor fibers of CN-XII. The spinal motor fibers arising from cervical spinal levels C_1 to C_3 unite into a common trunk, known as the *ansa cervicalis* (ansa hypoglossi). The ansa cervicalis is a set of spinal nerves that are anatomically part of the cervical plexus. Fibers of the ansa cervicalis are carried by CN-XII and together innervate both hyoid and laryngeal elevator, as well as hyoid and laryngeal depressor muscles. These hyoid and laryngeal elevators are the geniohyoid and the thyrohoid muscles. Both are innervated by CN-XII, and by the fibers that arise from cervical spinal level C_1 of the ansa cervicalis. The hyoid and laryngeal depressors are the sternothyroid, the sternohyoid, and the omohyoid muscles. The sternothyroid muscle is innervated by CN-XII, and by the fibers that arise from cervical spinal levels C_2 to C_3 of the ansa cervicalis. The sternohyoid and the omohyoid muscles are innervated by the fibers that arise from cervical spinal levels C_2 to C_3 of the ansa cervicalis.

Upper motor neuron damage to the corticobulbar fiber tracts that innervate the hypoglossal nucleus of CN-XII will result in a lateral deviation of the tongue at rest, which will be toward the side of the mouth that is opposite to the side of the damage. Lower motor neuron damage to CN-XII will also result in a lateral deviation of the tongue at rest, but toward the side of the mouth that corresponds to the same side of the damage. Lower motor neuron damage to CN-XII will result in flaccid paralysis and atrophy of the tongue musculature, on the same side of the tongue musculature as the side of the damage.

Chapter Summary

- In this chapter, the general organization of the nervous system was provided.
- In this chapter, the neuron was defined as the single, genetic, anatomic, trophic, and fundamental (functional) unit of the nervous system.
- In this chapter, the parts of a neuron were defined anatomically and functionally.
- In this chapter, the types of neurons were defined, based on morphological and functional distinctions.
- In this chapter, the terms nucleus (nuclei), tract (tracts), ganglion (ganglia), and nerve (nerves) were defined anatomically and functionally.
- In this chapter, the chemical synapse was defined, as were the terms presynaptic and postsynaptic.
- In this chapter, the terms excitatory postsynaptic potential (EPSP), and inhibitory postsynaptic potential (IPSP) were defined. The distinction between

slow potentials and fast potentials was also elucidated.

- In this chapter, the terms polarization, depolarization, and hyperpolarization were defined.
- In this chapter, saltatory conduction and the action potential were both defined. The different stages of the action potential were also elucidated.
- In this chapter, the types of regulated ion channels responsible for neuron-to-neuron, as well as for neuron-to-muscle or neuron-to-organ communication were discussed.
- In this chapter, the role of chemical neurotransmitters was elucidated.
- In this chapter, the distinction between the central nervous system (CNS) and the peripheral nervous system (PNS) was defined and elucidated both anatomically and functionally.
- In this chapter, the distinction between upper motor neurons and lower motor neurons was elucidated both anatomically and functionally.
- In this chapter, the 12 pairs of cranial nerves (CNs) were defined both anatomically and functionally. To summarize:
  - The olfactory nerve (CN-I) serves the special sense of olfaction, or smell. The optic nerve (CN-II) communicates the special sense of visual information to the CNS.
  - The oculomotor nerve (CN-III), the trochlear nerve (CN-IV), and the abducens nerve (CN-VI) provide motor

innervation to the skeletal muscles that move the eyes.

- The trigeminal nerve (CN-V) provides special-skeletal (branchial) motor innervation to the muscles of mastication, the tensor tympani and the tensor veli palatini muscle. CN-V also communicates general-sensory information from all of the head and neck, the face, the mouth, and the eyes to the CNS.
- The facial-intermediate nerve (CN-VII), through its facial motor division, provides special-skeletal (branchial) motor control of the muscles of facial expression. The intermediate division of CN-VII communicates the special gustatory sense (taste) from the anterior two-thirds of the tongue. The intermediate division also provides general-visceral motor (autonomic) innervation to the submandibular, sublingual, and lacrimal glands, as well as the nasal mucosa and paranasal sinuses. In addition, the general-sensory part of the intermediate division communicates sensory information from specific parts of the head.
- The vestibulo-cochlear nerve (CN-VIII) is responsible for mediating the two special-sensory functions of hearing (auditory) and balance (vestibular).
- The glossopharyngeal nerve (CN-IX) provides special-skeletal (branchial) motor,

general-visceral (autonomic) motor, general-visceral sensory, general-sensory, and special-sensory functions. The special-skeletal (branchial) motor division innervates the stylopharyngeus muscle and the superior pharyngeal constrictor muscle. The general-visceral (autonomic) motor division innervates the parotid gland. The general-visceral sensory division communicates sensory information from the posterior one-third of the tongue, the palatine tonsils, the Eustachian tube, and the carotid sinus, and provides sensory innervation to the same structures of the pharynx innervated by motor divisions of cranial nerves nine (CN-IX) and ten (CN-X) as part of the pharyngeal plexus. The general-sensory division of CN-IX communicates sensory information from specific parts of the head and the special-sensory division of CN-IX communicates taste information from near the base of the tongue.

- The vagus nerve (CN-X) provides special-skeletal (branchial) motor, general-visceral (autonomic) motor, general-visceral sensory, general-sensory, and special-sensory functions. Special-skeletal (branchial) motor functions of CN-X include all those that are provided by the motor branch of the pharyngeal division, the external branch of the superior laryngeal division, and the motor branch of the inferior (or recurrent) laryngeal division of CN-X. General-visceral (autonomic) motor functions of CN-X include all those resulting from the extensive and important innervation of the thoracic and abdominal viscera that is provided by CN-X. General-visceral sensory functions of CN-X include those that are provided by the sensory branch of the pharyngeal-sensory division, the internal branch of the superior laryngeal division, and the sensory branch of the inferior (or recurrent) division. The general-sensory division of CN-X communicates sensory information from specific parts of the head, and the special-sensory division of CN-X communicates taste information from the epiglottis and parts of the laryngopharynx.

- The spinal accessory nerve (CN-XI) is composed of two special-skeletal (branchial) motor divisions. These are the cranial (internal) division and the spinal (external) division. The cranial division of CN-XI joins with the inferior (recurrent) division of CN-X and innervates all of the intrinsic skeletal muscles of the larynx, except the cricothyroid. The cranial division of CN-XI also joins with the pharyngeal-motor division of CN-X as part of the pharyngeal plexus to innervate all of the skeletal muscles of the pharynx and soft palate (velum) involved in swallowing (deglutition), except for the stylopharyngeus and tensor veli palatini. The spinal division of CN-XI innervates the sternocleidomastoid and trapezius muscles.

- The hypoglossal nerve (CN-XII) is general-motor in function and innervates the intrinsic and extrinsic musculature of the tongue, with the exception of the palatoglossus muscle. Together with the ansa cervicalis, CN-XII also innervates the geniohyoid, thyrohoid, sternothyroid, sternohyoid, and omohyoid muscles.

Bibliography

Carpenter, M. B., & Sutin, J. (1983). *Human neuroanatomy* (8th ed.). Balitmore, MD: Williams & Wilkins.

Kandel, E. R., Schwartz, J. H., Jessell, T. M., Siegelbaum, S. A., & Hudspeth, A. J. (2013). *Principles of neural science* (5th ed.). New York, NY: McGraw-Hill Medical.

Nolte, J. (2009). *The human brain: An introduction to its functional anatomy* (6th ed.). Philadelphia, PA: Mosby-Elsevier.

Seikel, J. A., King, D. W., & Drumright, D. G. (2005). *Anatomy and physiology for speech, language, and hearing* (3rd ed.). New York, NY: Thomson Delmar Learning.

Wilson-Pauwels, L., Akesson, E. J., & Stewart, P. A. (1988). *Cranial nerves: Anatomy and clinical comments*. Toronto, Ontario, Canada: B. C. Decker.

Chapter 10

Anatomy and Physiology of Hearing

Alphabetized Listing of Key Terms Discussed in Chapter 10

acoustic reflex	corpus callosum	stria vascularis
auditory cortex	efferent system	summating potential
auditory nerve	osseous spiral lamina	temporal
basilar membrane	ossicular chain	temporal bone
biological amplifier	outer and inner hair cells	traveling wave
brainstem nuclei		Type I auditory fibers
cochlear microphonic	pinna	Type II auditory fibers

Introduction

The identification, location, and function of various structures within the auditory system are fundamental to our overall knowledge of this and all other sensory systems. This opening sentence could be interpreted as a description of anatomy and physiology of hearing.

Hearing is a complex process that is critical to our everyday well-being. As humans we can hear an extremely wide range of frequencies and intensities. We can also discriminate small changes in intensity (on the order of 1 dB) and frequency (on the order of a few Hz). Even more amazing is the fact that the normal human auditory system can pick out sounds embedded in noise and understand what someone is saying across the room at large social gatherings (i.e., the cocktail party effect). These hearing skills, which we all take for granted, are a result of the ear (peripheral system) and the brain (central system) working together with great precision.

Understanding the structure and function of the peripheral and central components of this system is the goal of much current research. It also is critical for advances in the diagnosis and treatment of disorders of the auditory system. An appreciation and understanding of auditory anatomy and physiology allow one to identify the location of the disordered region within the auditory system. This in turn provides insight as to the nature of the disorder that can lead to effective treatment. It is safe to say that understanding disorders of the auditory system is an essential skill for the audiologist and hearing care professional, that is dependent on a substantial knowledge of the structure and function of this system.

One of the keys to the appropriate orientation of the auditory system is the understanding of the anatomical planes. These anatomical planes provide reference to the location of a structure by direction (Figure 10–1). As shown, superior is above, inferior below, anterior in front, posterior in back, lateral to the side, and medial toward the middle. However, for four-legged animals these designations do not work so well; hence, terms such as rostral (toward the head), caudal (toward the tail), dorsal (along the backside), ventral (along the belly), distal (away from the center), and proximal (toward the center) are used. Also, commonly used in brain images including radiology are terms such as coronal (cuts from side to side), sagittal (cuts from front to back), and transverse (cuts along the horizontal plane).

The Peripheral Auditory System

The Temporal Bone

The temporal bone, often overlooked in studying hearing anatomy, is a part of the cranium and either houses or supports most of the key structures of the auditory periphery. It is an integral part of the skull base and is composed of four fairly distinct bone segments. The squamous portion is part of the lateral cranium immediately superior to the ear canal (external auditory meatus). The bony ear canal (medial aspect of the canal) is another segment of the temporal bone and constitutes the tympanic portion. Directly posterior to the tympanic portion is the mastoid segment, which is characterized by numerous air cells. The final segment discussed here is the petrous portion that houses the middle ear, the cochlea, and the vestibular apparatus. It is a wedge-shaped structure that courses medially in the base of the skull and divides the posterior cranial fossa from the middle cranial fossa.

Viewing the posterior side of the petrous portion of the temporal bone, there are a number of key structures. The opening to the internal auditory meatus (IAM), also termed the porous acousticus, is located about two-thirds of the way along this structure and courses in a lateral to medial direction. Through this opening in the temporal bone exits the auditory, vestibular, and facial nerves that project to their respective sensory nuclei in the brainstem (lateral, caudal pons). Also located on the posterior aspect of the petrous bone just lateral to the IAM opening is the opening for the vestibular and cochlear aqueducts. These openings are identified by small recesses that are often difficult to view in the posterior side of the petrous bone (Anson & Donaldson, 1981).

The main functions of the temporal bone are to provide a framework of support for the outer, middle, and inner ears as well as the seventh and eighth

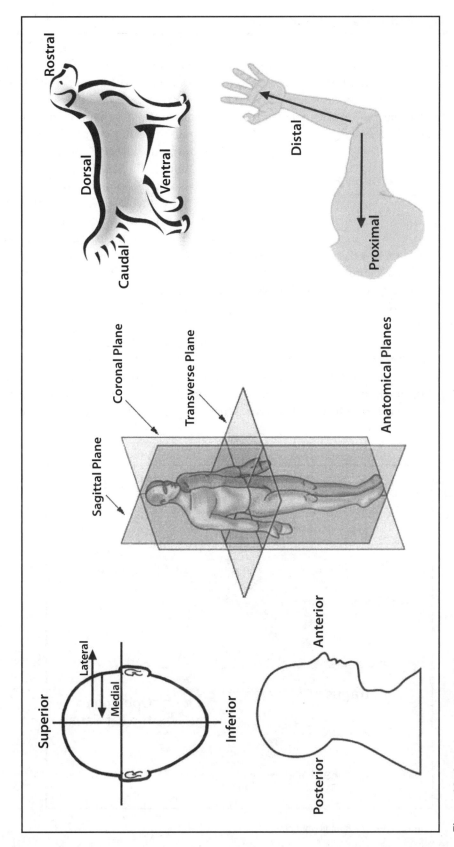

Figure 10–1. Various anatomical planes.

cranial nerves; to support and stabilize these structures; and to provide protection for most of the anatomic structures within the auditory periphery that support hearing processes.

The Outer Ear

Structure

The outer or external ear includes the pinna or auricle (Figure 10–2) and the external auditory meatus (EAM), or ear canal (Figure 10–3). The pinna is rather oblongated, "C"-shaped, and composed of a flexible cartilage that is covered with skin. The structure of the pinna takes on a shape that conforms to the underlying cartilage, with numerous folds and recesses. These folds and

recesses constitute specific anatomic sites or areas within the pinna for which particular terms are used. Referring back to the "C"-shaped structure of the pinna, the outer circular part of the "C" is termed the *helix* and just inside of the helix is the *antihelix*. The deepest recess of the pinna is the *concha*, which leads to the opening to the ear canal. Anterior to the concha is a protective flap called the *tragus*, which can be pressed into the opening of the ear canal to serve as a form of protection. Inferior and posterior to the tragus is a prominent fold of cartilage termed the *antitragus*. At the most inferior aspect of the pinna is the *ear lobe*—probably the softest and most flexible of the pinna's structures. The various structures of the pinna are innervated by the fifth (trigeminal) and seventh (facial/

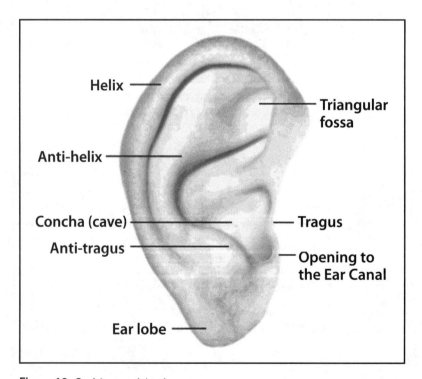

Figure 10–2. A human right pinna.

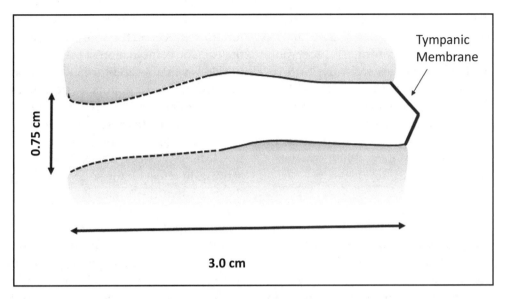

Figure 10–3. The external auditory meatus. Note the angles of the tympanic membrane, providing a slanted and concave structure. The dotted area corresponds to the cartilaginous and the solid line, to the bony portion of the ear canal. Copyright retained by Frank Musiek.

intermediate) cranial nerves (Musiek & Baran, 2007; Zemlin, 1998).

The anatomy of the pinna becomes clinically relevant when taking earmold impressions and the subsequent fabrication of the earmold. Variances in the pinna's fine structure can be well-defined using the anatomy discussed above. This in turn can provide better and more precise communication between the audiologist or hearing instrument specialist and the earmold manufacturer concerning the need for attention to a particular area or areas of the earmold to be created or modified. This should result in a better fit, and ultimately, a more satisfactory hearing aid experience for the patient.

The second structure in the external ear is the EAM. This outer ear structure is shaped like a tube and averages 2.5 to 3 cm in length and 0.75 cm in diameter in the adult human (see Figure 10–3). It originates at the concha and ends at the tympanic membrane. The EAM is not straight, but rather curves like an elongated letter "S" that is lying on its side. However, it is important to note that there is great variation in the shape of the EAM in humans. Visual inspection of this structure will reveal some EAMs that are relatively straight, whereas in other instances the EAM will be observed to be curvier. Pulling up and back (in adults) on the posterior aspect of the pinna can help straighten the ear canal for visual inspection with otoscopy. This procedure can prove to be especially helpful when one is visually inspecting an ear canal that is quite curvy in nature (see Musiek & Baran, 2007; Zemlin, 1998, for details).

The foundation of the outer third (approximately) of the ear canal is cartilaginous, whereas the foundation of the medial two-thirds (approximately) is bony. The entire length of the ear canal is covered by an epidermal lining, and the outer third contains hair follicles and glands that secrete a waxy substance (i.e., cerumen). Innervation of the EAM comes from the fifth (trigeminal), seventh (facial/intermediate), and ninth (glossopharyngeal) and tenth (vagus) cranial nerves (see Chapter 9), making the EAM sensitive to tactile stimulation (Møller, 2000; Musiek & Baran, 2007; Zemlin, 1998).

Function of the Outer Ear

The pinna's main function is to help funnel sounds from the environment into the smaller diameter EAM. Because of its unique structure and size, the pinna tends to result in a slight enhancement of sounds in the vicinity of 5000 Hz (Shaw & Teranishi, 1968). This enhancement (see Chapter 8) occurs because the unique configuration of the pinna in terms of its ridges and recesses results in a more efficient collection of sound in the higher frequency range, and the wavelengths of lower frequency sounds are essentially larger than the pinna and can pass around this structure more readily than those of higher frequency sounds (Musiek & Baran, 2007). The pinna also helps with sound localization (see Chapter 8) by creating complex resonances that change as the location of the sound source changes (Blauert, 1983).

The EAM helps to protect the ear with its debris-catching cilia (hair follicles) and cerumen, and it also serves as an acoustic resonator. The EAM peak resonance is around 3000 to 4000 Hz in the adult (see Chapter 7). At these frequencies, there is a gain of 10 to 15 dB in the acoustic signal with little or no gain at the frequencies below 1000 Hz (Dallos, 1973).

It also should be mentioned that in addition to the pinna and the EAM, the head, and even the torso can exert differential effects on the sounds reaching the ear. The combination of these effects provides valuable auditory information that the normal auditory system uses to help identify the source of a sound (i.e., directional hearing). Most notable of the directional hearing effects is the head-shadow effect, which can have a significant effect on the sound reaching the ear when the sound is originating from a source located on one side of the head versus the other (see Chapters 7 and 8). Take for example the situation where one has a sound being presented in a sound-field to the right side of the head. In this case, the sound would have almost direct access to the right ear, but the head would interfere with the sound that is traveling to the left ear. The end result would be that the sound reaching the left ear would be of a lower intensity (especially at high frequencies) than the sound arriving at the right ear. The central auditory system is capable of detecting and analyzing these types of intensity differences, as well as "small" times of arrival differences (see Chapters 7 and 8) that occur as a result of the farther distance that the signal has to travel to reach one ear versus the other, to identify the source of a sound (see Musiek & Baran, 2007, for additional discussion).

The Middle Ear (Tympanum)

Structure

The tympanic membrane (TM) marks the beginning of the middle ear, and it is oval shaped and concave in its appearance (Figure 10–4). In the adult human, it averages 8 to 10 mm in diameter, with

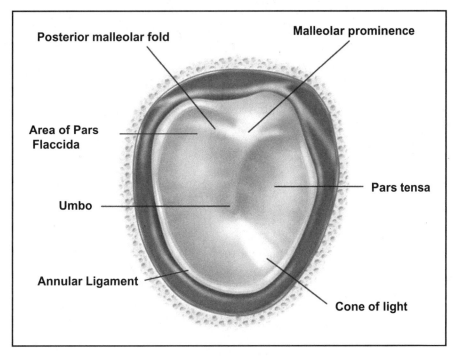

Figure 10–4. A human right tympanic membrane. Courtesy of Tom Dolan, medical illustrator, University of Kentucky.

a slightly larger diameter along the vertical axis than along the horizontal axis. The membrane has three layers and measures about 0.1 mm in thickness (Gelfand, 1997; Zemlin, 1998). These three layers include the epidermal (outer), the fibrous (middle), and the membranous (mucosal lining) layers. The fibrous layer is thicker in the center portion of the TM and thinner in the superior portion of this membrane. This "thinner" area is called the *pars flaccida*, which is the most elastic portion of the TM. For the most part, the remainder of the TM is stiffer due to more fibers and is called the *pars tensa* (see Yost, 2000).

The TM has several important anatomic landmarks in addition to the pars flaccida and the pars tensa. The annular ligament is the rim around the TM, which anchors the membrane to the wall of the ear canal. The manubrium of the malleus attaches to the TM in its upper center portion, and the umbo is located in the center of the TM and indicates the point of attachment for the most lateral aspect of the malleus. Coursing inferiorly and in a slightly lateral direction is the cone of light, which simply is the reflection of the otoscopic light that is reflected off of the TM during otoscopy. If observed otoscopically, the location of the cone of light would be viewed in the superior-posterior (or anterior-inferior) quadrant of the TM.

The middle ear (Figure 10–5) is, in part, identified by a cavity within the temporal bone (sometimes called the tympanum) that is bordered by the bony capsule of the cochlea medially and

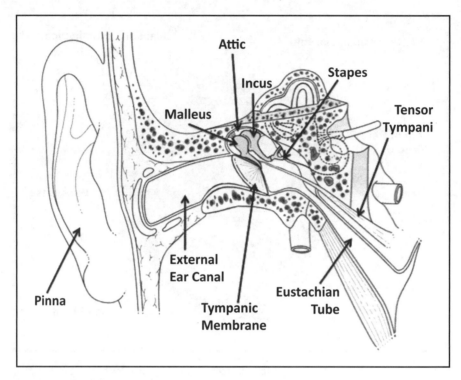

Figure 10–5. Outer and middle ear structures including the ossicular chain.

aspects of the temporal bone superiorly (attic), anteriorly, and posteriorly. The medial wall of the middle ear has two openings, the oval window (superior) and the round window (inferior), which are separated by the promontory. The ossicular chain, perhaps the most obvious structure in the middle ear, is composed of three bones: the malleus, the incus, and the stapes. Each of these bones has a detailed anatomy (see Musiek & Baran, 2007, for review). The stapes, the final bone in the ossicular chain, covers the oval window, and the round window is covered by flexible membrane (also known as a secondary tympanic membrane) (Musiek & Baran, 2007; Zemlin, 1998).

In the anterior, inferior middle ear cavity is the opening to the Eustachian tube. This tube connects the middle ear cavity with the posterior aspect of the nasopharynx. Also located in the middle ear are the stapedius muscle tendon, which arises from the posterior wall of the middle ear and connects to the head of the stapes, and the tendon of the tensor tympani muscle, which courses through the middle ear cavity to connect to the malleus (see Chapter 9). In addition, a branch of the facial-motor nerve that innervates the stapedius muscle (the smallest muscle in the body) transverses the middle ear space.

Function of the Middle Ear and Related Structures

Due to its concave structure, (see Figure 10–3), the TM has a rather complex displacement pattern that accommodates a wide range of frequencies and intensities (see Zemlin, 1998, for more in-depth explanation). Maximum displacement of the TM occurs in different areas and is dependent on the frequency of the sound stimulus. At high frequencies, the TM tends to vibrate in segments, whereas at low frequencies, there is less segmental vibration and the TM tends to vibrate more as a single unit (Gelfand, 1998).

A variety of functions are associated with the middle ear. The middle ear is an air-filled cavity. The volume of air within this cavity acts as a filter that limits or alters the transmission of some low-frequency sounds through the system. The structure also contributes to some complex resonance interactions with the ear canal and the pinna, altering the transmission of sound across the frequency range. The end result is primarily an increase in the intensity of the high-frequency components reaching the cochlea when these are compared to the levels represented in the original signal arriving at the outer ear.

The ossicular chain transmits vibrations from the eardrum (tympanic membrane) to the cochlea. The stapes, the final bone in the ossicular chain, transmits and enhances these vibrations to the cochlea by horizontally rotating around an axis (a rocking-like movement) at high intensities, whereas a more piston-like movement of the stapes occurs for (primarily) low intensities. The former type of movement may be related to stapedius muscle contraction, which occurs at high intensities (see Musiek & Baran, 2007, and Gelfand, 1998, for details). The ossicular chain also serves to stabilize movements related to the vibrations that are transmitted (Musiek & Baran, 2007).

The Eustachian tube's main function is to allow fresh air into the middle ear cavity and balance the air pressure in the middle ear tympanum to that of the atmosphere. This is done when a person opens his or her mouth or swallows. These actions result in contractions of the tensor veli palatini and levator veli palatini muscles (Chapter 9) which open the Eustachian tube (Zemlin, 1998).

Transformer Action

Sound travels through air which represents a low impedance medium. However, in hearing, sound (changes in air pressure) must be directed to penetrate the fluid-filled cochlea which has much higher impedance (see Chapter 5). Therefore, without some help from the transformer action of the middle ear, most of the acoustic energy reaching the cochlea would be reflected back out of the ear. Three mechanisms contribute to the middle ear transformer effects: (1) an area ratio advantage between the TM (which is larger) and the stapes' footplate, (2) a lever advantage created by the angles of middle ear bones, and (3) a "buckling" advantage due to the concave structure of the TM. The area ratio advantage relates to the fact that the TM has a much greater area than the stapes, which is the point of energy transfer to the inner ear. The area ratio of TM to stapes footplate is about 22:1, but the pars flaccida of the TM likely contributes little to this area ratio; hence, the effective ratio is estimated to be about 17:1 (or 18.6:1). This area ratio focuses energy at the stapes, thus increasing the input greatly at this point in the auditory system (Gelfand, 1998; von Békésy, 1960). The lever advantage is created by the way the malleus and incus interact. The gain in force is related to the longer handle of the malleus (manubrium) moving the shorter handle of the incus (long process) for about a 1.3:1 ratio advantage. Finally, the buckling action relates to the inward curvature of the TM, which on vibration imparts energy to the malleus. When this happens the TM moves proportionally more than the malleus (i.e., a "buckling effect"). The smaller displacement at the malleus in reference to the TM creates a greater gain in force (Musiek & Baran, 2007). These three transformer mechanisms allow greater energy to be directed to the fluid-filled cochlea than would be the case if these mechanisms did not exist or did not function appropriately. If these mechanisms are compromised individually or collectively, then a conductive hearing loss is expected.

The Acoustic Reflex

Stapedius muscle contraction is the endpoint of the acoustic reflex (AR). Because the stapedius muscle is located in the middle ear, it is reasonable to discuss this important reflex in this section of this chapter. However, it is important to highlight that the AR involves both peripheral and central mechanisms (Figure 10–6).

The AR pathway starts with sound entering the external ear and passing through the middle ear to the cochlea. The auditory nerve picks up the impulses from the cochlea and directs them to the ventral segment of the cochlear nucleus. The ventral cochlear nucleus then sends a fiber tract directly to the ipsilateral facial nerve nuclei and another branch to the contralateral superior olivary complex. The cochlear nucleus also sends fibers to the ipsilateral superior olivary complex, which then connects to its contralateral counterpart. The ipsilateral superior olivary complex connects to the facial nerve nuclei on both sides, and the contralateral superior olive also has input to the facial nerve nuclei. Hence, there is bilateral input to the facial nerve nuclei resulting in bilateral acoustic reflexes even if there is only monaural stimulation (see Chapter 9). From the facial nerve nuclei the AR follows an efferent course back to the stapedius muscle in the middle ear (Borg, 1973).

Møller (2000) and Borg (1973), two excellent researchers on the acoustic reflex (AR), provide great accounts of the nature and physiology of the AR. Probably the most popular explanation offered for the purpose of the acoustic reflex is that it serves to attenuate high-intensity sounds and therefore may help to protect the inner ear. As has been documented by Møller (2000), the higher the intensity of an acoustic signal above the reflex threshold intensity, the greater the contraction of the AR, at least for individuals with normal auditory and facial nerve function. In humans with normal auditory function, the AR is initiated at 70 to 90 dB HL for tonal stimuli and frequencies from 250 to 4000 Hz (also see Chapter 9). Stimulus frequency has little or no differential effects on the level of the threshold of the AR that is measured. The amplitude of the AR is largest for bilateral stimulation followed by ipsilateral and then contralateral stimulations (see Musiek & Baran, 2007). The latency of the AR also is variable and depends on a host of factors including stimulus type, intensity level, frequency, and how it is recorded.

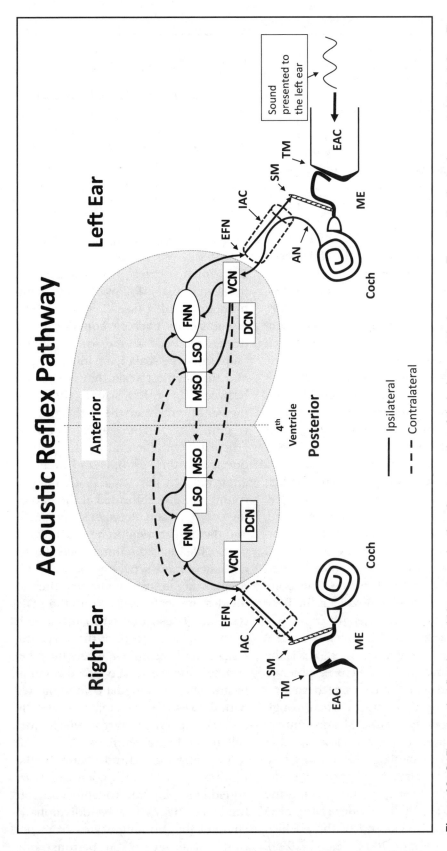

Figure 10–6. The acoustic reflex shown within an approximation of a cross section of the brainstem at the lower pons. The vertical dotted line represents the midline at the brainstem level. (AN, auditory nerve [internal auditory canal]; Coch, cochlea; DCN, dorsal cochlear nucleus; EAC, external auditory canal; EFN, facial nerve, efferent; FNN, facial nerve nuclei; IAC, internal auditory canal; LSO, lateral superior olive; ME, middle ear; MSO, medial superior olive; SM, stapedius muscle; TM, tympanic membrane; VCN, ventral cochlear nucleus.) Copyright retained by Frank Musiek.

The Cochlea

Structure: The Bony Cochlea

The cochlea is a bony snail-shell-shaped structure that is located within the petrous portion of the temporal bone. Inside this snail-like shell are fluids (endolymph and perilymph), special cells (hair and supporting cells), membranes (basilar, tectorial, Reissner's), nerve fibers, blood vessels, and special epithelium. The cochlea makes up part of the inner ear that also includes the vestibular apparatus (see also Chapter 9). The latter structure has a highly identifiable external bony structure that includes the three semicircular canals and the less obvious areas for the utricle and saccule. The bony cochlea has two openings in the shell: the oval window (superior) and round window as previously mentioned (Zemlin, 1998).

Inside the bony cochlear shell is a spiral-shaped osseous structure called *the osseous spiral lamina* (OSL). The OSL is shaped like an evergreen tree with the basal part of the cochlea located where lower branches would be and the apical part of the cochlea located toward the top of the tree. The bony cochlea is about 1 cm wide at the base and about 0.5 cm in length from base to apex. The "spiral" has from 2.2 to 2.9 turns in the human. The modiolus is the central part of the structure, which is composed of perforated bone that allows auditory nerve fibers to exit through small openings in the OSL and connect to the hair cells. The OSL has a shelf that spirals up the modiolus like a corkscrew. This bony shelf is the supporting structure for the basilar membrane and the limbus. This shelf is wider at the base than at the apical end of the cochlea (Musiek & Baran, 2007; Zemlin, 1998).

Function: The Bony Cochlea

In general, the osseous or bony cochlea is a framework of support and protection for the membranous cochlea and the auditory nerve fibers. Because of its position, the promontory, a bony protrusion between oval and round window, protects the round window.

Structure: The Membranous Cochlea

The bony cochlea provides a spiral framework that is followed by the membranous cochlea (see Chapter 9). The membranous cochlea contains three ducts called scalae: the scala vestibuli (superior), the scala tympani (inferior), and the smallest scala that is situated between the other scalae, the scala media (often termed the cochlear duct) (Figure 10–7). The stapes' footplate articulates with the oval window, which opens into the vestibule and transfers energy down the scala vestibuli. The round window is located at the end of the scala tympani. Reissner's membrane and the basilar membrane (BM) divide the cochlea into the three ducts. Reissner's membrane separates the scala vestibuli from the scala media, and the BM divides the scala media from the scala tympani. These ducts run the length of the cochlea except at the very end, termed the *helicotrema*, where the scala vestibuli and the scala tympani communicate. The scala media communicates with the vestibular system (specifically the saccule) via a narrowed channel called the ductus reuniens.

Two important fluid channels, the vestibular (VA) and cochlear (CA) aqueducts, play key roles in cochlear function. The VA is an endolymphatic channel that communicates from the posterior surface of the petrous bone

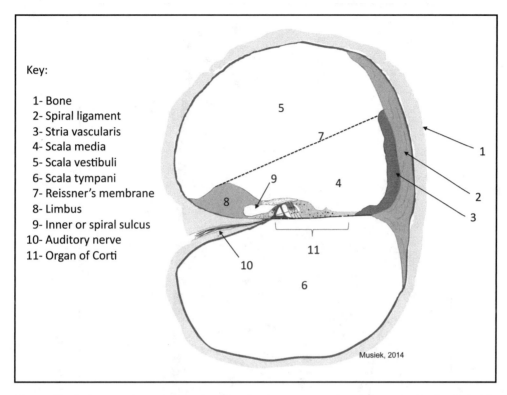

Key:

1- Bone
2- Spiral ligament
3- Stria vascularis
4- Scala media
5- Scala vestibuli
6- Scala tympani
7- Reissner's membrane
8- Limbus
9- Inner or spiral sulcus
10- Auditory nerve
11- Organ of Corti

Musiek, 2014

Figure 10–7. A cross section of the cochlea revealing key structures. Copyright retained by Frank Musiek.

to the saccule. The VA encompasses the endolymphatic duct and sac. The CA, which also opens to the petrous bone's posterior surface, courses to the scala tympani near the round window. This channel contains perilymph (a fluid highly similar to cerebral spinal fluid), which is found where it opens to the petrous bone surface

The two main fluids in the cochlea are endolymph (in the scala media) and perilymph (in the scala vestibuli and scala tympani). Endolymph is high in potassium and low in sodium, and perilymph has just the opposite chemical concentrations.

The BM is innervated by about 24,000 to 30,000 auditory fibers and is 25 to 35 mm in length in the adult human. The BM supports the organ of Corti, the actual end organ for hearing. At its apex, the BM is wider than at its base (0.36 mm versus 0.04 mm). The BM is also stiffer at the base than the apex (Buser & Imbert, 1992; Musiek & Baran, 2007)

Reissner's membrane is essentially avascular, has two layers of cells, and is impermeable. From base to apex Reissner's membrane becomes wider like the BM; however, the scala media becomes smaller and the "shelf" of the spiral lamina narrower as one moves from the base to the apex.

The organ of Corti is composed of supporting structures, sensory cells, membranes, and nerve fibers (Figure 10–8). This structure courses the length of the cochlea. Directly superior to the organ of Corti is the tectorial membrane,

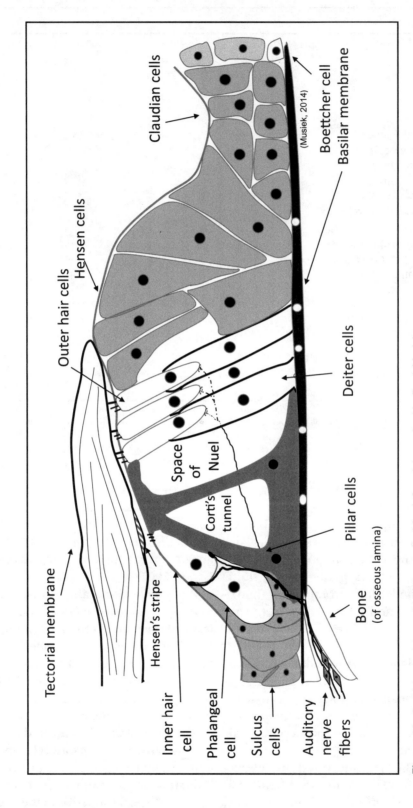

Figure 10–8. Major structures within the organ of Corti. Copyright retained by Frank Musiek.

which interacts with the stereocilia of the outer hair cells and is anchored to the upper lip of the limbus. It appears that the tectorial membrane does not articulate with the stereocilia of the inner hair cells. On its underside and just above the inner hair cells' stereocilia is a bulge termed *Hensen's stripe*. This bulge in the membrane's underside reduces the distance between the tops of the stereocilia and the tectorial membrane and may play a role in stimulation of the inner hair cells (see discussion later).

The reticular lamina is like a roof and is composed of tightly packed cells and forms a protective barrier above the sensory and supporting cells of the organ of Corti. The stereocilia of the hair cells protrude through the lamina. The reticular lamina is composed of phalanges of the Deiter's cells, the inner and outer border cells, as well as the tops of the pillar cells. The reticular lamina keeps the endolymph from penetrating the internal structures of the organ of Corti. Hence, only the stereocilia and not the hair cells themselves are bathed in endolymph, which has a +80 mV charge.

The lateral wall of the cochlear duct where the stria vascularis and spiral ligament reside will be discussed next. The stria vascularis is thought to play key roles in the production and absorption of endolymph. It is composed of three layers of cells. Marginal cells make up the first layer and are linked to ion channels and pumps. The intermediate cell layer is lateral to the marginal cells and contains melanin, and the basal cell layer is next to the spiral ligament. The cells in these three cell layers all are critical for the function of the cochlea. In summary, the metabolism of the inner ear is very dependent on the stria (Slepecky, 1996).

The spiral ligament extends throughout the cochlea and covers the lateral wall of the scala media. It also extends inferiorly to the upper scala tympani. This structure supplies support to the lateral aspect of the BM as well as for Reissner's membrane.

Sensory Cells

There are two types of sensory cells in the cochlea: inner and outer hair cells (IHCs, OHCs). The OHCs are organized in multiple rows (3 to 5), and the IHCs have only one row. These hair cells are located on the lateral and medial sides of the pillar cells, respectively. There are about 3,500 IHCs and 12,000 OHCs that course the length of the cochlea. Stereocilia are located at the top of both types of hair cells. The OHCs structure is surely different from that of the IHC (see Figure 10–8). The OHCs are rather elongated tube-like structures that vary in length. The OHCs in the high-frequency regions of the cochlea are shorter than those located in the low-frequency regions (Geisler, 1998). Located within the OHCs are contractile proteins such as actin, myosin, prestin, and tubulin. There are also unique microstructures along the outer walls of the OHCs called cisterns. These cisterns and special proteins (mentioned earlier) allow for rapid expansion and contractile movements of the cells (discussed later). The OHCs usually have in the vicinity of a −60 mV electrical charge and have potassium ion channels. The OHCs have a cuticular plate on top that supports the stereocilia that connect to the underside of the tectorial membrane. Each OHC has three rows of stereocilia with a greater number of cilia at the base than at the apex (about

150 to 50). These cilia are stiff and form a "W" shape when looking down on the top of the hair cell.

The IHCs are structured differently from OHCs. Also, they have more mitochondria and utilize calcium and potassiumion ion channels. Moreover, they do not have contractile proteins and cisterns. The IHCs have a −40 mV charge and about 50 to 70 stereocilia per cell, which are arranged in a "U" shape. The IHCs typically have three rows of stereocilia that are graded in length, and the stereocilia are longer at the apex of the organ of Corti than at its base.

It is key to realize that OHCs and IHCs have stereocilia that have pores (channels) that open when stimulated. This allows positive K ions to pass into the cell resulting in depolarization. Tip-links are small filament bands that open the pores upon movement in a certain direction. The tip-links are likely to be located toward the top of the stereocilia. Cross-links are similar in structure to tip-links, but they connect the stereocilia closer to their midpoints. This situation allows the stereocilia to move in unison and also supplies some overall support for this movement (Geisler, 1998).

The hair cells are tuned so that cells located more basally respond to high-frequency sounds, whereas the more apically situated cells respond to lower frequency sounds (see Gelfand, 1998 for details and review).

Supporting Cells

Supporting cells are located along the organ of Corti and include pillar cells, Deiter's cells, phalangeal cells, Hensen's cells, Claudian cells, border cells, and Boettcher's cells (Musiek & Baran, 2007; Slepecky, 1996). Next to the limbus are the border cells that divide the IHCs from the inner sulcus. The phalangeal cells support the IHCs and have stalks that separate these cells. These stalks or phalanges give rise to a flattened apical plate that contributes to the reticular lamina. A similar structure is observed in the case of the Deiter's cells, which support the OHCs. The inner and outer pillar cells enclose the tunnel of Corti and, because of their triangular structure, enhance the stiffness of this region where there is considerable movement of the BM. The space of Nuel is located next to the outer pillar cells. The lateral segment of the BM is where the Hensen's cells, the cells of Claudius, and the lesser known Boettcher's cells are found. These all lend support to the lateral aspect of the BM. Between the most lateral OHCs and the Hensen's cells is a space called the outer tunnel.

Function: The Membranous Cochlea

By way of overview, the physiology of the cochlea can be separated into two major areas of study: cochlear mechanics and cochlear electrophysiology. Although these two areas of function will be presented separately, it is important to realize that cochlear mechanics and electrophysiology are interdependent and function smoothly as part of a larger continuum that helps make up the hearing experience. Some key broad-based functions of the cochlea change vibrotactile energy to electrical energy and code for intensity, frequency, and time. These functions require both mechanical and electrophysiologic processing.

Cochlear Mechanics

The ossicular chain's vibratory energy is imparted to the cochlea through the stapes' motion at the oval window. Key to starting mechanical functions of the cochlea is that as the stapes pushes in (compression wave) or out (rarefaction wave) of the oval window, the round window membrane accommodates this movement. This interaction between the oval and round windows cannot be compromised without affecting the cochlear hearing processes.

The input from the stapes displaces the fluid in the cochlea in a manner that creates a traveling wave (TW) that moves down the length of the cochlea. The speed of the TW decreases as it moves from the base to the apex of the cochlea. This TW causes an activation of subsequent mechanical and electrochemical processes in the cochlea. Frequency can be coded in the cochlea in two ways, by place and by periodicity (temporally). The place theory, which was first described by von Békésy (1960), argued that sounds traveled down the BM and that frequency was coded by the point of maximum displacement of the BM by the traveling wave (TW), with high frequencies being represented more basally and low frequencies more apically. The TW reaches its maximum deflection at the place where the resonance of the BM matches the stimulating sound. This maximum deflection refers to the maximum amplitude point for the envelope. The difficulty with the place theory was that the tuning required for behavioral frequency discrimination was not consistent with the sharpness of the TW envelope; however, this problem was mostly resolved with the discovery of the biological amplifier that will be discussed later.

Frequency also can be coded temporally. That is, the rapid movement of the BM (fine structure) is associated with the cycles of the acoustic stimulus that stimulate the hair cells and subsequently the auditory nerve fibers accordingly. For example, if a 200-Hz tone were presented to the ear, the BM would move 200 times per second and the hair cells and auditory nerve would be stimulated and would fire at the same rate. This kind of frequency coding may work feasibly for low-frequency tones, but not well for high-frequency stimuli as the firing rates needed to code high-frequency sounds are likely to exceed the physiologic capacities of the hair cells. Hence, common thinking is that temporal or periodicity processing and place of maximum displacement work well for low frequencies but that, as the frequency of the stimulus increases, the place principle becomes more dominant (Geisler, 1998; Musiek & Baran, 2007; von Békésy, 1960; Yost, 2000).

Amplitude of the TW is the manner in which intensity is represented in the cochlea—the greater the intensity of the signal, the greater the amplitude of the TW envelope. However, with increases in intensity the displacement of the BM is not linear. The TW envelope has greater damping on the apical side; hence, the TW envelope has a sharper reduction in amplitude on the apical side than is reflected in the increase in amplitude on the basal side. When intensity increases, not only does the vertical displacement increase, but so does the width of the envelope. This action results in more hair cells being stimulated and in turn, more neural elements being activated. Because of the broader displacement of the envelope at high intensities, there is a decrease in the sharpness of the peak of the TW resulting in poorer frequency selectivity.

Nonlinearity associated with the BM (and hearing in general) is an important concept (see Chapter 6). As mentioned earlier, as intensity increases, so does BM displacement, but not in a linear fashion. At low intensities, there is proportionately more displacement of the BM than at high intensities. Like intensity, the representation of frequency on the BM is not linear. An octave change for a high frequency sound on the basal part of the BM requires less space than an octave change at the low-frequency end of the BM. This nonlinearity can be viewed as a natural "compression" within the cochlea for both intensity and frequency (see Musiek & Baran, 2007; Yost, 2000).

Hair Cell Mechanics

Perhaps the hair cells' main function is to convert vibratory energy into electrical energy so that the nervous system can utilize these signals. This mechanical activity starts at the stereocilia. The OHCs stereocilia are embedded in (penetrate) the underside of the tectorial membrane. If a TW is a compression wave, the BM will be deflected downward. Because the tectorial membrane and the BM are attached at different sites, a downward movement of the BM will result in the tectorial membrane pulling the stereocilia toward the limbus (or, medial aspect of the organ of Corti). Recall, at the stereocilia level, downward movements result in the tip-links closing the channels of the stereocilia. As a result, no chemical transduction can evolve and the hair cell cannot depolarize. However, when the BM moves upward, such as is seen when the stimulus is a rarefaction wave, the tectorial membrane pulls the stereocilia in the opposite direction and the channels open up allowing K^+ ions to enter the cells, starting the depolarizing process (Geisler, 1998).

Please note that the IHCs are not embedded in the tectorial membrane; hence, their stimulation related to the BM movement is somewhat different. The most popular theory is that there is a complex fluid flow between the reticular lamina and Hensen's stripe on the underside of the tectorial membrane (see Figure 10–8). This fluid flow is increased in its effectiveness due to the restricted area created by Hensen's stripe. The fluid movement causes the deflection of the stereocilia of the IHCs in the same direction for compression and rarefaction sound waves as the OHCs, which starts the transduction process in the IHCs (Geisler, 1998; Musiek & Baran, 2007).

The hair cells, both inner and outer, are responsible for the transduction process. However, they do have different functions. As mentioned earlier, the OHCs have contractile proteins and cell wall structures that allow them to expand and contract. These cells will contract on upward deflection of the BM and expand on the downward movement. Because the OHCs are connected to the BM via their Deiter's cells, when they contract the result is the enhanced movement of the BM in an upward direction. Just the opposite happens when the BM moves downward. This creates an overall greater displacement of the BM and makes the incoming sound greater in intensity—a type of amplifier, hence, the name the *biological or cochlear amplifier*. This biological amplifier is activated only for low-intensity sounds. Therefore, one might say that it contributes to the compression of intensity in the cochlea. As only a very narrow area of the BM is moved by OHC contraction/expansion, the cochlear amplifier modifies the BM's response for only a very small range of frequencies. Hence, the biological amplifier not only amplifies sounds in the cochlea, it also sharpens the tuning of the BM for low-intensity sounds by modifying the cochlear response for only a narrow range of frequencies (Salvi, Clock Eddins, & Wang, 2007).

The expansion and contraction of OHCs results in another interesting phenomenon in hearing. The biological amplifier creates small acoustical signals that are propagated back out of the cochlea in a reverse mechanical process. This reverse-acoustic energy vibrates the middle ear bones, moves the tympanic membrane, and results in subaudible sounds in the ear canal. These subaudible sounds can be picked up by a microphone and recorded and displayed. These signals are otoacoustic emissions (OAEs). Hence, OHC motility is linked to these OAEs (see Chapter 6). If the OHCs are damaged, OAEs usually are absent, therefore resulting in some sensorineural hearing loss (Salvi et al., 2007).

Interestingly, the intensity range of OAEs is 30 to 40 dB, about the same as the intensity range of the OHCs; that is, a hearing loss of 30 to 40 dB or more will result in absent OAEs. Furthermore, it is known that damage to IHCs, the auditory nerve, or the central mechanisms will not compromise OAEs (Geisler, 1998; Musiek & Baran, 2007).

The IHCs do not have motile properties like the OHCs, but they do play a major role in the transduction and coding of high-intensity acoustic signals. Perhaps too simply stated, the IHCs seem to take over where the OHCs leave off in terms of intensity coding.

Although OHCs often are damaged by high-intensity sounds, IHCs frequently survive. The IHCs carry much of the information about sounds that reach the ear onto the central auditory nervous system based on their reaction to high-intensity sounds and their rich neural supply.

Cochlear Electrophysiology

Cochlear mechanics initiates the transduction of vibratory energy to electrical energy. To recap, the BM moving upward as a result of a rarefaction sound wave results in shearing of the stereocilia of the hair cells by the tectorial membrane. This process results in the stereocilia being pushed away from the limbus and opens the pores of the stereocilia via increased tension on the tip-links. This pore opening allows K^+ ions to flow in and start the depolarization process (i.e., the hair cell fires). Downward deflection of the BM by a compression wave creates an opposite situation from what was just described and hyperpolarization takes place (i.e., the hair cell does not fire).

Three cochlear potentials are associated with hair cell depolarization. These include the endocochlear or resting potential, the cochlear microphonic (CM), and the summating potential (SP). The endocochlear potential is the electrical gradient that can be measured when the hair cell is not depolarizing, hyperpolarizing, or recovering from hyperpolarization. In this state, the hair cell is at about a –70 mV charge while the scala media (endolymph) is at about a +80 mV charge. This large differential in electrical charges, the endocochlear potential, is likely maintained by the intermediate cells of the stria vascularis. The endocochlear potential also is responsible for moving the K$^+$ ions through the mechanical channels (pores) of the stereocilia, which initiates the depolarization process. Hallowell Davis proposed a "battery model" many years ago that had as its main feature the stria vascularis as the energy source to maintain the intra- and extracellular charges in the cochlea (Davis, 1965; Wangemann, 2002a, 2002b).

The next cochlear potential that will be discussed is the cochlear microphonic (CM), which was brought to prominence in auditory science by the classic experiment of Wever and Bray (1930). The CM is a summation of hair cell responses from along the BM to a sound stimulus (Salvi et al., 2007). As Wever and Bray demonstrated, the CM faithfully mimics the sound stimulus. This is one of the key characteristics in defining the nature of the CM. The CM occurs almost instantly and has little fatigability. Because the CM mimics the stimulus, positive and negative polarity stimuli will yield positive and negative polarity CMs. Therefore, if alternating polarity signals are averaged together, they essentially will cancel out this response.

Salvi et al. (2007) nicely reviews some key characteristics of the CM. The CM is generated primarily by the OHCs; however, there is some contribution from the IHCs. The CM, depending on how it is recorded, can be obtained close to behavioral threshold—this is especially the case when using transtympanic electrocochleography. The CM amplitude generally increases monotically with intensity increases up to about 60 to 80 dB SPL, but then it "rolls over" slightly at higher intensities. The frequency of the stimulus will influence the amplitude of the CM. Recall that the higher frequencies do not produce as large a response as the low frequencies. Low-frequency stimuli are capable of producing a CM at all three turns of the cochlea, whereas high-frequency stimuli precipitate responses only at the basal turn, a finding that is consistent with TW physiology.

The summating potential (SP) follows the CM in time. It is a DC potential that is generated by the OHCs and IHCs; however, the IHCs have a greater contribution to the SP than they do for the CM. The SP can be positive or negative depending if one is recording from the scala tympani or the scala vestibuli. This sometimes makes far-field recordings, such as is done with electrocochleography, difficult to understand and interpret. The SP can be recorded at low-intensity levels when the recoding electrode is in or near the cochlea. However, in far-field recordings it is not often observed at low-intensity levels. At high intensities, the SP continues to increase in amplitude without the rollover effects noted for the CM. The SP cannot be cancelled out by an alternating polarity like the CM. It has been shown that in disorders such as cochlear hydrops the SP increases in amplitude (Clark & Ohlemiller, 2008; Dallos, 1973; Salvi et al., 2007).

The tuning curves of the IHCs and OHCs are sharp and similar to each other. These tuning curve responses are consistent with the vibration patterns and tuning of the BM (see Salvi et al., 2007).

The hair cells synapse with postsynaptic receptors (see Chapter 9) on the auditory nerve. It appears that the hair cells' (afferent) neurotransmitter is glutamate (see Clark & Ohlemiller, 2008).

The Auditory Nerve

Once the cochlea has done its part and has transduced the acoustic signal to electrical impulses and set up frequency and intensity codes, this information is then forwarded to the auditory nerve (AN). The AN, which preserves the cochlear codes, passes this information on to the brainstem, which is part of the central auditory system.

Structure

The AN connects the cochlea to the brainstem (Figure 10–9). The AN is part of the eighth cranial nerve, which also includes vestibular nerve fibers from the vestibular apparatus (also see Chapter 9). As Møller (2000) adroitly reviews in the adult human, the AN is approximately 22 to 26 mm long. The course of the afferent AN from the cochlea to the brainstem is not as simple as one may think. The AN fibers connect to the hair cells at their dendritic processes and from there course medially through the small openings in the shelf of the osseous spiral lamina called the habenula perforata. The AN continues medially to an enlarged cavity called Rosenthal's canal, which is where the spiral ganglion is located. The AN fibers proceed to form a trunk within the modiolus and then on into the internal auditory meatus (IAM) where they join the vestibular nerve (superior and inferior divisions) and facial nerve trunks. All these nerves course to the cerebellopontine angle (CPA) and then input to the cochlear nucleus in the brainstem (Møller, 2000).

There are two types of AN fibers, Types I and II. The Type I fibers connect to the IHCs and make up 90% of all AN fibers. The Type II fibers connect only to OHCs and are only 10% of the total AN population The Type I AN fibers are myelinated, but the Type II fibers, for the most part, are not (Musiek & Baran, 2007; Spoendlin, 1972).

In a general sense, the tonotopic organization of the AN nerve reveals high frequencies on the outside of the nerve bundle and low frequencies in the core or middle (see Figure 10–9). However, upon closer inspection, the tonotopic organization is revealed to be more of a spiral following the spiral organization of the cochlea (Møller, 2000).

Function

If a tone burst is presented to the ear, the AN will respond by firing over the time period of the stimulus. The pattern of firing rate over time is called a poststimulus time histogram (PSTH). In a PSTH, time is represented on the x-axis and the amplitude of neural firing is represented on the y-axis. The latency of the auditory nerve compound action potential (CAP) of the AN decreases with increases in the intensity of the stimulus. Usually, the latency of the CAP response is between 1 and 2 ms for a moderately intense click stimulus. The CAP is probably best known as wave I of the auditory brainstem response (ABR) or the CAP of an electrocochleographic recording (Møller, 2000; Musiek & Baran, 2007).

As earlier discussed, frequency is coded in the AN by place or firing rate (periodicity or temporal coding). Temporal coding is dependent on phase-locking, which means that the nerve fiber fires at the same point on the acoustic waveform. However, this does not mean that the nerve fiber fires on

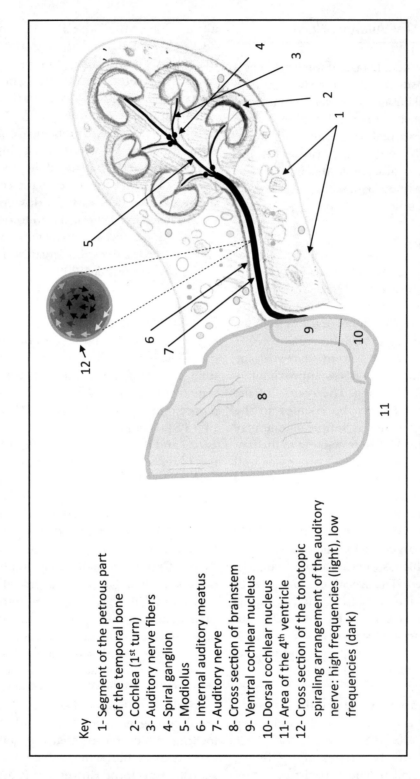

Key

1- Segment of the petrous part
   of the temporal bone
2- Cochlea (1st turn)
3- Auditory nerve fibers
4- Spiral ganglion
5- Modiolus
6- Internal auditory meatus
7- Auditory nerve
8- Cross section of brainstem
9- Ventral cochlear nucleus
10- Dorsal cochlear nucleus
11- Area of the 4th ventricle
12- Cross section of the tonotopic
    spiraling arrangement of the auditory
    nerve: high frequencies (light), low
    frequencies (dark)

Figure 10–9. Aucitory nerve pathway from the cochlea through the internal auditory meatus to the brainstem. Copyright retained by Frank Musiek.

every cycle of the waveform. If the refractory period (time period of successive firings) of the nerve fiber is too long, it may not be capable of firing on every cycle. In this case, the fiber may fire on every other or every third or fourth cycle. The cycles that are missed by one fiber are picked up by other available fibers of the AN. In aggregate, all cycles will be coded by AN fibers. This kind of frequency coding is commonly referred to as the volley principle (reviewed by Musiek & Baran, 2007).

The characteristic frequency (CF) is the frequency to which the nerve fiber responds best, which usually is its lowest threshold (see Chapter 5). The farther away from the CF the stimulus is, the greater the intensity is required for the nerve fiber to respond. Therefore, if one plots the intensity needed for the nerve fiber to fire as one moves gradually away from the CF (both on the low- and high-frequency sides), a physiologic tuning curve (TC) can be established. Tuning curves relate the frequency selectivity of the nerve fiber —that is, the sharper the TC, the better is the frequency selectivity. Auditory nerve TCs are usually sharp at the high frequencies and broader at low frequencies unless there is damage to the OHCs of the cochlea or damage to the AN itself (Gelfand, 1998).

Intensity coding at the AN level is related to the spontaneous firing rate (SFR) of the neurons. Much of the work by Liberman (1978) as well as Kim and Parham (1991, 1997) have allowed a categorization of AN firing rates related to intensity coding. These authors relate that there is a range of SFRs with the lowest being less than 10 and the highest being about 100 spikes per second. Liberman (1978) divided AN SFRs into

three categories: low = 0 to 0.5, medium = 0.5 to 18, and high ≥18 spikes per second. The high SFRs respond best to low-intensity sounds, and the low SFRs respond best to high-intensity sounds. It is the combination of the low, medium, and high SFR neurons that allow the AN (in total) to have a relatively linear firing rate response to intensities from threshold to near 100 dB SPL. Hence, as intensities increase, so does the firing rate of the neuron and also more neurons respond (relating to the TW size).

One of the key phenomena of AN function is that of adaptation (see Chapter 8). Adaptation is the decrease in the amplitude of the AN action potential over time during stimulation, without a change in the stimulus characteristics. Adaptation is a neural phenomenon, which is greater at high frequencies compared to low frequencies (Keidel, Kallert, & Korth, 1983). Damage to the AN increases adaptation.

The Central Auditory Nervous System

As one proceeds from a caudal to rostral orientation in the auditory system, more neurons are observed that respond to acoustic stimuli. The central auditory system contains dramatically more auditory neurons than the AN. These neurons essentially increase in number and connections as one ascends the central auditory system (neural arborization). This marked increase in auditory neurons from thousands at the AN level to practically millions in the auditory regions of the brain speaks to the high redundancy and complex functioning of the auditory brain (Figure 10–10).

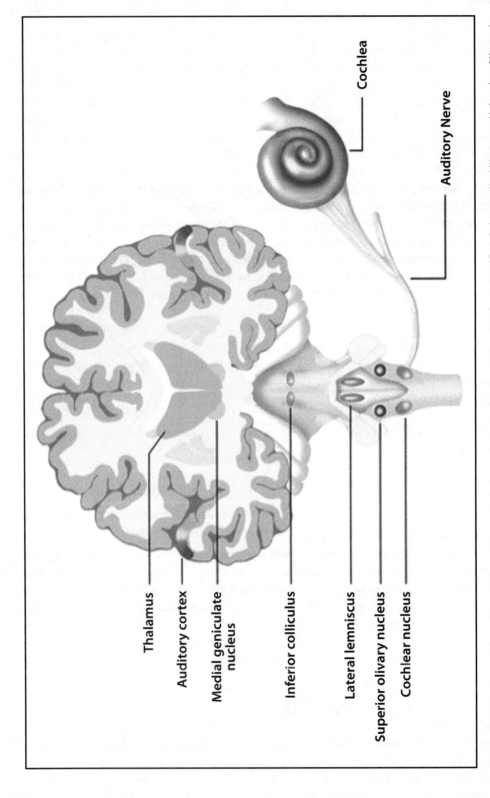

Figure 10–10. Coronal view of the auditory pathways including brainstem, subcortex, and cortex. Courtesy of Tom Dolan, medical illustrator, University of Kentucky.

The increase in neurons is likely needed as, at this level, some difficult demands are made on the central auditory system.

The Cochlear Nucleus

Structure

The auditory pathway of the brainstem (Figure 10–11) is introduced by the cochlear nucleus (CN). It is the first structure one will observe of the central auditory system and is located on the lateral aspect of the caudal-most pons just above the termination of the medulla. It is composed of three major nuclei groups: the dorsal cochlear nucleus (DCN), the posterior ventral cochlear nucleus (PVCN), and the anterior ventral cochlear nucleus (AVCN). The AN fibers project to the CN and enter between the AVCN and PVCN in an area termed the *root entry zone*. There are a variety of cell types in the

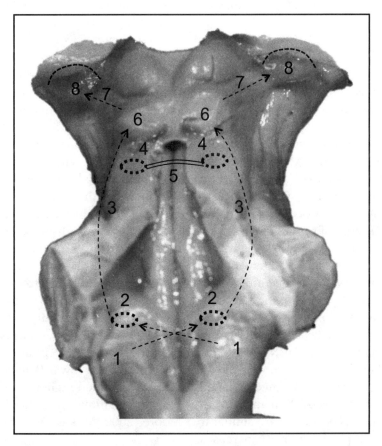

Figure 10–11. A posterior view of the auditory brainstem showing the ascending auditory pathway (*dotted lines*) and structures. (Key: 1 = the cochlear nucleus, 2 = area of superior olivary complex (*dotted circles*), 3 = lateral lemniscus, 4 = nuclei of lateral lemniscus, 5 = commissure of Probst, 6 = inferior colliculus, 7 = Brachium of inferior colliculus, 8 = medial geniculate body.) Copyright retained by Frank Musiek.

CN (i.e., pyramidal, octopus, globular, multipolar, etc.) which are located in specific areas of this auditory structure. The neural outputs from the CN are both ipsilateral and contralateral with the latter being larger and more numerous. There are three major contralateral routes exiting the CN. The ventral and intermediate stria arising from the AVCN and PVCN project primarily to the opposite superior olivary complex (SOC), and to a lesser degree to the ipsilateral SOC. The dorsal stria, from the DCN, projects primarily to the opposite lateral lemniscus (LL) tract (Pickles, 1988).

Function

The various cell types in the CN are responsible for modifying or maintaining the input firing pattern over time or over the PSTH (poststimulatory time histogram) from the AN. However, the PSTHs generated from the cells in the CN take on a variety of forms indicating sophisticated processing of the AN input. This kind of processing happens at each level of the auditory system. The CN has a tonotopic arrangement that is patterned by the projections of the AN. In general, and simplified, the low frequencies are in the lateral areas and the high frequencies are in the medial dorsal regions of the DCN, PVCN, and AVCN. Therefore, each section of the CN has its own tonotopic arrangement (see Musiek & Baran, 2007; Romand & Avan, 1997). The TCs of the CN are similar to those of the AN. As intensity increases, the firing rate of CN neurons tends to increase rather linearly over about a 30- to 40-dB range; however, some neurons have a greater range of response. The CN neurons can phase lock for tones up

to the 3000- to 4000-Hz range, indicating capacity for good temporal resolution. The CN is represented by wave III of the ABR, which occurs about 1.5 to 2 msec after wave I (generated by the auditory nerve) in individuals with normal auditory function.

The Superior Olivary Complex

Structure

Following the CN, the superior olivary complex (SOC) is observed in the ascending central auditory pathway in the brainstem. This complex structure receives heavy input from the contralateral CN as mentioned earlier. Although the SOC is at the same level as the CN, it cannot be seen on the surface of the brainstem as it is located deep in the pons. The main structures in this complex are the lateral superior olive (LSO), the medial superior olive (MSO), the nuclei of the trapezoid body, and groups of periolivary nuclei surrounding the lateral and medial olive. For the most part, there are only three cell types in the SOC—much less than in the CN. In the LSO, high frequencies are located medially and low frequencies are represented laterally, whereas for the MSO the high frequencies are represented toward the ventral end and the low frequencies toward the dorsal end. The LSO is tuned higher than the MSO (based on animal data) (Møller, 2000; Moore, 2000; Musiek & Baran, 2007).

Function

The SOC is the prominent structure for bilateral representation of monaural acoustic input. This permits precise comparisons of ipsilateral and contralateral inputs along time, intensity, and to some degree, frequency domains. This sets up the cuing (for the rest of the central auditory system) of time and intensity differences that are essential for sound lateralization (within the head) and sound localization functions (see Chapter 8). The terms interaural timing (ITD) and intensity differences (IID) have become entrenched in describing localization and lateralization functions. Fusion is another function of the SOC that can be defined as the combination and integration of information from the two ears. For example, if one ear could hear only high frequencies and the other ear only low frequencies, the SOC could combine these inputs allowing hearing along the entire frequency spectrum.

The TCs of the SOC are sharp and sensitive to change. Further frequency analysis has to do with place in the SOC as mentioned earlier. As one would expect, the SOC neurons have good phase locking—similar to the phase-locking capabilities of CN neurons. Intensity coding for the SOC also is similar to that of the CN. The SOC is represented in large part by wave IV of the ABR; however, this auditory structure also may contribute to other ABR waves. Finally, the SOC plays a major role in the acoustic reflex (discussed earlier) and in masking level differences (Møller, 2000).

The Lateral Lemniscus

Structure

The lateral lemniscus (LL) and the nuclei of the LL (NLL) represent two anatomic entities. The LL refers to the major pathway on each side of the brainstem that courses from the caudal pons to the midbrain (inferior colliculus) which carries the majority of all neural impulses from lower nuclei to more rostral nuclei. In the LL, the contralateral fibers are far greater in number than are the ipsilateral fibers. The NLL has two main parts: the ventral (VNLL) and dorsal (DNLL) divisions. The VNLL division receives projections from the AVCN and the trapezoid body contralaterally, and the DNLL receives projections from the SOC and AVCN ipsilaterally. Neural projections from these nuclei are primarily ipsilateral and course to the IC (Møller, 2000; Schwartz, 1992). It is worthy to note that many fibers from the CN and SOC bypass the NLL. Stellate, multipolar, globular, elongated, and ovoid cells are found in the NLL (Covey & Casseday, 1986).

Function

One concept that is true is that the tonotopic arrangement of the NLL is poorly understood with several different kinds of arrangements being hypothesized (see Musiek & Baran, 2007, for discussion). The NLL is known to be sensitive to interaural time differences, preserving this function from the SOC. The NLL is also the primary generator of wave V of the ABR. This is the largest and most consistent wave of the ABR (Møller, 2000).

Inferior Colliculus

Structure

Superior to the NLL is the easily observed inferior colliculus (IC). The IC is situated within the relatively small midbrain but is the largest of the ascending brainstem auditory nuclei. It has three divisions, including the central nucleus, the dorsal nucleus, and the lateral nucleus (Morest & Oliver, 1984). The central nucleus is the key auditory player, although the other divisions also contribute to hearing. The IC essentially receives major inputs from all of the more caudal nuclei in the pons, both ipsilaterally and contralaterally. The IC is on the receiving end of the acoustic chiasm. Mostly disc-shaped and stellate cells are found in the IC's central nucleus. The projections from the IC primarily run ipsilaterally to the medial geniculate body (MGB) in the thalamus via a large pathway—the brachium; however, there are also contralateral projections that often course through the commissure of the IC (Ehret, 1997; Musiek & Baran, 2007).

Function

As highly documented, the central nucleus of the IC has a tonotopic organization that runs dorsolaterally to ventromedially for low to high characteristic frequencies (Winer, 1992). The TCs of the IC are mostly sharp and some even double peaked, indicating complex frequency coding. There are both monotonic and nonmonotonic intensity functions found in the IC. Although most fibers increase firing rate with increases in intensity over a wide range, some fibers "roll over" (decrease firing rate) at sensation levels of less than 10 dB (Popelár & Syka, 1982). This provides a large range of intensity functions for the IC—perhaps more than is seen for other auditory brainstem nuclei.

The neurons in the IC are regarded as good temporal processors. The IC has a large population of neurons that are sensitive to amplitude and frequency tone modulations (as compared to steady-state tones). As one might expect based on information provided above, the IC also is sensitive to interaural time and intensity differences similar to the neurons of the SOC; hence, it also plays an important role in localization and binaural hearing (Ehret, 1997; Erulkar, 1959).

The Medial Geniculate Body

Structure

On the underside of the thalamus is a relatively large auditory structure—the medial geniculate body (MGB) (see Morest, 1965, for classic descriptions). Highlighting the MGB is the clear divisions into dorsal, ventral, and medial segments with the ventral being the "most" auditory by comparison to the other nuclei groups. The dorsal and medial segments are multisensory, but both of these segments have large areas of auditory representations. It is important to note here that the main projections from the IC are ipsilateral with the key input from the central nucleus coursing to the ventral portion of the MGB (Morest, 1965; Winer, 1992).

Output projections from the MGB take several courses. The ventral segment fibers lead to the primary auditory cortex, the medial segment fibers course to the insula, and the dorsal segment fibers project to the secondary auditory areas, insula, and even primary auditory cortex (Musiek & Baran, 2007; Streitfeld, 1980). There also are connections from the MGB to the amygdala, at least in some animals (LeDoux, 1986). Cell types in the ventral MGB are predominately large bushy cells and small stellate cells (Winer, 1992).

Function

Tonotopically the ventral MGB reveals low frequencies laterally and high frequencies medially. The TCs are multiformed—broad, narrow, multipeaked, with some that are "unusual" (Musiek & Baran, 2007).

Intensity coding in the MGB features mostly nonmonotonic fibers. This differs somewhat from previously discussed intensity coding for lower nuclei. This could mean less activity for high intensities at this level within the auditory system. There also is a decrease in phase locking (temporal processing) at the MGB compared to other nuclei, with the majority of MGB fibers locking onto low-frequency stimuli. However, the MGB (especially the ventral segment) is sensitive to interaural time and intensity differences similar to more caudal auditory nuclei. Excitatory and inhibitory interactions at the MGB for contralateral and ipsilateral stimulations, respectively, enhance localization processing (Musiek & Baran, 2007).

The MGB contributes to the middle latency response (MLR). However, other nuclei in the thalamic area and auditory cortex may also contribute to the MLR (McGee, Kraus, Littman, & Nicol, 1992).

Auditory Cortex and Subcortex

Structure

Though not always the case, the subcortex for purposes of this chapter includes the brain structures between the MGB and the auditory cortex. The internal capsule is an important auditory pathway through which the auditory tracts project to the cortex and associated areas. The internal capsule is bordered medially by the caudate nucleus and lateral ventricle, and laterally by the putamen and globus pallidus, which together are termed the lenticular nucleus. Lateral to the lenticular nucleus is the external capsule and the insula. Within the external capsule is the claustrum, which is gray matter that is responsive to acoustic stimuli (Musiek, 1986).

Neurons from the ventral and dorsal portions of the MGB course through the internal capsule to the primary and secondary auditory areas, and the medial segment of the MGB sends fibers that proceed beneath the internal capsule then turn laterally under the lenticular nucleus to reach the external capsule and insula (Roullier, 1997).

The use of imaging studies in humans has changed the view of the auditory cortex. These authors feel it is difficult and somewhat arbitrary to define primary and secondary areas. Hence, areas of the cortex that have been shown to be highly responsive to acoustic stimuli are discussed here. A key structure is the lateral or Sylvian fissure (Figure 10–12) that separates the superior temporal lobe from the frontal and parietal lobes. Located deep in the posterior half of the Sylvian fissure are Heschl's gyrus and the planum temporale. Other structures that are considered auditory are the (central) gyri of the inferior parietal lobe, the inferior-posterior frontal lobule, the supramarginal gyrus, the angular gyrus, and portions of the superior temporal gyrus (posterior two-thirds). Also the insula should be considered as an auditory responsive area (see Bamiou, Musiek, & Luxon, 2003).

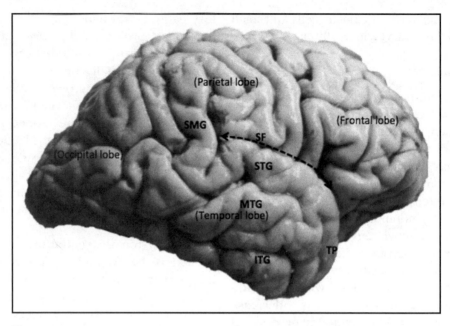

Figure 10–12. A right lateral view of the human brain focusing on the temporal lobe. (SMG, supramarginal gyrus; SF, Sylvian fissure; STG, superior temporal gyrus; MTG, middle temporal gyrus; ITG, inferior temporal gyrus; TP, temporal pole.) Copyright retained by Frank Musiek.

Heschl's gyrus is often considered the primary auditory cortex in humans (Figure 10–13). There can be from one to three gyri composing Heschl's gyrus in an individual brain. Generally, the left Heschl's gyrus is larger than the right (Campain & Minckler, 1976; Musiek & Reeves, 1990). The planum temporale is located immediately posterior to Heschl's gyrus and immediately anterior to the supramarginal gyrus. It also is larger on the left than right side (Geschwind & Levitsky, 1968). The insula is a cortex medial to the mesial temporal lobe. It has a series of long and short gyri with adjacent sulci. It is also larger on the left than right sides (Mesulam & Mufson, 1985). As alluded to earlier, the insula has been viewed as a key structure in auditory function (Bamiou et al., 2003).

There is also a different more recent view of the anatomy of the auditory cor-tex, termed the core-belt arrangement (Kaas, Hackett, & Tramo, 1999). The core is the main auditory region, sur-rounded by a belt and parabelt. There is an outflow of fibers from the core to the belt and parabelt regions. Primarily the connections to other parts of the brain are via the parabelt region (see Musiek & Baran, 2007).

There are intra- and interhemispheric connections involving the cerebral audi-tory areas. The interhemispheric con-nections are presented later. The main intrahemispheric connection is via the arcuate fasciculus, which is part of the longitudinal fasciculus. This tract courses from the area around the supra-marginal gyrus (often referred to as Wernicke's area) to the frontal lobe, picking up neural connections along the way. This is how Heschl's gyrus con-veys impulses to the frontal lobe.

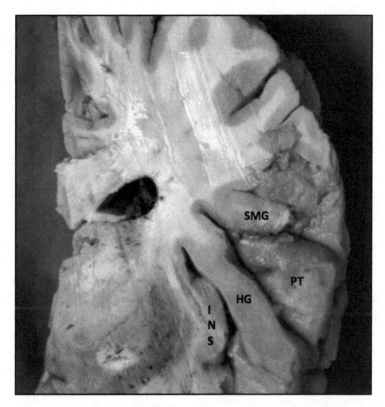

Figure 10–13. Looking down on the top of the superior temporal gyrus, often termed the superior temporal plane, showing key structures. (INS, insula; HG, Heschl's gyrus; PT, planum temporale; SMG, supramarginal gyrus [partial].) Copyright retained by Frank Musiek.

Function

The tonotopic arrangement of Heschl's gyrus reveals the low frequencies in the lateral aspect and the high frequencies in the medial posterior aspect (Musiek & Baran, 2007). The core-belt organization, however, is different. The core has anterior, middle, and posterior segments with the anterior and posterior segments running from low to high in a lateral to medial manner. The middle segment runs low to high in a posterior to anterior manner (Hackett, Preuss, & Kaas, 2001). The TCs of the auditory cortex are sharp and multipeaked. In regard to intensity coding, the auditory cortex has both monotonic and nonmonotonic fibers. Generally, as intensity increases, most fibers fire at a higher rate and more fibers respond. Some, however, do "roll over" with intensity increases. At the cortex, there also may be some interesting interactions for intensity increases involving inhibitory fibers. In other words, inhibition may result in decreases rather than increases in firing rate and numbers of fibers activated (see Musiek & Baran, 2007).

The auditory cortex responds better to modulated tones (see Chapter 6) than to steady-state tones (Evans & Whitfield, 1964). The cortical neurons also respond better to slow as opposed to fast modulation rates (<50 per second). Most auditory cortex fibers can respond to periodicities (pure tone cycles) but only up to 100 Hz. However, individual abrupt stimuli like click responses are much faster (Phillips & Hall, 1990). The overall capacity of cortical neurons to temporally process sounds is not as fast as is observed for more caudal auditory structures.

The auditory cortices play an important role in localization. Time and intensity differences are utilized to trigger localization processes, and there appears to be stronger cortical activity for contralateral compared to ipsilateral directed signals (see Musiek & Baran, 2007).

A number of evoked potentials are relevant to the function of the auditory cortex and subcortex. The MLR is generated from the thalmo-cortical pathway and auditory cortex. The late potentials N1,P2 also are generated by the auditory cortex. Although the event-related potentials (P300, MMN) likely have numerous generators, the auditory cortex certainly plays a role in these responses (McPherson, 1996; Musiek & Baran, 2007).

The Corpus Callosum

Structure

The corpus callosum (CC) is the largest commissure in the brain connecting the two hemispheres and is responsible for transferring information from one hemisphere to the other (Figure 10–14) (see Musiek & Baran, 2007). The CC is heavily myelinated and in adult humans is about 6.5 cm anterior to posterior and is about 1 cm in thickness. Its fibers run from cortex to cortex. Some connect to the same locus in the other hemi-

sphere (homolateral fibers), and some connect to other regions (heterolateral fibers). The CC is organized to transfer information from every main area of the hemisphere; hence, it has different anatomical regions (see Figure 10–14). The posterior sixth of the CC is the splenium where visual fibers from the occipital lobes cross. Just anterior to the splenium is the isthmus or sulcus (a thinned region) where auditory fibers from the temporal lobe reside. Proceeding anteriorly is a division known as the trunk or body where somatosensory and motor fibers from the parietal lobe cross. Anterior to the trunk is the genu for frontal lobe and olfactory fibers. Beneath the genu is the anterior commissure for which there is much controversy regarding the fiber types, but they could be auditory or olfactory.

Function

The key function of the CC is the transfer of impulses between the two hemispheres. There are both excitatory and inhibitory fibers within the CC. The heavily myelinated fibers that are excitatory have an interhemispheric transfer time (ITT) of 3 to 6 msec, and the inhibitory fibers may have an ITT of more than 100 msec. The ITT in humans changes with age. The best ITT is found in teenagers, with individuals who are older and younger yielding increased ITTs (Salamy, 1978).

The transfer of information from one hemisphere to the other can be critical to our perception. Each hemisphere is dominant for certain processes, and it is the timely exchange of these processes that allows the brain to work efficiently. A relevant example of this exchange of hemispheric information is the dich-

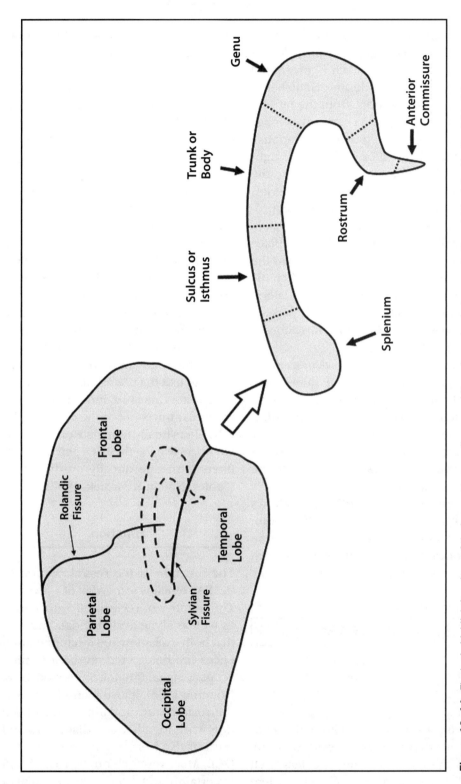

Figure 10–14. The brain highlighting views of the human corpus callosum and its main anatomical segments. Copyright retained by Frank Musiek.

otic listening for speech. The definition of dichotic listening was provided in Chapter 8. When speech is presented in the dichotic mode, the right hemisphere receives input from the left ear and the left hemisphere receives input from the right ear. If a verbal response is required, the information in the right hemisphere must be transferred to the speech hemisphere, which is the left hemisphere. If this function is compromised, a left ear deficit in dichotic listening will result. This deficit takes place because the ipsilateral pathways to the cortex are suppressed during dichotic listening, leaving only the contralateral system to function for speech perception (Kimura, 1961; Musiek, Kibbe, & Baran, 1984).

Recent research also has demonstrated that the CC may play a role in modulating the functions (inhibitory-excitatory) in each hemisphere. Although it is difficult at this time to theorize how this may influence various auditory processes, it seems to be an exciting avenue for future research. Needless to say, the CC plays important roles in audition. It allows the efficient exchange of information across all sensory systems and therefore is critical to both auditory and speech perception processing.

The Efferent System

Structure

Coursing along a similar tract as the afferent auditory system is the descending or efferent auditory system (EAS). This system is smaller and less well understood than is the afferent system just discussed. The EAS starts at the auditory cortex where it likely has several areas of input including fibers from secondary auditory regions. It courses caudally through the internal capsule and on to the MGB where some reciprocal routes to the cortex are noted. The EAS fibers descend to the inferior colliculus where more reciprocal connections involving the MGB and cortex are present. It then descends farther along the LL and into the area around the SOC where it becomes known as the olivocochlear bundle (OCB).

The OCB can be divided into two main descending tracts, the lateral olivocochlear (LOC) and medial olivocochlear (MOC) systems. The LOC is primarily an ipsilateral route and the MOC a contralateral route to the cochlea. These ipsilateral and contralateral routes descend from the OCB area to the cochlear nucleus, exit the brainstem via the internal auditory meatus, and run along the vestibular tracts out to the cochlea. The LOC fibers finally terminate on the afferent fibers leaving the IHCs and the MOC fibers terminate directly on the OHCs (Sahley, Nodar, & Musiek, 1997).

Function

The function of the rostral portion of the EAS remains somewhat of a mystery. The number of reciprocal connections as well as some available data indicate that both excitation and inhibition influences can be exerted on the incoming acoustic signal (Mitani, Shimokouchi, & Nomura, 1983). It also seems likely that the rostral and caudal portions of the EAS work together and that the rostral portion also has some influence on the OCB. More research on the rostral EAS is certainly indicated as it may play a subtle, but important, role in hearing that is yet to be discovered.

The caudal EAS, which we will refer to as the OCB, was first studied over 50 years ago by Galambos (1956). Galambos demonstrated that if the OCB was stimulated electrically in animals, it resulted in reduced firing rates of the AN fibers. These findings have been interpreted to mean that the OCB may have inhibitory influences on the afferent auditory system. It was discovered that the OCB also could be stimulated and the same effect measured if an acoustic signal was presented to one ear and a noise was presented to the opposite ear (Folsom & Owsley, 1987). This has become known as the *suppression effect* and can be measured using otoacoustic emissions or evoked potentials in humans.

Activation of the OCB also has been shown to enhance hearing in noise (Kawase & Liberman, 1993). If the OCB is activated either electrically (as was done in the Galambos study) or by contralateral noise when a listener is being asked to detect a signal in noise, the detection threshold will improve relative to the conditions in which the OCB is not stimulated. A number of experimental studies have shown similar effects, and this phenomenon is now considered to be one of the mechanisms that allows hearing in noisy situations to be enhanced (see Musiek & Baran, 2007; Sahley et al., 1997).

Vascular Supply for the Auditory System

The Peripheral System

Functions of the peripheral and central auditory systems are highly dependent on blood supply. The external ear's blood supply comes from branches of the external carotid artery, whereas the middle ear receives its blood supply from branches of the internal carotid. The cochlea and AN's vascular supply comes from the vertebral basilar system.

The pinna and external auditory meatus are supplied mostly, but not exclusively, by the superficial temporal artery and posterior auricular artery. There is some controversy regarding the tympanic membrane's blood supply, but playing key roles are branches of the deep auricular and maxillary arteries. The middle ear (soft tissue) receives vascular input from branches of the internal carotid, maxillary (tympanic branch), posterior auricular (mastoid branch), and middle meningeal (petrosal branch) arteries, as well as branches of the ascending pharyngeal and pterygoid arteries (Anson & Donaldson, 1981; Clark & Ohlemiller, 2008; Musiek & Baran, 2007).

The internal auditory or labyrinthine artery (IAA), which is a main branch of the basilar or anterior inferior cerebellar artery (AICA) (brainstem), is key for blood supply of the cochlea and AN. The IAA divides within the IAM to cochlear and vestibular branches, which supply the auditory and vestibular nerves before proceeding externally to the cochlea. The cochlear artery branches into the spiral modiolar artery (SMA) and the cochlea-vestibular artery (CVA). The SMA spirals around the modiolus giving off branches en route, and the CVA coils following the cochlea. These two main vessels give off branches that make up the network of radiating arterioles that supplies much of the cochlea (Musiek & Baran, 2007; Smith, 1973). These arteries have as their counterpart veins and collecting venules in similar anatomic areas, which return the impure blood back to the main veins and onto the heart.

The Central System

The central auditory nervous system, in terms of its vascular supply, can be segmented into the brainstem and cortex. The brainstem auditory structures are supplied by the vertebral basilar system and the cortex by the internal carotid system. In the brainstem, the vertebral arteries, which course rostrally on both sides of the spine, join together to form the basilar artery a few millimeters below the pontomedullary junction. The basilar artery is located on the ventral side of the brainstem. The basilar artery gives off the anterior inferior cerebellar artery (AICA), which with circumferential branches supplies blood to the cochlear nucleus. Smaller branches off the basilar artery called paramedial or pontine penetrating arteries, penetrate the pons to supply the SOC and some of the LL deep in the pons (Waddington, 1974).

Proceeding rostrally another main branch of the basilar artery is the superior cerebellar artery, which indirectly supplies the LL and the IC. The MGB is most likely supplied by the posterior thalamic group of arteries, which are a multivessel complex arising from the posterior cerebral artery (Musiek & Baran, 2007; Waddington, 1974).

The auditory cortex and associated areas are supplied with blood primarily by the middle cerebral artery (MCA). The MCA has anterior, middle, and posterior temporal arteries that branch to cover the anterior, middle, and posterior temporal lobes. The MCA also has central sulcus branch that supplies the parietal lobe. The angular artery feeds the angular gyrus and possibly the supramarginal gyrus. The insula's vascular supply comes from the fronto-opercular artery (from anterior MCA), which branches into a variety of insular arteries. The corpus callosum's anterior four-fifths has as its vascular supply the pericallosal artery, a branch of the MCA, and its posterior one-fifth is supplied by the posterior cerebral artery (Musiek & Baran, 2007; Waddington, 1974).

Chapter Summary

In this chapter:

- Anatomical planes and directions of orientation were defined and illustrated.
- The structure (anatomy) of the peripheral auditory system was defined and illustrated, beginning with the temporal bone, and continuing with the outer ear, the middle ear, the inner ear, and finally, the Type I and Type II auditory fibers of the collective auditory nerve, which is also the auditory division of the eighth cranial nerve.
- The separate functions (physiology) of the outer ear, the middle ear, and the inner ear were described. This included descriptions of cochlear and hair cell mechanics, as well as cochlear electrophysiology.
- Some of the functional properties of the auditory nerve were discussed.
- The structures (anatomy) of the central auditory nuclei and fiber

pathways, from the cochlear nucleus to the primary auditory cortex of the brain (Heschl's gyrus), were defined, discussed, and illustrated. The functions (physiology) of the central auditory nuclei and fiber pathways, from the cochlear nucleus to the primary auditory cortex of the brain (Heschl's gyrus), were also discussed.

■ The participation of the insular cortex (insula), the claustrum, and the external capsule (association) fiber pathway were briefly discussed in relation to auditory function.

■ The extensive commissural fiber tracts of the corpus callosum were illustrated and discussed in reference to dichotic listening.

■ The efferent olivocochlear fiber pathways were briefly discussed, as well as the vascular anatomy of the peripheral and central auditory systems.

References

Anson, B. J., & Donaldson, J. A. (1981). *The surgical anatomy of the temporal bone and ear* (3rd ed.). Philadelphia, PA: W. B. Saunders.

Bamiou, D. E., Musiek, F. E., & Luxon, L. M. (2003). The insula (Island of Reil) and its role in auditory processing: Literature review. *Brain Research Reviews, 42*(2), 143–154.

Blauert, J. (1983). *Spatial hearing. The psychophysics of human sound localization.* Cambridge, MA: MIT Press.

Borg, E. (1973). On the neuronal organization of the acoustic middle ear reflex. A physiological and anatomical study. *Brain Research, 49*(1), 101–123.

Buser, P. A., & Imbert, M. (1992). *Audition.* Cambridge, MA: MIT Press.

Campain, R., & Minckler, J. (1976). A note on the gross configurations of the human auditory cortex. *Brain and Language, 3*(2), 318–323.

Clark, W. W., & Ohlemiller, K. K. (2008). *Anatomy and physiology of hearing for audiologists.* Clifton Park, NY: Thomson Delmar Learning.

Covey, E., & Casseday, J. H. (1986). Connectional basis for frequency representation in the nuclei of the lateral lemniscus of the bat *Eptesicus fuscus. Journal of Neuroscience, 6*(10), 2926–2940.

Dallos, P. (1973). *The auditory periphery: Biophysics and physiology.* New York, NY: Academic Press.

Davis, H. (1965). A model for transducer action in the cochlea. *Cold Spring Harbor Symposia on Quantitative Biology, 30,* 181–190.

Ehret, G. (1997). The auditory midbrain, a "shunting-yard" of acoustical information processing. In G. Ehret & R. Romand (Eds.), *The central auditory system* (pp. 259–303). New York, NY: Oxford University Press.

Erulkar, S. D. (1959). The responses of single units of the inferior colliculus of the cat to acoustic stimulation. *Proceedings of the Royal Society of London B Biological Sciences, 150*(940), 336–355.

Evans, E. F., & Whitfield, I. C. (1964). Classification of unit responses in the auditory cortex of the unanaesthetized and unrestrained cat. *Journal of Physiology, 171,* 476–493.

Folsom, R. C., & Owsley, R. M. (1987). N1 action potentials in humans. Influence of simultaneous contralateral stimulation. *Acta Otolaryngologica, 103*(3–4), 262–265.

Galambos, R. (1956). Suppression of auditory nerve activity by stimulation of efferent fibers to the cochlea. *Journal of Neurophysiology, 19*(5), 424–437.

Geisler, C. D. (1998). *From sound to synapse: Physiology of the mammalian ear.* New York, NY: Oxford University Press.

Gelfand, S. A. (1997). *Essentials of audiology.* New York, NY: Thieme Medical.

Gelfand, S. A. (1998). *Hearing: An introduction to psychological and physiological acoustics* (3rd ed.). New York, NY: Marcel Dekker.

Geschwind, N., & Levitsky, W. (1968). Human brain: Left-right asymmetries in temporal speech region. *Science, 161*(837), 186–187.

Hackett, T. A., Preuss, T. M., & Kaas, J. H. (2001). Architectonic identification of the core region in auditory cortex of macaques, chimpanzees, and humans. *Journal of Comparative Neurology, 441*(3), 197–222.

Kaas, J. H., Hackett, T. A., & Tramo, M. J. (1999). Auditory processing in primate cerebral cortex. *Current Opinion in Neurobiology, 9*(2), 164–170.

Kawase, T., & Liberman, M. C. (1993). Antimasking effects of the olivocochlear reflex. I. Enhancement of compound action potentials to masked tones. *Journal of Neurophysiology, 70*(6), 2519–2532.

Keidel, W. D., Kallert, S., & Korth, M. (1983). *The physiological bases of hearing* (pp. 82–108). New York, NY: Thieme-Stratton.

Kim, D. O., & Parham, K. (1991). Auditory nerve spatial encoding of high frequency pure tones: Population response profiles derived from d' measure associated with nearby places along the cochlea. *Hearing Research, 52*(1), 167–179.

Kim, D. O., & Parham, K. (1997). Physiology of the auditory nerve. In M. J. Crocker (Ed.), *Encyclopedia of acoustics* (pp. 1331–1378). New York, NY: Wiley.

Kimura, D. (1961). Some effects of temporal lobe damage on auditory perception. *Canadian Journal of Psychology, 15,* 156–165.

LeDoux, J. E. (1986). The neurobiology of emotion. In J. E. LeDoux & W. Hirst (Eds.), *Mind and brain: Dialogues in cognitive neuroscience* (pp. 342–346).

Cambridge, UK: Cambridge University Press.

Liberman, M. C. (1978). Auditory-nerve response from cats raised in low-noise chamber. *Journal of the Acoustical Society of America, 63*(2), 442–455.

McGee, T., Kraus, N., Littman, T., & Nicol, T. (1992). Contributions of medial geniculate body subdivisions to the middle latency response. *Hearing Research, 61*(1–2), 147–154.

McPherson, D. L. (1996). *Late potentials of the auditory system.* San Diego, CA: Singular.

Mesulam, M., & Mufson, E. (1985). The insula of Reil in man and monkey architectonics, connectivity, and function. In E. G. Jones & A. Peters (Eds.), *Cerebral cortex* (Vol. 4, pp. 179–226). New York, NY: Plenum Press.

Mitani, A., Shimokouchi, M., & Nomura, S. (1983). Effects of stimulation of the primary auditory cortex upon colliculogeniculate neurons in the inferior colliculus of the cat. *Neuroscience Letters, 42*(2), 185–189.

Møller, A. R. (2000). *Hearing: Its physiology and pathophysiology.* New York, NY: Academic Press.

Moore, J. K. (2000). Organization of the human superior olivary complex. *Microscopy Research and Technique, 51*(4), 403–412.

Morest, D. K. (1965). The laminar structure of the medial geniculate body of the cat. *Journal of Anatomy, 99,* 143–160.

Morest, D. K., & Oliver, D. L. (1984). The neuronal architecture of the inferior colliculus in the cat: Defining the functional anatomy of the auditory midbrain. *Journal of Comparative Neurology, 222*(2), 209–236.

Musiek, F. E. (1986). Neuroanatomy, neurophysiology, and central auditory assessment. Part II: The cerebrum. *Ear and Hearing, 7*(5), 283–294.

Musiek, F. E., & Baran, J. A. (2007). *The auditory system: Anatomy, physiology, and clinical correlates.* Boston, MA: Allyn & Bacon.

Musiek, F. E., Kibbe, K., & Baran, J. A. (1984). Neuroaudiological results from split-brain patients. *Seminars in Hearing, 5*(3), 219–229.

Musiek, F. E., & Reeves, A. G. (1990). Asymmetries of the auditory areas of the cerebrum. *Journal of the American Academy of Audiology, 1*(4), 240–245.

Phillips, D. P., & Hall, S. E. (1990). Response timing constraints on the cortical representation of sound time structure. *Journal of the Acoustical Society of America, 88*(3), 1403–1411.

Pickles, J. O. (1988). *An introduction to the physiology of hearing* (2nd ed.). London, UK: Academic Press.

Popelár, J., & Syka, J. (1982). Response properties of neurons in the inferior colliculus of the guinea-pig. *Acta Neurobiologiae Experimentalis, 42*(4–5), 299–310.

Romand, R., & Avan, P. (1997). Anatomical and functional aspects of the cochlear nucleus. In G. Ehret & R. Romand (Eds.), *The central auditory system* (pp. 97–192). New York, NY: Oxford University Press.

Roullier, E. (1997). Functional organization of the auditory pathways. In G. Ehret & R. Romand (Eds.), *The central auditory system* (pp. 3–65). New York, NY: Oxford University Press.

Sahley, T. L., Nodar, R. H., & Musiek, F. E. (1997). *Efferent auditory system*. San Diego, CA: Singular.

Salamy, A. (1978). Commissural transmission: Maturational changes in humans. *Science 200*(4348), 1409–1411.

Salvi, R. J., Clock Eddins, A. C., & Wang, J. (2007) Cochlear physiology II: Mostly electrophysiology. In F. E. Musiek & J. A. Baran, *The auditory system: Anatomy, physiology, and clinical correlates* (pp. 112–149). Boston, MA: Allyn & Bacon.

Schwartz, I. R. (1992). Superior olivary complex in the lateral lemniscal nuclei. In D. B. Webster, A. N. Popper, & R. R. Fey (Eds.), *The cochlea* (pp. 117–167). New York, NY: Springer-Verlag.

Shaw, E. A. G., & Teranishi, R. (1968). Sound pressure generated in an external ear replica and real human ears by a nearby point source. *Journal of the Acoustical Society of America, 44*(1), 240–249.

Slepecky, N. (1996). Cochlear structure. In P. Dallos, A. N. Popper, & R. R. Fay (Eds.), *The cochlea* (pp. 44–129). New York, NY: Springer-Verlag.

Smith, C. A. (1973). Vascular patterns of the membranous labyrinth. In A. J. D. De Lorenzo (Ed.), *Vascular disorders and hearing defects* (pp. 1–22). Baltimore, MD: University Park Press.

Spoendlin, H. (1972). Innervation densities of the cochlea. *Acta Otolaryngologica, 73*(2), 235–248.

Streitfeld, B. D. (1980). The fiber connections of the temporal lobe with emphasis on Rhesus monkey. *International Journal of Neuroscience, 11*(1), 51–71.

von Békésy, G. (1960). *Experiments in hearing*. New York, NY: McGraw-Hill.

Waddington, M. (1974). *The atlas of cerebral angiography with anatomic correlation*. Boston, MA: Little, Brown.

Wangemann, P. (2002a). K+ cycling and the endocochlear potential. *Hearing Research, 165*(1–2), 1–9.

Wangemann, P. (2002b). K(+) cycling and its regulation in the cochlea and the vestibular labyrinth. *Audiology and Neurotology, 7*(4), 199–205.

Wever, E. G., & Bray, C. W. (1930). Action currents in the auditory nerve in response to acoustic stimulation. *Proceedings of the National Academy of Sciences of the United States of America, 16*(5), 344–350.

Winer, J. A. (1992). The functional architecture of the medial geniculate body and primary auditory cortex. In D. B. Webster, A. N. Popper, & R. R. Fay (Eds.), *The mammalian auditory pathway: Neuroanatomy* (pp. 222–409). New York, NY: Springer-Verlag.

Yost, W. A. (2000). *Fundamentals of hearing: An introduction* (4th ed.). San Diego, CA: Academic Press.

Zemlin, W. R. (1998). *Speech and hearing science: Anatomy and physiology* (4th ed.). Boston, MA: Allyn & Bacon.

Appendix A

Exponential and Scientific Notation

Section A1.
Conversion From Conventional to Exponential Notation

Numbers That Are Exact Multiples of Ten

As illustrated in Table A1–1, a simple rule for converting conventional multiples of 10 for values greater than or equal to (≥) 1.00 into equivalent, exponential notation is to count the number of zeros in the conventional notation that directly follow the 1, up to the decimal point. The number of zeros counted to the right of the 1 up to the decimal point for such values will be the (positive) exponent for the base (Mullin, Gerace, Mestre, & Velleman, 2003). For instance, as illustrated in Table A1–1, at one extreme the number 1.00 written in conventional notation has no zeros (or zero, zeros) directly to the right (of the 1), up to the decimal point. Therefore, 1.00 is rewritten in exponential notation as 10^0. At the other extreme, the number 10,000,000,000 written in conventional notation has 10 zeros between the 1 and the decimal point. Therefore,

Table A1–1. Conversion to Exponential Notation

Conventional	Exponential
0.0000000001	10^{-10}
0.000000001	10^{-9}
0.00000001	10^{-8}
0.0000001	10^{-7}
0.000001	10^{-6}
0.00001	10^{-5}
0.0001	10^{-4}
0.001	10^{-3}
0.01	10^{-2}
0.1	10^{-1}
1.00	10^0
10	10^1
100	10^2
1,000	10^3
10,000	10^4
100,000	10^5
1,000,000	10^6
10,000,000	10^7
100,000,000	10^8
1,000,000,000	10^9
10,000,000,000	10^{10}

10,000,000,000 is equal to 10^{10} when expressed in exponential notation.

A somewhat different approach may be taken when converting conventional integer multiples of 10 for values less than (<) 1.00, into equivalent exponential notation. Once more, a simple rule is to count the number of decimal places in the conventional value that would be required to put the decimal point to the right of the 1, to create the whole number 1.00 (Mullin et al., 2003). The number of places counted then becomes the exponent in the exponential equivalent for the value. The exponent in this case will take a negative sign. Alternatively, for values that are <1.00, the number of zeros counted directly to the right of the decimal point, up to the number 1 for the value written in conventional notation, will always be one less than the absolute value of the exponent, which will again take a negative sign. For instance, as illustrated in Table A1–1, at one extreme the number 0.1 in conventional notation would require that the decimal point be moved only one place to the right to create the whole number 1.00. Therefore, 0.1 is equal to 10^{-1} in exponential notation. Alternatively, the number 0.1 also has no zeros that directly follow the decimal point. Since the number of zeros directly to the right of the decimal point in conventional notation is one less than the absolute value of the exponent, then 0 + 1 = 1 place, and 0.1 is again equal to 10^{-1} when expressed in exponential notation.

At the other extreme, the number 0.0000000001, written in conventional notation, would require that the decimal point be moved 10 places to the right in order to create the whole number 1.00. Therefore, 0.0000000001 is equal to 10^{-10} expressed in exponential notation. It is also clear that the number 0.0000000001 has nine zeros directly to the right of the decimal point. Since the number of zeros to the right of the decimal in conventional notation is one less than the absolute value of the exponent, 9 + 1 = 10, and 0.0000000001 is again equal to 10^{-10} expressed in exponential notation.

Section A2. Operating Principles in the Use of Exponents

I. Multiplication

First: For any base values X and Y, and the exponential value of zero: any base value raised to an exponent of zero, is equal to 1 (Giancoli, 2005).

Therefore, $X^0 = 1$; $Y^0 = 1$

Second: For any base values X and Y and the exponential value of one: any base value raised to an exponential value of one is equal to the base value (Giancoli, 2005).

Therefore, $X^1 = X$; $Y^1 = Y$

Example: $10^0 = 1$; $2^0 = 1$

Example: $10^1 = 10$; $2^1 = 2$

Third: To determine the product of two quantities, each consisting of a common base raised to a specified exponential value, the product of the two quantities is simply the (common) base raised to the sum of the separate exponential values (Giancoli, 2005).

Therefore, for any base values X and Y and any exponential values a to c: the product of X^a and X^b is simply $X^{(a+b)}$; and the product of Y^b and Y^c is simply $Y^{(b+c)}$.

In addition, for any base values X and Y and any exponential values a to c: the product of X^a and X^{-b} is simply $X^{a+(-b)}$; the product of Y^{-b} and Y^c is simply $Y^{-b+(c)}$.

Example: $(10^3)(10^4) = 10^{3+4} = 10^7$

Example: $(2^4)(2^5) = 2^{4+5} = 2^9$

Example: $(10^3)(10^{-4}) = 10^{3+(-4)} = 10^{-1}$

Example: $(2^{-4})(2^5) = 2^{-4+(5)} = 2^1$

However, for any base values X and Y, and any exponential values a to c: the product of X^a and Y^b is the product of the separate quantities of X^a and Y^b, and the product of X^a and Y^{-b} is the product of the separate quantities of X^a and Y^{-b} (Giancoli, 2005).

Example: $(10^3)(2^4) = 10^3 \times 2^4$

Example: $(10^3)(2^{-4}) = 10^3 \times 2^{-4}$

Also, for any base values X and Y, and any exponential values a to c: the product of X^a and Y^a is $(XY)^a$ (Giancoli, 2005).

Example: $(10^3)(2^3) = (10 \times 2)^3$

II. Exponentiation

If: $(X^a)^b$;
Then: $(X^a)^b = X^{ab}$;

Example: $(10^3)^5 = 10^{15}$
(Durrant & Lovrinic, 1995)

III. Division

First: For any base values X and Y, and any exponential values a to c:

$$1/X^a = X^{-a} \text{ and } 1/Y^{-b} = Y^b$$
$$\text{(Giancoli, 2005).}$$

In addition:

$$(X^c)(X^{-c}) = X^c/X^c = X^0 = 1$$

Example:

$$1/10^3 = 10^{-3} \text{ and } \tfrac{1}{2}^{-4} = 2^4$$

Example:

$$(10^5)(10^{-5}) = 10^5/10^5 = 10^0 = 1$$

Second: To divide two quantities, each consisting of a common base raised to a specified exponential value, the division of the two quantities will simply be the (common) base raised to the difference of the separate exponential values found in the numerator and denominator, respectively (Giancoli, 2005).

Therefore, for any base values X and Y, and any exponential values a to c: the division of X^a and X^b (or X^a/X^b) is simply $X^{(a-b)}$; and the division of Y^b and Y^c (or Y^b/Y^c) is simply $Y^{(b-c)}$; but the division of X^a and Y^b (or X^a/Y^b) is the division of the separate quantities of X^a and Y^b.

Example:

$$10^3/10^4 = 10^{(3-4)} = 10^{-1}$$

Example:

$$10^3/2^4 = (10^3) \div (2^4)$$

In addition, for any base values X and Y, and any exponential values a to c:

the division of X^a and X^{-b} (or X^a/X^{-b}) is $X^{a-(-b)}$ or simply $X^{(a+b)}$; and the division of Y^{-b} and Y^c (or Y^{-b}/Y^c) is $Y^{(-b)-(c)}$ or simply $Y^{-(b+c)}$; but the division of X^a and Y^{-b} (or X^a/Y^{-b}) is the division of the separate quantities of X^a and Y^{-b} (Giancoli, 2005).

Example:

$$10^3/10^{-4} = 10^{(3)-(-4)} = 10^{(3+4)} = 10^7$$

Example:

$$2^{-4}/2^5 = 2^{(-4)-(5)} = 2^{-(4+5)} = 2^{-9}$$

Example:

$$10^3/2^{-4} = (10^3) \div (2^{-4})$$

IV. Combining Multiple Exponents

For any base values X and Y, and any exponential values a to c: $(X^a)^b = X^{ab}$; and $(Y^b)^c = Y^{bc}$ (Giancoli, 2005).

Example:

$$(10^3)^4 = 10^{(3 \times 4)} = 10^{12}$$

Example:

$$(2^4)^5 = 2^{(4 \times 5)} = 2^{20}$$

Section A3.
Conversion From Conventional
to Scientific Notation

A few simple steps can be followed for converting conventional values into scientific notation.

First: With conventional quantities that are ≥ 1.00, such as 1,200,000 or 350,000, the decimal point must always be assumed. That is, the decimal point in such cases is said to be implicit or implied (Durrant & Lovrinic, 1995). Therefore, these three conventionally expressed quantities should be viewed as 1.00, 200,000.00, and 350,000.00, respectively.

Second: The number of places that the decimal point must be moved to the left to create the simple coefficient (i.e., from 1.000 to 9.999), will also be the positive value taken by the exponent to which the base will be raised. Since the decimal point in 200,000.00 must be moved five places to the left to create the coefficient 2.00, the number 200,000.00 equals 2×10^5 when expressed in scientific notation. Similarly, the decimal point in the number 350,000.00 must be moved five places to the left to create the coefficient 3.5 (Mullin et al., 2003; Speaks, 1999). Therefore, 350,000.00 equals 3.5×10^5 when expressed in scientific notation. However, the decimal place in the number 1.00 is not moved to create the simple coefficient, and the number of places is zero. Therefore, 1.00 is simply 1×10^0 when written in scientific notation, as shown in Table A3–1.

As yet another example, in the number 56,789, the decimal point must be moved four places to the left to create the simple coefficient 5.6789. Therefore, 56,789.00 may be rewritten as 5.6789×10^4 to be expressed in scientific notation. Other examples of values ≥ 1.00 that are expressed in scientific notation are presented in Tables A3–1 and A3–2.

For values <1.00, the decimal point is always explicit, rather than implicit. In the numbers 0.00002 and 0.0000000001,

Table A3–1. Conversion to Exponential or Scientific Notation

Conventional	Exponential	Scientific
0.0000000001	10^{-10}	1×10^{-10}
0.000000001	10^{-9}	1×10^{-9}
0.00000001	10^{-8}	1×10^{-8}
0.0000001	10^{-7}	1×10^{-7}
0.000001	10^{-6}	1×10^{-6}
0.00001	10^{-5}	1×10^{-5}
0.0001	10^{-4}	1×10^{-4}
0.001	10^{-3}	1×10^{-3}
0.01	10^{-2}	1×10^{-2}
0.1	10^{-1}	1×10^{-1}
1.00	10^{0}	1×10^{0}
10	10^{1}	1×10^{1}
100	10^{2}	1×10^{2}
1,000	10^{3}	1×10^{3}
10,000	10^{4}	1×10^{4}
100,000	10^{5}	1×10^{5}
1,000,000	10^{6}	1×10^{6}
10,000,000	10^{7}	1×10^{7}
100,000,000	10^{8}	1×10^{8}
1,000,000,000	10^{9}	1×10^{9}
10,000,000,000	10^{10}	1×10^{10}

the total number of places that the decimal point would be moved to the right to create the simple coefficient is also the negative value taken by the exponent, to which the base is raised for transformation into scientific notation (Mullin et al., 2003). Therefore, 0.00002 becomes 2×10^{-5}, and 0.0000000001 becomes 1×10^{-10} when expressed in scientific notation (see Table A3–1).

Similarly, in the value 0.000056789, the decimal point would be moved five places to the right to create the simple coefficient 5.6789. Therefore, 0.000056789 may be rewritten in scientific notation as 5.6789×10^{-5}. Additional examples of numbers that are <1.00 and expressed in scientific notation are also presented in Tables A3–1 and A3–2.

Table A3–2. Additional Examples of Scientific Notation Conversion

Conventional	Scientific	Conventional	Scientific
0.00000098765	9.8765×10^{-7}	9.8765	9.8765×10^{0}
0.0000012345	1.2345×10^{-6}	12.345	1.2345×10^{1}
0.000056789	5.6789×10^{-5}	567.89	5.6789×10^{2}
0.0000098765	9.8765×10^{-6}	98.765	9.8765×10^{1}
0.000012345	1.2345×10^{-5}	123.45	1.2345×10^{2}
0.00056789	5.6789×10^{-4}	5678.9	5.6789×10^{3}
0.000098765	9.8765×10^{-5}	987.65	9.8765×10^{2}
0.00012345	1.2345×10^{-4}	1234.5	1.2345×10^{3}
0.0056789	5.6789×10^{-3}	56789	5.6789×10^{4}
0.00098765	9.8765×10^{-4}	9876.5	9.8765×10^{3}
0.0012345	1.2345×10^{-3}	12345	1.2345×10^{4}
0.056789	5.6789×10^{-2}	567890	5.6789×10^{5}
0.0098765	9.8765×10^{-3}	98765	9.8765×10^{4}
0.012345	1.2345×10^{-2}	123450	1.2345×10^{5}
0.56789	5.6789×10^{-1}	5678900	5.6789×10^{6}
0.098765	9.8765×10^{-2}	987650	9.8765×10^{5}
0.12345	1.2345×10^{-1}	1234500	1.2345×10^{6}
5.6789	5.6789×10^{0}	56789000	5.6789×10^{7}
0.98765	9.8765×10^{-1}		
1.2345	1.2345×10^{0}		
56.789	5.6789×10^{1}		

Section A4. Working With Scientific Notation

I. Multiplication With Scientific Notation

To determine the product of any two numbers using scientific notation:

First: Transform both numbers into scientific notation;

Second: Separate the two coefficients from the two base values raised to their separate exponential values, then organize the equation to multiply the product of the coefficients by the product of the exponential values;

Third: Obtain the product of the two coefficients only;

Fourth: Using the operating principles of exponents, obtain the product of the two base values raised to their separate exponential values;

Fifth: Multiply the products of the coefficients and the base values raised to their separate exponential values;

Sixth: Obtain and express the final value (Durrant & Lovrinic, 1995; Mullin et al., 2003).

Example: Find the product of 5,000 and 3:

First:

$$5{,}000 \times 3 = (5 \times 10^3) \times (3 \times 10^0)$$

Second: $= (5 \times 3) \times (10^3 \times 10^0)$

Third: $= (15) \times (10^3 \times 10^0)$
$\quad\quad$ [or $(15) \times 10^{-3} \times 1$]

Fourth: $= (15) \times (10^{3+0}) = (15) \times (10^3)$

Fifth: $= 15 \times 10^3$

Sixth: $= 15{,}000$

Example: Find the product of 3,000 and 0.20:

First:

$$3{,}000 \times 0.20 = (3 \times 10^3) \times (2 \times 10^{-1})$$

Second: $= (3 \times 2) \times (10^3 \times 10^{-1})$

Third: $= (6) \times (10^3 \times 10^{-1})$

Fourth: $= (6) \times (10^{3-1}) = (6) \times (10^2)$

Fifth: $= 6 \times 10^2$

Sixth: $= 600$

Example: Find the product of 0.032 and 0.0025:

First:

$$0.032 \times 0.0025 =$$
$$(3.2 \times 10^{-2}) \times (2.5 \times 10^{-3})$$

Second: $= (3.2 \times 2.5) \times (10^{-2} \times 10^{-3})$

Third: $= (8) \times (10^{-2} \times 10^{-3})$

Fourth: $= (8) \times (10^{-2 + (-3)})$
$\quad\quad\quad = (8) \times (10^{-5})$

Fifth: $= 8 \times 10^{-5}$

Sixth: $= 0.00008$

II. Division With Scientific Notation

To determine the quotient of any two numbers using scientific notation:

First: Transform both numbers into scientific notation;

Second: Separate the two coefficients from the two base values raised to their separate exponential values, then set up the equation to multiply the quotient of the coefficients by the quotient of the exponential values;

Third: Obtain the quotient of the two coefficients only;

Fourth: Using the operating principles of exponents, obtain the quotient of the two base values raised to their separate exponential values;

Fifth: Find the product of the quotients of the coefficients and the quotients of the base values, raised to their separate exponential values;

Sixth: Obtain and express the final value (Durrant & Lovrinic, 1995; Mullin et al., 2003).

Example: Find the quotient of 8,000 and 5:

First:

$$8,000 \div 5 = (8 \times 10^3) \div (5 \times 10^0)$$

Second: $= (8 \div 5) \times (10^3 \div 10^0)$

Third: $= (1.6) \times (10^3 \div 10^0)$

Fourth: $= (1.6) \times (10^{3-0})$
$= (1.6) \times (10^3)$

Fifth: $= 1.6 \times 10^3$

Sixth: $= 1,600$

Example: Find the quotient of 0.005 and 2,500:

First:

$$0.005 \div 2500 = (5 \times 10^{-3}) \div (2.5 \times 10^3)$$

Second: $= (5 \div 2.5) \times (10^{-3} \div 10^3)$

Third: $= (2) \times (10^{-3} \div 10^3)$

Fourth: $= (2) \times (10^{-3-(3)})$
$= (2) \times (10^{-6})$

Fifth: $= 2 \times 10^{-6}$

Sixth: $= 0.000002$

Example: Find the quotient of 2,500 and 0.05:

First:

$$2,500 \div 0.05 = (2.5 \times 10^3) \div (5 \times 10^{-2})$$

Second: $= (2.5 \div 5) \times (10^3 \div 10^{-2})$

Third: $= (0.5) \times (10^3 \div 10^{-2})$

Fourth: $= (0.5) \times (10^{3-(-2)})$
$= (0.5) \times (10^5)$

$= (5 \times 10^{-1}) \times (1 \times 10^5)$

$= (5 \times 1) \times (10^{-1} \times 10^5)$
$= (5) \times (10^{-1+5})$

Fifth: $= 5 \times 10^4$

Sixth: $= 50,000$

References

Durrant, J. D., & Lovrinic, J. H (1995). *Bases of hearing science* (3rd ed). Baltimore, MD: Williams & Wilkins.

Giancoli, D. C. (2005). *Physics: Principles with applications* (6th ed.). Upper Saddle River, NJ: Prentice Hall.

Mullin, W. J., Gerace, W. J., Mestre, J. P., & Velleman, S. L. (2003). *Fundamentals of sound with applications to speech and hearing*. Boston, MA: Allyn & Bacon.

Speaks, C. E. (1999). *Introduction to sound: Acoustics for the hearing and speech sciences* (3rd ed.). San Diego, CA: Singular.

Appendix B

Logarithms

Section B1. The Characteristic and the Mantissa

Recall that the conversion of any value into scientific notation is a rather simple process that includes exponential notation (Durrant & Lovrinic, 1995). To convert to scientific notation, a number is first translated into the product of a simple coefficient, and a base (10) which is raised to an exponential power. When the logarithm is found for a number converted into scientific notation, the exponent of the base becomes the *characteristic of the log*. The log of the simple coefficient becomes the *mantissa*

of the log. As indicated previously, the mantissa is separated from the characteristic by the decimal point (Durrant & Lovrinic, 1995). An illustration of the characteristic of a log is presented in Table B1–1. The values presented were borrowed from Table A3–1 in Appendix A. Since each of the numbers presented in the example set are exact multiples of 10, the conversion to scientific notation is a simple process. Importantly, note that in each case, the characteristic of the log is a whole number integer, and it is located to the left of the decimal point. The mantissa, located to the right of the decimal in each of these particular cases, will always be zero.

Table B1–1. Examples of Conversion from Conventional to Scientific to Logarithmic Notation

Conventional Notation	Scientific Notation	Logarithm charac.↓ ↓mantissa
1,000	1×10^3	3.00
10,000	1×10^4	4.00
100,000	1×10^5	5.00
0.001	1×10^{-3}	−3.00
0.01	1×10^{-2}	−2.00
0.1	1×10^{-1}	−1.00

The reason for this is explained by the following.

The expression:

$$\log 1 \times 10^5$$

should be understood to mean:

$$\log 1.00 + \log 10^5$$

The log of the expression 10^5 (or 5) becomes the characteristic, and the log of the simple coefficient 1.00 (or 0), becomes the mantissa, with characteristic and mantissa separated by a decimal point. In this simple example, since the log of $10^5 = 5$ (characteristic), and the log of $1.00 = 0$ (mantissa), the log of 1×10^5 is simply $5 + 0.00$ or 5.00.

The previous example illustrated that when quantities are exact multiples of 10, the mantissa of the log takes a zero value. There are also instances when the characteristic of the log will have a zero value. Recall from Table 2–5 in the body of the text (see Chapter 2) that logs of whole numbers less than 10 are decimal values, having characteristics that are zero. An explanation of why the characteristics are zero in these instances will serve to stress the importance of converting numbers into scientific notation prior to obtaining logarithms.

The expression   log 5

should be understood to mean

$$\log 5.00 \times 10^0 = \log 5.00 + \log 10^0$$

The log of the exponential value 10^0 becomes the characteristic of the final log (i.e., 0), and the log of the simple coefficient 5.00 becomes the mantissa of the final log. The log of 10^0 is equal to zero and the zero is the characteristic of the final log. However, consulting with a table of logarithms (see Tables B3–2, B3–3, B3–4, and B3–5 below) or using a calculator, it is easy to determine that the log of $5.00 = .698$ (mantissa). Therefore, the log of 5×10^0 is simply $0 + .698$ or 0.698.

Section B2.
Working With Logarithms

Most calculators will compute a logarithm for any number. A condensed table of common logs is presented as Table B3–2 in Section B3 of this appendix. The logs shown in the table have been computed for numbers ranging from 1.0 to 9.9 (Giancoli, 2005). Note that the numbers in question are separated by equal (decimal) intervals. The decimal intervals are shown horizontally in the first row to the right of Column N, by the values 0.0 to 0.9. These decimal values should be used in conjunction with the whole number values (1 to 9) found in Column N. The table furnishes logs for the values between each whole number, to one decimal place. The characteristic of each of the logs shown (for the numbers 1 through 9.9) in Table B3–1A is understood to be zero. Therefore, it should be noted that the row to the right of the whole number 1 presents the logs for the numbers 1.0 to 1.9. Also, the second row presents the logs for numbers ranging from 2.0 to 2.9, and so forth.

Rules in the Use of Logarithms

Mathematical principles used in computational operations with exponential notation and/or scientific notation also apply to computations involving logarithms. Several rules in the use of logarithms are found below (Durrant & Lovrinic, 1995).

Finding Logs for Positive Numbers Less Than 10

Find the log of 5.5. Using Table B3–2 in Section B3, this is easily accomplished by first finding the row that corresponds to the whole number 5 along the far left column. Next, locate the column that falls under the decimal value, 0.5. The site in the table where row 5 and column 0.5 intersect provides the mantissa for the log of 5.5. Once more, the characteristic of the log is understood to be zero. Confirm that the log of 5.5 is equal to 0.740. This is true, of course, because $10^{0.740} = 5.5$. Note also that the logs for the values 1 through 9 found in the table column 0.0 are the same logs presented in Example Set 2–4 in the body of the text of Chapter 2.

Finding Logs for Exact Multiples of 10

As indicated earlier, a logarithm obtained for a number converted to scientific notation will consist of a characteristic, which is the exponent of the base, and a mantissa, which is the log of the simple coefficient. The importance of converting a number to scientific notation prior to obtaining its log should become obvious. The characteristics of each of the logs presented in Table B3–2 found in Section B3 are zero, because each number shown is less than 10. Now examine the values shown in Tables B3–3, B3–4, and B3–5 of Section B3. Note that each of the numbers is equal to a value of 10 or greater (i.e., 10–90; 100–900, etc.), and that each value shown is also an even multiple of 10. Note also that in Tables B3–3, B3–4, and B3–5 in Section B3, the mantissas of the logs are the same as, and have not changed from the mantissas presented in Table B3–2 for each of the whole number values 1 through 9. What in fact does change across each of these values are the characteristics of each log.

Example Set B2–1 illustrates the uncomplicated procedure for finding the logs of 50, 500, and 5,000, as provided in Tables B3–3, B3–4, and B3–5 from Section B3. *Note that in each case, the value in question is first converted to scientific notation.* Recall as well that the log 5 = 0.699, as indicated in Table B3–2.

Example Set B2–1

Find: log 50

$$\log 50 = \log 5 \times 10$$
$$= \log 10 + \log 5; \text{ or } 1 + 0.699$$

Therefore,

$$\log 50 = 1.699$$

Find: log 500

$$\log 500 = \log 5 \times 10^2$$
$$= \log 10^2 + \log 5; \text{ or } 2 + 0.699$$

Therefore,

$$\log 500 = 2.699$$

Find: log 5,000

$$\log 5,000 = \log 5 \times 10^3$$
$$= \log 10^3 + \log 5; \text{ or } 3 + 0.699$$

Therefore,

$$\log 5,000 = 3.699$$

Finding Logs for Additional Numbers Greater Than 10

The information provided in Table B3–2 may also be used to find logarithms for a wide range of numbers. Once again, converting a number to scientific notation prior to obtaining the log greatly simplifies the process. For instance, examine the small selection of problems presented in Example Set B2–2.

Example Set B2–2

Find: log 12

$$\log 12 = \log 1.2 \times 10$$
$$= \log 10^1 + \log 1.2; \text{ or } 1 + 0.079$$

Therefore

$$\log 12 = 1.079$$

Find: log 46

$$\log 46 = \log 4.6 \times 10$$
$$= \log 10^1 + \log 4.6; \text{ or } 1 + 0.663$$

Therefore,

$$\log 46 = 1.663$$

Find: log 6,900

$$\log 6{,}900 = \log 6.9 \times 10^3$$
$$= \log 10^3 + \log 6.9; \text{ or } 3 + 0.839$$

Therefore,

$$\log 6{,}900 = 3.839$$

Find: log 87,000

$$\log 87{,}000 = \log 8.7 \times 10^4$$
$$= \log 10^4 + \log 8.7; \text{ or } 4 + 0.940$$

Therefore,

$$\log 87{,}000 = 4.940$$

Finding Logs for Positive Numbers Less Than 1

While logarithms are not defined for negative numbers, numbers that exist between zero and one will always have negative logs (Mullin, Gerace, Mestre, & Velleman, 2003). That is, the exponent to which 10 must be raised to yield a decimal value will always consist of a negative number. The logarithms of a small sample of decimal values are presented in Table B3–6 of Section B3. The logs shown in Table B3–6 have been computed for numbers ranging from 0.01 to 0.99. Note that the numbers in question are separated by equal intervals, out to two decimal places only. The decimal intervals are shown horizontally in the first row to the right of the N (row N), by the values 0.00 to 0.09. The decimal values to two places (hundredths) should be used in conjunction with the tenth decimal values (0.0 to 0.9) found in column N. It should be noted that the row to the right of 0.0 provides the negative logs for the decimal values 0.01 to 0.09. The second row (to the right of 0.1) provides the negative logs for the decimal values ranging from 0.1 to 0.19. The row to the right of 0.2 presents the negative logs for the decimal values ranging from 0.2 to 0.29, and so forth.

Find the log of 0.55 using Table B3–6 in Section B3. This is easily accomplished by first finding the row that corresponds to the decimal value 0.5

along the left column. Next, locate the column that falls under the decimal value, 0.05. The site in the table where row 0.5 and column 0.05 intersect provides the mantissa for the log of 0.55. The characteristic of the log in this case is understood to be zero. Confirm that the log of 0.55 is equal to -0.259. This is true of course, because $10^{-0.259} = 0.55$.

When log tables for decimal values are not available, it may be less cumbersome to use a calculator for adding the positive mantissa with a negative characteristic when computing the logarithm for decimal values. Notwithstanding, when computing the logs of decimal values, the procedures are essentially the same as in the previous instances. The first step is always to transform the value to be solved into scientific notation. Examples illustrating the procedures that may be followed for finding logs of decimals are presented in Example Set B2–3. The log values originally shown in Table B3–2 in Section B3, combined with the conversion of numbers to scientific notation can be very useful. Example Set B2–3 illustrates solutions to a few types of log problems involving decimals.

Example Set B2–3

Find: log 0.12

$$\log 0.12 = \log 1.2 \times 10^{-1}$$
$$= \log 10^{-1} + \log 1.2; \text{ or } -1 + 0.079$$

Therefore,

$$\log 0.12 = -0.921$$

_____

Find: log 0.046

$$\log 0.046 = \log 4.6 \times 10^{-2}$$
$$= \log 10^{-2} + \log 4.6; \text{ or } -2 + 0.663$$

Therefore,

$$\log 0.046 = -1.337$$

_____

Find: log 0.0069

$$\log 0.0069 = \log 6.9 \times 10^{-3}$$
$$= \log 10^{-3} + \log 6.9; \text{ or } -3 + 0.839$$

Therefore,

$$\log 0.0069 = -2.161$$

_____

Find: log 0.00087

$$\log 0.00087 = \log 8.7 \times 10^{-4}$$
$$= \log 10^{-4} + \log 8.7; \text{ or } -4 + 0.940$$

Therefore,

$$\log 0.00087 = -3.06$$

Section B3.
Antilogarithms (Antilogs)

As indicated previously, common logarithms are generally used in hearing science with the understanding that base values are always 10. Recall that the common logarithm (or $\log_{10}$) of a value expressed in conventional notation (Y) was defined as the exponential power (n) that a base X (10) needed to be raised to in order to obtain the value Y. Therefore, if Y represents the conventional expression of a number, and $Y = 10^n$; then the logarithm to the base 10 (or $\log_{10}$) of the value Y is simply the exponent n of the base 10, or

If: $10^n = Y$; then $\log_{10}Y = n$

It also happens that the conventional expression Y of a number is equivalent to and is labeled the antilog$_x$ (antilog to the base X) of the exponent n, in the X^n. When using common logarithms,

antilog$_{10}$ $n = Y$

Therefore,

If: $10^n = Y$;

Then: antilog$_{10}$ $n = Y$

And: 10^n = antilog$_{10}$ n

Simply put, the common antilog to the base 10 of a number expressed in exponential notation (10^n) is equal to the same quantity as 10^n expressed in con-

ventional notation, or simply Y (Speaks, 1999). This point is illustrated in Table B3–1 using the same base 10 quantities presented previously in Example Set 2–1, taken from Chapter 2.

Table B3–1. Examples of the Base 10 Antilog of Some Common Exponents

antilog$_{10}$ n	$= 10^n$
0.0001	$= 10^{-4}$
0.001	$= 10^{-3}$
0.01	$= 10^{-2}$
0.1	$= 10^{-1}$
1.00	$= 10^0$
10	$= 10^1$
100	$= 10^2$
1,000	$= 10^3$
10,000	$= 10^4$

Table B3–2. Table of Logarithms

N	0.0	0.1	0.2	0.3	0.4	0.5	0.6	0.7	0.8	0.9
1	.000	.041	.079	.114	.146	.176	.204	.230	.255	.279
2	.301	.322	.342	.362	.380	.398	.415	.431	.447	.462
3	.477	.491	.505	.519	.531	.544	.556	.568	.580	.591
4	.602	.613	.623	.633	.643	.653	.663	.672	.681	.690
5	.699	.708	.716	.724	.732	.740	.748	.756	.763	.771
6	.778	.785	.792	.799	.806	.813	.820	.826	.833	.839
7	.845	.851	.857	.863	.869	.875	.881	.886	.892	.898
8	.903	.908	.914	.919	.924	.929	.935	.940	.944	.949
9	.954	.959	.964	.968	.973	.978	.982	.987	.991	.996

Table B3–3. Table of Logarithms for The Numbers 10 to 90 In Increments of 10

N	0.0
10	1.000
20	1.301
30	1.477
40	1.602
50	1.699
60	1.778
70	1.845
80	1.903
90	1.954

Table B3–4. Table of Logarithms for The Numbers 100 to 900 In Increments of 100

N	0.0
100	2.000
200	2.301
300	2.477
400	2.602
500	2.699
600	2.778
700	2.845
800	2.903
900	2.954

Table B3–5. Table of Logarithms for The Numbers 1000 to 9000 In Increments of 1000

N	0.0
1000	3.000
2000	3.301
3000	3.477
4000	3.602
5000	3.699
6000	3.778
7000	3.845
8000	3.903
9000	3.954

Table B3–6. Table of Logarithms for Values <1.00 (0.01 to 0.99)

N	0.00	0.01	0.02	0.03	0.04	0.05	0.06	0.07	0.08	0.09
0		−2.00	−1.69	−1.52	−1.39	−1.30	−1.22	−1.15	−1.09	−1.04
0.1	−1.00	−.958	−.920	−.886	−.853	−.823	−.795	−.769	−.744	−.721
0.2	−.698	−.677	−.657	−.638	−.619	−.602	−.585	−.568	−.552	−.537
0.3	−.522	−.508	−.494	−.481	−.468	−.455	−.443	−.431	−.420	−.408
0.4	−.397	−.387	−.376	−.366	−.356	−.346	−.337	−.327	−.318	−.309
0.5	−.301	−.292	−.283	−.270	−.267	−.259	−.251	−.244	−.236	−.229
0.6	−.221	−.214	−.207	−.200	−.193	−.187	−.180	−.173	−.167	−.161
0.7	−.154	−.148	−.142	−.136	−.130	−.124	−.119	−.113	−.107	−.102
0.8	−.096	−.091	−.086	−.080	−.075	−.070	−.065	−.060	−.055	−.050
0.9	−.045	−.040	−.036	−.031	−.026	−.022	−.017	−.013	−.008	−.004

Rules for Computations With Logarithms

The same mathematical principles found in operations using exponential notation or scientific notation that were presented in sections of Appendix A also form the basis of rules that apply to computations involving logarithms (Giancoli, 2005; Mullin et al., 2003; Speaks, 1999).

Rule I

If: 10^x = a; and 10^y = b;
Then: a × b = $10^{x + y}$

Example:

If: 10^4 = 10,000; and $10^{0.301}$ = 2
Then: $10{,}000 × 2 = 10^{4 + 0.301} = 10^{4.301}$

Rule II

If: 10^x = a; and 10^y = b;
Then: log (ab) = log a + log b;

Example:

If: 10^4 = 10,000; and $10^{0.301}$ = 2
Then: log (10,000 × 2 or 20,000)
= log 10,000 + log 2 = 4 + 0.301
= 4.301

Rule III

If: 10^x = a; and 10^y = b;
Then: log (ab) = $x + y$

Example:

If: 10^4 = 10,000; and $10^{0.301}$ = 2

Then: log (10,000 × 2 or 20,000)
= 4 + 0.301 = 4.301

Rule IV

If 10^x = a; and 10^y = b;
Then: log (a/b) = log a − log b;
or log (a/b) = $x − y$

Example:

If: 10^4 = 10,000; and $10^{0.301}$ = 2
Then: log (10,000/2 or 5000)
= 4 − 0.301 = 3.699

Rule V

If: a^x = b;
Then: log a^x = x log a

Example 1:

If: 10^4 = 10,000
Then: log 10^4 = 4 × log 10^1
= 4 × 1 = 4

Example 2:

If: $10^{0.301}$ = 2
Then: log $10^{0.301}$ = 0.301 × log 10^1
= 0.301 × 1 = 0.301

Rule VI: Exponentiation

If: log $(10)^x$;
Then: log $(10)^x$ = x log (10);

(Durrant & Lovrinic, 1995)

Example:

If: log $(10)^5$
Then: log $(10)^5$ = 5 log (10)
= log $(10)^5$ = 5; and 5 (1) = 5

References

Durrant, J. D., & Lovrinic, J. H. (1995). *Bases of hearing science* (3rd ed.). Baltimore, MD: Williams & Wilkins.

Giancoli, D. C. (2005). *Physics: Principles with applications* (6th ed.). Upper Saddle River, NJ: Prentice Hall.

Mullin, W. J., Gerace, W. J., Mestre, J. P., & Velleman, S. L. (2003). *Fundamentals of sound with applications to speech and hearing.* Boston, MA: Allyn & Bacon.

Speaks, C. E. (1999). *Introduction to sound: Acoustics for the hearing and speech sciences* (3rd ed.). San Diego, CA: Singular.

Appendix C

Exponents With Metric Prefixes

See Table C–1 on the following page.

Table C–1. Table of Exponential Prefixes, Symbols, and Exponential Derivations

Factor	Prefix	Symbol	Derivation
$10^{-24} =$	yocto	(y)	$= 1 \div 10^{24}$
$10^{-21} =$	zepto	(z)	$= 1 \div 10^{21}$
$10^{-18} =$	atto	(a)	$= 1 \div 10^{18}$
$10^{-15} =$	femto	(f)	$= 1 \div 10^{15}$
$10^{-12} =$	pico	(p)	$= 1 \div 10^{12}$
$10^{-9} = 0.000000001$	nano	(n)	$= 1 \div 10^{9}$
$10^{-6} = 0.000001$	micro	(μ)	$= 1 \div [10 \times 10 \times 10 \times 10 \times 10 \times 10]$
$10^{-5} = 0.00001$			$= 1 \div [10 \times 10 \times 10 \times 10 \times 10]$
$10^{-4} = 0.0001$			$= 1 \div [10 \times 10 \times 10 \times 10]$
$10^{-3} = 0.001$	milli	(m)	$= 1 \div [10 \times 10 \times 10]$
$10^{-2} = 0.01$	centi	(c)	$= 1 \div [10 \times 10]$
$10^{-1} = 0.1$	deci	(d)	$= 1 \div [10 \times 1]$
$10^{0} = 1$	mono		$= 1 \times 1$
$10^{1} = 10$	deca	(da)	$= 1 \times 10$
$10^{2} = 100$	hecto	(h)	$= 10 \times 10$
$10^{3} = 1,000$	kilo	(k)	$= 10 \times 10 \times 10$
$10^{4} = 10,000$			$= 10 \times 10 \times 10 \times 10$
$10^{5} = 100,000$			$= 10 \times 10 \times 10 \times 10 \times 10$
$10^{6} = 1,000,000$	mega	(M)	$= 10 \times 10 \times 10 \times 10 \times 10 \times 10$
$10^{9} = 1,000,000,000$	giga	(G)	$= 1 \times 10^{9}$
$10^{12} =$	tera	(T)	$= 1 \times 10^{12}$
$10^{15} =$	peta	(P)	$= 1 \times 10^{15}$
$10^{18} =$	exa	(E)	$= 1 \times 10^{18}$
$10^{21} =$	zetta	(Z)	$= 1 \times 10^{21}$
$10^{24} =$	yotta	(Y)	$= 1 \times 10^{24}$

Source: Giancoli, D. C. (2005). *Physics: Principles with applications* (6th ed.). Upper Saddle River, NJ: Prentice Hall.

Index

Note: Page numbers in **bold** reference non-text material.